The Council of State Governments

STATE DIRECTORY

Directory III—
Administrative Officials 2015

The Council of State Governments
2760 Research Park Drive
Lexington, KY 40511-8482

Contact the Publication Sales Department at
1-800-800-1910 or sales@csg.org to order:

Directory I—Elective Officials 2015,

Directory II—Legislative Leadership, Committees and Staff 2015,

Directory III—Administrative Officials 2015

or mailing lists of state government officials.

Since 1933, The Council of State Governments has served our nation's state leaders by providing a forum for "sharing capitol ideas." As the only state services organization spanning all three branches of government, CSG offers a unique look into the issues shaping state policy and legislation from the national and regional perspectives. This unique arrangement contributes to a strong national presence for CSG, creating unparalleled opportunities to network, collaborate and form problem-solving partnerships.

The Council of State Governments Officers

President **Gov. Brian Sandoval**, Nev.

Chair **Sen. Carl Marcellino**, N.Y. ▪ *Chair-Elect* **Sen. Beau McCoy**, Neb. ▪ *Vice Chair* **Sen. Kelvin Atkinson**, Nev.

The Council of State Governments

David Adkins, Executive Director CEO

2760 Research Park Drive ▪ Lexington, KY 40511-8482 ▪ (859) 244-8000 ▪ Fax: (859) 244-8001 ▪ www.csg.org

---

Eastern Office	**Midwestern Office**	**Southern Office**	**Western Office**	**Washington Office**
Wendell M. Hannaford, Director	*Michael H. McCabe, Director*	*Colleen Cousineau, Director*	*Edgar E. Ruiz, Director*	
22 Cortlandt Street, 22nd Floor	701 East 22nd Street, Suite 110	P.O. Box 98129	1107 9th Street, Suite 730	444 N. Capitol Street, N.W., Suite 401
New York, NY 10007	Lombard, IL 60148	Atlanta, GA 30359	Sacramento, CA 95814	Washington, DC 20001
(212) 482-2320	(630) 925-1922	(404) 633-1866	(916) 553-4423	(202) 624-5460
Fax: (212) 482-2344	Fax: (630) 925-1930	Fax: (404) 633-4896	Fax: (916) 446-5760	Fax: (202) 624-5452
www.csgeast.org	www.csgmidwest.org	www.slcatlanta.org	www.csgwest.org	www.csgdc.org

Editorial Staff

Kelley Arnold ▪ Jessica Clay ▪ Eric Lancaster ▪ Heather Perkins

*Special thanks to the CSG regional offices
and the clerks and secretaries of the legislature for each state.*

Table of Contents

How to Use This Directory

This annual directory provides basic information about elected and appointed officials with primary responsibility in more than 110 state government functions. The directory includes names, addresses, telephone, fax and e-mail addresses. The information is organized alphabetically by function (e.g., Labor) and by state and U.S. jurisdiction name. Generally, there is one entry per function for each state or U.S. jurisdiction. State names and jurisdictions are not listed if there is not a corresponding entry for a given section.

CSG collected the information for the 2015 directory between May and June 2015. The data contained in this volume was compiled through one of three methods. First, national associations were given the opportunity to provide a roster for the directory. For those categories that did not have rosters provided, the information was gathered through two other methods. Each state and territory was sent a survey requesting updated information for their administrative officials. If states did not respond to the surveys, CSG staff collected the updated information from state-sponsored websites or phone calls to state offices.

Party Abbreviations

D	Democrat
R	Republican
REFORM	Reform
C	Covenant
I	Independent
L	Libertarian
S	Statehood
ICM	Independent Citizen Movement
DFL	Democratic-Farmer-Labor
NP	Nonpartisan
P	Progressive
NPP	New Progressive Party
PDP	Popular Democratic Party
PIP	Puerto Rican Independent Party
RA	Rural Alaskan
TRIBAL	Delegate representing a Native American tribe
U	Unenrolled

Adjutant General

The executive or administrative head of the state's military service.

ALABAMA
Maj. Gen. Perry G. Smith Sr.
Adjutant General
National Guard
1720 Congressman W.L. Dickinson Drive
Montgomery, AL 36109
P: (334) 271-7200
F: (334) 213-7511
E: perry.g.smith
@us.army.mil

ALASKA
Maj. Gen. Thomas H. Katkus
Adjutant General
Department of Military & Veterans Affairs
P.O. Box 5800
Fort Richardson, AK 99505
P: (907) 428-6003
F: (907) 428-6019
E: thomas.katkus
@us.army.mil

ARIZONA
Michael McGuire
Adjutant General
Department of Emergency & Military Affairs
5636 East McDowell Road
Phoenix, AZ 85008
P: (602) 267-2710
F: (602) 267-2715

ARKANSAS
Maj. Gen. William D. Wofford
Adjutant General
Military Department
Camp Robinson, Box 16
North Little Rock, AR 72199
P: (510) 212-5001
F: (510) 212-5009
E: william.d.wofford
@ar.ngb.army.mil

CALIFORNIA
Maj. Gen. David Baldwin
Adjutant General
Military Department
P.O. Box 269101
Sacramento, CA 95826
P: (916) 854-3533
F: (916) 854-3671
E: david.s.baldwin
@us.army.mil

COLORADO
Maj. Gen. H. Michael Edwards
Adjutant General
Department of Military Affairs
6848 South Revere Parkway
Centennial, CO 80112
P: (720) 250-1500
F: (720) 250-1509
E: howard.edwards
@ang.af.mil

CONNECTICUT
Maj. Gen. Thaddeus J. Martin
Adjutant General
Military Department
360 Broad Street
Hartford, CT 06105
P: (860) 524-4953
F: (860) 524-4898
E: thad.martin@us.army.mil

DELAWARE
Maj. Gen. Francis D. Vavala
Adjutant General
National Guard
First Regiment Road
Wilmington, DE 19808
P: (302) 326-7001
F: (302) 326-7196
E: frank.vavala
@de.ngb.army.mil

DISTRICT OF COLUMBIA
Maj. Gen. Errol R. Schwartz
Commanding General
National Guard
2001 East Capitol Street, Southeast
Washington, DC 20003
P: (202) 685-9798
F: (202) 685-9794
E: errol.r.schwartz
@us.army.mil

FLORIDA
Maj. Gen. Emmett R. Titshaw Jr.
Adjutant General
Department of Military Affairs
P.O. Box 1008
St. Augustine, FL 32085
P: (904) 823-0101
F: (904) 823-0149
E: emmett.titshaw
@fl.ngb.army.mil

GEORGIA
Mr. James B. Butterworth
Director
Department of Defense
935 East Confederate Avenue, Southeast
Atlanta, GA 30316
P: (404) 635-7008
E: jim.butterworth
@gema.ga.gov

GUAM
Maj. Gen. Benny M. Paulino
Adjutant General
National Guard
430 Army Drive, Building 300
Barrigada, GU 96913
P: (671) 735-0406
F: (671) 734-4081
E: benny.m.paulino
@us.army.mil

HAWAII
Maj. Gen. Darryl D.M. Wong
Adjutant General
Department of Defense
3949 Diamond Head Road
Honolulu, HI 96816
P: (808) 733-4246
F: (808) 733-4499
E: darryll.wong
@hickarm.af.mil

IDAHO
Maj. Gen. Gary L. Sayler
Adjutant General
Military Division
4040 West Guard Street
Boise, ID 83705
P: (208) 422-5242
F: (208) 422-6179
E: gary.sayler@ang.af.mil

ILLINOIS
Brigadier General Daniel M. Krumrei
Adjutant General
Office of the Adjutant General
1301 North MacArthur Boulevard
Springfield, IL 62702
P: (217) 761-3500
F: (217) 761-3736

INDIANA
Maj. Gen. R. Martin Umbarger
Adjutant General
Adjutant General's Office
2002 South Holt Road
Indianapolis, IN 46241
P: (317) 247-3559
F: (317) 247-3540
E: marty.umbarger
@us.army.mil

IOWA
Maj. Gen. Timothy E. Orr
Adjutant General
Office of the Adjutant General
7105 Northwest 70th Avenue
Johnston, IA 50131
P: (515) 252-4211
F: (515) 252-4787
E: timothy.orr@us.army.mil

KANSAS
Maj. Gen. Lee E. Tafanelli (R)
Adjutant General
Adjutant General's Department
2800 Southwest Topeka Boulevard
Topeka, KS 66611
P: (785) 274-1001
F: (785) 274-1682
E: lee.tafanelli
@us.army.mil

KENTUCKY
Maj. Gen. Edward W. Tonini
Adjutant General
Department of Military Affairs
100 Minuteman Parkway
Frankfort, KY 40601
P: (502) 607-1558
F: (502) 607-1271
E: edward.tonini
@us.army.mil

LOUISIANA
Brigadier General Glenn Curtis
Adjutant General
National Guard
304 F Street
Pineville, LA 71360
P: (318) 641-3863
F: (318) 641-3865
E: glenn.curtis@us.army.mil

MAINE
Brigadier General James D. Campbell
Adjutant General
Office of the Adjutant General
Camp Keyes
Augusta, ME 04333
P: (207) 430-6000
F: (207) 626-4509

MARYLAND
Maj. Gen. James A. Adkins
Adjutant General
Military Department
5th Regiment Armory
Baltimore, MD 21201
P: (410) 576-6097
F: (410) 576-6079
E: james.a.adkins
@us.army.mil

Adjutant General

MASSACHUSETTS
Maj. Gen. Leon Scott Rice
Adjutant General
National Guard
2 Randolph Road
Hanscom AFB, MA 01731
P: (339) 202-3900

MICHIGAN
Maj. Gen. Gregory J.
    Vadnais
Adjutant General
Department of Military &
Veterans Affairs
3411 North Martin Luther King
Boulevard
Lansing, MI 48906
P: (517) 481-8083
F: (517) 481-8125
E: gregory.vadnais
    @us.army.mil

MINNESOTA
Maj. Gen. Richard C. Nash
Adjutant General
Department of Military Affairs
20 West 12th Street
St. Paul, MN 55155
P: (651) 268-8924
F: (651) 282-4541
E: rick.nash@us.army.mil

MISSISSIPPI
Maj. Gen. Augustus Collins
Adjutant General
National Guard
1410 Riverside Drive
Jackson, MS 39202
P: (601) 313-6232
F: (601) 313-6251
E: augustus.collins
    @us.army.mil

MISSOURI
Maj. Gen. Stephen L. Danner
Adjutant General
National Guard
2302 Militia Drive
Jefferson City, MO 65101
P: (573) 638-9710
F: (573) 638-9722
E: stephen.l.danner
    @us.army.mil

MONTANA
Maj. Gen. Matthew T. Quinn
Adjutant General
Office of the Adjutant General
P.O. Box 4789
Fort Harrison, MT 59636
P: (406) 324-3010
F: (406) 324-4800

NEBRASKA
Maj. Gen. Daryl L. Bohac
Adjutant General
National Guard
2433 Northwest 24th Street
Lincoln, NE 68524
P: (402) 309-8105
F: (402) 309-7147

NEVADA
William R. Burks
Adjutant General
National Guard
2460 Fairview Drive
Carson City, NV 89701
P: (775) 887-7302
F: (775) 887-7315
E: william.ross.burks
    @us.army.mil

NEW HAMPSHIRE
Maj. Gen. William N.
    Reddel III
Adjutant General
National Guard
1 Minuteman Way
Concord, NH 03301
P: (603) 225-1200
F: (603) 225-1257
E: william.n.reddel
    @us.army.mil

NEW JERSEY
Michael L. Cunniff
Adjutant General
Department of Military &
Veterans' Affairs
101 Eggert Crossing Road
Lawrenceville, NJ 08648
P: (609) 530-6957
F: (609) 530-7191

NEW MEXICO
Brigadier General Andrew E.
    Salas
Adjutant General
Office of the Adjutant General
47 Bataan Boulevard
Santa Fe, NM 87505
P: (505) 474-1210
F: (505) 474-1355

NEW YORK
Maj. Gen. Patrick A. Murphy
Adjutant General
Division of Military & Naval
Affairs
330 Old Niskayuna Road
Latham, NY 12110
P: (518) 786-4502
F: (518) 786-4325
E: pat.murphy@us.army.mil

NORTH CAROLINA
Maj. Gen. Gregory A. Lusk
Adjutant General
National Guard
1636 Gold Star Drive
Raleigh, NC 27607
P: (919) 664-6101
F: (919) 664-6430
E: greg.lusk@us.army.mil

NORTH DAKOTA
Maj. Gen. David A.
    Sprynczynatyk
Adjutant General
National Guard
Fraine Barracks
P.O. Box 5511
Bismarck, ND 58506
P: (701) 333-2002
F: (701) 333-2017
E: david.sprynczynatyk
    @us.army.mil

OHIO
Maj. Gen. Deborah A.
    Ashenhurst
Adjutant General
National Guard
2825 West Dublin Granville
Road
Columbus, OH 43235
P: (614) 336-7070
F: (614) 336-7074
E: deborah.ashenhurst
    @us.army.mil

OKLAHOMA
Maj. Gen. Myles L. Deering
Director
National Guard
P.O. Box 53067
Oklahoma City, OK 73152
P: (405) 521-3684
F: (405) 521-6533
E: mdeering
    @odva.state.ok.us

OREGON
Maj. Gen. Daniel R.
    Hokanson
Adjutant General
Office of the Adjutant General
P.O. Box 14350
Salem, OR 97301
P: (503) 584-3991
F: (503) 584-3987

PENNSYLVANIA
Maj. Gen. Wesley E.
    Craig Jr.
Adjutant General
Department of Military &
Veterans Affairs
Fort Indiantown Gap
Annville, PA 17003
P: (717) 861-8502
F: (717) 861-8481
E: wesley.craig@us.army.mil

PUERTO RICO
Colonel Juan J.
    Medina-Lamela
Adjutant General
Office of the Adjutant General
P.O. Box 9023786
San Juan, PR 00902
P: (787) 289-1631
F: (787) 723-6360

RHODE ISLAND
Maj. Gen. Kevin R. McBride
Adjutant General
National Guard
645 New London Avenue
Cranston, RI 02920
P: (401) 275-4102
F: (401) 275-4338
E: kevin.r.mcbride
    @us.army.mil

SOUTH CAROLINA
Maj. Gen. Robert E.
    Livingston Jr.
Adjutant General
National Guard
1 National Guard Road
Columbia, SC 29201
P: (803) 299-2500
F: (803) 806-4468
E: bob.livingston
    @us.army.mil

SOUTH DAKOTA
Maj. Gen. Timothy A. Reisch
Adjutant General
Department of Military &
Veterans Affairs
2823 West Main Street, Building
420
Rapid City, SD 57702
P: (605) 737-6702
F: (605) 737-6677
E: tim.reisch@us.army.mil

TENNESSEE
Maj. Gen. Terry M. Haston
Adjutant General
Military Department
P.O. Box 41502
Nashville, TN 37204
P: (615) 313-3001
F: (615) 313-3100
E: terry.max.haston
@us.army.mil

TEXAS
Maj. Gen. John F. Nichols
Adjutant General
Adjutant General's Department
P.O. Box 5218
Austin, TX 78763
P: (512) 782-5006
F: (512) 782-5578
E: john.f.nichols1
@us.army.mil

U.S. VIRGIN ISLANDS
Mr. Renaldo Rivera
Adjutant General
National Guard
4031 La Grande Princess, Lot
1B
Christiansted, VI 00820
P: (340) 712-7710
F: (340) 712-7709
E: renaldo.rivera
@us.army.mil

UTAH
Maj. Gen. Jefferson S.
Burton
Adjutant General
Office of the Adjutant General
12953 South Minuteman Drive
Draper, UT 84020
P: (801) 432-4402
F: (801) 432-4677

VERMONT
Maj. Gen. Steven A. Cray
Adjutant General
Office of the Adjutant General
789 Vermont National Guard
Road
Colchester, VT 05446
P: (802) 338-3124
F: (802) 338-3425

VIRGINIA
Maj. Gen. Daniel E.
Long Jr.
Adjutant General
National Guard
5901 Beulah Road
Sandston, VA 23150
P: (804) 236-7880
F: (804) 236-7901
E: chip.long@us.army.mil

WASHINGTON
Maj. Gen. Bret D. Daugherty
Adjutant General
Office of the Adjutant General
One Militia Drive, Building One
Camp Murray, WA 98430
P: (253) 512-8201
F: (253) 512-7727

WEST VIRGINIA
Maj. Gen. James A. Hoyer
Adjutant General
Army National Guard
1703 Coonskin Drive
Charleston, WV 25311
P: (304) 561-6317
F: (304) 561-6327
E: james.hoyer@us.army.mil

WISCONSIN
Brigadier General Donald P.
Dunbar
Adjutant General
Department of Military Affairs
P.O. Box 8111
Madison, WI 53704
P: (608) 242-3003
F: (608) 242-3111
E: donald.p.dunbar
@us.army.mil

WYOMING
Maj. Gen. Kenneth L. Reiner
Adjutant General
Military Department
5410 Bishop Boulevard
Cheyenne, WY 82009
P: (307) 772-5234
F: (307) 772-5010
E: luke.reiner@us.army.mil

Administration

Umbrella agency of administration that coordinates administrative services provided to state agencies.

ALABAMA
Mr. Bill Newton
Acting Director
Department of Finance
State Capitol
600 Dexter Avenue, Suite N-105
Montgomery, AL 36130
P: (334) 242-7230
F: (334) 353-3300
E: bill.newton
   @budget.alabama.gov

ALASKA
Mr. Sheldon Fisher
Commissioner
Department of Administration
P.O. Box 110200
Juneau, AK 72203
P: (907) 465-2200
E: Sheldon.Fisher
   @alaska.gov

ARIZONA
Mr. Kevin Donnellan
Acting Director
Department of Administration
100 North 15th Avenue, Suite 401
Phoenix, AZ 85007
P: (602) 542-1500
E: kevin.donnellan
   @azdoa.gov

ARKANSAS
Ms. Carla Wooley-Haugen
Administrative Services
Administrator
Department of Finance &
Administration
P.O. Box 2485
Little Rock, AR 72203
P: (501) 324-9057
E: Carla.Wooley-Haugen
   @dfa.arkansas.gov

CALIFORNIA
Mr. Esteban Almanza
Acting Director
Department of General Services
707 Third Street
West Sacramento, CA 95605
E: esteban.almanza
   @dgs.ca.gov

COLORADO
Ms. Kara Veitch
Interim Executive Director
Department of Personnel &
Administration
1525 Sherman Street, 5th Floor
Denver, CO 80203
P: (303) 866-4434
E: kara.veitch@state.co.us

CONNECTICUT
Ms. Melody A. Currey
Commissioner
Department of Administrative
Services
165 Capitol Avenue
Hartford, CT 06106
P: (860) 713-5100
F: (860) 713-7481
E: Melody.Currey@ct.gov

DELAWARE
Ms. Ann Shepard Visalli
Director
Office of Management &
Budget
Haslet Armory
122 Martin Luther King Jr.
Boulevard S.
Dover, DE 19901
P: (302) 739-4204
F: (302) 739-5661
E: Ann.Visalli@state.de.us

DISTRICT OF COLUMBIA
Mr. Jonathan Kayne
Interim Director
Department of General Services
2000 14th Street, Northwest, 8th
Floor
Washington, DC 20009
P: (202) 727-2800
E: dgs@dc.gov

FLORIDA
Mr. Chad Poppell
Secretary
Department of Management
Services
4050 Esplande Way, Suite 250
Tallahassee, FL 32399
P: (850) 414-8941
E: Chad.poppell
   @dms.myflorida.com

GEORGIA
Mr. Sid Johnson
Commissioner
Department of Administrative
Services
200 Piedmont Avenue, 1804
West Tower
Atlanta, GA 30334
P: (404) 656-5514
E: sid.johnson@doas.ga.gov

HAWAII
Mr. Douglas Murdock
Comptroller
Department of Accounting &
General Services
1151 Punchbowl Street, Room
412
Honolulu, HI 96813
P: (808) 586-0400
F: (808) 586-0775
E: dags@hawaii.gov

IDAHO
Mr. Keith Reynolds
Acting Director
Department of Administration
650 West State Street, Room
100
Len B. Jordan Building, P.O.
Box 83720
Boise, ID 83720
P: (208) 332-1824
E: keith.reynolds
   @adm.idaho.gov

ILLINOIS
Mr. Tom Tyrrell
Acting Director
Department of Central
Management Services
100 West Randolph, 4th Floor
JRTC 4-500
Chicago, IL 60601
P: (312) 814-2648
E: tom.tyrrell@illinois.gov

INDIANA
Ms. Jessica Robertson
Commissioner
Department of Administration
402 West Washington Street,
Room W478
Indianapolis, IN 46204
P: (317) 233-1494
E: jrobertson@idoa.in.gov

IOWA
Ms. Janet Phipps
Director
Department of Administrative
Services
1305 East Walnut Street
Hoover Building, 3rd Floor
Des Moines, IA 50319
P: (515) 725-2205
E: janet.phipps@iowa.gov

KANSAS
Mr. Jim Clark
Interim Chief Information
Technology Officer
Department of Administration
900 Southwest Jackson, Room
751S
Topeka, KS 66612
P: (785) 296-3011
E: jim.clark@da.ks.gov

KENTUCKY
Ms. Lori Hudson Flanery
Secretary
Department of Finance &
Administration Cabinet
383 Capitol Annex
Frankfort, KY 40601
P: (502) 564-4240
F: (502) 564-5856
E: Lori.Flanery@ky.gov

LOUISIANA
Ms. Kristy H. Nichols
Commissioner of Administration
Department of Administration
1201 North Third Street
Claiborne Building
Baton Rouge, LA 70802
P: (225) 342-7000
E: doacommissioner@la.gov

MAINE
Mr. Richard W. Rosen
Commissioner
Department of Administration &
Financial Services
78 State House Station
Augusta, ME 04333
P: (207) 624-7800
E: richard.rosen@maine.gov

MARYLAND
Ms. Gail Bassette
Secretary
Department of General Services
301 West Preston Street, Room
1401
Baltimore, MD 21201
P: (410) 767-4960

MASSACHUSETTS
Ms. Kristen Lepore
Secretary
Executive Office for
Administration & Finance
State House, Room 373
Boston, MA 02133
P: (617) 727-2040
F: (617) 727-2779
E: kristen.lepore
   @state.ma.us

MICHIGAN
Mr. David Behen
Chief Information Officer &
Department Director
Department of Technology,
Management & Budget
320 South Walnut Street, 2nd
Floor
P.O. Box 30026
Lansing, MI 48909
P: (517) 373-3209
E: behend@michigan.gov

MINNESOTA
Mr. Matt Massman
Commissioner
Department of Administration
116 Veterans Service Building
20 West 12 Street
St. Paul, MN 55155
P: (651) 201-3421
E: Matt.Massman@state.mn.us

MISSISSIPPI
Mr. Kevin J. Upchurch
Executive Director
Department of Finance &
Administration
P.O. Box 267
Jackson, MS 39205
P: (601) 359-3402
F: (601) 359-2405
E: Kevin.Upchurch
　@dfa.ms.gov

MISSOURI
Mr. Dougles E. Nelson
Commissioner
Office of Administration
201 West Capitol Avenue
Jefferson City, MO 65101
P: (573) 751-1851
E: doug.nelson@oa.mo.gov

MONTANA
Hon. Sheila Hogan
Director
Department of Administration
P.O. Box 200101
Helena, MT 59620
P: (406) 444-3033
F: (406) 444-6194
E: shogan@mt.gov

NEBRASKA
Mr. Byron L. Diamond
Director
Department of Administrative
Services
State Capitol, Room 1315
Lincoln, NE 68509
P: (402) 471-2331
E: byron.diamond
　@nebraska.gov

NEVADA
Mr. James Wells
Interim Director
Department of Administration
Balsdel Building, Room 200
209 East Musser Street
Carson City, NV 89701
P: (775) 684-0222
F: (775) 684-0260
E: budget@admin.nv.gov

NEW HAMPSHIRE
Ms. Linda M. Hodgdon
Commissioner
Department of Administrative
Services
25 Capitol Street
State House Annex, Room 120
Concord, NH 03301
P: (603) 271-3201
F: (603) 271-6600
E: linda.hodgdon@nh.gov

NEW JERSEY
Ms. Charlene M. Holzbaur
Director
Office of Management &
Budget
Department of the Treasury
33 West State Street, P.O. Box
221
Trenton, NJ 08625
P: (609) 292-6746
F: (609) 633-8179
E: charlene.holzbaur
　@treas.state.nj.us

NEW MEXICO
Mr. Ed Burckle
Cabinet Secretary
General Services Department
P.O. Box 6850
Santa Fe, NM 87502
P: (505) 827-2000
E: ed.burckle@state.nm.us

NEW YORK
Ms. RoAnn M. Destito
Commissioner
Office of General Services
41st Floor, Corning Tower
Empire State Plaza
Albany, NY 12242
P: (518) 474-3899
E: roann.destito@ogs.ny.gov

NORTH CAROLINA
Mr. Bill Daughtridge Jr.
Secretary
Department of Administration
116 West Jones Street, Suite
5106
MSC 1301
Raleigh, NC 27699
P: (919) 807-2425
F: (919) 733-9420
E: bill.daughtridge
　@doa.nc.gov

NORTH DAKOTA
Ms. Pam Sharp
Director
Office of Management &
Budget
600 East Boulevard Avenue
Department 110
Bismarck, ND 58505
P: (701) 328-4606
F: (701) 328-3230
E: psharp@nd.gov

OHIO
Mr. Robert Blair
Director
Department of Administrative
Services
30 East Broad Street, Suite 4040
Columbus, OH 43215
P: (614) 466-6511
F: (614) 644-8151
E: Robert.Blair
　@das.ohio.gov

OREGON
Mr. George M. Naughton
Chief Operating Officer
Department of Administrative
Services
155 Cottage Street, Northeast,
U10
Salem, OR 97301
P: (503) 378-5460
F: (503) 373-7643
E: george.m.naughton
　@oregon.gov

PENNSYLVANIA
Ms. Sharon Minnich
Secretary
Governor's Office of
Administration
207 Finance Building
Harrisburg, PA 17102
P: (717) 772-5174
E: sminnich@pa.gov

RHODE ISLAND
Mr. Michael DiBiase
Department of Administration
One Capitol Hill
Providence, RI 02908
P: (401) 222-2280
E: michael.dibiase
　@doa.ri.gov

SOUTH CAROLINA
Ms. Marcia S. Adams
Executive Director
Budget & Control Board
1200 Senate Streer, Suite 600
Columbia, SC 29201
P: (803) 734-2320
F: (803) 734-2117
E: madams@oed.sc.gov

SOUTH DAKOTA
Mr. Paul Kinsman
Commissioner
Bureau of Administration
500 East Capital Avenue
Pierre, SD 57501
P: (605) 773-3688
F: (605) 773-3887
E: paul.kinsman@state.sd.us

TENNESSEE
Mr. Bob Oglesby
Commissioner
Department of General Services
22nd Floor, 312 8th Avenue,
North
Nashville, TN 37243
P: (615) 741-2081
E: bob.oglesby@tn.gov

TEXAS
Mr. Harvey Hilderbran
Executive Director
Facilities Commission
1711 San Jacinto
P.O. Box 13047
Austin, TX 78711
P: (512) 463-3446
E: Harvey.Hilderbran
　@tfc.state.tx.us

UTAH
Ms. Kimberly Hood
Executive Director
Department of Administrative
Services
350 North State Street
Salt Lake City, UT 84114
P: (801) 538-3010
F: (801) 538-3844
E: khood@utah.gov

VERMONT
Mr. Justin Johnson
Secretary of Administration
Agency of Administration
109 State Street
Montpelier, VT 05609
P: (802) 828-3322
E: justin.johnson
　@state.vt.us

VIRGINIA
Mr. Richard F. Sliwoski
Director
Department of General Services
1100 Bank Street, Suite 420
Richmond, VA 23219
P: 804-786-3311
F: 804-371-8305
E: richard.sliwoski
　@dgs.virginia.gov

Administration

WASHINGTON
Mr. Christopher Liu
Director
Department of Enterprise
Services
P.O. Box 41401
Olympia, WA 98504
P: (360) 407-9201
E: chris.liu@des.wa.gov

WEST VIRGINIA
Mr. Jason Pizatella
Secretary
Department of Administration
1900 Kanawha Boulevard East,
Building 1
Room E-119
Charleston, WV 25305
P: (304) 558-4331
E: jason.c.pizatella@wv.gov

WISCONSIN
Mr. Scott Neitzel
Secretary
Department of Administration
10th Floor, 101 East Wilson
Street
Madison, WI 53703
P: (608) 266-1741
E: scott.neitzel
    @wisconsin.gov

WYOMING
Mr. Dean Fausset
Director
Department of Administration &
Information
2001 Capitol Avenue
Cheyenne, WY 82002
P: (307) 777-6414
F: (307) 777-3633
E: dean.fausset@wyo.gov

Aging

Develops and strengthens services for the aged and conducts or promotes research into their problems.

ALABAMA
Mr. Neal Morrison
Commissioner
Department of Senior Services
201 Monroe Street, Suite 350
P.O. Box 301851
Montgomery, AL 36130
P: (334) 242-4985
F: (334) 242-5594

ALASKA
Mr. Duane Mayes
Director
Senior & Disabilities Services
Department of Health & Social
Services
550 West 8th Street
Anchorage, AK 99501
P: (907) 269-2083
F: (907) 269-3688
E: duane.mayes@alaska.gov

AMERICAN SAMOA
Tifimalae Ale
Director
Territorial Administration on
Aging
American Samoa Government
Pago Pago, AS 96799
P: (684) 633-1251
F: (684) 633-2533

ARIZONA
Ms. Lynn Larson
Assistant Director
Division of Aging & Adult
Services
Department of Economic
Security
1789 West Jefferson, No. 950A
Phoenix, AZ 85007
P: (602) 542-2591
F: (602) 542-6575

ARKANSAS
Mr. Craig Cloud
Director, Division of Aging and
Adult Services
Department of Human Services
700 Main Street, 5th Floor, S530
P.O. Box 1437
Little Rock, AR 72203
P: (501) 682-2441
F: (501) 682-8155

COLORADO
Mr. Todd Coffey
Director
Commission on Aging
Department of Human Services
1575 Sherman Street, 10th Floor
Denver, CO 80203
P: (303) 866-2750
F: (303) 866-2696
E: Todd.Coffey@state.co.us

CONNECTICUT
Ms. Elizabeth B. Ritter
Commissioner
State Department on Aging
Department of Social Services
25 Sigourney Street
Hartford, CT 06106
P: (860) 424-5322
F: (860) 424-5301
E: Elizabeth.Ritter
    @cga.ct.gov

DELAWARE
Ms. Lisa Bond
Deputy Director
Division of Services for Aging
& Adults with Physical
Disabilities
Department of Health & Social
Services
1901 North DuPont Highway
New Castle, DE 19720
P: (302) 255-9351
F: (302) 255-4445

DISTRICT OF COLUMBIA
Mr. John Thompson
Executive Director
Office on Aging
500 K Street, Northeast
Washington, DC 20002
P: (202) 724-5622
F: (202) 724-4979

FLORIDA
Mr. Sam Verghese
Secretary
Department of Elder Affairs
4040 Esplanade Way, Suite 315
Tallahassee, FL 32399
P: (850) 414-2000
F: (850) 414-2004

GEORGIA
Mr. James Bulot
Director
Division of Aging Services
Department of Human Services
2 Peachtree Street, Northwest,
9th Floor
Atlanta, GA 30303
P: (404) 657-5258
F: (404) 657-5285

GUAM
Mr. Arthur U. San Agustin
Senior Citizens Administrator,
Division of Senior Citizens
Department of Public Health &
Social Services
130 University Drive, Suite 8
University Castle Mall
Mangilao, GU 96913
P: (671) 735-7011
F: (671) 735-7316
E: chiefdsc
    @dphss.govguam.net

HAWAII
Ms. Terri Byers
Director
Executive Office on Aging
No. 1 Capitol District
250 South Hotel Street, Suite
406
Honolulu, HI 96813
P: (808) 586-0100
F: (808) 586-0185

IDAHO
Ms. Sam Haws
Administrator
Commission on Aging
341 West Washington, 3rd Floor
P.O. Box 83720
Boise, ID 83720
P: (208) 334-3833 Ext. 226
F: (208) 334-3033

ILLINOIS
Mr. John K. Holton
Director
Department on Aging
One Natural Resources Way,
Suite 100
Springfield, IL 62702
P: (217) 785-2870
F: (217) 785-4477

INDIANA
Ms. Yonda Synder
Director, Division of Aging
Family & Social Services
Administration
402 West Washington Street
P.O. Box 7083
Indianapolis, IN 46207
P: (317) 232-7123
F: (307) 232-7867

KANSAS
Ms. Kari Bruffett
Acting Secretary
Department for Aging &
Disability Services
New England Building
503 South Kansas Avenue
Topeka, KS 66603
P: (785) 296-4986
F: (785) 296-0256
E: kari.bruffett
    @kdads.ks.gov

KENTUCKY
Ms. Deborah Anderson
Commissioner
Department for Aging &
Independent Living
Cabinet for Health & Family
Services
275 East Main Street, 3E-E
Frankfort, KY 40621
P: (502) 564-6930
F: (502) 564-4595
E: Deborah.anderson2@ky.gov

LOUISIANA
Ms. Karen Ryder
Assistant Director
Governor's Office of Elderly
Affairs
525 Florida, 4th Floor
Baton Rouge, LA 70801
P: (225) 342-7100
F: (225) 342-7133

MAINE
Mr. Ricker Hamilton
Deputy Commissioner of
Programs
Department of Health & Human
Services
221 State Street
Augusta, ME 04333
P: (207) 287-3707
F: (207) 287-3005
E: ricker.hamilton
    @maine.gov

MARYLAND
Ms. Rona E. Kramer
Secretary
Department of Aging
301 West Preston Street, Suite
1007
Baltimore, MD 21201
P: (410) 767-1100
F: (410) 333-7943

Aging

MASSACHUSETTS
Ms. Alice Bonner
Secretary
Executive Office of Elder
Affairs
One Ashburton Place
Boston, MA 02108
P: (617) 222-7417
F: (617) 727-9368

MICHIGAN
Ms. Kari Sederburg
Director
Office of Services to the Aging
300 East Michigan Avenue, 3rd
Floor
Lansing, MI 48913
P: (517) 373-8230
F: (517) 373-4092

MINNESOTA
Ms. Jean Wood
Director, Board on Aging
Department of Human Services
Aging & Adult Services
Division
P.O. Box 64976
St. Paul, MN 55164
P: (651) 431-2500
F: (651) 431-7453
E: jean.wood@state.mn.us

MISSISSIPPI
Ms. Melinda Bertucci
Director
Division of Aging & Adult
Services
Department of Human Services
750 North State Street
Jackson, MS 39202
P: (601) 359-4929
F: (601) 359-4370

MISSOURI
Ms. Celesta Hartgraves
Director
Division of Senior & Disability
Services
Department of Health and
Senior Services
P.O. Box 570
Jefferson City, MO 65102
P: (573) 526-3626
F: (573) 751-8687

MONTANA
Mr. Charles Rehbein
Aging Services Bureau Chief,
Office on Aging
Senior & Long Term Care
Division
Public Health and Human
Services
111 Sanders Street, P.O. Box
4210
Helena, MT 59604
P: (406) 444-7788
F: (406) 444-7743
E: crehbein@mt.gov

NEBRASKA
Ms. Cynthia Brammeier
Administrator
State Unit on Aging, State
Health & Human Services
301 Centennial Mall, South
P.O. Box 95026
Lincoln, NE 68509
P: (402) 471-4624
F: (402) 471-4619

NEVADA
Ms. Jane Gruner
Administrator
Aging & Disability Services
Division
3416 Goni Road, Building
D-132
Carson City, NV 89706
P: (775) 687-4210
F: (775) 687-4264
E: jgruner@adsd.nv.gov

NEW HAMPSHIRE
Ms. Sheri Rockburn
Acting Associate Commissioner
Department of Health & Human
Services
Brown Building
129 Pleasant Street
Concord, NH 03301

NEW JERSEY
Mr. Lowell Arye
Deputy Commissioner
Department of Human Services
222 South Warren Street
P.O. Box 700
Trenton, NJ 08625
P: (609) 292-9265
F: (609) 292-3824

NEW MEXICO
Mr. Gino Rinaldi
Secretary
Aging & Long-Term Services
Department
2550 Cerrillos Road
Santa Fe, NM 87505
P: (505) 476-4799
F: (505) 476-4750

NEW YORK
Ms. Corinda Crossdale
Director
State Office for the Aging
Two Empire State Plaza
Albany, NY 12223
P: (518) 474-7012
F: (518) 474-1398

NORTH CAROLINA
Ms. Suzanne Merrill
Acting Director
Division of Aging & Adult
Services
Department of Health & Human
Services
2101 Mail Service Center, 693
Palmer Dr.
Raleigh, NC 27699
P: (919) 855-3401
F: (919) 733-0443

NORTH DAKOTA
Ms. Cindy Marihart
Director
Aging Services Division
Department of Human Services
1237 West Divide Avenue, Suite
6
Bismarck, ND 58501
P: (701) 328-4607
F: (701) 328-8744

**NORTHERN MARIANA
ISLANDS**
Mr. Melvin Faiao
Acting Director
Commonwealth of the Northern
Mariana Islands
Office on Aging
P.O. Box 502178
Saipan, MP 96950
P: (670) 233-1320
F: (670) 233-1327

OHIO
Ms. Bonnie Kantor-Burman
Director
Department of Aging
50 West Broad Street, 9th Floor
Columbus, OH 43215
P: (614) 466-7246
F: (614) 995-1049

OKLAHOMA
Mr. Lance A. Robertson
Director
Aging Services Division
Department of Human Services
2401 Northwest 23rd Street,
Suite 40
Oklahoma City, OK 73107
P: (405) 521-2281
F: (405) 521-5805
E: lance.robertson
    @okdhs.org

OREGON
Ms. Mike McCormick
Director
Aging & People with
Disabilities Program
Department of Human Services
500 Summer Street, Northeast,
E12
Salem, OR 97301
P: (503) 945-5858
F: (503) 373-7823

PENNSYLVANIA
Ms. Teresa Osborne
Secretary
Department of Aging
555 Walnut Street, 5th Floor
Harrisburg, PA 17101
P: (717) 783-6128
F: (717) 783-6842

PUERTO RICO
Dr. Carmen Delia
    Sanchez Salgado
Ombudsman
Office for Elderly Affairs
P.O. Box 191179
San Juan, PR 00919
P: (787) 721-6121
F: (787) 725-2919

RHODE ISLAND
Mr. Charles J. Fogarty
Director
Division of Elderly Affairs
Hazard Building
74 West Road
Cranston, RI 02920
P: (401) 462-0565
F: (401) 462-0503

SOUTH CAROLINA
Sen. J. Yancey McGill (D)
Director
Lieutenant Governor's Office on
Aging
1301 Gervais Street, Suite 350
Columbia, SC 29201
P: (803) 734-9900
F: (803) 734-9886
E: mcgill@aging.sc.gov

SOUTH DAKOTA
Ms. Marilyn Kinsman
Administrator
Office of Adult Services &
Aging
Department of Social Services
700 Governors Drive
Pierre, SD 57501
P: (605) 773-3656
F: (605) 773-6834
E: marilyn.kinsman
    @state.sd.us

TENNESSEE
Mr. Jim Shulman
Executive Director
Commission on Aging &
Disability
Andrew Jackson Building
500 Deaderick Street, Suite 825
Nashville, TN 37243
P: (615) 741-2056 Ext. 134
F: (615) 741-3309
E: jim.shulman@tn.gov

TEXAS
Mr. Jon Weizenbaum
Commissioner
Department of Aging &
Disability Services
701 West 51st Street
P.O. Box 149030
Austin, TX 78714
P: (512) 438-3030
F: (512) 438-3011

U.S. VIRGIN ISLANDS
Ms. Murlean Van Beverhoudt
Administrator, Senior Citizen
Affairs Administration
Department of Human Services
Knud Hansen Complex,
Building A
1303 Hospital Ground
St. Thomas, VI 00820
P: (340) 774-0930 Ext. 4342
F: (340) 772-9849

UTAH
Mr. Nels Holmgren
Director
Division of Aging & Adult
Services
Department of Human Services
195 North 1950 West
Salt Lake City, UT 84116
P: (801) 538-3921
F: (801) 538-4395
E: nholmgren@utah.gov

VERMONT
Ms. Monica Hutt
Commissioner
Department of Disabilities,
Aging & Independent Living
Weeks Building
103 South Main Street
Waterbury, VT 05676
P: (802) 871-3350
F: (802) 871-3281

VIRGINIA
Mr. James Rothrock
Commissioner
Department for Aging &
Rehabilitative Services
8004 Franklin Farms Drive
Henrico, VA 23229
P: (804) 662-7010
F: (804) 662-7644

WASHINGTON
Mr. Bill Moss
Assistant Secretary
Aging & Long Term Support
Administration
Department of Social & Health
Services
P.O. Box 45050
Olympia, WA 98504
P: (360) 725-2260
F: (360) 407-0304

WEST VIRGINIA
Mr. Robert Roswall
Commissioner
Bureau of Senior Services
3003 Town Center Mall
1900 Kanawha Boulevard, East
Charleston, WV 25305
P: (304) 558-3317
F: (304) 558-5609

WISCONSIN
Ms. Carrie Molke
Director, Bureau on Aging and
Disability Resources
Department of Health Services
One West Wilson Street, Room
551
P.O. Box 7851
Madison, WI 53707
P: (608) 267-5267
F: (608) 267-3203

WYOMING
Ms. Heather Babbitt
Senior Administrator
Aging Division
Department of Health
6101 Yellowstone Road, Suite
186
Cheyenne, WY 82001
P: (307) 777-7995
F: (307) 777-5340

Agriculture

Enforces agriculture laws and administers agricultural programs in the state.

ALABAMA
Hon. John McMillan (R)
Commissioner
Department of Agriculture & Industries
Richard Beard Building
1445 Federal Drive
Montgomery, AL 36107
P: (334) 240-7100
F: (334) 240-7190

ALASKA
Ms. Franci Havemeister
Director
Division of Agriculture
Department of Natural Resources
1800 Glenn Highway, Suite 12
Palmer, AK 99645
P: (907) 761-3867
F: (907) 745-7112

AMERICAN SAMOA
Ms. Lealao Purcell
Director
Department of Agriculture
American Samoa Government
Industrial Parkway
Tafuna, AS 96779
P: (684) 699-9272

ARIZONA
Mr. Mark W. Killian
Director
Department of Agriculture
1688 West Adams
Phoenix, AZ 85007
P: (602) 542-5729
F: (602) 542-5420

ARKANSAS
Mr. Wes Ward
Secretary of Agriculture
Agriculture Department
1 Natural Resources Drive
Little Rock, AR 72205
P: (501) 683-4851
F: (501) 683-4852

CALIFORNIA
Ms. Karen Ross
Secretary
Department of Food & Agriculture
1220 N Street, Suite 400
Sacramento, CA 95814
P: (916) 654-0433
F: (916) 654-0403

COLORADO
Mr. Don Brown
Commissioner
Department of Agriculture
305 Interlocken Parkway
Broomfield, CO 80021
P: (303) 869-9000
F: (303) 466-2867

CONNECTICUT
Mr. Steven Reviczky
Commissioner
Department of Agriculture
165 Capitol Avenue
Hartford, CT 06106
P: (860) 713-2500
F: (860) 713-2514

DELAWARE
Mr. Ed Kee
Secretary
Department of Agriculture
2320 South DuPont Highway
Dover, DE 19901
P: (302) 698-4501
F: (302) 697-6287

FLORIDA
Hon. Adam H. Putnam (R)
Commissioner
Department of Agriculture & Consumer Services
The Capitol, PL-10
400 South Monroe Street
Tallahassee, FL 32399
P: (850) 488-3022
F: (850) 922-4936

GEORGIA
Mr. Gary Black
Commissioner
Department of Agriculture
19 Martin Luther King Jr. Drive, SW
204 Agricultural Building
Atlanta, GA 30334
P: (404) 656-3600
F: (404) 651-8206

GUAM
Ms. Mariquita F. Taitague
Director
Department of Agriculture
163 Dairy Road
Mangilao, GU 96913
P: (671) 734-3942
F: (671) 734-6569

HAWAII
Mr. Scott Enright
Chairperson
Department of Agriculture
1428 South King Street
Honolulu, HI 96814
P: (808) 973-9560
F: (808) 973-9613

IDAHO
Ms. Celia R. Gould
Director
State Department of Agriculture
2270 Old Penitentiary Road
P.O. Box 790
Boise, ID 83701
P: (208) 332-8500
F: (208) 332-2170

ILLINOIS
Mr. Philip Nelson
Acting Director
Department of Agriculture
State Fairgrounds
P.O. Box 19281
Springfield, IL 62794
P: (217) 782-2172
F: (217) 785-4505

INDIANA
Mr. Ted McKinney
Director
State Department of Agriculture
One North Capitol Avenue
Suite 600
Indianapolis, IN 46204
P: (317) 448-5023
F: (317) 232-1362

IOWA
Mr. Bill Northey
Secretary of Agriculture
Department of Agriculture & Land Stewardship
Wallace Building
502 East 9th Street
Des Moines, IA 50319
P: (515) 281-5321
F: (515) 281-6236

KANSAS
Ms. Jackie McClaskey
Secretary
Department of Agriculture
1320 Research Park Drive
Manhattan, KS 66502
P: (785) 564-6700
F: (785) 296-8389

KENTUCKY
Hon. James Comer (R)
Commissioner
Department of Agriculture
105 Corporate Drive
Frankfort, KY 40601
P: (502) 573-0450
F: (502) 573-0046
E: ag.web@ky.gov

LOUISIANA
Dr. Michael G. Strain
Commissioner
Department of Agriculture & Forestry
P.O. Box 631
Baton Rouge, LA 70821
P: (225) 922-1234
F: (225) 923-4880
E: commissioner
@ldaf.state.la.us

MAINE
Mr. Walter E. Whitcomb
Commissioner
Department of Agriculture, Conservation & Forestry
28 State House Station
18 Elkins Lane
Augusta, ME 04333
P: (207) 287-3419
F: (207) 287-7548
E: dacf@maine.gov

MARYLAND
Mr. Joe Bartenfelder
Secretary
Department of Agriculture
50 Harry S. Truman Parkway
Annapolis, MD 21401
P: (410) 841-5880
E: joe.bartenfelder
@maryland.gov

MASSACHUSETTS
Mr. John Lebeaux
Commissioner
Department of Agricultural Resources
251 Causeway Street, Suite 500
Boston, MA 02114
P: (617) 626-1720
F: (617) 626-1850

MICHIGAN
Ms. Jamie Clover Adams
Director
Department of Agriculture & Rural Development
525 West Allegan Street
P.O. Box 30017
Lansing, MI 48909
P: (517) 284-5716
F: (517) 335-1423

MINNESOTA
Mr. Dave Frederickson
Commissioner
Department of Agriculture
Freeman Office Building
625 Robert Street North
St. Paul, MN 55155
P: (651) 201-6219
F: (651) 201-6118

MISSISSIPPI
Hon. Cindy Hyde-Smith (R)
Commissioner
Department of Agriculture &
Commerce
121 North Jefferson Street
Jackson, MS 39201
P: (601) 359-1100
F: (601) 354-7710

MISSOURI
Mr. Richard Fordyce
Director
Department of Agriculture
P.O. Box 630
Jefferson City, MO 65102
P: (573) 751-5617
F: (573) 751-1784

MONTANA
Mr. Ron De Yong
Director
Department of Agriculture
302 North Roberts
Helena, MT 59620
P: (406) 444-3144
F: (406) 444-5409
E: agr@mt.gov

NEBRASKA
Mr. Greg Ibach
Director
Department of Agriculture
301 Centennial Mall South
P.O. Box 94947
Lincoln, NE 68509
P: (402) 471-2341
F: (402) 471-6876

NEVADA
Mr. Jim Barbee
Director
Department of Agriculture
405 South 21st Street
Sparks, NV 89431
P: (775) 353-3600
F: (775) 668-1178

NEW HAMPSHIRE
Ms. Lorraine Merrill
Commissioner
Department of Agriculture,
Markets & Food
P.O. Box 2042
Concord, NH 03302
P: (603) 271-3551
F: (603) 271-1109

NEW JERSEY
Mr. Douglas H. Fisher
Secretary of Agriculture
Department of Agriculture
P.O. Box 330
John Fitch Plaza
Trenton, NJ 08625
P: (609) 292-3976
F: (609) 292-3978

NEW MEXICO
Mr. Jeff Witte
Director/Secretary
Department of Agriculture
MSC 3189
P.O. Box 30005
Las Cruces, NM 88003
P: (575) 646-3007
F: (575) 646-8120

NEW YORK
Mr. Richard A. Ball
Commissioner
Department of Agriculture &
Markets
10B Airline Drive
Albany, NY 12235
P: (518) 457-2771

NORTH CAROLINA
Mr. Steve Troxler
Commissioner
Department of Agriculture &
Consumer Services
1001 Mail Service Center
Raleigh, NC 27699
P: (919) 707-3000
F: (919) 733-1141

NORTH DAKOTA
Mr. Doug Goehring
Commissioner
Department of Agriculture
600 East Boulevard Avenue
Department 602
Bismarck, ND 58505
P: (701) 328-2231
F: (701) 328-4567
E: ndda@nd.gov

OHIO
Mr. David Daniels
Director
Department of Agriculture
8995 East Main Street
Reynoldsburg, OH 43068
P: (614) 466-2732
F: (614) 466-6124

OKLAHOMA
Mr. Jim Reese
Secretary
Department of Agriculture,
Food & Forestry
P.O. Box 528804
Oklahoma City, OK 73152
P: (405) 522-5719
F: (405) 522-0909

OREGON
Ms. Katy Coba
Director
Department of Agriculture
635 Capitol Street, Northeast
Salem, OR 97301
P: (503) 986-4552
F: (503) 986-4750

PENNSYLVANIA
Mr. Russell Redding
Secretary
Department of Agriculture
2301 North Cameron Street
Harrisburg, PA 17110
P: (717) 772-2853
F: (717) 705-8402

PUERTO RICO
Ms. Myrna Comas Pagan
Secretary
Department of Agriculture
P.O. Box 10163
San Jaun, PR 00908
P: (787) 721-2120
F: (787) 723-8512

RHODE ISLAND
Mr. Kenneth Ayars
Chief
Division of Agriculture, DEM
235 Promenade Street, Room
370
Providence, RI 02908
P: (401) 222-2781 Ext. 4500
F: (401) 222-6047

SOUTH CAROLINA
Mr. Hugh E. Weathers
Commissioner
Department of Agriculture
Wade Hampton Office Building
P.O. Box 11280
Columbia, SC 29211
P: (803) 734-2179
F: (803) 734-2192

SOUTH DAKOTA
Mr. Lucas Lentsch
Secretary
Department of Agriculture
523 East Capitol
Pierre, SD 57501
P: (605) 773-5425
F: (605) 773-5926

TENNESSEE
Mr. Julius Johnson
Commissioner
Department of Agriculture
Melrose Station
P.O. Box 40627
Nashville, TN 37204
P: (615) 837-5100
F: (615) 837-5333

TEXAS
Hon. Sid Miller (R)
Commissioner
Department of Agriculture
P.O. Box 12847
Capitol Station
Austin, TX 78711
P: (512) 463-7567
F: (512) 463-1104

U.S. VIRGIN ISLANDS
Mr. Carlos A. Robles
Commissioner
Department of Agriculture
#1 Estate Lower Love
Kingshill
St. Croix, VI 00850
P: (340) 778-0991

UTAH
Ms. LuAnn Adams
Commissioner
Department of Agriculture &
Food
350 North Redwood Road
P.O. Box 146500
Salt Lake City, UT 84114
P: (801) 538-7100
F: (801) 538-7126

VERMONT
Mr. Chuck Ross
Secretary
Agency of Agriculture, Food &
Markets
116 State Street
Montpelier, VT 05620
P: (802) 828-3521
F: (802) 828-2361

VIRGINIA
Ms. Sandy Adams
Commissioner
Department of Agriculture &
Consumer Services
102 Governor Street
Richmond, VA 23219
P: (804) 786-3501
F: (804) 371-2945

Agriculture

WASHINGTON
Mr. Bud Hover
Director
State Department of Agriculture
1111 Washington Street SE, 2nd
Floor
P.O. Box 42560
Olympia, WA 98504
P: (360) 902-1887
F: (360) 902-2092
E: dhover@agr.wa.gov

WEST VIRGINIA
Mr. Walt Helmick
Commissioner
Department of Agriculture
1900 Kanawha Boulevard, East
State Capitol, Room E-28
Charleston, WV 25305
P: (304) 558-3550
F: (304) 558-2203
E: whelmick@wvda.us

WISCONSIN
Mr. Ben Brancel
Secretary
Department of Agriculture,
Trade & Consumer Protection
2811 Agriculture Drive
P.O. Box 8911
Madison, WI 53708
P: (608) 224-5012
F: (608) 224-5045

WYOMING
Mr. Doug Miyamoto
Director
Department of Agriculture
2219 Carey Avenue
Cheyenne, WY 82002
P: (307) 777-6569
F: (307) 777-6593

Alcohol and Substance Abuse

Plans, establishes and administers programs for the prevention, treatment, and rehabilitation of alcohol and/or drug and other abusers.

ALABAMA
Ms. Beverly Bell-Shambley
Associate Commissioner
Division of Mental Health &
Substance Abuse Services
100 North Union Street
P.O. Box 301410
Montgomery, AL 36130
P: (334) 242-3454
F: (334) 242-0725

ALASKA
Mr. Albert Wall
Director
Division of Behavioral Health
P.O. Box 110620
Juneau, AK 99811
P: (907) 465-4841
F: (907) 465-2668
E: albert.wall@alaska.gov

AMERICAN SAMOA
Dr. Taeaoafua Meki Solomona
Director
Department of Human & Social
Services
P.O. Box 997534
Pago Pago, AS 96799
P: (684) 633-1664
F: (684) 633-7449
E: mtsolomona@dhss.as

ARIZONA
Mr. Cory Nelson
Deputy Director
Division of Behavioral Health
Services
Department of Health Services
150 North 18th Avenue, Suite
500
Phoenix, AZ 85007
P: (602) 364-4566
F: (602) 542-1062
E: cory.nelson@azdhs.gov

ARKANSAS
Mr. Charlie Green
Director
Division of Behavioral Health
Services
305 South Palm Street
Little Rock, AR 72205
P: (501) 686-9981
F: (501) 686-9182
E: charlie.green
    @dhs.arkansas.gov

CALIFORNIA
Mr. Michael Cunningham
Acting Director
Substance Use Disorder
Services
1501 Capitol Avenue, MS 4000
P.O. Box 997413
Sacramento, CA 95899
P: (916) 440-7800
E: michael.cunningham
    @cdph.ca.gov

COLORADO
Mr. Patrick K. Fox
Acting Director
Office of Behavioral Health
Department of Human Services
3824 West Princeton Circle
Denver, CO 80236
P: (303) 866-7655
F: (303) 866-7090
E: patrick.fox@state.co.us

CONNECTICUT
Dr. Miriam E.
    Delphin-Rittmon
Commissioner
Department of Mental Health &
Addiction Services
410 Capitol Avenue, 4th Floor
P.O. Box 341431
Hartford, CT 06134
P: (860) 418-6850
F: (860) 418-6691
E: Miriam.delphin-rittmon
    @ct.gov

DELAWARE
Dr. Kevin A. Huckshorn
Director
Division of Substance Abuse &
Mental Health
Main Building
1901 North DuPont Highway
New Castle, DE 19720
P: (302) 255-9399
F: (302) 255-4428
E: Kevin.Huckshorn
    @state.de.us

DISTRICT OF COLUMBIA
Mr. Stephen T. Baron
Director
Department of Behavioral
Health
64 New York Avenue Northeast,
3rd Floor
Washington, DC 20002
P: (202) 673-2200
F: (202) 673-3433
E: steve.baron@dc.gov

FLORIDA
Mr. Rob Siedlecki
Department of Children &
Families
1317 Winewood Boulevard
Building 1, Room 202
Tallahassee, FL 32399
P: (850) 414-9065
F: (850) 487-2239
E: rob_siedlecki
    @dcf.state.fl.us

GEORGIA
Mr. Frank W. Berry III
Commissioner
Department of Behavioral
Health & Developmental
Disabilities
2 Peachtree Street, Northwest
Suite 24.290
Atlanta, GA 30303
P: (404) 463-7945
F: (770) 408-5480
E: fwberry@dbhdd.ga.gov

GUAM
Mr. Don Sabang
Supervisor
Department of Mental Health &
Substance Abuse
Drug & Alcohol Treatment
J&G Commercial Center, Suite
105F
Hagatna, GU 96910
P: (671) 475-5439
F: (671) 477-7782
E: don.sabang
    @mail.dmhsa.guam.gov

IDAHO
Ms. Kathy Skippen
Manager
Behavioral Health Substance
Use Disorders Unit
3rd Floor, Pete T. Cenarrusa
Building
450 West State Street
Boise, ID 83720
P: (208) 334-6676
F: (208) 332-7291
E: skippenk@dhw.idaho.gov

ILLINOIS
Ms. Theodora Binion-Taylor
Director
Division of Alcoholism &
Substance Abuse
401 South Clinton, 2nd Floor
Chicago, IL 60607
P: (312) 814-2300
F: (312) 814-3838
E: DHSASA4@dhs.state.il.us

INDIANA
Mr. Kevin Moore
Director
Division of Mental Health &
Addiction
Family & Social Services
Administration
402 West Washington Street,
Room W353
Indianapolis, IN 46204
P: (317) 232-7860
F: (317) 233-1986
E: kevin.moore@fssa.in.gov

IOWA
Mr. Gerd W. Clabaugh
Interim Director
Health Promotion & Chronic
Disease Prevention
Lucas State Office Building
321 East 12th Street
Des Moines, IA 50319
P: (515) 281-7689
F: (515) 281-4958
E: gerd.clabaugh
    @idph.iowa.gov

KANSAS
Mr. Bill Rein
Commissioner
Behavioral Health Services
915 Southwest Harrison, 9th
Floor South
Topeka, KS 66612
P: (785) 296-7228

LOUISIANA
Dr. Rochelle Head-Dunham
Assistant Secretary/Medical
Director
Office of Behavioral Health
Department of Health &
Hospitals
P. O. Box 629
Baton Rouge, LA 70821
P: (225) 342-2540
F: (225) 342-5066
E: rochelle.dunham@la.gov

Alcohol and Substance Abuse

MAINE
Mr. Guy R. Cousins
Director
Office of Adult Mental Health
Services, Department of Health
& Human Services
#11 State House Station
41 Anthony Avenue
Augusta, ME 04333
P: (207) 287-2595
F: (207) 287-4334
E: guy.cousins@maine.gov

MARYLAND
Ms. Gayle Jordan-Randolph
Deputy Secretary
Behavioral Health &
Disabilities
Department of Health & Mental
Hygiene
201 West Preston Street
Baltimore, MD 21201
P: (410) 767-3167

MASSACHUSETTS
Mr. Michael Botticelli
Assistant Commissioner for
Substance Abuse Services
Department of Public Health
250 Washington Street
Boston, MA 02108
P: (617) 624-5111
F: (617) 624-5261

MICHIGAN
Ms. Lynda Zeller
Deputy Director
Mental Health & Substance
Abuse Administration
Department of Community
Health
320 South Walnut Street
Lansing, MI 48913
P: (517) 335-0196
F: (517) 335-4798
E: zellerl2@michigan.gov

MINNESOTA
Mr. Dave Hartford
Assistant Commissioner
Chemical & Mental Health
Services
P.O. Box 0988
St. Paul, MN 55164
P: (651) 431-2323
F: (651) 431-7455
E: dave.hartford
   @state.mn.us

MISSISSIPPI
Mr. Herbert Loving
Director
Bureau of Alcohol & Drug
Services
1101 Robert E. Lee Building
239 North Lamar Street
Jackson, MS 39201
P: (601) 359-6224
F: (601) 359-6295
E: hloving@msdmh.org

NEBRASKA
Dr. Scot L. Adams
Director
Division of Behavioral Health,
Department of Health & Social
Services
301 Centennial Mall South, 3rd
Floor
P.O. Box 95026
Lincoln, NE 68509
P: (402) 471-8553
F: (402) 471-9449
E: scot.adams@nebraska.gov

NEVADA
Mr. Richard Whitley
Administrator
Division of Public & Behavioral
Health
4150 Technology Way, Suite
300
Carson City, NV 89706
P: (775) 684-4224
F: (775) 684-4211
E: rwhitley@health.nv.gov

NEW HAMPSHIRE
Mr. Joseph P. Harding
Director
Bureau of Drug & Alcohol
Services
Department of Health & Human
Services
105 Pleasant Street
Concord, NH 03301
P: (603) 271-6104
F: (603) 271-6116
E: jharding
   @dhhs.state.nh.us

NEW JERSEY
Ms. Lynn A. Kovich
Assistant Commissioner
Division of Mental Health &
Addiction Services
Department of Human Services
222 South Warren Street, 3rd
Floor
Trenton, NJ 08625
P: (609) 777-0702
F: (609) 341-2302
E: lynn.kovich
   @dhs.state.nj.us

NEW MEXICO
Mr. Brent Earnest
Cabinet Secretary
Human Services Department
P.O. Box 2348
Santa Fe, NM 87504
P: (505) 827-7750

NEW YORK
Ms. Arlene Gonzalez-Sanchez
Commissioner
Office of Alcoholism &
Substance Abuse Services
1450 Western Avenue
Albany, NY 12203
P: (518) 473-3460
F: (518) 457-5474

NORTH CAROLINA
Dr. Courtney M. Cantrell
Director
Division of Mental Health,
Developmental Disabilities &
Substance Abuse Services
Department of Health & Human
Services
3001 Mail Service Center
Raleigh, NC 27699
P: (919) 733-7011
F: (919) 508-0951
E: courtney.m.cantrell
   @dhhs.nc.gov

NORTH DAKOTA
Ms. Kris Storbeck
Substance Abuse Treatment
Administrator
Division of Mental Health &
Substance Abuse Services
1237 West Divide Avenue, Suite
1C
Bismarck, ND 58501
P: (701) 328-8982
F: (701) 328-8969
E: kstorbeck@nd.gov

**NORTHERN MARIANA
ISLANDS**
Mr. Joseph P. Villagomez
Secretary of Public Health
Department of Public Health
P.O. Box 500409
Saipan, MP 96950
P: (670) 234-8950
F: (670) 234-8930
E: jkvsaipan@aol.com

OHIO
Ms. Tracy J. Plouck
Director
Department of Mental Health &
Addiction Services
30 East Broad Street, 36th Floor
Columbus, OH 43215
P: (614) 466-2337
F: (614) 752-9453
E: tracy.plouck
   @mha.ohio.gov

OKLAHOMA
Mr. Steven Buck
Deputy Commissioner,
Communications & Prevention
Services
Department of Mental Health &
Substance Abuse Services
1200 Northeast 13th Street
P.O. Box 53277
Oklahoma City, OK 73152
P: (405) 522-3908
F: (405) 522-3650
E: sbuck@odmhsas.org

OREGON
Dr. Pam Martin
Director
Addictions & Mental Health
Division
State Health Authority
500 Summer Street Northeast,
E86
Salem, OR 97301
P: (503) 945-5879
F: (503) 378-8467
E: pamela.a.martin
   @dhsoha.state.or.us

PENNSYLVANIA
Mr. Gary Tennis
Secretary
Department of Drug & Alcohol
Programs
Health & Welfare Building
625 Forster Street, 9th Floor
West
Harrisburg, PA 17120
P: (717) 783-8200
F: (717) 787-6285

RHODE ISLAND
Ms. Maria Montanaro
Director
Department of Behavioral
Healthcare, Developmental
Disabilities & Hospitals
Barry Hall
14 Harrington Road
Cranston, RI 02920
P: (401) 462-2339
F: (401) 462-3204
E: maria.montanaro
   @bhddh.ri.gov

SOUTH CAROLINA
Mr. Bob Toomey
Director
Department of Alcohol & Other
Drug Abuse Services
2414 Bull Street
P.O. Box 8268
Columbia, SC 29202
P: (803) 896-5555
F: (803) 896-5557
E: btoomey@daodas.sc.gov

SOUTH DAKOTA
Ms. Tiffany Wolfgang
Division Director of Behavioral
Health
Division of Behavioral Health
Services
811 East 10th Street,
Department 9
Sioux Falls, SD 57103
P: (605) 367-5078
F: (605) 367-5239
E: Tiffany.Wolfgang
　@state.sd.us

TENNESSEE
Mr. E. Douglas Varney
Commissioner
Department of Mental Health &
Substance Abuse Services
Andrew Jackson Building
Nashville, TN 37243
P: (615) 532-6503
F: (615) 532-6514
E: Doug.Varney@tn.gov

TEXAS
Ms. Lauren Lacefield Lewis
Assistant Commissioner of
Mental Health & Substance
Abuse
Mental Health & Substance
Abuse Services
P.O. Box 149347
Austin, TX 78714
P: (512) 206-5145
F: (512) 206-5306
E: lauren.lacefieldlewis
　@dshs.state.tx.us

UTAH
Mr. Doug Thomas
Director
Division of Substance Abuse &
Mental Health
Department of Human Services
195 North 1950 West
Salt Lake City, UT 84116
P: (801) 538-4298
F: (801) 538-9892
E: dothomas@utah.gov

VERMONT
Ms. Barbara A. Cimaglio
Deputy Commissioner for
Alcohol & Drug Abuse
Programs
Division of Alcohol & Drug
Abuse Programs
108 Cherry Street, Room 202
P.O. Box 70, Drawer 27
Burlington, VT 05402
P: (802) 951-1258
F: (802) 863-7425
E: Barbara.Cimaglio
　@state.vt.us

VIRGINIA
Dr. Debra Ferguson
Commissioner
Department of Behavioral
Health & Developmental
Services
1220 Bank Street
P.O. Box 1797
Richmond, VA 23218
P: (804) 786-3921
F: (804) 371-6638
E: debra.ferguson
　@dbhds.virginia.gov

WEST VIRGINIA
Mr. Damon Iarossi
Deputy Commissioner
Bureau for Behavioral Health &
Health Facilities
350 Capitol Street, Room 350
Charleston, WV 25301
P: (304) 356-4811
F: (304) 558-1008

WISCONSIN
Ms. Joyce Bohn Allen
Director, Bureau of Prevention
Treatment and Recovery
Division of Mental Health &
Substance Abuse Services
1 West Wilson Street, Room
#850
Madison, WI 53707
P: (608) 266-1351
F: (608) 266-2579
E: joyce.allen
　@wisconsin.gov

WYOMING
Ms. Chris Newman
Senior Administrator
Behavioral Health Division
Department of Health
6101 Yellowstone Road, Suite
220
Cheyenne, WY 82002
P: (307) 777-6494
F: (307) 777-5849
E: chris.newman@wyo.gov

Alcoholic Beverage Control

Administers and enforces the laws governing the manufacturing, distribution, and dispensing of alcoholic beverages.

ALABAMA
Mr. H. Mac Gipson
Administrator
Alcoholic Beverage Control
Board
2715 Gunter Park Drive West
Montgomery, AL 36109
P: (334) 277-0569
F: (334) 277-2150

ALASKA
Ms. Cynthia Franklin
Director
Alcoholic Beverage Control
Board
2400 Viking Drive
Anchorage, AK 99501
P: (907) 269-0351

ARIZONA
Mr. John Cocca
Director
Department of Liquor Licenses
& Control
800 West Washington Street, 5th
Floor
Phoenix, AZ 85007
P: (602) 542-9032
F: (602) 542-5707

ARKANSAS
Mr. Carl Kirkland
Director, ABC Enforcement
Alcoholic Beverage Control
Division
1509 West 7th Street
Little Rock, AR 72201
P: (501) 682-1105
F: (501) 682-2221

Mr. Bud Roberts
Director, ABC Administration
Alcoholic Beverage Control
Division
1509 West 7th Street
Little Rock, AR 72201
P: (501) 682-8174
F: (501) 682-2221

CALIFORNIA
Mr. Timothy Gorsuch
Director
State Alcoholic Beverage
Control
3927 Lennane Drive, Suite 100
Sacramento, CA 95834
P: (916) 419-2512
F: (916) 419-2599
E: timothy.gorsuch
    @abc.ca.gov

COLORADO
Mr. Patrick Maroney
Director
Liquor & Tobacco Enforcement
Division
Department of Revenue
1881 Pierce Street, Suite 108
Lakewood, CO 80214
P: (303) 205-2934
F: (303) 205-2341

CONNECTICUT
Mr. John Suchy
Director
State Division of Liquor Control
165 Capitol Avenue
Hartford, CT 06106
P: (860) 713-6217
F: (860) 713-7235
E: John.Suchy@ct.gov

DELAWARE
Mr. John H. Cordrey
Commissioner
State Alcoholic Beverage
Control
Carvel State Building
820 North French Street
Wilmington, DE 19801
P: (302) 577-5222
F: (302) 577-3204
E: john.cordrey@state.de.us

DISTRICT OF COLUMBIA
Mr. Fred Moosally
Director
Alcoholic Beverage Regulation
Administration
2000 14th Street Northwest
Suite 400-South
Washington, DC 20009
P: (202) 442-4355
F: (202) 442-9563
E: abra@dc.gov

FLORIDA
Mr. Thomas Philpot
Director
Division of Alcoholic Beverages
& Tobacco
1940 North Monroe Street
Tallahassee, FL 32399
P: (850) 717-1107
F: (850) 922-5175

GEORGIA
Mr. Howard A. Tyler
Director, Alcohol & Tobacco
Division
Department of Revenue
1800 Century Center Boulevard,
Northeast
Room 4235
Atlanta, GA 30345
P: (404) 417-4902
F: (404) 417-4901
E: atdiv@dor.ga.gov

HAWAII
Mr. Franklin Don
    Pacarro Jr.
Administrator
Liquor Commission, City &
County of Honolulu
711 Kapiolani Boulevard, Suite
600
Honolulu, HI 96813
P: (808) 768-7303
F: (808) 768-7311

Mr. Gerald T. Rapozo
Director
Liquor Control Commission,
County of Kauai
4444 Rice Street, Suite 120
Lihue, HI 96766
P: (808) 241-4966
F: (808) 241-6585
E: liquor@kauai.gov

Mr. Franklyn L. Silva
Director
Department of Liquor Control,
County of Maui
2145 Kaohu Street, Room 105
Wailuku, HI 96793
P: (808) 243-7772
F: (808) 243-7558
E: liquor@mauicounty.gov

Mr. Gerald Takase
Director
Department of Liquor Control,
County of Hawaii
Hilo Lagoon Centre
101 Aupuni Street, Suite 230
Hilo, HI 96720
P: (808) 961-8218
F: (808) 961-8684
E: cohdlc@co.hawaii.hi.us

IDAHO
Mr. Jeffrey R. Anderson
Director
State Liquor Division
1349 East Beechcraft Court
Boise, ID 83716
P: (208) 947-9402
F: (208) 947-9401
E: info@idaholottery.com

Lt. Russell Wheatley
Bureau Chief, ABC
Alcohol Beverage Control
State Police
700 South Stratford Drive, Suite
115
Meridian, ID 83642
P: (208) 884-7062
F: (208) 884-7096

ILLINOIS
Ms. Mary McNulty
Commission Secretary
Liquor Control Commission
100 West Randolph Street, Suite
7-801
Chicago, IL 60601
P: (312) 814-1801
F: (312) 814-2241

INDIANA
Mr. David Cook
Chair
Alcohol & Tobacco
Commission
302 West Washington Street,
Room E114
Indianapolis, IN 46204
P: (317) 232-2462
F: (317) 234-1520

IOWA
Mr. Stephen Larson
Administrator
Alcoholic Beverages Division
1918 Southeast Hulsizer Road
Ankeny, IA 50021
P: (515) 281-7402
F: (515) 281-7372
E: larson@iowabd.com

KANSAS
Mr. Dean Reynoldson
Director
Department of Revenue
Docking State Office Building
915 Southwest Harrison, Room
214 North
Topeka, KS 66625
P: (785) 296-4388
F: (785) 296-7185
E: dean.reynoldson
    @kdor.ks.gov

KENTUCKY
Mr. Frederick Higdon
Commissioner
Department of Alcoholic
Beverage Control
1003 Twilight Trail, Suite A-2
Frankfort, KY 40601
P: (502) 564-4850
F: (502) 564-1442
E: Frederick.higdon@ky.gov

Alcoholic Beverage Control

LOUISIANA
Mr. Troy Hebert
Commissioner
Office of Alcohol & Tobacco
Control
Department of Revenue
8585 Archives Avenue, Suite
220
Baton Rouge, LA 70809
P: (225) 925-4054
F: (225) 925-3975
E: troy.herbert@atc.la.gov

MARYLAND
Hon. Peter Franchot (D)
Comptroller
Office of the Comptroller
L.L. Goldstein Treasury
Building
P.O. Box 466
Annapolis, MD 21404
P: (410) 260-7801
F: (410) 974-3808
E: mdcomptroller
   @comp.state.md.us

Mr. Jeffrey A. Kelly
Director
Field Enforcement Division
80 Calvert Street
Annapolis, MD 21404
P: (410) 260-7104
F: (410) 974-5564
E: jakelly@comp.state.md.us

MASSACHUSETTS
Mr. Ralph Sacramone
Executive Director
Alcoholic Beverage Control
Commission
239 Causeway Street, First Floor
Boston, MA 02114
P: (617) 727-3040 Ext. 731
F: (617) 727-1510

MICHIGAN
Mr. Andrew J. Deloney
Chair
Liquor Control Commission
525 West Allegan
Lansing, MI 48933
P: (517) 284-6310
F: (517) 763-0057
E: ajdeloney@michigan.gov

MISSISSIPPI
Ms. Patsy Holeman
Director
Alcoholic Beverage Control
Division
P.O. Box 540
Madison, MS 39130
P: (601) 856-1302
F: (601) 856-1390

Mr. J. Ed Morgan
Commissioner of Revenue
Department of Revenue
P.O. Box 22828
Jackson, MS 39225
P: (601) 923-7400
F: (601) 923-7423

MISSOURI
Mr. Lafayette E. Lacy
State Supervisor
Division of Alcohol & Tobacco
Control
Department of Public Safety
1738 East Elm Street
Jefferson City, MO 65101
P: (573) 526-4540
F: (573) 526-4369
E: lafayette.lacy
   @dps.mo.gov

MONTANA
Ms. Shawna Helfert
Administrator, Liquor Control
Division
Department of Revenue
Sam W. Mitchell Building
125 North Roberts Street, 3rd
Floor
Helena, MT 59601
P: (406) 444-1464
F: (406) 444-0718
E: shelfert@state.mt.gov

NEBRASKA
Mr. Hobert B. Rupe
Executive Director
Liquor Control Commission
301 Centennial Mall South, 5th
Floor
Lincoln, NE 68509
P: (402) 471-2574
F: (402) 471-2814
E: hobert.rupe@nebraska.gov

NEVADA
Ms. JoLynn Smith
Supervisor
Department of Taxation
1550 East College Parkway,
Suite 115
Carson City, NV 89706
P: (775) 684-2029
F: (775) 684-2020

NEW HAMPSHIRE
Mr. Joseph W. Mollica
Chair
State Liquor Commission
Storrs Street - Robert J. Hart
Building
Concord, NH 03302
P: (603) 271-3134
F: (603) 271-1107
E: joseph.mollica
   @liquor.state.nh.us

NEW JERSEY
Mr. Michael I. Halfacre
Director
Division of Alcoholic Beverage
Control
Department of Law & Public
Safety
140 East Front Street, 5th Floor
Trenton, NJ 08625
P: (609) 984-2830
F: (609) 633-6078
E: michael.halfacre
   @lps.state.nj.us

NEW MEXICO
Ms. Mary Kay Root
Director
Alcohol & Gaming Division
Regulation & Licensing
Department
2550 Cerrillos Road, 2nd Floor
Santa Fe, NM 87505
P: (505) 476-4550
F: (505) 476-4595
E: MaryKay.Root@state.nm.us

NORTH CAROLINA
Mr. Robert A. Hamilton
Chief Administrator
Alcoholic Beverage Control
Commission
4307 Mail Service Center
Raleigh, NC 27699
P: (919) 779-8323
F: (919) 662-3583

NORTH DAKOTA
Mr. Blane Braunberger
Supervisor, Alcoholic Beverages
Office of State Tax Commission
600 East Boulevard Avenue
Department 127
Bismarck, ND 58505
P: (701) 328-3011
F: (701) 328-1283
E: bbraunberger@nd.gov

OHIO
Mr. Peter Patitsas
Division Counsel
Division of Liquor Control
6606 Tussing Road
Reynoldsburg, OH 43068
P: (614) 995-3420
F: (614) 644-2480

OKLAHOMA
Mr. A. Keith Burt
Director
Alcoholic Beverage Laws
Enforcement Commission
3812 North Santa Fe
Suite 200
Oklahoma City, OK 73118
P: (405) 521-3484
F: (405) 521-6578
E: kburt@able.ok.gov

OREGON
Mr. Steve Marks
Executive Director
Liquor Control Commission
9079 Southeast McLoughlin
Boulevard
Portland, OR 97222
P: (503) 872-5062
F: (503) 872-5266

PENNSYLVANIA
Mr. John E. Metzger
Executive Director
Liquor Control Board
Northwest Office Building
901 Capitol Street
Harrisburg, PA 17124
P: (717) 787-7114
F: (717) 772-3725

RHODE ISLAND
Ms. Maria D'Alessandro
Deputy Director of Securities,
Commercial Licensing, Racing
& Athletics
Division of Commercial
Licensing - Liquor Enforcement
& Compliance
1511 Pontiac Avenue, Building
69-1
Cranston, RI 02920
P: (401) 462-9506
F: (401) 462-9532

SOUTH CAROLINA
Ms. Tammy Young
Supervisor, ABL Section
Alcoholic Beverage Licensing
Department of Revenue
300 Outlet Pointe Boulevard,
Suite A
Columbia, SC 29210
P: (803) 898-5864
F: (803) 898-5899

Alcoholic Beverage Control

SOUTH DAKOTA
Mr. Michael Houdyshell
Director
Department of Revenue
445 East Capital Avenue
Pierre, SD 57501
P: (605) 773-3311
F: (605) 773-6729

TENNESSEE
Mr. E. Keith Bell
Director
Alcoholic Beverage
Commission
500 James Robertson Parkway
Davy Crockett Tower, 3rd Floor
Nashville, TN 37243
P: (615) 741-1602
F: (615) 741-0847
E: keith.bell@tn.gov

TEXAS
Ms. Sherry Cook
Executive Director
Alcoholic Beverage
Commission
5806 Mesa Drive
Austin, TX 78731
P: (512) 206-3366
F: (512) 206-3203
E: sherry.cook
   @tabc.state.tx.us

UTAH
Mr. Salvador Petilos
Executive Director
Department of Alcoholic
Beverage Control
1625 South 900 West
Salt Lake City, UT 84130
P: (801) 977-6800
F: (801) 977-6888
E: spetilos@utah.gov

VERMONT
Mr. William Goggins
Director, Education, Licensing
& Enforcement
Department of Liquor Control
13 Green Mountain Drive
Montpelier, VT 05620
P: (802) 828-2339

VIRGINIA
Mr. Jeffrey Painter
Chair
State Alcoholic Beverage
Control
2901 Hermitage Road
Richmond, VA 23220
P: (804) 213-4404
F: (804) 213-4411

WASHINGTON
Ms. Jane Rushford
Board Chair
State Liquor Control Board
3000 Pacific Avenue, Southeast
Olympia, WA 98504
P: (360) 664-1711
F: (360) 586-3190

WEST VIRGINIA
Mr. Ronald M. Moats
Acting Commissioner
Alcohol Beverage Control
Administration
322 70th Street Southeast
Charleston, WV 25304
P: (304) 558-2481
F: (304) 558-0081
E: ronald.m.moats@wv.gov

WISCONSIN
Ms. Justin Shemanski
Criminal Investigation Section
Chief
Department of Revenue
2135 Rimrock Road
Madison, WI 53713
P: (608) 266-0286
F: (608) 261-6240
E: justin.shemanski
   @revenue.wi.gov

WYOMING
Mr. Greg Cook
Administrator
Liquor Distribution Division
Department of Revenue
6601 Campstool Road
Cheyenne, WY 82002
P: (307) 777-6448
F: (307) 777-6255
E: greg.cook@wyo.gov

Arbitration and Mediation

Promotes the settlement of a variety of labor disputes.

ALABAMA
Mr. Fitzgerald Washington
Commissioner
Department of Labor
649 Monroe Street
Montgomery, AL 36131
P: (334) 242-8990

ALASKA
Ms. Heidi Drygas
Commissioner
Department of Labor &
Workforce Development
P.O. Box 111149
Juneau, AK 99811
P: (907) 465-2700
F: (907) 465-2784
E: heidi.drygas@alaska.gov

AMERICAN SAMOA
Mr. Le'i S. Thompson
Director
Department of Human
Resources
Executive Office Building
AP Lutali, 2nd Floor
Pago Pago, AS 96799
P: (684) 644-4485
F: (684) 633-1139
E: sonnythompson
    @samoatelco.com

COLORADO
Ms. Ellen Golombek
Executive Director
Department of Labor &
Employment
633 17th Street, Suite 201
Denver, CO 80202
P: (303) 318-8020
F: (303) 318-8047
E: Ellen.Golombek
    @state.co.us

CONNECTICUT
Ms. Sharon Palmer
Commissioner
Department of Labor
200 Folly Brook Boulevard
Westerfield, CT 06109
P: (860) 263-6505
F: (850) 263-6529
E: sharon.palmer@ct.gov

DELAWARE
Mr. John McMahon
Secretary of Labor
Department of Labor
4425 North Market Street
Wilmington, DE 19802
P: (302) 761-8000
F: (302) 761-6621
E: john.mcmahon@state.de.us

FLORIDA
Mr. Mike Hogan
Chair
Public Employees Relations
Commission
4050 Esplanade Way, Room 150
Tallahassee, FL 32399
P: (850) 488-8641
F: (850) 488-9704
E: mike.hogan
    @perc.myflorida.com

GEORGIA
Hon. Mark Butler (R)
Commissioner
Department of Labor
148 International Boulevard
Northeast
Atlanta, GA 30303
P: (404) 232-7300
F: (404) 656-2683
E: commissioner@gdol.ga.gov

GUAM
Mr. Manuel Q. Cruz
Director
Department of Labor
Government of Guam
P.O. Box 9970
Tamuning, GU 96931
P: (671) 647-6510
F: (671) 674-6517

Mr. Tony A. Lamorena V
Director
Civil Service Commission
P.O. Box 3156
Hagatna, GU 96932
P: (671) 647-1855
F: (671) 647-1867

IDAHO
Mr. Kenneth D. Edmunds
Director
Department of Labor
317 West Main Street
Boise, ID 83735
P: (208) 334-6110
F: (208) 334-6430
E: kenneth.edmunds
    @labor.idaho.gov

ILLINOIS
Ms. Melissa Mlynski
Executive Director
Labor Relations Board
160 North LaSalle Street, Suite
S-400
Chicago, IL 60601
P: (217) 785-4017
F: (312) 793-6989

INDIANA
Mr. Rick J. Ruble
Commissioner
Department of Labor
402 West Washington Street,
Room W195
Indianapolis, IN 46204
P: (317) 232-2655
F: (317) 233-3790
E: rruble@dol.in.gov

IOWA
Mr. Michael A. Mauro
Commissioner
Division of Labor Services
1000 East Grand Avenue
Des Moines, IA 50319
P: (515) 281-3447
F: (515) 281-4698
E: michael.mauro
    @iwd.iowa.gov

KANSAS
Ms. Lana Gordon
Secretary of Labor
Department of Labor
401 Southwest Topeka
Boulevard
Topeka, KS 66603
P: (785) 296-5058
F: (785) 368-5289
E: lana.gordon@dol.ks.gov

KENTUCKY
Ms. Jodie M. Craig
Program Coordinator
Labor-Management Relations &
Mediation
1047 U.S. Highway 127 South
Suite 4
Frankfort, KY 40601
P: (502) 564-3203
F: (502) 696-1897
E: jodie.craig@ky.gov

LOUISIANA
Mr. Curt Eysink
Executive Director
Workforce Commission
1001 North 23rd Street
P.O. Box 94094
Baton Rouge, LA 70804
P: (225) 342-3111
F: (225) 342-3778
E: owd@lwc.la.gov

MAINE
Ms. Jeanne Paquette
Commissioner
Department of Labor
54 State House Station
Augusta, ME 04333
P: (207) 623-7900
F: (207) 623-7934
E: jeanne.paquette
    @maine.gov

MASSACHUSETTS
Ms. Susan M. Jeghelian
Executive Director
Office of Public Collaboration
100 Morrissey Boulevard
McCormack Building, 1st Floor,
Room 627
Boston, MA 02125
P: (617) 287-4047
F: (617) 287-4049
E: susan.jeghelian@umb.edu

MICHIGAN
Ms. Ruthanne Okun
Director
Bureau of Employment
Relations
Cadillac Place, Suite 2-750
3026 West Grand Boulevard
Detroit, MI 48202
P: (313) 456-3519
F: (313) 456-3511
E: okunr@michigan.gov

MINNESOTA
Mr. Josh Tilsen
Commissioner
Bureau of Mediation Services
1380 Energy Lane, Suite 2
St. Paul, MN 55108
P: (651) 649-5436
E: josh.tilsen@state.mn.us

MONTANA
Hon. Sheila Hogan
Director
Department of Administration
P.O. Box 200101
Helena, MT 59620
P: (406) 444-3033
F: (406) 444-6194
E: shogan@mt.gov

NEBRASKA
Ms. Annette Hord
Clerk/Administrator
Commission of Industrial
Relations
301 Centennial Mall South
P.O. Box 94864
Lincoln, NE 68509
P: (402) 471-2934
F: (402) 471-6597
E: annette.hord
    @nebraska.gov

Arbitration and Mediation

NEVADA
Mr. Philip E. Larson
Chair
Local Government
Employee-Management
Relations Board
Department of Business &
Industry
2501 East Sahara Avenue, Suite
203
Las Vegas, NV 89104
P: (702) 486-4504
F: (702) 486-4355
E: emrb@business.nv.gov

NEW HAMPSHIRE
Mr. James W. Craig
Commissioner of Labor
Department of Labor
95 Pleasant Street
Concord, NH 03301
P: (603) 271-3171
F: (603) 271-6852
E: jcraig@labor.state.nh.us

NEW JERSEY
Mr. Harold Wirths
Commissioner
Department of Labor &
Workforce Development
P.O. Box 110
Trenton, NJ 08625
P: (609) 292-2323
F: (609) 633-9271
E: hal.wirths
    @dol.state.nj.us

NEW MEXICO
Ms. Celina Bussey
Secretary
Department of Workforce
Solutions
401 Broadway, Northeast
P.O. Box 1928
Albuquerque, NM 87103
P: (505) 841-8405
F: (505) 841-8491
E: celina.bussey
    @state.nm.us

NORTH CAROLINA
Hon. Cherie K. Berry (R)
Commissioner
Department of Labor
1101 Mail Service Center
Raleigh, NC 27699
P: (919) 807-2796
F: (919) 733-7640
E: cherie.berry
    @labor.nc.gov

NORTH DAKOTA
Ms. Bonnie Storbakken
Commissioner of Labor
Department of Labor
600 East Boulevard Avenue
Department 406
Bismarck, ND 58505
P: (701) 328-2660
F: (701) 328-2031
E: bstorbakken@nd.gov

**NORTHERN MARIANA
ISLANDS**
Ms. Edith DeLeon Guerrero
Secretary
Department of Labor
Capitol Hill
Saipan, MP 96950
P: (670) 664-3196
F: (670) 664-3197
E: gov.wia1@gtepacifica.net

OHIO
Mr. Robert Blair
Director
Department of Administrative
Services
30 East Broad Street, Suite 4040
Columbus, OH 43215
P: (614) 466-6511
F: (614) 644-8151
E: Robert.Blair
    @das.ohio.gov

OKLAHOMA
Hon. Mark Costello (R)
Commissioner of Labor
Department of Labor
3017 North Stiles, Suite 100
Oklahoma City, OK 73105
P: (405) 521-6100
F: (405) 521-6018
E: mark.costello
    @labor.ok.gov

OREGON
Ms. Kathryn A. Logan
Chair
Employment Relations Board
Old Garfield School Building,
Suite 400
528 Cottage Street, Northeast
Salem, OR 97301
P: (503) 378-3807
F: (503) 373-0021
E: Kathryn.Logan
    @state.or.us

PENNSYLVANIA
Ms. Kathy M. Manderino
Secretary
Department of Labor & Industry
651 Boas Street, Room 1700
Harrisburg, PA 17121
P: (717) 787-5279
F: (717) 787-8826

PUERTO RICO
Mr. Vance Thomas
Secretary
Department of Labor & Human
Resources
P.O. Box 195540
Hato Rey, PR 00918
P: (787) 754-2119
F: (787) 753-9550

SOUTH CAROLINA
Ms. Richele Taylor
Director
Department of Labor, Licensing
& Regulation
P.O. Box 11329
Columbia, SC 29211
P: (803) 896-4390
F: (803) 896-4393

SOUTH DAKOTA
Ms. Marcia Hultman
Secretary
Department of Labor &
Regulation
700 Governors Drive
Pierre, SD 57501
P: (605) 773-3101
F: (605) 773-6184
E: marcia.hultman
    @state.sd.us

TENNESSEE
Mr. Burns Phillips
Commissioner
Department of Labor &
Workforce Development
220 French Landing Drive
Nashville, TN 37243
P: (615) 741-6642
F: (615) 741-5078
E: burns.phillips@tn.gov

TEXAS
Mr. Larry E. Temple
Executive Director
Workforce Commission
101 East 15th Street
Austin, TX 78778
P: (512) 463-0735
F: (512) 475-2321
E: larry.temple
    @twc.state.tx.us

UTAH
Ms. Sherrie M. Hayashi
Commissioner & Department
Director
Labor Commission
160 East 300 South, 3rd Floor
P.O. Box 146600
Salt Lake City, UT 84114
P: (801) 530-6848
F: (801) 530-6390
E: shayashi@utah.gov

VERMONT
Mr. Timothy J. Noonan
Executive Director
Labor Relations Board
133 State Street
Monpelier, VT 05633
P: (802) 828-2700
F: (802) 828-2392
E: tim.noonan@state.vt.us

VIRGINIA
Mr. William Burge
Assistant Commissioner/Acting
Commissioner
Department of Labor & Industry
600 East Main Street, Room 207
Richmond, VA 23219
P: (804) 786-2377
F: (804) 371-6524

WASHINGTON
Mr. Joel Sacks
Director
Department of Labor &
Industries
P.O. Box 44000
Olympia, WA 98504
P: (360) 902-5799
F: (360) 902-5792
E: joel.sacks@lni.wa.gov

WEST VIRGINIA
Mr. John R. Junkins
Acting Commissioner
Division of Labor
Department of Commerce
749 B, Building 6, Capitol
Complex
Charleston, WV 25305
P: (304) 558-7890
F: (304) 558-2415
E: john.r.junkins@wv.gov

WISCONSIN
Mr. Reggie Newson
Secretary
Department of Workforce
Development
201 East Washington Avenue
GEF-1, Room A400, P.O. Box
7946
Madison, WI 53707
P: (608) 266-3131
F: (608) 266-1784
E: reggie.newson
    @dwd.wisconsin.gov

Archives

Identifies, acquires, preserves and makes available state government records of continuing historical and research value.

ALABAMA
Mr. Steve Murray
Director
Department of Archives & History
624 Washington Avenue
P.O. Box 300100
Montgomery, AL 36130
P: (334) 242-4441
E: steve.murray
    @archives.alabama.gov

ALASKA
Mr. Dean Dawson
State Archivist
State Archives
P.O. Box 110525
Juneau, AK 99811
P: (907) 465-2270
F: (907) 465-2465
E: dean.dawson@alaska.gov

Ms. Heidi Drygas
Commissioner
Department of Labor & Workforce Development
P.O. Box 111149
Juneau, AK 99811
P: (907) 465-2700
F: (907) 465-2784
E: heidi.drygas@alaska.gov

AMERICAN SAMOA
Mr. James Hemphill
Territorial Archivist
Office of Archives & Records Management
American Samoa Government
Pago Pago, AS 96799
P: (684) 699-6848
F: (684) 699-6849
E: James.Himphill@la.as.gov

ARIZONA
Ms. Karen Axsom
Director, Labor Department
Industrial Commission
800 West Washington Street
Phoenix, AZ 85007
P: (602) 542-4515
F: (602) 542-7889
E: LaborAdmin@azica.gov

Dr. Melanie Sturgeon
Division Director
State Library, Archives & Public Records
History & Archives Division
1901 West Madison
Phoenix, AZ 85009
P: (602) 926-3720
F: (602) 256-7982
E: services@lib.az.us

ARKANSAS
Ms. Lisa Speer
Director
History Commission
One Capitol Mall, Suite 2B215
Little Rock, AR 72201
P: (501) 682-6900
F: (501) 682-6916
E: lisa.speer@arkansas.gov

CALIFORNIA
Ms. Nancy Lenoil
Chief
State Archives
1020 O Street
Sacramento, CA 95814
P: (916) 653–7715
F: (916) 653–7363
E: nlenoil@sos.ca.gov

COLORADO
Mr. George Orlowski
State Archivist
State Archives
Department of Personnel & Administration
1525 Sherman Street
Denver, CO 80203
P: (303) 866-2550
F: (303) 866-2257
E: george.orlowski
    @state.co.us

CONNECTICUT
Ms. Lizette Pelletier
State Archivist
State Library & Archives
231 Capitol Avenue
Hartford, CT 06106
P: (860) 566-1100 Ext. 304
E: lizette.pelletier@ct.gov

DELAWARE
Mr. Stephen M. Marz
Director
Public Archives
121 Martin Luther King Jr. Blvd., North
Dover, DE 19901
P: (302) 744-5000
F: (302) 739-8436

DISTRICT OF COLUMBIA
Ms. Deborah A. Carroll
Director
Department of Employment Services
4058 Minnesota Avenue, Northeast
Washington, DC 20019
P: (202) 724-7000
F: (202) 673-6993
E: does@dc.gov

Mr. Clarance Davis
Administrator
District of Columbia Archives
1300 Naylor Court, Northwest
Washington, DC 20001
P: (202) 671-1105
F: (202) 727-6076
E: archives@dc.gov

FLORIDA
Mr. Gerard Clark
Bureau Chief
Archives & Record Management
R.A. Gray Building
Tallahassee, FL 32399
P: (850) 245-6639
F: (850) 245-6744
E: Gerard.Clark
    @DOS.MyFlorida.com

GEORGIA
Mr. Christopher M. Davidson
Director
The Georgia Archives
5800 Jonesboro Road
Morrow, GA 30260
P: (678) 364-3710
F: (678) 364-3860

HAWAII
Ms. Susan E. Shaner
State Archivist
Department of Accounting & General Services
Kekauluohi Bldg., Iolani Palace Grounds
364 South King Street
Honolulu, HI 96813
P: (808) 586-0329
F: (808) 586-0330
E: archives@hawaii.gov

Ms. Linda Chu Takayama
Director
Department of Labor & Industrial Relations
830 Punchbowl Street
Honolulu, HI 96813
P: (808) 586-8844
F: (808) 586-9099
E: dlir.director@hawaii.gov

IDAHO
Mr. David Matte
Acting State Archivist
State Archives
2205 Old Penitentiary Road
Boise, ID 83712
P: (208) 514-2328
F: (208) 334-2626
E: david.matte
    @ishs.idaho.gov

ILLINOIS
Mr. David A. Joens
Director
State Archives
Margaret Cross Norton Building
Capitol Complex
Springfield, IL 62756
P: (217) 782-4682
F: (217) 524-3930

INDIANA
Mr. Jim Corridan
Director/State Archivist
Commission on Public Records
402 West Washington Street, Room W472
Indianapolis, IN 46204
P: (317) 232-3380
F: (317) 233-1713
E: jcorridan@icpr.IN.gov

IOWA
Mr. Anthony Jahn
State Archivist
Historical Society of Iowa
Capitol Complex
East 6th & Locust Street
Des Moines, IA 50319
P: (515) 281-4895
F: (515) 282-0502
E: anthony.jahn@iowa.gov

KANSAS
Ms. Matt Veatch
Division Director
State Archives
Historical Society
6425 Southwest 6th Avenue
Topeka, KS 66615
P: (785) 272-8681 Ext. 271
F: (785) 272-8682
E: mveatch@kshs.org

KENTUCKY
Ms. Barbara Teague
State Archivist & Records Administrator
Department for Libraries & Archives
Public Records Division
300 Coffee Tree Road
Frankfort, KY 40601
P: (502) 564-8300 ext.249
F: (502) 564-5773
E: barbara.teague@ky.gov

LOUISIANA
Dr. Florent Hardy Jr.
State Archivist
State Archives
Office of the Secretary of State
3851 Essen Lane
Baton Rouge, LA 70809
P: (225) 922-1200
F: (225) 922-0433
E: florent.hardy
   @sos.louisiana.gov

MAINE
Mr. Dave Cheever
State Archivist
State Archives
84 State House Station
Augusta, ME 04333
P: (207) 287-5790
F: (207) 287-6035
E: david.cheever@maine.gov

MARYLAND
Mr. Timothy Baker
Acting State Archivist
State Archives
350 Rowe Boulevard
Annapolis, MD 21401
P: (410) 260-6402
F: (410) 974-2525
E: tim.baker@maryland.gov

MASSACHUSETTS
Dr. John D. Warner Jr.
Archivist of the Commonwealth
State Archives
Secretary of the Commonwealth
220 Morrissey Boulevard
Boston, MA 02125
P: (617) 727-2816
F: (617) 288-8429
E: john.warner
   @sec.state.ma.us

MICHIGAN
Mr. Mark Harvey
State Archivist
Archives of Michigan
Library & Historical Center
702 West Kalamazoo Street
Lansing, MI 48913
P: (517) 373-1415
E: HarveyM@michigan.gov

MINNESOTA
Mr. Shawn Rounds
State Archivist
State Archives
Historical Society
345 West Kellogg Boulevard
St. Paul, MN 55102
P: (651) 259-3265
F: (651) 296-9961
E: shawn.rounds@mnhs.org

MISSISSIPPI
Ms. Katherine Blount
Executive Director
Department of Archives &
History
200 North Street
P.O. Box 571
Jackson, MS 39205
P: (601) 576-6850
F: (601) 576-6964
E: blount@mdah.state.ms.us

MISSOURI
Mr. John Dougan
State Archivist
State Archives
600 West Main Street
P.O. Box 1747
Jefferson City, MO 65102
P: (573) 751-3280
F: (573) 526-7333
E: archref@sos.mo.gov

MONTANA
Jodie Foley
State Archivist
Historical Society, Research
Center
225 North Roberts Street
Helena, MT 59620
P: (406) 444-7482
F: (406) 444-5297
E: jofoley@mt.gov

NEBRASKA
Ms. Gayla Koerting
State Archivist
Historical Society
P.O. Box 82554
Lincoln, NE 68501
P: (402) 471-4783
E: gayla.koerting
   @nebraska.gov

NEVADA
Mr. Jeffrey M. Kintop
Assistant Administrator
State Library & Archives
Department of Administration
100 North Stewart Street
Carson City, NV 89701
P: (775) 684-3410
F: (775) 684-3371
E: jkintop@admin.nv.gov

NEW HAMPSHIRE
Mr. Brian Nelson Burford
Director & State Archivist
Division of Archives & Records
Management
Department of State
71 South Fruit Street
Concord, NH 03301
P: (603) 271-2236
F: (603) 271-2272
E: archives@sos.nh.gov

NEW JERSEY
Mr. Joseph Klett
Chief of Archives
Division of Archives & Records
Management
225 W. State Street, Level 2
P.O. Box 307
Trenton, NJ 08625
P: (609) 292-9507
F: (609) 292-9105
E: joseph.klett
   @sos.state.nj.us

NEW MEXICO
Ms. Linda Trujillo
State Records Administrator
State Records Center &
Archives
1205 Camino Carlos Rey
Santa Fe, NM 87507
P: (505) 476-7912
E: LindaM.Trujillo
   @state.nm.us

NEW YORK
Mr. Mario J. Musolino
Acting Commissioner
Department of Labor
W. Averell Harriman State
Office Campus
Building 12
Albany, NY 12240
P: (518) 457-9000
F: (518) 485-6297
E: mario.musolino
   @labor.state.ny.us

Mr. Thomas J. Ruller
Interim State Archivist
State Archives
Cultural Education Center,
Room 9D46
Albany, NY 12230
P: (518) 473-7091
F: (518) 473-7058
E: tom.ruller
   @mail.nysed.gov

NORTH CAROLINA
Dr. Kevin Cherry
Director of Archives & Records
Office of Archives & History
109 East Jones Street
4614 Mail Service Center
Raleigh, NC 27699
F: (919) 715-7274
E: kevin.cherry@ncdcr.gov

NORTH DAKOTA
Ms. Ann B. Jenks
State Archivist
State Historical Society
612 East Boulevard Avenue
Bismarck, ND 58505
P: (701) 328-2666
F: (701) 328-3710
E: ajenks@nd.gov

NORTHERN MARIANA ISLANDS
Mr. Christopher Todd
CNMI Archives
CNMI Archives
P.O. Box 501250
Saipan, MP 96950
P: (670) 237-6799
E: christopher.todd
   @marianas.edu

OHIO
Mr. Fred Previts
State Archivist
Historical Society
800 East 17th Avenue
Columbus, OH 43211
P: (614) 297-2536
F: (614) 297-2546
E: fprevits@ohiohistory.org

OKLAHOMA
Ms. Jan Davis
Administrator
Archives & Records
Department of Libraries
200 Northeast 18th Street
Oklahoma City, OK 73105
P: (405) 522-3191
E: jdavis
   @oltn.odl.state.ok.us

OREGON
Ms. Mary Beth Herkert
State Archivist
State Archives
Secretary of State
800 Summer Street, Northeast
Salem, OR 97310
P: (503) 378-5196
F: (503) 373-0953
E: mary.e.herkert
   @state.or.us

Archives

PENNSYLVANIA
Mr. David Carmichael
State Archivist
Historical & Museum
Commission
350 North Street
Harrisburg, PA 17120
P: (717) 783-5796
E: dcarmichea@pa.gov

RHODE ISLAND
Mr. Scott Jensen
Director
Department of Labor & Training
Center General Complex
1511 Pontiac Avenue
Cranston, RI 02920
P: (401) 462-8000
F: (401) 462-8872
E: director-dlt@dlt.ri.gov

Ms. R. Gwenn Stearn
State Archivist & Public Records
Administrator
State Archives
337 Westminster Street
Providence, RI 02903
P: (401) 222-2353
F: (401) 222-3199
E: statearchives@sos.ri.gov

SOUTH CAROLINA
Mr. Eric Emerson
Director
Department of Archives &
History
8301 Parklane Road
Columbia, SC 29223
P: (803) 896-6187
F: (803) 896-6167
E: eemerson
    @scdah.state.sc.us

SOUTH DAKOTA
Ms. Chelle Somsen
State Archivist
State Archives
State Historical Society
900 Governors Drive
Pierre, SD 57501
P: (605) 773-5521
F: (605) 773-6041
E: chelle.somsen
    @state.sd.us

TENNESSEE
Mr. Charles A. Sherrill
State Librarian & Archivist
State Library & Archives
403 7th Avenue, North
Nashville, TN 37243
P: (615) 741-7996
F: (615) 532-9293
E: Chuck.Sherrill@tn.gov

TEXAS
Mr. Jelain Chubb
State Library & Archives
Commission
State Library & Archives
Commission
P.O. Box 12516
Austin, TX 78711
P: (512) 463-5467
E: jchubb@tsl.texas.gov

U.S. VIRGIN ISLANDS
Ms. Ingrid Bough
Territorial Director of Libraries,
Archives & Museums
Division of Libraries, Archives
& Museums
C/o Florence Williams Public
Library
1122 King Street, Christiansted
St. Croix, VI 00820
P: (304) 773-5715
F: (304) 773-5327
E: ingrid.bough@dpnr.vi.gov

Ms. Catherine Ann Hendry
Commissioner of Labor
Department of Labor
4401 Sion Farm
Christiansted, VI 00820
P: (340) 773-1994
F: (340) 773-0094
E: chendry@vidol.gov

UTAH
Ms. Patricia
    Smith-Mansfield
Director
Division of State Archives &
Records Service
346 South Rio Grande
Salt Lake City, UT 84101
P: (801) 531-3850
F: (801) 531-3854
E: pmansfie@utah.gov

VERMONT
Ms. Tanya Marshall
State Archivist & Director
Archives & Records
Administration
1078 U.S. Route 2, Middlesex
Montpelier, VT 05633
P: (802) 828-0405
F: (802) 828-3710
E: tanya.marshall
    @sec.state.vt.us

VIRGINIA
Ms. Sandra Treadway
State Librarian
The Library of Virginia
800 East Broad Street
Richmond, VA 23219
P: (804) 692-3535
F: (804) 692-3594
E: Sandra.Treadway
    @lva.virginia.gov

WASHINGTON
Mr. Steve Excell
State Archivist
Office of the Secretary of State
State Archives
P.O. Box 40238
Olympia, WA 98504
P: (360) 586-1492
E: steve.excell@sos.wa.gov

WEST VIRGINIA
Mr. Joe Geiger
Director, Archives & History
Division of Culture & History
The Culture Center, Capitol
Complex
1900 Kanawha Boulevard, East
Charleston, WV 25305
P: (304) 558-0230
F: (304) 558-2779
E: Joe.N.Geiger@wv.gov

WISCONSIN
Mr. Matt Blessing
Director
Library-Archives Division
816 State Street
Madison, WI 53706
P: (608) 264-6480
F: (608) 264-6486
E: matt.blessing
    @wisconsinhistory.org

WYOMING
Mr. Michael Strom
State Archivist
Department of State Parks &
Cultural Resources
2301 Central Avenue
Cheyenne, WY 82002
P: (307) 777-7020
F: (307) 777-7044
E: michael.strom@wyo.gov

Attorney General

The chief legal officer of the state who represents the state or its offices in all litigation.

ALABAMA
Hon. Luther Strange (R)
Attorney General
Office of the Attorney General
501 Washington Avenue
P.O. Box 300152
Montgomery, AL 36130
P: (334) 242-7300

ALASKA
Hon. Craig Richards
   (appointed)
Attorney General
Office of the Attorney General
P.O. Box 110300
Juneau, AK 99811
P: (907) 465-2133
F: (907) 465-2075

AMERICAN SAMOA
Hon. Talauega Eleasalo V.
   Ale
   (appointed)
Attorney General
Office of the Attorney General
American Samoa Government
Exeuctive Office Building,
Utulei
Pago Pago, AS 96799
P: (684) 633-4163

ARIZONA
Hon. Mark Brnovich (R)
Attorney General
Office of the Attorney General
1275 West Washington Street
Phoenix, AZ 85007
P: (602) 542-4266
F: (602) 542-4085

ARKANSAS
Hon. Leslie Rutledge (R)
Attorney General
Office of the Attorney General
323 Center Street, Suite 200
Little Rock, AR 72201
P: (800) 482-8982
F: (501) 682-8084

CALIFORNIA
Hon. Kamala Harris (D)
Attorney General
Office of the Attorney General
1300 I Street, Sutie 1740
Sacramento, CA 95814
P: (916) 445-9555

COLORADO
Hon. Cynthia Coffman (R)
Attorney General
Office of the Attorney General
Ralph L. Carr Colorado Judicial
Center
1300 Broadway, 10th Floor
Denver, CO 80203
P: (720) 508-6000
F: (720) 508-6030
E: attorney.general
   @state.co.us

CONNECTICUT
Hon. George C. Jepsen (D)
Attorney General
Office of the Attorney General
55 Elm Street
Hartford, CT 06106
P: (860) 808-5318

DELAWARE
Hon. Matthew Denn (D)
Attorney General
Office of the Attorney General
Carvel State Office Building
820 North French Street
Wilmington, DE 19801
P: (302) 577-8338
E: matthew.denn@state.de.us

DISTRICT OF COLUMBIA
Hon. Karl A. Racine
   (appointed)
Attorney General
Office of the Attorney General
441 4th Street, Northwest
Suite 1100S
Washington, DC 20001
P: (202) 727-3400
F: (202) 347-8922
E: oag@dc.gov

FLORIDA
Hon. Pam Bondi (R)
Attorney General
Office of the Attorney General
The Capitol, PL 01
Tallahassee, FL 32399
P: (850) 414-3300
F: (954) 712-4826

GEORGIA
Hon. Sam S. Olens (R)
Attorney General
Office of the Attorney General
40 Capitol Square, Southwest
Atlanta, GA 30334
P: (404) 656-3300
F: (404) 657-8733
E: AGOlens@law.ga.gov

GUAM
Hon. Elizabeth
   Barrett-Anderson
Attorney General
Office of the Attorney General
590 South Marine Corps Drive
ITC Building, Suite 706
Tamuning, GU 96913
P: (671) 475-3324
F: (671) 472-2493
E: law@guamag.org

HAWAII
Hon. Doug Chin (D)
   (appointed)
Attorney General
Office of the Attorney General
425 Queen Street
Honolulu, HI 96813
P: (808) 586-1500

IDAHO
Hon. Lawrence Wasden (R)
Attorney General
Office of the Attorney General
Statehouse
Boise, ID 83720
P: (208) 334-2400
F: (208) 854-8071

ILLINOIS
Hon. Lisa Madigan (D)
Attorney General
Office of the Attorney General
James R. Thompson Center
100 West Randolph Street
Chicago, IL 60601
P: (312) 814-3000

INDIANA
Hon. Greg Zoeller (R)
Attorney General
Office of the Attorney General
Indiana Government Center
South
302 West Washington Street, 5th
Floor
Indianapolis, IN 46204
P: (317) 232-6201
F: (317) 232-7979
E: Constituent@atg.in.gov

IOWA
Hon. Tom Miller (D)
Attorney General
Office of the Attorney General
Hoover State Office Building
1305 East Walnut
Des Moines, IA 50319
P: (515) 281-5164
F: (515) 281-4209

KANSAS
Hon. Derek Schmidt (R)
Attorney General
Office of the Attorney General
120 Southwest 10th Avenue, 2nd
Floor
Topeka, KS 66612
P: (785) 296-2215
F: (785) 296-6296

KENTUCKY
Hon. Jack Conway (D)
Attorney General
Office of the Attorney General
700 Capitol Avenue
Capitol Building, Suite 118
Frankfort, KY 40601
P: (502) 696-5300
F: (502) 564-2894
E: attorney.general
   @ag.ky.gov

LOUISIANA
Hon. James D. Caldwell (R)
Attorney General
Office of the Attorney General
P.O. Box 94095
Baton Rouge, LA 70804
P: (225) 326-6000
F: (225) 326-6797
E: executive@ag.state.la.us

MAINE
Hon. Janet T. Mills (D)
Attorney General
Office of the Attorney General
State House Station 6
Augusta, ME 04333
P: (207) 626-8800

MARYLAND
Hon. Brian E. Frosh (D)
Attorney General
Office of the Attorney General
200 Saint Paul Place
Baltimore, MD 21202
P: (410) 576-6300
F: (410) 576-6404
E: oag@oag.state.md.us

MASSACHUSETTS
Hon. Maura Healey (D)
Attorney General
Office of the Attorney General
1 Ashburton Place
Boston, MA 02108
P: (617) 727-2200

MICHIGAN
Hon. Bill Schuette (R)
Attorney General
Office of the Attorney General
525 West Ottawa Street
P.O. Box 30212
Lansing, MI 48909
P: (517) 373-1110

Attorney General

MINNESOTA
Hon. Lori Swanson (DFL)
Attorney General
Office of the Attorney General
State Capitol, Suite 102
St. Paul, MN 55155
P: (651) 296-3353
F: (651) 297-4193
E: attorney.general
    @state.mn.us

MISSISSIPPI
Hon. Jim Hood (D)
Attorney General
Office of the Attorney General
Department of Justice
P.O. Box 220
Jackson, MS 39205
P: (601) 359-3680
E: msag05@ago.state.ms.us

MISSOURI
Hon. Chris Koster (D)
Attorney General
Office of the Attorney General
Supreme Court Building
207 West High Street
Jefferson City, MO 65101
P: (573) 751-3321
F: (573) 751-0774

MONTANA
Hon. Tim Fox (R)
Attorney General
Office of the Attorney General
Justice Building
215 North Sanders
Helena, MT 59620
P: (406) 444-2026
F: (406) 444-3549
E: contactdoj@mt.gov

NEBRASKA
Hon. Doug Peterson (R)
Attorney General
Office of the Attorney General
State Capitol
P.O. Box 98920
Lincoln, NE 68509
P: (402) 471-2682
F: (402) 471-3297

NEVADA
Hon. Adam Paul Laxalt (R)
Attorney General
Office of the Attorney General
Old State Capitol Building
100 North Carson Street
Carson City, NV 89701
P: (775) 684-1100
F: (775) 684-1108
E: aginfo@ag.state.nv.us

NEW HAMPSHIRE
Hon. Joseph Foster (D)
    (appointed)
Attorney General
Office of the Attorney General
33 Capitol Street
Concord, NH 03301
P: (603) 271-3658
F: (603) 271-2110
E: attorneygeneral
    @doj.nh.gov

NEW JERSEY
Hon. John Jay Hoffman (R)
    (appointed)
Acting Attorney General
Office of the Attorney General
Hughes Justice Complex, 25
Market Street
P.O. Box 080
Trenton, NJ 08625
P: (609) 292-8740

NEW MEXICO
Hon. Hector H. Balderas (D)
Attorney General
Office of the Attorney General
P.O. Drawer 1508
Santa Fe, NM 87504
P: (505) 827-6000
F: (505) 827-5826

NEW YORK
Hon. Eric T.
    Schneiderman (D)
Attorney General
Office of the Attorney General
Department of Law
The Capitol, 2nd Floor
Albany, NY 12224
P: (518) 474-7330

NORTH CAROLINA
Hon. Roy A. Cooper III (D)
Attorney General
Office of the Attorney General
Department of Justice
P.O.Box 629
Raleigh, NC 27602
P: (919) 716-6400
F: (919) 716-6750
E: rcooper@ncdoj.gov

NORTH DAKOTA
Hon. Wayne Stenehjem (R)
Attorney General
Office of the Attorney General
State Capitol
600 East Boulevard Avenue
Bismarck, ND 58505
P: (701) 328-2210
F: (701) 328-2226
E: wstenehjem@nd.gov

**NORTHERN MARIANA
ISLANDS**
Hon. Edward Manibusan
Attorney General
Office of the Attorney General
Administration Building
P.O. Box 10007
Saipan, MP 96950
P: (670) 664-2341

OHIO
Hon. Mike DeWine (R)
Attorney General
Office of the Attorney General
State Office Tower
30 East Broad Street
Columbus, OH 43266
P: (614) 466-4320

OKLAHOMA
Hon. Scott Pruitt (R)
Attorney General
Office of the Attorney General
313 Northeast 21st Street
Oklahoma City, OK 73105
P: (405) 521-3921

OREGON
Hon. Ellen Rosenblum (D)
Attorney General
Office of the Attorney General
Justice Building
1162 Court Street, Northeast
Salem, OR 97301
P: (503) 378-6002
F: (503) 378-4017

PENNSYLVANIA
Hon. Kathleen Kane (D)
Attorney General
Office of the Attorney General
1600 Strawberry Square
Harrisburg, PA 17120
P: (717) 787-3391
F: (717) 787-8242

PUERTO RICO
Hon. Cesar R.
    Miranda-Rodriguez
Attorney General
Office of the Attorney General
G.P.O. Box 902192
San Juan, PR 00902
P: (787) 721-2900

RHODE ISLAND
Hon. Peter F. Kilmartin (D)
Attorney General
Office of the Attorney General
150 South Main Street
Providence, RI 02903
P: (401) 274-4400

SOUTH CAROLINA
Hon. Alan Wilson (R)
Attorney General
Office of the Attorney General
Rembert C. Dennis Office
Building
P.O. Box 11549
Columbia, SC 29211
P: (803) 734-3970

SOUTH DAKOTA
Hon. Marty J. Jackley (R)
Attorney General
Office of the Attorney General
1302 East Highway 14, Suite 1
Pierre, SD 57501
P: (605) 773-3215
F: (605) 773-4106
E: atghelp@state.sd.us

TENNESSEE
Hon. Herbert Slatery III
    (appointed)
Attorney General
Office of the Attorney General
425 5th Avenue North
Nashville, TN 37243
P: (615) 741-3491
F: (615) 741-2009

TEXAS
Hon. Ken Paxton (R)
Attorney General
Office of the Attorney General
P.O. Box 12548
Austin, TX 78711
P: (512) 463-2100
F: (512) 475-2994
E: ken.paxton
    @texasattorneygeneral.gov

U.S. VIRGIN ISLANDS
Hon. Terri Griffiths
    (appointed)
Acting Attorney General
Office of the Attorney General
Department of Justice, G.E.R.S.
Complex
34-38 Kronprinsdens Gade
St. Thomas, VI 00802
P: (340) 774-5666
F: (340) 774-9710

UTAH
Hon. Sean D. Reyes (R)
Attorney General
Office of the Attorney General
State Capitol, Room 236
Salt Lake City, UT 84114
P: (801) 538-9600
F: (801) 538-1121
E: uag@utah.gov

VERMONT
Hon. William H. Sorrell (D)
Attorney General
Office of the Attorney General
109 State Street
Montpelier, VT 05609
P: (802) 828-3171
F: (802) 828-3187

VIRGINIA
Hon. Mark R. Herring (D)
Attorney General
Office of the Attorney General
900 East Main Street
Richmond, VA 23219
P: (804) 786-2071

WASHINGTON
Hon. Bob Ferguson (D)
Attorney General
Office of the Attorney General
1125 Washington Street,
Southeast
P.O. Box 40100
Olympia, WA 98504
P: (360) 753-6200
F: (360) 664-0228
E: bob.ferguson@atg.wa.gov

WEST VIRGINIA
Hon. Patrick Morrisey (R)
Attorney General
Office of the Attorney General
State Capitol
1900 Kanawha Boulevard, East
Charleston, WV 25305
P: (304) 558-2021
F: (304) 558-0140

WISCONSIN
Hon. Brad Schimel (R)
Attorney General
Office of the Attorney General
State Capitol, Suite 114 East
P.O. Box 7857
Madison, WI 53707
P: (608) 266-1221

WYOMING
Hon. Peter K. Michael
    (appointed)
Attorney General
Office of the Attorney General
State Capitol Building
Cheyenne, WY 82002
P: (307) 777-7841
F: (307) 777-6869

Auditor

Determines that governmental funds are handled appropriately and assesses how effectively government organizations are achieving their purposes.

Information provided by:

National Association of State Auditors, Comptrollers & Treasurers
Kinney Poynter
Executive Director
449 Lewis Hargett Circle
Suite 290
Lexington, KY 40503
P: (859) 276-1147
F: (859) 278-0507
kpoynter@nasact.org
www.nasact.org

ALABAMA

Mr. Ronald L. Jones
Chief Examiner
Department of Examiners of Public Accounts
50 North Ripley Street, Room 3201
Montgomery, AL 36104
P: (334) 242-9200
F: (334) 353-1436
E: ron.jones
@examiners.alabama.gov

Hon. Jim Zeigler (R)
State Auditor
Office of the State Auditor
State Capitol, Room S-101
600 Dexter Avenue
Montgomery, AL 36130
P: (334) 242-7010
F: (334) 242-7650
E: jim.zeigler
@auditor.alabama.gov

ALASKA

Hon. Kris Curtis
Legislative Auditor
Division of Legislative Audit
P.O. Box 113300
Juneau, AK 99811
P: (907) 465-3830
F: (907) 465-2347

AMERICAN SAMOA

Liua Fatuesi
Territorial Audit Office
Executive Office Building
AP Lutali - 2nd Floor
Pago Pago, AS 96799
P: (684) 633-5191
F: (684) 633-1039

ARIZONA

Hon. Debra K. Davenport
Auditor General
Office of the Auditor General
2910 North 44th Street, Suite 410
Phoenix, AZ 85018
P: (602) 553-0333
F: (602) 553-0051
E: ddavenport@azauditor.gov

ARKANSAS

Mr. Roger A. Norman
Legislative Auditor
Legislative Audit
State Capitol
500 Woodlane Street, Suite 172
Little Rock, AR 72201
P: (501) 683-8600
F: (501) 683-8605
E: roger.norman
@arklegaudit.gov

CALIFORNIA

Hon. Elaine M. Howle
State Auditor
Office of the State Auditor
621 Capitol Mall, Suite 1200
Sacramento, CA 95814
P: (916) 445-0255 Ext. 342
F: (916) 323-0913
E: elaineh@bsa.ca.gov

COLORADO

Hon. Diane E. Ray
State Auditor
Office of the State Auditor
1525 Sherman Street, 7th Floor
Denver, CO 80203
P: (303) 869-2800
F: (303) 869-3060
E: diane.ray@state.co.us

CONNECTICUT

Hon. John C. Geragosian
State Auditor
Office of the Auditors of Public Accounts
State Capitol
210 Capitol Avenue
Hartford, CT 06106
P: (860) 240-8651
F: (860) 240-8655
E: john.geragosian
@cga.ct.gov

Hon. Robert M. Ward
State Auditor
Office of the Auditors of Public Accounts
State Capitol
210 Capitol Avenue
Hartford, CT 06106
P: (860) 240-8653
F: (860) 240-8655
E: robert.ward@cga.ct.gov

DELAWARE

Hon. R. Thomas
   Wagner Jr. (R)
Auditor of Accounts
Office of the Auditor of Accounts
401 Federal Street
Townsend Building, Suite 1
Dover, DE 19901
P: (302) 739-5055
F: (302) 739-6707
E: r.thomas.wagner
@state.de.us

DISTRICT OF COLUMBIA

Hon. Kathleen Patterson
Auditor
Office of the Auditor
717 14th Street, Northwest
Suite 900
Washington, DC 20005
P: (202) 727-3600
F: (202) 724-8814
E: kathleen.patterson
@dc.gov

FLORIDA

Hon. David W. Martin
Auditor General
Office of the Auditor General
111 West Madison Street
Pepper Building, Room G-75
Tallahassee, FL 32399
P: (850) 488-5534
F: (850) 488-6975
E: davidmartin
@aud.state.fl.us

GEORGIA

Mr. Greg S. Griffin
State Auditor
Department of Audits and Accounts
270 Washington Street, Southwest
Suite 4-113
Atlanta, GA 30334
P: (404) 656-2174
F: (404) 651-9448
E: griffin@audits.ga.gov

GUAM

Hon. Doris Flores Brooks
Public Auditor
Office of Public Accountability
DNA Building, Suite 401
238 Archbishop Flores Street
Hagatna, GU 96910
P: (671) 475-0390, Ext. 207
F: (671) 472-7951
E: dfbrooks@guamopa.org

HAWAII

Ms. Jan K. Yamane
Acting State Auditor
Office of the State Auditor
465 South King Street, Room 500
Honolulu, HI 96813
P: (808) 587-0800
F: (808) 587-0830
E: auditors2
@auditor.state.hi.us

IDAHO

Mr. Rakesh Mohan
Director
Office of Performance Evaluations
954 West Jefferson Street
10th Street Entrance, 2nd Floor
Boise, ID 83720
P: (208) 332-1470
F: (208) 332-1471
E: rmohan@ope.idaho.gov

Ms. April Renfro
Division Manager
Legislative Services - Audit Division
P.O. Box 83720
Boise, ID 83720
P: (208) 334-4826
F: (208) 334-2034
E: arenfro@lso.idaho.gov

ILLINOIS

Hon. William G. Holland
Auditor General
Office of the Auditor General
Iles Park Plaza
740 East Ash Street
Springfield, IL 62703
P: (217) 782-3536
F: (217) 785-8222
E: auditor@mail.state.il.us

INDIANA

Mr. Paul D. Joyce
State Examiner
State Board of Accounts
302 West Washington Street, Room E-418
Indianapolis, IN 46204
P: (317) 232-2524
F: (317) 232-4711

IOWA
Ms. Mary Mosiman
Auditor of State
Office of the Auditor of State
Room 111, State Capitol
Building
Des Moines, IA 50319
P: (515) 281-5385
F: (515) 242-6134

KANSAS
Mr. Scott E. Frank
Legislative Post Auditor
Legislative Division of Post
Audit
800 Southwest Jackson Street
Suite 1200
Topeka, KS 66612
P: (785) 296-5180
F: (785) 296-4482
E: scott.frank@lpa.ks.gov

KENTUCKY
Hon. Adam Edelen (D)
Auditor of Public Accounts
Office of the Auditor of Public
Accounts
209 St. Clair Street
Frankfort, KY 40601
P: (502) 564-5841
F: (502) 564-2912
E: adam.edelen
    @auditor.ky.gov

LOUISIANA
Hon. Daryl G. Purpera
Legislative Auditor
Office of the Legislative Auditor
P.O. Box 94397
1600 North 3rd Street
Baton Rouge, LA 70804
P: (225) 339-3839
F: (225) 339-3870
E: dpurpera@lla.la.gov

MAINE
Hon. Pola Buckley
State Auditor
Office of the State Auditor
66 State House Station
Augusta, ME 04333
P: (207) 624-6250
F: (207) 624-6273

MARYLAND
Mr. Thomas J. Barnickel III
Legislative Auditor
Office of Legislative Audits
301 West Preston Street, Room
1202
Baltimore, MD 21201
P: (410) 946-5900
F: (410) 946-5998
E: tbarnickel
    @ola.state.md.us

MASSACHUSETTS
Hon. Suzanne M. Bump (D)
Auditor of the Commonwealth
Office of the Auditor of the
Commonwealth
State House, Room 230
Boston, MA 02133
P: (617) 727-2075
F: (617) 727-2383
E: suzanne.bump
    @sao.state.ma.us

MICHIGAN
Hon. Doug Ringler
Auditor General
Office of the Auditor General
201 North Washington Square
Victor Center, Suite 600
Lansing, MI 48913
P: (517) 334-8050
F: (517) 334-8079
E: dringler
    @audgen.michigan.gov

MINNESOTA
Mr. James Nobles
Legislative Auditor
Office of the Legislative Auditor
Centennial Office Building
658 Cedar Street, 1st Floor South
St. Paul, MN 55155
P: (651) 296-4711
F: (651) 296-4713
E: james.nobles@state.mn.us

Hon. Rebecca Otto (DFL)
State Auditor
Office of the State Auditor
525 Park Street, Suite 500
St. Paul, MN 55103
P: (615) 296-2551
F: (615) 296-4755
E: rebecca.otto@state.mn.us

MISSISSIPPI
Mr. Max Arinder
Executive Director
Joint Committee on
Performance
Evaluation & Expenditure
Review
P.O. Box 1204
Jackson, MS 39215
P: (601) 359-1226
F: (601) 359-1420
E: arinder@peer.state.ms.us

Hon. Stacey E.
    Pickering (R)
State Auditor
Office of the State Auditor
Woolfolk Building, Suite 801
501 North West Street, P.O. Box
956
Jackson, MS 39205
P: (601) 576-2641
F: (601) 576-2650
E: stacey.pickering
    @osa.ms.gov

MISSOURI
Ms. Nicole Galloway
State Auditor
Office of thc State Auditor
State Capitol, Room 224
Jefferson City, MO 65102
P: (573) 751-4824
F: (573) 751-6539

MONTANA
Hon. Tori M. Hunthausen
Legislative Auditor
Legislative Audit Division
State Capitol Building, Room
160
P.O. Box 201705
Helena, MT 59620
P: (406) 444-3122
F: (406) 444-9784
E: thunthausen@mt.gov

NEBRASKA
Hon. Charlie Janssen (R)
Auditor of Public Accounts
Office of the Auditor of Public
Accounts
Room 2303, State Capitol
P.O. Box 98917
Lincoln, NE 68509
P: (603) 271-2389
F: (402) 471-3301
E: charlie.janssen
    @nebraska.gov

NEVADA
Hon. Paul V. Townsend
Legislative Auditor
Legislative Counsel Bureau
401 South Carson Street
Carson City, NV 89701
P: (775) 684-6815
F: (775) 684-6435
E: townsend@lcb.state.nv.us

NEW HAMPSHIRE
Mr. Jeffry A. Pattison
Legislative Budget Assistant
Office of Legislative Budget
Assistant
State House, Room 102
107 North Main Street
Concord, NH 03301
P: (603) 271-3161
F: (603) 271-1097
E: jeff.pattison
    @leg.state.nh.us

NEW JERSEY
Hon. Stephen M. Eells
State Auditor
Office of the State Auditor
P.O. Box 067
Trenton, NJ 08625
P: (609) 847-3470
F: (609) 633-0834
E: seells@njleg.org

Mr. Marc Larkins
Acting State Comptroller
Office of the State Comptroller
P.O. Box 024
Trenton, NJ 08625
P: (609) 984-2888
F: (609) 292-2017

NEW MEXICO
Hon. Timothy Keller (D)
State Auditor
Office of the State Auditor
2540 Camino Edward Ortiz,
Suite A
Santa Fe, NM 87505
P: (505) 476-3800
F: (505) 827-3512

Mr. Charles Sallee
Deputy Director
Legislative Finance Committee
416 Capitol Building
Santa Fe, NM 87503
P: (505) 986-4550
F: (505) 986-4644
E: charles.sallee
    @nmlegis.gov

NEW YORK
Hon. Thomas P. DiNapoli (D)
Comptroller
Office of the State Comptroller
110 State Street
Albany, NY 12236
P: (518) 474-4040
F: (518) 474-3004
E: tdinapoli
    @osc.state.ny.us

Auditor

Mr. Andrew SanFilippo
Office of the State Comptroller -
State & Local Accountability
110 State Street
Albany, NY 12236
P: (518) 474-4040
F: (518) 474-3004

NORTH CAROLINA
Hon. Beth Wood (D)
State Auditor
Office of the State Auditor
2 South Salisbury Street
20601 Mail Service Center
Raleigh, NC 27699
P: (919) 807-7500
F: (919) 807-7600
E: Beth_Wood@ncauditor.net

NORTH DAKOTA
Hon. Robert R. Peterson (R)
State Auditor
Office of the State Auditor
600 East Boulevard Avenue, 3rd
Floor
Bismarck, ND 58505
P: (701) 328-2241
F: (701) 328-1406
E: rpeterso@nd.gov

**NORTHERN MARIANA
ISLANDS**
Mr. Michael S. Pai
Public Auditor
Office of the Public Auditor
P.O. Box 501399
Saipan, MP 96950
P: (670) 322-6481
F: (670) 322-7812
E: mpai@opacnmi.com

OHIO
Hon. David A. Yost (R)
Auditor of State
Office of Auditor of State
88 East Broad Street, 5th Floor
P.O. Box 1140
Columbus, OH 43216
P: (614) 466-4514
F: (614) 466-4490
E: contactus
   @auditor.state.oh.us

OKLAHOMA
Hon. Gary Jones (R)
State Auditor & Inspector
Office of the State Auditor &
Inspector
2300 North Lincoln Boulevard
State Capitol Building, Room
100
Oklahoma City, OK 73105
P: (405) 521-3495
F: (405) 521-3426
E: gjones@sai.ok.gov

OREGON
Mr. Gary Blackmer
Director
Division of Audits
255 Capitol Street, Northeast
Suite 500
Salem, OR 97310
P: (503) 986-2355
F: (503) 378-4829
E: gary.blackmer
   @state.or.us

PENNSYLVANIA
Hon. Eugene DePasquale (D)
Auditor General
Department of the Auditor
General
Finance Building, Room 229
Harrisburg, PA 17120
P: (717) 787-2543
F: (717) 783-4407
E: auditorgen
   @auditorgen.state.pa.us

Mr. Philip R. Durgin
Executive Director
Legislative Budget & Finance
Committee
400 Finance Building
P.O. Box 8737
Harrisburg, PA 17105
P: (717) 783-1600
F: (717) 787-5487
E: pdurgin@palbfc.us

PUERTO RICO
Ms. Yesmin Valdivieso-Galib
Comptroller
Office of the Comptroller
P.O. Box 366069
San Juan, PR 00963
P: (787) 250-3300
F: (787) 751-6768
E: ocpr@ocpr.gov.pr

RHODE ISLAND
Mr. Dennis E. Hoyle
Auditor General
Office of the Auditor General
86 Weybosset Street
Providence, RI 02903
P: (401) 222-2435 Ext. 3038
F: (401) 222-2111
E: ag@oag.ri.gov

SOUTH CAROLINA
Hon. Richard H. Gilbert Jr.
Interim State Auditor
Office of the State Auditor
1401 Main Street, Suite 1200
Columbia, SC 29201
P: (803) 253-4160 Ext. 203
F: (803) 343-0723
E: rgilbert@osa.state.sc.us

Mr. Earle Powell
Director
Legislative Audit Council
1331 Elmwood Avenue, Suite
315
Columbia, SC 29201
P: (803) 253-7612
F: (803) 253-7639

SOUTH DAKOTA
Mr. Martin Guindon
Auditor General
Department of Legislative Audit
500 East Capitol Avenue
Pierre, SD 57501
P: (605) 773-3595
F: (605) 773-6454
E: marty.guindon
   @state.sd.us

TENNESSEE
Mr. Justin P. Wilson
Comptroller of the Treasury
Office of the Comptroller of the
Treasury
505 Deaderick Street, Suite
1500
Nashville, TN 37243
P: (615) 741-2501
F: (615) 741-7328
E: justin.wilson@tn.gov

TEXAS
Hon. John Keel
State Auditor
State Auditor's Office
1501 North Congress, 4th Floor
P.O. Box 12067
Austin, TX 78701
P: (512) 936-9500
F: (512) 936-9400
E: eguzman@sao.state.tx.us

U.S. VIRGIN ISLANDS
Mr. Steven G.
   Van Beverhoudt
Inspector General
Office of the Inspector General
2315 Kronprindsens Gade #75
Charlotte Amalie
St. Thomas, VI 00802
P: (340) 774-3388
F: (340) 774-6431
E: svanbeverhoudt@viig.org

UTAH
Hon. John Dougall (R)
State Auditor
Office of the State Auditor
East Office Building, Suite E310
P.O. Box 142310
Salt Lake City, UT 84114
P: (801) 538-1360
F: (801) 538-1383
E: jdougall@utah.gov

Mr. John Schaff
Auditor General
Office of the Legislative Auditor
General
W315 State Capitol Complex
P.O. Box 140151
Salt Lake City, UT 84114
P: (801) 538-1033 Ext. 103
F: (801) 538-1063
E: jschaff@utah.gov

VERMONT
Hon. Douglas R. Hoffer (D)
State Auditor
Office of the State Auditor
132 State Street
Montpelier, VT 05633
P: (802) 828-2281
F: (802) 828-2198
E: doug.hoffer@state.vt.us

VIRGINIA
Mr. Hal Greer
Director
Joint Legislative Audit &
Review Commission
General Assembly Building
910 Capitol Street, Suite 1100
Richmond, VA 23218
P: (804) 371-4589
F: (804) 371-0101

Ms. Martha Mavredes
Auditor of Public Accounts
Office of the Auditor of Public
Accounts
P.O. Box 1295
Richmond, VA 23218
P: (804) 225-3350
F: (804) 225-3357
E: martha.mavredes
   @apa.virginia.gov

WASHINGTON
Honourable Jan Jutte
Acting State Auditor
Office of the State Auditor
P.O. Box 40021
Olympia, WA 98504
P: (360) 902-0370
F: (360) 753-0646
E: auditor@sao.wa.gov

Mr. Keenan Konopaski
Legislative Auditor
Joint Legislative Audit &
Review Committee
1300 Quince Street, Southeast
Olympia, WA 98504
P: (360) 786-5187
F: (360) 786-5180
E: keenan.konopaski
   @leg.wa.gov

WEST VIRGINIA
Mr. Aaron Allred
Legislative Manager &
Legislative Auditor
Legislative Auditor's Office
State Capitol Complex
Building 1, E-132
Charleston, WV 25305
P: (304) 347-4800
F: (304) 347-4815
E: aaron.allred
    @wvlegislature.gov

WISCONSIN
Mr. Joe Chrisman
State Auditor
Legislative Audit Bureau
22 East Mifflin Street, Suite 500
Madison, WI 53703
P: (608) 266-2818
F: (608) 267-0410
E: joe.chrisman
    @legis.wisconsin.gov

WYOMING
Mr. Jeffrey C. Vogel
Director
Department of Audit
Herschler Building
3rd Floor, East Wing
Cheyenne, WY 82002
P: (307) 777-5312
F: (307) 777-5341
E: jvogel
    @wyaudit.state.wy.us

Banking

Administers laws regulating the operation of banking institutions in the state.

ALABAMA
Mr. John D. Harrison
Superintendent
Banking Department
P.O. Box 4600
Montgomery, AL 36103
P: (334) 242-3452
F: (334) 242-3500
E: john.harrison
   @banking.alabama.gov

ALASKA
Ms. Kevin Anselm
Director
Division of Banking &
Securities
Division of Banking &
Securities
P.O. Box 110807
Juneau, AK 99811
P: (907) 465-2521
F: (907) 465-2549
E: kevin.anselm@alaska.gov

AMERICAN SAMOA
Hon. Lolo Matalasi
   Moliga (I)
Governor
Development Bank of American
Samoa
Executive Office Building,
Third Floor
Utulei
Pago Pago, AS 96799
P: (684) 633-4116
F: (684) 633-2269

ARIZONA
Mr. Lauren W. Kingry
Superintendent of Financial
Institutions
Department of Financial
Institutions
2910 North 44th Street, Suite
310
Phoenix, AZ 85018
P: (602) 771-2770
F: (602) 381-1225
E: lkingry@azdfi.gov

ARKANSAS
Mr. B. Edmond Waters
Securities Commissioner
Securities Department
Heritage West Building, Suite
300
201 East Markham Street
Little Rock, AR 72201
P: (501) 324-9260
F: (501) 324-9268
E: ewaters
   @securities.arkansas.gov

CALIFORNIA
Ms. Jan Lynn Owen
Commissioner
Department of Business
Oversight
1515 K Street, Suite 200
Sacramento, CA 95814
P: (866) 275-2677
F: (916) 322-1559

DELAWARE
Mr. Robert A. Glen
Commissioner
Office of State Bank
Commissioner
555 East Lockerman Street
Dover, DE 19901
P: (302) 739-4235
F: (302) 739-3609
E: Dawn.Hollinger
   @state.de.us

DISTRICT OF COLUMBIA
Mr. Chester A. McPherson
Acting Commissioner
Department of Insurance,
Securities & Banking
Government of the District of
Columbia
810 First Street Northeast, Suite
701
Washington, DC 20002
P: (202) 727-8000
F: (202) 535-1196
E: disb@dc.gov

GEORGIA
Mr. Kevin Hagler
Commissioner
Department of Banking &
Finance
2990 Brandywine Road, Suite
200
Atlanta, GA 30341
P: (770) 986-1633
F: (770) 986-1654
E: khagler@dbf.state.ga.us

GUAM
Mr. John P. Camacho
Director
Department of Revenue &
Taxation
Director's Office
P.O. Box 23607
GMF, GU 96921
P: (671) 635-1817
F: (671) 633-2643
E: jpcamacho@revtax.gov.gu

HAWAII
Ms. Iris Ikeda Catalani
Commissioner
Division of Financial
Institutions
King Kalakaua Building
335 Merchant Street, Room 221
Honolulu, HI 96813
P: (808) 586-2820
F: (808) 586-2818
E: dfi@dcca.hawaii.gov

IDAHO
Mr. Gavin M. Gee
Director
Department of Finance
800 Park Boulevard, Suite 200
P.O. Box 83720
Boise, ID 83720
P: (208) 332-8010
F: (208) 332-8097
E: gavin.gee
   @finance.idaho.gov

ILLINOIS
Mr. Michael Mannion
Division Director
Division of Banking
100 West Randolph, 9th Floor
Chicago, IL 60601
P: (312) 793-3000
F: (312) 793-0756

INDIANA
Mr. Dennis L. Bassett
Public Finance Director
Department of Financial
Institutions
One North Capitol, Suite 900
Indianapolis, IN 46204
P: (317) 233-4332
F: (317) 232-6786
E: DeBassett@ifa.IN.gov

IOWA
Mr. James M. Schipper
Superintendent
Division of Banking
200 East Grand Avenue, Suite
300
Des Moines, IA 50309
P: (515) 281-4014
F: (515) 281-4862
E: jschipper
   @idob.state.ia.us

KANSAS
Mr. Deryl Schuster
Commissioner
Office of the State Banking
Commissioner
700 Jackson, Suite 300
Topeka, KS 66603
P: (785) 296-2266
F: (785) 296-0168

KENTUCKY
Mr. Charles A. Vice
Commissioner
Department of Financial
Institutions
1025 Capital Center Drive, Suite
200
Frankfort, KY 40601
P: (502) 573-3390
F: (502) 573-8787
E: charles.vice@ky.gov

LOUISIANA
Mr. John P. Ducrest
Commissioner
Office of Financial Institutions
8660 United Plaza Boulevard,
Suite 200
P.O. Box 94095
Baton Rouge, LA 70804
P: (225) 925-4660
F: (225) 925-4524
E: ofila@ofi.la.gov

MAINE
Mr. Lloyd P. LaFountain III
Superintendent
Bureau of Financial Institutions
Professional & Financial
Regulation
36 State House Station
Augusta, ME 04333
P: (207) 624-8570
F: (207) 624-8590
E: lloyd.p.lafountain.III
   @maine.gov

MARYLAND
Mr. Gordon Cooley
Acting Commissioner of
Financial Regulation
Division of Financial
Regulation
500 North Calvert Street, Room
402
Baltimore, MD 21202
P: (410) 230-6001
F: (410) 333-0475
E: gordon.cooley
   @maryland.gov

MASSACHUSETTS
Mr. David Cotney
Commissioner
Division of Banks
1000 Washington Street,
10th Floor
Boston, MA 02118
P: (617) 956-1500
F: (617) 956-1599

MICHIGAN
Ms. Ann Flood
Director
Department of Insurance &
Financial Services
611 West Ottawa, 3rd Floor
P.O. Box 30220
Lansing, MI 48909
P: (517) 373-0220
F: (517) 335-4978
E: difs-info@michigan.gov

MINNESOTA
Mr. Mike Rothman
Commissioner
Department of Commerce
85 East 7th Place, Suite 500
St. Paul, MN 55101
P: (651) 539-1638
F: (651) 296-4328
E: commerce.commissioner
@state.mn.us

MISSISSIPPI
Ms. Charlotte Corley
Commissioner
Department of Banking and
Consumer Finance
P. O. Box 12129
Jackson, MS 39236
P: (601) 321-6901

MISSOURI
Ms. Debbie Hardman
Acting Commissioner of Finance
Division of Finance
Truman State Office Building,
Room 630
P.O. Box 716
Jefferson City, MO 65102
P: (573) 751-3242
F: (573) 751-9192
E: finance@dof.mo.gov

MONTANA
Ms. Melanie Hall
Commissioner
Division of Banking &
Financial Institutions
301 South Park, Suite 316
P.O. Box 200546
Helena, MT 59620
P: (406) 841-2920
F: (406) 841-2930
E: mghall@mt.gov

NEBRASKA
Mr. Mark Quandahl
Director
Department of Banking &
Finance
1230 O Street, Suite 400
P.O. Box 95006
Lincoln, NE 68509
P: (402) 471-2845
E: mark.quandahl
@nebraska.gov

NEVADA
Mr. George E. Burns
Commissioner
Financial Institutions Division
Department of Business &
Industry
2785 East Desert Inn Road, Suite
180
Las Vegas, NV 89121
P: (702) 486-4120
F: (702) 486-4563
E: gburns@fid.state.nv.us

NEW HAMPSHIRE
Mr. Glenn A. Perlow
Commissioner
Banking Department
53 Regional Drive, Suite 200
Concord, NH 03301
P: (603) 271-3561
F: (603) 271-1090
E: nhbd@banking.state.nh.us

NEW JERSEY
Mr. Kenneth E. Kobylowski
Commissioner
Department of Banking &
Insurance
State of New Jersey
20 West State Street, P.O. Box
325
Trenton, NJ 08625
P: (609) 292-7272
F: (609) 984-5273
E: commissioner
@dobi.state.nj.us

NORTH CAROLINA
Mr. Ray Grace
Commissioner of Banks
Banking Commission
316 West Edenton Street
4309 Mail Service Center
Raleigh, NC 27699
P: (888) 384-3811
F: (919) 733-6918
E: rgrace@nccob.gov

NORTH DAKOTA
Mr. Robert J. Entringer
Commissioner
Department of Financial
Institutions
2000 Schafer Street, Suite G
Bismarck, ND 58501
P: (701) 328-9933
F: (701) 328-0290
E: rentring@nd.gov

OHIO
Mr. Charles J. Dolezal
Superintendent
Division of Financial
Institutions
Department of Commerce
77 South High Street, 21st Floor
Columbus, OH 43215
P: (614) 728-8400
F: (614) 728-0380
E: webdfi-cf
@com.state.oh.us

OKLAHOMA
Mr. Mick Thompson
Commissioner
State Banking Department
2900 North Lincoln Boulevard
Oklahoma City, OK 73105
P: (405) 521-2782
F: (405) 522-2993
E: mick.thompson
@banking.ok.gov

OREGON
Mr. David C. Tatman
Division Administrator
Division of Finance &
Corporate Securities
Consumer & Business Services
350 Winter Street, Northeast,
Room 410
Salem, OR 97301
P: (503) 947-7475
F: (503) 947-7862
E: david.c.tatman
@oregon.gov

PENNSYLVANIA
Ms. Robin Weissmann
Secretary
Department of Banking &
Securities
17 North 2nd Street, Suite 1300
Harrisburg, PA 17101
P: (717) 787-2665

PUERTO RICO
Mr. Rafael Blanco
Commissioner of Financial
Institutions
Office of the Commissioner of
Financial Institutions
Commonwealth of Puerto Rico
P.O. Box 11855
San Juan, PR 00910
P: (787) 723-8004
F: (787) 723-4042
E: comisionado
@ocif.gobierno.pr

SOUTH CAROLINA
Mr. Louie A. Jacobs
Commissioner of Banking
Office of the Commissioner of
Banking
1205 Pendleton Street, Suite 305
Columbia, SC 29201
P: (803) 734-2001
F: (803) 734-2013

SOUTH DAKOTA
Mr. Bret Afdahl
Director
Division of Banking
Department of Labor &
Regulation
1601 North Harrison Avenue,
Suite 1
Pierre, SD 57501
P: (605) 773-3421
F: (866) 326-7504
E: banking@state.sd.us

TENNESSEE
Mr. Greg Gonzales
Commissioner
Department of Financial
Institutions
414 Union Street, Suite 1000
Nashville, TN 37219
P: (615) 741-5603
F: (615) 253-6306
E: Greg.Gonzales@tn.gov

TEXAS
Mr. Charles G. Cooper
Commissioner
Department of Banking
2601 North Lamar Boulevard
Austin, TX 78705
P: (512) 475-1325
F: (512) 475-1313
E: executive@dob.texas.gov

Banking

UTAH
Mr. G. Edward Leary
Commissioner
Department of Financial
Institutions
324 South State Street, Suite
201
P.O. Box 146800
Salt Lake City, UT 84114
P: (801) 538-8830
F: (801) 538-8894
E: ELEARY@utah.gov

VERMONT
Ms. Susan L. Donegan
Commissioner
Department of Financial
Regulation
89 Main Street
Montpelier, VT 05620
P: (802) 828-3301
F: (802) 828-3306
E: susan.donegan
    @state.vt.us

VIRGINIA
Mr. E. Joseph Face Jr.
Commissioner of Financial
Institutions
Bureau of Financial Institutions
1300 East Main Street, Suite
800
P.O. Box 640
Richmond, VA 23218
P: (804) 371-9657
F: (804) 371-9416
E: joe.face
    @scc.virginia.gov

WASHINGTON
Mr. Scott Jarvis
Director
Department of Financial
Institutions
P.O. Box 41200
Olympia, WA 98504
P: (360) 902-8700
F: (360) 586-5068
E: confsec@dfi.wa.gov

Ms. Gloria McVey
Acting Director of Banks
Division of Banks
Department of Financial
Institutions
P.O. Box 41200
Olympia, WA 98504
P: (360) 902-8704
F: (360) 753-6070
E: banks@dfi.wa.gov

WEST VIRGINIA
Ms. Sara M. Cline
Commissioner of Banking
Division of Financial
Institutions
900 Pennsylvania Avenue, Suite
306
Charleston, WV 25302
P: (304) 558-2294
F: (304) 558-0442
E: scline@wvdob.org

WISCONSIN
Mr. Michael Mach
Administrator
Division of Banking
P.O. Box 7876
Madison, WI 53707
P: (608) 261-7578
F: (608) 267-6889
E: Mike.Mach
    @dfi.wisconsin.gov

WYOMING
Mr. Albert L. Forkner
State Banking Commissioner
Division of Banking
Herschler Building, 3rd Floor,
East Wing
122 West 25th Street
Cheyenne, WY 82002
P: (307) 777-7797
F: (307) 777-3555
E: albert.forkner@wyo.gov

Borders Management

Oversees and regulates the flow of transportation and immigration over state and international borders.

AMERICAN SAMOA
Hon. Talauega Eleasalo V.
    Ale
Attorney General
Office of the Attorney General
American Samoa Government
Exeuctive Office Building,
Utulei
Pago Pago, AS 96799
P: (684) 633-4163

FLORIDA
Mr. Rick Swearingen
Commissioner
Department of Law
Enforcement
2331 Phillips Road
P.O. Box 1489
Tallahassee, FL 32302
P: (850) 410-7001
E: RickSwearingen
    @fdle.state.fl.us

GUAM
Mr. Pedro A.
    Leon Guerrero Jr.
Director
Customs & Quarantine Agency
Building 13-16, 17 Mariner
Drive, Tiyan
Barrigada, GU 96932
P: (671) 475-6202
F: (671) 475-6227

KANSAS
Mr. Mark Bruce
Superintendent
Highway Patrol
122 Southwest 7th Street
Topeka, KS 66603
P: (785) 296-6800
F: (785) 296-3049

MASSACHUSETTS
Colonel Richard D. McKeon
Superintendent
State Police
470 Worcester Road
Framingham, MA 01702
P: (508) 820-2300
F: (617) 727-6874

MINNESOTA
Ms. Ramona Dohman
Commissioner
Department of Public Safety
445 Minnesota Street, Suite
1000
St. Paul, MN 55101
P: (651) 201-7160
F: (651) 297-5728
E: Mona.Dohman@state.mn.us

MISSOURI
Mr. Lane Roberts
Director
Department of Public Safety
Office of the Director
P.O. Box 749
Jefferson City, MO 65102
P: (573) 751-4905
F: (573) 751-5399

MONTANA
Hon. Tim Fox (R)
Attorney General
Department of Justice
Justice Building
215 North Sanders
Helena, MT 59620
P: (406) 444-2026
F: (406) 444-3549
E: contactdoj@mt.gov

NEW HAMPSHIRE
Mr. John J. Barthelmes
Commissioner
Department of Safety
James H. Hayes Safety Building
33 Hazen Drive
Concord, NH 03305
P: (603) 223-3889
F: (603) 271-3903
E: john.barthelmes
    @dos.nh.gov

NORTH DAKOTA
Ms. Debbie LaCombe
State Director
Homeland Security Division
Fraine Barracks Lane, Building
35
P.O. Box 5511
Bismarck, ND 58504
P: (701) 328-8100
F: (701) 328-8181
E: dlacombe@nd.gov

SOUTH CAROLINA
Ms. Christy Hall
Acting Secretary of
Transportation
Department of Transportation
Silas N. Pearman Building
955 Park Street
Columbia, SC 29201
P: (803) 737-2314
F: (803) 737-2038

U.S. VIRGIN ISLANDS
Mr. Carlton Dowe
Executive Director
Port Authority
8074 Lindbergh Bay
P.O. Box 301707
St. Thomas, VI 00803
P: (340) 774-1629
F: (340) 774-0025
E: info@viport.com

UTAH
Mr. Chad Sheppick
Director
Motor Carriers Division
Department of Transportation
4501 South 2700 West, P.O. Box
148240
Salt Lake City, UT 84114
P: (801) 965-4156
F: (801) 965-4847
E: csheppick@utah.gov

VIRGINIA
Mr. John F. Reinhart
CEO & Executive Director
Port Authority
600 World Trade Center
Norfolk, VA 23510
P: (757) 683-8000
F: (757) 683-8500
E: jreinhart
    @portofvirginia.com

WASHINGTON
Maj. Gen. Timothy J.
    Lowenberg
Adjutant General
Military Department
One Militia Drive, Building One
Camp Murray, WA 98430
P: (253) 512-8201
F: (253) 512-8497
E: timothy.lowenberg
    @us.army.mil

Budget

Collects and analyzes budget
requests and supporting
materials and prepares the
executive budget documents.

ALABAMA
Mr. Kelly Butler
Assistant State Budget Officer
Executive Budget Office
P.O. Box 302610
Montgomery, AL 36130
P: (334) 242-7230
F: (334) 242-3776
E: kelly.butler
    @budget.alabama.gov

ALASKA
Ms. Pat Pitney
Director
Office of Management &
Budget
P.O. Box 110020
Juneau, AK 99811
P: (907) 465-4660
F: (907) 465-3640
E: pat.pitney@alaska.gov

ARIZONA
Mr. Lorenzo Romero
Director
Governor's Office of Strategic
Planning & Budgeting
1700 West Washington, 6th
Floor
Phoenix, AZ 85007
P: (602) 542-5383
F: (602) 542-5381
E: romero@az.gov

ARKANSAS
Mr. Larry Walther
Director
Department of Finance &
Administration
1509 West 7th Street
DFA Building, Room 401
Little Rock, AR 72201
P: (501) 682-2242
F: (501) 682-1029
E: larry.walther
    @dfa.arkansas.gov

CALIFORNIA
Mr. Michael Cohen
Director
Department of Finance
915 L Street
Sacramento, CA 95814
P: (916) 445-4141
E: michael.cohen@dof.ca.gov

COLORADO
Mr. Henry Sobanet
Director
Office of State Planning &
Budgeting
200 East Colfax, Room 111
Denver, CO 80203
P: (303) 866-3317
F: (303) 866-3044
E: henry.sobanet
    @state.co.us

CONNECTICUT
Mr. Benjamin Barnes
Secretary
Office of Policy & Management
450 Capitol Avenue
Hartford, CT 06106
P: (860) 418-6500
F: (860) 418-6487
E: Ben.Barnes@Ct.gov

DELAWARE
Ms. Ann Shepard Visalli
Director
Office of Management &
Budget
Haslet Armory
122 Martin Luther King Jr.
Boulevard S.
Dover, DE 19901
P: (302) 739-4204
F: (302) 739-5661
E: Ann.Visalli@state.de.us

FLORIDA
Ms. Cynthia Kelly
State Budget Director
Office of Policy & Budget
The Capitol
400 South Monroe Street, PL05
Tallahassee, FL 32399
P: (850) 487-1880

GEORGIA
Ms. Teresa MacCartney
Director
Governor's Office of Planning &
Budget
270 Washington Street,
Southwest
Suite 8057A
Atlanta, GA 30334
P: (404) 656-3820
F: (404) 656-7198
E: teresa.maccartney
    @opb.state.ga.us

HAWAII
Hon. Wesley Machida
Director of Finance
Department of Budget &
Finance
P.O. Box 150
Honolulu, HI 96810
P: (808) 586-1518
F: (808) 586-1976
E: hi.budgetandfinance
    @hawaii.gov

IDAHO
Ms. Jani Revier
Administrator
Division of Financial
Management
P.O. Box 83720
Boise, ID 83720
P: (208) 334-3900
F: (208) 334-2438
E: jani.revier
    @dfm.idaho.gov

ILLINOIS
Mr. Tim Nuding
Director
Governor's Office of
Management & Budget
401 South Spring
603 Stratton Building
Springfield, IL 62706
P: (217) 782-4520
F: (217) 524-4876

INDIANA
Mr. Brian E. Bailey
Director
State Budget Agency
200 West Washington Street,
Room 212
Indianapolis, IN 46204
P: (317) 234-8538
F: (317) 233-3323
E: bbailey@gov.in.gov

IOWA
Mr. David Roederer
Director
Department of Management
State Capitol
Des Moines, IA 50319
P: (515) 281-3322
E: david.roederer@iowa.gov

KANSAS
Mr. Shawn Sullivan
Director
Division of the Budget
900 Southwest Jackson, Suite
504
Topeka, KS 66612
P: (785) 296-2436
F: (785) 296-0231
E: shawn.sullivan
    @budget.ks.gov

KENTUCKY
Ms. Jane Driskell
State Budget Director
Office of the State Budget
Director
702 Capitol Avenue
Room 284, Capitol Annex
Frankfort, KY 40601
P: (502) 564-7300
F: (502) 564-6684

LOUISIANA
Mr. Barry Dusse
Director
Office of Planning & Budget
P.O. Box 94095
Baton Rouge, LA 70804
P: (225) 342-7005
F: (225) 342-7220
E: barry.dusse@la.gov

MAINE
Ms. Melissa Gott
State Budget Director
Bureau of the Budget
3rd Floor, Burton M. Cross
Building
58 State House Station
Augusta, ME 04333
P: (207) 624-7810
E: Melissa.L.Gott@maine.gov

MARYLAND
Mr. David R. Brinkley
Secretary
Department of Budget &
Management
45 Calvert Street, 1st Floor
Annapolis, MD 21401
P: (410) 260-7041
F: (410) 974-2585
E: David.Brinkley
    @maryland.gov

MASSACHUSETTS
Ms. Kristen Lepore
Secretary
Executive Office for
Administration & Finance
State House, Room 373
Boston, MA 02133
P: (617) 727-2040
F: (617) 727-2779
E: kristen.lepore
    @state.ma.us

MICHIGAN
Mr. John S. Roberts
State Budget Director
Department of Technology,
Management & Budget
111 South Capitol Avenue
Lansing, MI 48933
P: (517) 373-7560
F: (517) 241-5428
E: Contact-SBO@Michigan.gov

MINNESOTA
Mr. Myron Frans
Commissioner
Management & Budget
658 Cedar Street, Suite 400
St. Paul, MN 55155
P: (651) 201-8011
F: (651) 797-1300
E: myron.frans@state.mn.us

MISSISSIPPI
Ms. Sandra Lohrisch
Director
Office of Budget & Fund
Management
P.O. Box 267
Jackson, MS 39201
P: (601) 359-3927
F: (601) 359-6758
E: Sandra.Lohrisch
     @dfa.ms.gov

MISSOURI
Ms. Linda S. Luebbering
Director
Division of Budget & Planning
Capitol Building
Rooms 124/129
Jefferson City, MO 65102
P: (573) 751-3925
F: (573) 526-4811

MONTANA
Mr. Dan Villa
Budget Director
Office of Budget & Program
Planning
State Capitol, Room 277
P.O. Box 200802
Helena, MT 59620
P: (406) 444-3616
F: (406) 444-4670
E: dvilla@mt.gov

NEBRASKA
Mr. Byron L. Diamond
Director
Department of Administrative
Services
State Capitol, Room 1315
Lincoln, NE 68509
P: (402) 471-2331
E: byron.diamond
     @nebraska.gov

NEVADA
Mr. James Wells
Interim Director
Department of Administration
Balsdel Building, Room 200
209 East Musser Street
Carson City, NV 89701
P: (775) 684-0222
F: (775) 684-0260
E: budget@admin.nv.gov

NEW HAMPSHIRE
Ms. Vicki Quiram
Commissioner
Department of Administrative
Services
25 Capitol Street
State House Annex, Room 120
Concord, NH 03301
P: (603) 271-3201
F: (603) 271-6600
E: vicki.quiram@nh.gov

NEW JERSEY
Ms. Charlene M. Holzbaur
Director
Office of Management &
Budget
Department of the Treasury
33 West State Street, P.O. Box
221
Trenton, NJ 08625
P: (609) 292-6746
F: (609) 633-8179
E: charlene.holzbaur
     @treas.state.nj.us

NEW MEXICO
Mr. Michael Marcelli
Director
State Budget Division
Bataan Memorial Building,
Suite 190
407 Galisteo Street
Santa Fe, NM 87501
P: (505) 827-3640
F: (505) 827-3861
E: michael.marcelli
     @state.nm.us

NEW YORK
Ms. Mary Beth Labate
Budget Director
Division of the Budget
State Capitol
Albany, NY 12224
P: (518) 474-0580

NORTH CAROLINA
Mr. Lee Roberts
State Budget Director
Office of State Budget &
Management
116 West Jones Street
Raleigh, NC 27603
P: (919) 807-4700
E: lee.roberts@osbm.nc.gov

NORTH DAKOTA
Ms. Sheila Peterson
Director, Fiscal Management
Division
Fiscal Management Division
600 East Boulevard Avenue
Department 110
Bismarck, ND 58505
P: (701) 328-2680
F: (701) 328-3230
E: speterson@nd.gov

NORTHERN MARIANA
ISLANDS
Ms. Esther Fleming
Chief of Staff
Office of the Governor
Caller Box 10007, Capitol Hill
Saipan, MP 96950
P: (670) 664-2212
F: (670) 664-2211

OHIO
Mr. Timothy S. Keen
Director
Office of Budget &
Management
30 East Broad Street, 34th Floor
Columbus, OH 43215
P: (614) 752-2579
F: (614) 485-1058
E: tim.keen@obm.state.oh.us

OKLAHOMA
Ms. Jill Geiger
Budget Director
Office of State Finance
2300 North Lincoln Boulevard,
Room 122
Oklahoma City, OK 73105
P: (405) 521-2141
F: (405) 521-3902

OREGON
Ms. Kay Erickson
Budget Manager
Budget & Management Division
155 Cottage Street, Northeast,
U20
Salem, OR 97301
P: (503) 378-4588
E: Kay.L.Erickson
     @oregon.gov

PENNSYLVANIA
Mr. Randy Albright
Secretary of the Budget
Office of the Budget
19th Floor, 333 Market Street
Harrisburg, PA 17101
P: (717) 787-2542
F: (717) 783-3368

PUERTO RICO
Mr. Luis Batista Cruz
Director
Office of Management &
Budget
P.O. Box 9023228
San Juan, PR 00902
P: (787) 725-9420
F: (787) 722-0299

RHODE ISLAND
Mr. Thomas A. Mullaney
Director
Budget Office
Office of Management &
Budget
One Capitol Hill, 4th Floor
Providence, RI 02908
P: (401) 222-6414
F: (401) 222-6436
E: thomas.mullaney
     @budget.ri.gov

SOUTH CAROLINA
Ms. Brenda Hart
Interim Director
Executive Budget Office
1205 Pendleton Street, Suite 529
Columbia, SC 29201
P: (803) 734-2280
F: (803) 734-0645
E: bhart@budget.sc.gov

SOUTH DAKOTA
Mr. Jason C. Dilges
Chief Financial Officer &
Commissioner
Bureau of Finance &
Management
500 East Capitol Avenue
Pierre, SD 57501
P: (605) 773-3411
F: (605) 773-4711
E: jason.dilges@state.sd.us

TENNESSEE
Mr. Larry Martin
Commissioner
Department of Finance &
Administration
312 Rosa Parks Avenue, 21st
Floor
Nashville, TN 37243
P: (615) 741-2401
E: Larry.Martin@tn.gov

Budget

TEXAS
Ms. Kate McGrath
Director
Budget, Planning & Policy
Division
Office of the Governor
P.O. Box 12428
Austin, TX 78711
P: (512) 463-1778
F: (512) 463-1975

U.S. VIRGIN ISLANDS
Mr. Nellon Bowry
Director
Office of Management &
Budget
#41 Norre Gade
Emancipation Garden Station,
2nd Floor
St. Thomas, VI 00802
P: (340) 774-0750
F: (340) 778-8925
E: nellon.bowry@omb.vi.gov

UTAH
Ms. Kristen Cox
Executive Director
Governor's Office of
Management & Budget
State Capitol, Suite 150
P.O. Box 132210
Salt Lake City, UT 84114
P: (801) 538-1027
F: (801) 538-1547
E: kristencox@utah.gov

VERMONT
Mr. James B. Reardon
Commissioner
Department of Finance &
Management
109 State Street
Montpelier, VT 05609
P: (802) 828-2376
F: (802) 828-2428
E: jim.reardon@state.vt.us

VIRGINIA
Mr. Daniel Timberlake
Director
Department of Planning &
Budget
1111 East Broad Street
Room 5040
Richmond, VA 23219
P: (804) 786-7455
F: (804) 225-3291
E: dan.timberlake
   @dpb.virginia.gov

WASHINGTON
Mr. David Schumacher
Director
Office of Financial Management
P.O. Box 43113
Olympia, WA 98504
P: (360) 902-0555
F: (360) 664-2832
E: ofm.administration
   @ofm.wa.gov

WEST VIRGINIA
Mr. Mike McKown
Director
State Budget Office
Building 1, Room 310-W
Capitol Building
Charleston, WV 25305
P: (304) 558-0040
F: (304) 558-1588
E: Mike.P.McKown@wv.gov

WISCONSIN
Mr. Michael Heifetz
Administrator
Division of Executive Budget &
Finance
101 East Wilson Street, 10th
Floor
P.O. Box 7864
Madison, WI 53703
P: (608) 266-1035
F: (608) 267-0372
E: michael.heifetz
   @wisconsin.gov

Building Codes

Establishes and enforces standards of construction, materials and occupancy for all buildings.

ALABAMA
Ms. Katherine Lynn
Director
Building Commission
P.O. Box 301150
Montgomery, AL 36130
P: (334) 242-4082
F: (334) 242-4182

ARIZONA
Ms. Debra Blake
Director
Department of Fire, Building & Life Safety
1110 West Washington, Suite 100
Phoenix, AZ 85007
P: (602) 364-1003
F: (602) 364-1052

ARKANSAS
Mr. Tom Waller
Director
Manufactured Home Commission
101 East Capitol Avenue, Suite 210
Little Rock, AR 72201
P: (501) 324-9032
F: (501) 683-3538
E: Whit.Waller@arkansas.gov

CALIFORNIA
Mr. Richard Conrad
Manager
Division of the State Architect
Architectural Code & Building Systems
1102 Q Street, Suite 5100
Sacramento, CA 95814
P: (916) 324-7180
F: (916) 445-3521
E: Richard.Conrad
   @dgs.ca.gov

Mr. Chester Widom
State Architect
Division of the State Architect
1102 Q Street, Suite 5100
Sacramento, CA 95811
P: (916) 445-8100
F: (916) 445-3521
E: chester.widom@dgs.ca.gov

COLORADO
Ms. Alison George
Director
Division of Housing
Department of Local Affairs
1313 Sherman, Room 500
Denver, CO 80203
P: (303) 864-7810
F: (303) 864-7856
E: alison.george
   @state.co.us

CONNECTICUT
Mr. Joseph V. Cassidy
Acting State Building Inspector
Office of State Building Inspector
Division of Construction Services
165 Capitol Avenue, Room 265
Hartford, CT 06106
P: (860) 713-5900
F: (860) 713-7410
E: joseph.cassidy@ct.gov

DELAWARE
Mr. Grover P. Ingle
State Fire Marshal
Office of the State Fire Marshal
1537 Chestnut Grove Road
Dover, DE 19904
P: (302) 739-5665
F: (302) 739-3696
E: grover.ingle@state.de.us

DISTRICT OF COLUMBIA
Mr. Rabbiah Sabbakhan
Director
Department of Consumer & Regulatory Affairs
1100 4th Street, Southwest
Washington, DC 20024
P: (202) 442-4400
F: (202) 442-9445
E: dcra@dc.gov

FLORIDA
Mr. Ken L. Reecy
Director
Bureau of Housing & Community Development
Division of Community Development
Caldwell Building, 107 East Madison St.
Tallahassee, FL 32399
P: (850) 717-8436
F: (850) 922-5623
E: ken.reecy
   @deo.myflorida.com

GEORGIA
Mr. Theodore N. Miltiades
Office Director, Construction Codes
Planning & Environmental Management Division
Department of Community Affairs
60 Executive Park South, Northeast
Atlanta, GA 30329
P: (404) 679-3106
E: ted.miltiades@dca.ga.gov

HAWAII
Mr. Manuel P. Neves
Chair
State Fire Council
636 South Street
Honolulu, HI 96813
P: (808) 723-7101
F: (808) 723-7111

IDAHO
Mr. C. Kelly Pearce
Administrator
Division of Building Safety
1090 East Watertower Street, Suite 150
Meridian, ID 83642
P: (208) 334-3950
F: (877) 810-2840
E: kelly.pearce
   @dbs.idaho.gov

ILLINOIS
Ms. Lisa Mattingly
Division Staff
Building Codes & Regulations
3rd Floor Stratton
401 South Spring Street
Springfield, IL 62706
P: (217) 524-6408
F: (217) 524-4208
E: Lisa.Mattingly
   @illinois.gov

INDIANA
Mr. James L. Greeson
Division Director & State Fire Marshal
Division of Fire & Building Safety
Department of Homeland Security
302 West Washington Street, Room E241
Indianapolis, IN 46204
P: (317) 232-2226
E: jgreeson@dhs.in.gov

IOWA
Mr. Larry L. Noble
Commissioner
Department of Public Safety
215 East 7th Street
Des Moines, IA 50319
P: (515) 725-6182
E: noble@dps.state.ia.us

KANSAS
Mr. Douglas Jorgensen
State Fire Marshal
Office of the Fire Marshal
700 Southwest Jackson, Suite 600
Topeka, KS 66603
P: (785) 296-3401
F: (785) 296-0151

KENTUCKY
Mr. Ambrose Wilson IV
Commissioner
Department of Housing, Buildings & Construction
101 Sea Hero Road, Suite 100
Frankfort, KY 40601
P: (502) 573-0365
F: (502) 573-1057
E: ambrose.wilson@ky.gov

LOUISIANA
Mr. Mark A. Moses
Director
Office of Facility Planning & Control
Division of Administration
P.O. Box 94095
Baton Rouge, LA 70804
P: (225) 342-0820
F: (225) 342-7624
E: mark.moses@la.gov

MAINE
Mr. Robert V. LeClair
Executive Director
Manufactured Housing Board
Professional & Financial Regulation
35 State House Station
Augusta, ME 04333
P: (207) 624-8612
F: (207) 624-8637
E: manuhousing.board
   @maine.gov

MARYLAND
Mr. Ed Landon
Director, Codes Administration
Department of Housing & Community Development
100 Community Place, Room 3.641
Crownsville, MD 21032
P: (410) 514-7444
F: (410) 987-8902
E: landon@mdhousing.org

Building Codes

MASSACHUSETTS
Mr. Matthew Carlin
Commissioner
Department of Public Safety
One Ashburton Place, Room
1301
Boston, MA 02108
P: (617) 727-3200
F: (617) 727-5732

MICHIGAN
Mr. Irvin Poke
Executive Director
Bureau of Construction Codes
P.O. Box 30254
Lansing, MI 48909
P: (517) 241-9313
F: (517) 241-9308
E: pokei@michigan.gov

MINNESOTA
Mr. Steve Hernick
State Building Official
Construction Codes & Licensing
Department of Labor & Industry
443 Lafayette Road, North
St. Paul, MN 55155
P: (651) 284-5848
F: (651) 284-5749
E: steve.hernick
    @state.mn.us

MISSISSIPPI
Mr. Ricky Davis
Chief Deputy Fire Marshal
State Fire Marshal's Office
Insurance Department
660 North Street, Suite 100-B
Jackson, MS 39202
P: (601) 359-1061
F: (601) 359-1076
E: ricky.davis
    @mid.state.ms.us

MISSOURI
Mr. Justin Smith
Manager
Manufactured Housing &
Modular Unit Program
Public Service Commission
P.O. Box 360
Jefferson City, MO 65102
P: (573) 526-2833
F: (573) 522-2509
E: justin.smith@psc.mo.gov

MONTANA
Mr. Adam De Yong
Acting Division Administrator
Business Standards Division
Dept. of Labor & Industry
301 South Park, Room 430
Helena, MT 59620
P: (406) 841-2333

NEBRASKA
Mr. Mark Luttich
Director
Housing & Recreational
Vehicles
Public Service Commission
1200 N Street, Suite 300
Lincoln, NE 68508
P: (402) 471-3101
F: (402) 471-0254
E: mark.luttich
    @nebraska.gov

NEVADA
Mr. Bruce H. Breslow
Director
Department of Business &
Industry
555 East Washington Avenue,
Suite 4900
Las Vegas, NV 89101
P: (702) 486-2750
F: (702) 486-2758
E: breslow@business.nv.gov

NEW HAMPSHIRE
Mr. J. William Degnan
State Fire Marshal
Division of Fire Safety
Department of Safety
33 Hazen Drive
Concord, NH 03305
P: (603) 223-4289
F: (603) 223-4294
E: fmo@dos.nh.gov

NEW JERSEY
Mr. Edward Smith
Director
Division of Codes & Standards
Department of Community
Affairs
101 South Broad Street, P.O.
Box 802
Trenton, NJ 08625
P: (609) 292-7899
F: (609)-633-6729

NEW MEXICO
Ms. Lisa Martinez
Director
Construction Industries &
Manufactured Housing
Regulation & Licensing
Department
P.O. Box 25101
Santa Fe, NM 87504
P: (505) 476-4700
F: (505) 476-4685
E: lisa.martinez
    @state.nm.us

NEW YORK
Mr. Ronald E. Piester
Director
Division of Code Enforcement
& Administration
One Commerce Plaza
99 Washington Avenue
Albany, NY 12231
P: (518) 474-4073
F: (518) 486-4487
E: codes@dos.state.ny.us

NORTH CAROLINA
Mr. Chris Noles
Deputy Commissioner,
Engineering & Codes
Office of the State Fire Marshal
Department of Insurance
1202 Mail Service Center
Raleigh, NC 27699
P: (919) 661-5880 Ext.223
F: (919) 662-4414
E: chris.noles@ncdoi.gov

NORTH DAKOTA
Mr. Paul T. Govig
Director
Division of Community
Services
1600 East Century Avenue,
Suite 2
P.O. Box 2057
Bismarck, ND 58502
P: (701) 328-4499
F: (701) 328-2308
E: pgovig@nd.gov

**NORTHERN MARIANA
ISLANDS**
Mr. Donald Anderson
Building Safety Official
Building Safety Code Division
2nd Floor, Joeten Commercial
Center
Gualo Rai
Saipan, MP 96950
P: (670) 235-5827
F: (670) 235-6346

OHIO
Ms. Regina Hanshaw
Executive Secretary
Board of Building Standards
6606 Tussing Road
P.O. Box 4009
Reynoldsburg, OH 43068
P: (614) 644-2613
F: (614) 644-3147
E: regina.hanshaw
    @com.state.oh.us

OKLAHOMA
Mr. Robert Doke
State Fire Marshal
Office of the State Fire Marshal
2401 Northwest 23rd, Suite 4
Oklahoma City, OK 73107
P: (405) 522-5005
F: (405) 522-5028
E: robert.doke@fire.ok.gov

OREGON
Mr. Mark S. Long
Administrator
Building Codes Division
1535 Edgewater Street,
Northwest
P.O. Box 14470
Salem, OR 97309
P: (503) 373-7235
F: (503) 378-2322
E: Mark.Long@oregon.gov

PENNSYLVANIA
Mr. Mark Conte
Chief
Housing Standards Division
Community & Economic
Development
400 North Street, 4th Floor
Harrisburg, PA 17112
P: (717) 720-7416
F: (717) 783-4663
E: mconte@pa.gov

RHODE ISLAND
Mr. John P. Leyden
State Building Code
Commissioner
Building Code Commission
1 Capitol Hill, 2nd Floor
Providence, RI 02908
P: (401) 222-1129
F: (401) 222-2599
E: Jeanne.Enos@doa.ri.gov

SOUTH CAROLINA
Mr. Roger K. Lowe
Administrator
Building Codes Council
P.O. Box 11329
Columbia, SC 29211
P: (803) 896-4688
F: (803) 896-4814
E: roger.lowe@llr.sc.gov

SOUTH DAKOTA
Mr. Paul Merriman
State Fire Marshal
Department of Public Safety
118 West Capitol Avenue
Pierre, SD 57501
P: (605) 773-3562
F: (605) 773-6631
E: paul.merriman
    @state.sd.us

TENNESSEE
Mr. Gary L. West
Assistant Commissioner
Fire Prevention Division
Department of Commerce &
Insurance
500 James Robertson Parkway,
3rd Floor
Nashville, TN 37243
P: (615) 741-2981
F: (615) 741-1583
E: Fire.Prevention@TN.Gov

UTAH
Mr. Dan S. Jones
Bureau Manager, Uniform
Building Codes
Division of Occupational &
Professional Licensing
Department of Commerce
P.O. Box 146741
Salt Lake City, UT 84114
P: (801) 530-6720
F: (801) 530-6511
E: dansjones@utah.gov

VERMONT
Mr. Matthew Lindhiem
Fire Safety Building Engineer
Department of Fire Safety
Department of Public Safety
1311 U.S. Route 302, Suite 600
Barre, VT 05641
P: (802) 479-7561
F: (802) 479-7562
E: matthew.lindhiem
@state.vt.us

VIRGINIA
Mr. Emory Rodgers
Deputy Director of Building &
Fire Regulation
Department of Housing &
Community Development
501 North Second Street
Richmond, VA 23219
P: (804) 371-7000
F: (804) 371-7090
E: emory.rodgers
@dhcd.virginia.gov

WASHINGTON
Mr. Tim Nogler
Managing Director
State Building Code Council
1500 Jefferson Avenue,
Southeast
P.O. Box 41449
Olympia, WA 98504
P: (360) 407-9277
F: (360) 586-9088
E: tim.nogler@des.wa.gov

WEST VIRGINIA
Mr. Kenneth E. Tyree
State Fire Marshal
Office of the State Fire Marshal
1207 Quarrier Street, 2nd Floor
Charleston, WV 25301
P: (304) 558-2191
F: (304) 558-2537

WISCONSIN
Ms. Nancy Mistele
Division Administrator
Department of Safety &
Professional Services
Division of Industry Services
P.O. Box 2599
Madison, WI 53701
P: (608) 266-1816
F: (608) 266-9946
E: nancy.mistele@wi.gov

WYOMING
Mr. Lanny Applegate
State Fire Marshal
Department of Fire Prevention
& Electrical Safety
320 West 25th Street, 3rd Floor
Cheyenne, WY 82002
P: (307) 777-7288
F: (307) 777-7119
E: Lanny.applegate@wyo.gov

Campaign Finance Administration

Administers and enforces campaign finance laws.

ALABAMA
Hon. John Merrill (R)
Secretary of State
Office of the Secretary of State
P.O. Box 5616
Montgomery, AL 36103
P: (334) 242-7200
F: (334) 242-4993
E: john.merrill
    @sos.alabama.gov

ALASKA
Mr. Paul Dauphinais
Executive Director
Public Offices Commission
Department of Administration
2221 East Northern Lights,
Room 128
Anchorage, AK 99508
P: (907) 276-4176
F: (907) 276-7018
E: Paul.Dauphinais
    @alaska.gov

AMERICAN SAMOA
Mr. Tuaolo Manaia Fruean
Acting Director
Territorial Election Office
P.O. Box 3790
Pago Pago, AS 96799
P: (684) 699-3570
F: (684) 699-3574
E: Asgelect@samoatelco.com

ARKANSAS
Hon. Mark Martin (R)
Secretary of State
Office of the Secretary of State
256 State Capitol Building
Little Rock, AR 72201
P: (501) 682-1010
F: (501) 682-3510
E: info@sos.arkansas.gov

CALIFORNIA
Ms. Jana Lean
Chief of Elections
Elections Division
1500 11th Street, 5th Floor
Sacramento, CA 95814
P: (916) 657-2166
F: (916) 653-3214
E: jana.lean@sos.ca.gov

COLORADO
Mr. Judd Choate
Director of Elections
Elections Division
Department of State
1700 Broadway, Suite 200
Denver, CO 80290
P: (303) 894-2200
F: (303) 869-4861
E: judd.choate
    @sos.state.co.us

CONNECTICUT
Hon. Denise W. Merrill (D)
Secretary of State
Office of the Secretary of State
State Capitol Building, Room
104
Hartford, CT 06106
P: (860) 509-6200
F: (860) 509-6209
E: denise.merrill@ct.gov

DELAWARE
Ms. M. Elaine Manlove
State Election Commissioner
Office of the State Election
Commissioner
905 South Governors Avenue,
Suite 170
Dover, DE 19904
P: (302) 739-4277
F: (302) 739-6794
E: elaine.manlove
    @state.de.us

DISTRICT OF COLUMBIA
Ms. Cecily E.
    Collier-Montgomery
Director
Office of Campaign Finance
Frank D. Reeves Municipal
Building
2000 14th Street, Northwest,
Suite 433
Washington, DC 20009
P: (202) 671-0547
F: (202) 671-0658
E: ocf@dc.gov

FLORIDA
Hon. Kenneth Detzner (R)
Secretary of State
Office of the Secretary of State
500 South Bronough Street
Tallahassee, FL 32399
P: (850) 245-6500
F: (850) 245-6125
E: dossecretaryofstate
    @dos.myflorida.com

GUAM
Ms. Maria I.D. Pangelinan
Executive Director
Elections Commission
414 West Soledad Avenue
GCIC Building, Suite 200
Hagatna, GU 96910
P: (671) 477-9791
F: (671) 477-1895
E: vote@gec.guam.gov

HAWAII
Ms. Kristin E. Izumi-Nitao
Executive Director
Campaign Spending
Commission
Leiopapa A. Kamehameha
Building
235 South Beretania Street,
Room 300
Honolulu, HI 96813
P: (808) 586-0285
F: (808) 586-0288

IDAHO
Hon. Lawerence Denney (R)
Secretary of State
Office of the Secretary of State
P.O. Box 83720
Boise, ID 83720
P: (208) 334-2300
F: (208) 334-2282
E: ldenney@sos.idaho.gov

ILLINOIS
Mr. Steve Sandvoss
Executive Director
State Board of Elections
2329 South Macarthur
Boulevard
Springfield, IL 62704
P: (217) 782-4141
F: (217) 524-5574
E: ssandvoss
    @elections.il.gov

INDIANA
Mr. Trent Deckard
Co-Director
Election Division
Office of the Secretary of State
302 West Washington Street,
Room E-204
Indianapolis, IN 46204
P: (317) 232-3940
F: (317) 233-6793
E: tdeckard@iec.in.gov

Mr. J. Bradley King
Co-Director
Election Division
Office of the Secretary of State
302 West Washington Street,
Room E-204
Indianapolis, IN 46204
P: (317) 233-0929
F: (317) 233-6793
E: bking@iec.in.gov

IOWA
Ms. Megan Tooker
Executive Director
Ethics & Campaign Disclosure
Board
510 East 12th, Suite 1A
Des Moines, IA 50319
P: (515) 281-3489
F: (510) 281-4073
E: megan.tooker@iowa.gov

KANSAS
Ms. Carol E. Williams
Executive Director
Governmental Ethics
Commission
109 West 9th Street, Suite 504
Topeka, KS 66612
P: (785) 296-4219
F: (785) 296-2548
E: ethics@ethics.ks.gov

KENTUCKY
Ms. Sarah M. Jackson
Executive Director
Registry of Election Finance
140 Walnut Street
Frankfort, KY 40601
P: (502) 573-2226
F: (502) 573-5622
E: sarahm.jackson@ky.gov

LOUISIANA
Ms. Kathleen Allen
Ethics Administrator
Ethics Administration Program
617 North Third Street, Suite
10-36
P.O. Box 4368
Baton Rouge, LA 70821
P: (225) 219-5600
F: (225) 381-7271
E: kathleen.allen@la.gov

MAINE
Mr. Jonathan Wayne
Executive Director
Commission on Governmental
Ethics & Election Practices
135 State House Station
Augusta, ME 04333
P: (207) 287-4179
F: (207) 287-6775
E: Jonathan.Wayne@maine.gov

MARYLAND
Mr. Jared DeMarinis
Director
Division of Candidacy &
Campaign Finance
151 West Street, Suite 200
P.O. Box 6486
Annapolis, MD 21401
P: (410) 269-2853
F: (410) 974-5415
E: Jared.DeMarinis
    @maryland.gov

MASSACHUSETTS
Mr. Michael J. Sullivan
Director
Office of Campaign & Political
Finance
John W. McCormack Building
One Ashburton Place, Room 411
Boston, MA 02108
P: (617) 979-8300
F: (617) 727-6549
E: ocpf@cpf.state.ma.us

MICHIGAN
Mr. Christopher M. Thomas
Director
Bureau of Elections
Richard H. Austin Building,
First Floor
430 West Allegan Street
Lansing, MI 48918
P: (517) 335-2789
F: (517) 373-0941
E: ChristopherT
    @michigan.gov

MINNESOTA
Mr. Gary Goldsmith
Executive Director
Campaign Finance & Public
Disclosure Board
Centennial Office Building,
Suite 190
658 Cedar Street
St. Paul, MN 55155
P: (651) 539-1190
F: (651) 539-1196
E: gary.goldsmith
    @state.mn.us

MISSISSIPPI
Ms. Kim Turner
Senior Attorney
Elections Division
Secretary of State's Office
401 Mississippi Street
Jackson, MS 39201
P: (601) 359-5137
F: (601) 359-1499
E: Kim.Turner@sos.ms.gov

MISSOURI
Mr. James Klahr
Executive Director
Ethics Commission
3411A Knipp Drive
P.O. Box 1370
Jefferson City, MO 65102
P: (573) 751-2020
F: (573) 526-4506
E: helpdesk@mec.mo.gov

MONTANA
Mr. Jonathan R. Motl
Commissioner
Commissioner of Political
Practices
P.O. Box 202401
Helena, MT 59620
P: (406) 444-2942
F: (406) 444-1643
E: jmotl@mt.gov

NEBRASKA
Mr. Frank Daley
Executive Director
Accountability & Disclosure
Commission
P.O. Box 95086
Lincoln, NE 68509
P: (402) 471-2522
F: (402) 471-6599
E: frank.daley@nebraska.gov

NEVADA
Hon. Barbara Cegavske (R)
Secretary of State
Office of the Secretary of State
101 North Carson Stree, Suite 3
Carson City, NV 89701
P: (775) 684-5708
F: (775) 684-5724
E: sosexec@sos.nv.gov

NEW HAMPSHIRE
Hon. William M. Gardner (D)
Secretary of State
Office of the Secretary of State
State House, Room 204
Concord, NH 03301
P: (603) 271-3242
F: (603) 271-6316
E: kladd@sos.state.nh.us

NEW JERSEY
Mr. Jeffrey M. Brindle
Executive Director
Election Law Enforcement
Commission
P.O. Box 185
Trenton, NJ 08625
P: (609) 292-8700
F: (609) 777-1448
E: jeff.brindle
    @elec.state.nj.us

NEW MEXICO
Ms. Bobbi Shearer
Director
Bureau of Elections
Secretary of State's Office
325 Don Gaspar, Suite 300
Santa Fe, NM 87501
P: (505) 827-3600
F: (505) 827-8403
E: bobbi.shearer
    @state.nm.us

NEW YORK
Mr. Robert A. Brehm
Co-Director
State Board of Elections
40 North Pearl Street, Suite 5
Albany, NY 12207
P: (518) 474-8100
F: (518) 486-4068
E: Robert.Brehm
    @elections.ny.gov

Mr. Todd D. Valentine
Co-Director
State Board of Elections
40 North Pearl Street, Suite 5
Albany, NY 12207
P: (518) 474-8100
F: (518) 486-4068
E: Todd.Valentine
    @elections.ny.gov

NORTH CAROLINA
Ms. Kim Westbrook Strach
Executive Director
State Board of Elections
441 North Harrington Street
P.O. Box 27255
Raleigh, NC 27611
P: (919) 733-7173
F: (919) 715-0135
E: kim.strach@ncsbe.gov

NORTH DAKOTA
Ms. LeeAnn Oliver
Elections Specialist
Office of the Secretary of State
600 East Boulevard Avenue
Department 108, 1st Floor
Bismarck, ND 58505
P: (701) 328-4146
F: (701) 328-2992
E: loliver@nd.gov

**NORTHERN MARIANA
ISLANDS**
Mr. Michael S. Pai
Public Auditor
Office of the Public Auditor
P.O. Box 501399
Saipan, MP 96950
P: (670) 322-6481
F: (670) 322-7812
E: mpai@opacnmi.com

OHIO
Mr. J. Curtis Mayhew
Campaign Finance
Administrator
Office of the Secretary of State
180 East Broad Street, 16th
Floor
Columbus, OH 43215
P: (614) 466-3111

OREGON
Mr. Jim Williams
Director of Elections
Office of the Secretary of State
Public Service Building, Suite
501
Salem, OR 97301
P: (503) 986-1518
F: (503) 373-7414
E: James.R.Williams
    @state.or.us

PENNSYLVANIA
Mr. Jonathan M. Marks
Commissioner
Bureau of Commissions,
Elections & Legislation
Department of State
210 North Office Building
Harrisburg, PA 17120
P: (717) 787-5280
F: (717) 705-0721
E: RA-BCEL@pa.gov

PUERTO RICO
Mr. Angel A. Roman Gonzalez
Executive Director
State Election Commission
P.O. Box 195552
San Juan, PR 00919
P: (787) 777-8682
F: (787) 296-0173

RHODE ISLAND
Mr. Robert Kando
Executive Director
Board of Elections
50 Branch Avenue
Providence, RI 02904
P: (401) 222-2345
F: (401) 222-3135
E: campaignfinance
    @elections.ri.gov

SOUTH CAROLINA
Mr. Herbert R. Hayden Jr.
Executive Director
State Ethics Commission
5000 Thurmond Mall, Suite 250
Columbia, SC 29201
P: (803) 253-4192
F: (803) 253-7539
E: herb@ethics.state.sc.us

Campaign Finance Administration

TENNESSEE
Ms. Patricia Heim
Chair
Registry of Election Finance
404 James Robertson Parkway,
Suite 104
Nashville, TN 37243
P: (615) 741-7959
F: (615) 532-8905
E: registry.info@tn.gov

TEXAS
Ms. Natalia Luna Ashley
Executive Director
Ethics Commission
201 East 14th Street, 10th Floor
P.O. Box 12070
Austin, TX 78711
P: (512) 463-5800
F: (512) 463-5777

U.S. VIRGIN ISLANDS
Ms. Caroline Fawkes
Supervisor of Elections
Election System of the Virgin
Islands
P.O. Box 1499, Kingshill
St. Croix, VI 00851
P: (340) 773-1021
F: (340) 773-4523
E: caroline.fawkes@vi.gov

UTAH
Mr. Mark Thomas
Director of Elections
Office of the Lieutenant
Governor
Utah State Capitol Suite 220
P.O. Box 142325
Salt Lake City, UT 84114
P: (801) 538-1041
F: (801) 538-1133
E: mjthomas@utah.gov

VERMONT
Hon. Jim Condos (D)
Secretary of State
Office of the Secretary of State
128 State Street
Montpelier, VT 05633
P: (802) 828-2148
F: (802) 828-2496
E: jim.condos
    @sec.state.vt.us

VIRGINIA
Mr. Edgardo Cortes
Commissioner
Department of Elections
Washington Building
1100 Bank Street, First Floor
Richmond, VA 23219
P: (804) 864-8903
F: (804) 371-0194
E: edgardo.cortes
    @elections.virginia.gov

WASHINGTON
Mr. Fred Kiga
Interim Executive Director
Public Disclosure Commission
711 Capitol Way, #206
P.O. Box 40908
Olympia, WA 98504
P: (360) 664-2735
F: (360) 753-1112
E: Fred.Kiga@pdc.wa.gov

WISCONSIN
Mr. Kevin J. Kennedy
Executive Director & General
Counsel
Government Accountability
Board
P.O. Box 7984
Madison, WI 53707
P: (608) 266-8005
F: (608) 267-0500
E: gab@wi.gov

WYOMING
Hon. Ed Murray (R)
Secretary of State
Office of the Secretary of State
State Capitol Building, Room
106
200 West 24th Street
Cheyenne, WY 82002
P: (307) 777-7378
F: (307) 777-6217
E: secofstate@wyo.gov

Chief Information Officer

Oversees state information technology operations and develops, implements, and monitors state IT initiatives.

ALABAMA
Mr. Brunson White
Secretary of Information Technology
Office of Information Technology
100 North Union Street, Suite 980
Montgomery, AL 36130
P: (334) 242-3706
F: (334) 242-7331

ALASKA
Mr. Jim Bates
Director & Chief Information Officer
Division of Enterprise Technology Services
Department of Administration
P.O. Box 110206
Juneau, AK 99811
P: (907) 269-4744
F: (907) 465-3450
E: jim.bates@alaska.gov

ARIZONA
Mr. Mike Lettman
Acting State Chief Information Officer & Chief Information Security Officer
Department of Administration
100 North 15th Avenue, Suite 400
Phoenix, AZ 85007
P: (602) 542-0030

ARKANSAS
Mr. Mark Myers
Director & Chief Technology Officer
Department of Information Systems
One Capitol Mall
P.O. Box 3155
Little Rock, AR 72203
P: (501) 682-9990
F: (501) 682-4310

CALIFORNIA
Mr. Carlos Ramos
Chief Information Officer
Department of Technology
1325 J Street, Suite 1600
Sacramento, CA 95814
P: (916) 319-9223
F: (916) 324-1734
E: carlos.ramos
    @state.ca.gov

COLORADO
Ms. Suma Nallapati
Secretary of Technology & Chief Information Officer
Governor's Office of Information Technology
601 East 18th Avenue, Suite 250
Denver, CO 80203
P: (303) 764-7700
E: oit@state.co.us

CONNECTICUT
Mr. Mark D. Raymond
Chief Information Officer
Bureau of Enterprise Systems & Technology
Department of Administrative Services
55 Farmington Avenue
Hartford, CT 06105
P: (860) 622-2419
F: (860) 291-8665
E: mark.raymond@ct.gov

DELAWARE
Mr. James L. Collins
Chief Information Officer
Department of Technology & Information
801 Silver Lake Boulevard
Dover, DE 19904
P: (302) 739-9629
F: (302) 739-9686
E: james.collins
    @state.de.us

DISTRICT OF COLUMBIA
Mr. Tegene Baharu
Acting Chief Technology Officer
Office of the Chief Technology Officer
200 I Street, Southeast
Washington, DC 20003
P: (202) 727-7349
F: (202) 727-6857
E: octo@dc.gov

FLORIDA
Mr. Jason Allison
Executive Director & Chief Information Officer
Agency for State Technology
4050 Esplanade Way, Suite 115
Tallahassee, FL 32399
P: (850) 414-8521

GEORGIA
Mr. Calvin Rhodes
Executive Director & Chief Information Officer
Technology Authority
47 Trinity Avenue, Southwest
Atlanta, GA 30334
P: (404) 463-2340
F: (404) 463-2380
E: calvn.rhodes@gta.ga.gov

GUAM
Mr. William Castro
Director, Bureau of Statistics & Plans
Office of Technology
P.O. Box 884
Hagatna, GU 96932
P: (671) 475-1113
F: (671) 472-9508

HAWAII
Mr. Todd Nacapuy
Chief Information Officer
Office of Information Management & Technology
1177 Alakea Street, Room 305
Honolulu, HI 96813
P: (808) 586-6000

IDAHO
Mr. Robert L. Geddes
Director & Chief Information Officer
Department of Administration
650 West State Street, Room 100
Len B. Jordan Building, P.O. Box 83720
Boise, ID 83720
P: (208) 332-1824
F: (208) 334-5315
E: contact@cio.idaho.gov

INDIANA
Mr. Paul Baltzell
Chief Information Officer
Office of Technology
Government Center North
1000 North Senate Avenue, Room N551
Indianapolis, IN 46204
P: (317) 234-4392
F: (317) 324-0917
E: pbaltzell@iot.in.gov

IOWA
Mr. Bob Von Wolffradt
Director & Chief Information Officer
Office of the Chief Information Officer
Department of Administrative Services
1305 East Walnut Street
Des Moines, IA 50319
P: (515) 745-4873
F: (515) 281-6137
E: robert.vonwolffradt
    @iowa.gov

KANSAS
Mr. Jim Clark
Interim Chief Information Technology Officer
Office of Information Technology Services
900 Southwest Jackson, Room 751S
Topeka, KS 66612
P: (785) 296-3011
E: jim.clark@da.ks.gov

KENTUCKY
Mr. Parker Allen
Member Services Director
Commonwealth Office of Technology
Finance & Administration Cabinet
101 Cold Harbor Drive
Frankfort, KY 40601
P: (859) 514-9160

LOUISIANA
Mr. Richard Howze
State Chief Information Officer
Office of Technology Services
Division of Administration
P.O. Box 94095
Baton Rouge, LA 70804
P: (225) 342-7105
F: (225) 219-9465
E: cio@la.gov

MAINE
Mr. Jim Smith
Chief Information Officer
Office of Information Technology
Administrative & Financial Services
145 State House Station
Augusta, ME 04333
P: (207) 624-7568

Chief Information Officer

MARYLAND
Mr. David Garcia
Secretary of Information
Technology
Department of Information
Techology
45 Calvert Street
Annapolis, MD 21401
P: (410) 260-4088

MASSACHUSETTS
Mr. Bill Oates
Commonwealth Chief
Information Officer
Executive Office for
Administration & Finance
One Ashburton Place, 8th Floor
Boston, MA 02108
P: (617) 626-4434
F: (617) 626-4411

MICHIGAN
Mr. David Behen
Chief Information Officer &
Department Director
Department of Technology,
Management & Budget
320 South Walnut Street, 2nd
Floor
P.O. Box 30026
Lansing, MI 48909
P: (517) 373-3209
E: behend@michigan.gov

MINNESOTA
Mr. Tom Baden
Commissioner & Chief
Information Officer
Information Technology
Services
Centennial Office Building
658 Cedar Street
St. Paul, MN 55155
P: (651) 431-2917

MISSISSIPPI
Dr. Craig P. Orgeron
Chief Information Officer &
Executive Director
Department of Information
Technology Services
3771 Eastwood Drive
Jackson, MS 39211
P: (601) 432-8000
F: (601) 713-6380
E: craig.orgeron@its.ms.gov

MISSOURI
Mr. Tim Robyn
Chief Information Officer
Office of Administration
301 West High Street, Room
280
P.O. Box 809
Jefferson City, MO 65101
P: (573) 751-1504
F: (573) 751-3299
E: Tim.Robyn@oa.mo.gov

MONTANA
Mr. Ron Baldwin
Chief Information Officer
Information Technology
Services Division
125 North Roberts Street
P.O. Box 200113
Helena, MT 59620
P: (406) 444-2777
F: (406) 444-2701

NEBRASKA
Mr. Ed Toner
Chief Information Officer
Office of the Chief Information
Officer
501 South 14th Street
Lincoln, NE 68508
P: (402) 471-3717

NEVADA
Ms. Shannon Rahming
Interim Administrator
Enterprise Information
Technology Services
100 North Stewart Street, Suite
100
Carson City, NV 89701
P: (775) 684-5849

NEW HAMPSHIRE
Mr. Denis Goulet
Commissioner
Department of Information
Technology
27 Hazen Drive
Concord, NH 03301
P: (603) 223-5701

NEW JERSEY
Mr. E. Steven Emanuel
Chief Information Officer
Office of Information
Technology
200/300 Riverview Plaza
P.O. Box 212
Trenton, NJ 08625
P: (609) 777-5865
F: (609) 633-9100
E: steven.emanuel
@oit.state.nj.us

NEW MEXICO
Mr. Darryl Ackley
Secretary & Chief Information
Officer
Department of Information
Technology
715 Alta Vista Street
P.O. Box 22550
Santa Fe, NM 87502
P: (505) 827-0000
F: (505) 827-2948

NEW YORK
Ms. Maggie Miller
State Chief Information Officer
Office of Information
Technology Services
State Capitol, Empire State
Plaza
P.O. Box 2062
Albany, NY 12220
P: (518) 473-2658

NORTH CAROLINA
Mr. Chris Estes
Chief Information Officer
Office of Information
Technology Services
P.O. Box 17209
Raleigh, NC 27619
P: (919) 754-6576
E: chris.estes@nc.gov

NORTH DAKOTA
Mr. Mike J. Ressler
Chief Information Officer
Information Technology
Department
4201 Normandy Street
Bismarck, ND 58503
P: (701) 328-1000
F: (701) 328-1075
E: mressler@nd.gov

OHIO
Mr. Stuart R. Davis
Chief Information Officer &
Assistant Director
Office of Information
Technology
Department of Administrative
Services
30 East Broad Street, 39th Floor
Columbus, OH 43215
P: (614) 644-6446
F: (614) 728-5297
E: Stu.Davis@das.ohio.gov

OKLAHOMA
Mr. Bo Reese
Chief Information Officer
Office of Management &
Enterprise Services
3115 North Lincoln Boulevard
Oklahoma City, OK 73105
P: (405) 522-5722
F: (405) 521-3902

OREGON
Mr. Alex Pettit
Chief Information Officer
Department of Administrative
Services
Executive Building
155 Cottage Street Northeast, 4th
Floor
Salem, OR 97301
P: (503) 378-3175
F: (503) 378-3795
E: alex.pettit
@das.state.or.us

PENNSYLVANIA
Mr. John MacMillan
Deputy Secretary for
Information Technology & Chief
Information Officer
Office for Information
Technology
Governor's Office of
Administration
209 Finance Building
Harrisburg, PA 17120
P: (717) 787-5440
F: (717) 787-4523
E: cio@pa.gov

PUERTO RICO
Mr. Giancarlo Gonzalez
Chief Information Officer
Office of the Governor
P.O. Box 9023228
San Juan, PR 00902
P: (787) 977-9200

RHODE ISLAND
Mr. Thom Guertin
Chief Digital Officer
Office of Digital Excellence
Division of Information
Technology
One Capitol Hill
Providence, RI 02908
P: (401) 574-9220

SOUTH CAROLINA
Mr. Kyle Herron
Chief Operating Officer
Budget & Control Board
P.O. Box 12444
Columbia, SC 29211
P: (803) 896-0222
E: kherron@cio.sc.gov

SOUTH DAKOTA
Mr. David Zolnowsky
Commissioner
Bureau of Information &
Telecommunications
700 Governors Drive
Pierre, SD 57501
P: (605) 773-5110
F: (605) 773-6040

TENNESSEE
Mr. Mark Bengel
Chief Information Officer
Office for Information
Resources
Department of Finance &
Administration
312 Rosa L. Parks Avenue
Nashville, TN 37343
P: (615) 741-7951
F: (615) 532-0471

TEXAS
Mr. Todd Kimbriel
Interim Executive Director &
CIO
Department of Information
Resources
300 West 15th Street, Suite 1300
P.O. Box 13564
Austin, TX 78711
P: (512) 475-0579
F: (512) 475-4759

U.S. VIRGIN ISLANDS
Mr. Reuben Molloy
Chief Information Officer
Bureau of Information
Technology
#9059 Est. Castle Coakley
Christiansted, VI 00820
P: (340) 713-0354
F: (340) 719-1623

UTAH
Mr. Mark VanOrden
Chief Information Officer
Department of Technology
Services
1 State Office Buidling, Floor 6
Salt Lake City, UT 84114
P: (801) 538-3298
F: (801) 538-3622
E: mvanorden@utah.gov

VERMONT
Mr. Richard Boes
Commissioner & Chief
Information Officer
Department of Information &
Innovation
Agency of Administration
133 State Street
Montpelier, VT 05633
P: (802) 828-4141
F: (802) 828-3398
E: richard.boes@state.vt.us

VIRGINIA
Mr. Nelson Moe
Chief Information Officer
Information Technologies
Agency
Commonwealth Enterprise
Solutions Center
11751 Meadowville Lane
Chester, VA 23836
P: (804) 416-6004
F: (804) 416-6355
E: cio@vita.virginia.gov

WASHINGTON
Mr. Michael Cockrill
Chief Information Officer
Office of the Chief Information
Officer
210 11th Avenue Southwest,
Suite 300
P.O. Box 43113
Olympia, WA 98504
P: (360) 902-7325
F: (360) 664-0495
E: ocio@ofm.wa.gov

WEST VIRGINIA
Ms. Gale Given
Chief Technology Officer
Office of Technology
1900 Kanawha Boulevard, East
Capitol Complex, Building 5,
10th Floor
Charleston, WV 25305
P: (304) 558-8101
F: (304) 558-0136
E: Gale.Y.Given@wv.gov

WISCONSIN
Mr. David Cagigal
Chief Information Officer
Division of Enterprise
Technology
Department of Administration
P.O. Box 7844
Madison, WI 53707
P: (608) 261-8406
F: (608) 267-0626
E: David.Cagigal
@wisconsin.gov

WYOMING
Mr. Flint Waters
Chief Information Officer &
Director
Department of Enterprise
Technology Services
Emerson Building, Suite 214
2001 Capitol Avenue
Cheyenne, WY 82002
P: (307) 777-5840
F: (307) 777-3696
E: cio@wyo.gov

Chief Justice

The chief justice or judge of the state court of last resort.

ALABAMA
Hon. Roy Moore (R)
Chief Justice
Supreme Court
300 Dexter Avenue
Montgomery, AL 36104
P: (334) 229-0700

ALASKA
Hon. Dana Fabe
Chief Justice
Supreme Court
303 K Street
Anchorage, AK 99501
P: (907) 264-0622
F: (907) 264-0768

AMERICAN SAMOA
Hon. F. Michael Kruse
Chief Justice
High Court
Courthouse, P.O. Box 309
Pago Pago, AS 96799
P: (684) 633-1410
F: (684) 633-1318

ARIZONA
Hon. W. Scott Bales
Chief Justice
Supreme Court
1501 West Washington
Suite, 402
Phoenix, AZ 85007
P: (602) 542-9396

ARKANSAS
Hon. Jim Hannah
Chief Justice
Supreme Court
625 Marshall Street
Justice Building
Little Rock, AR 72201
P: (501) 682-6873
F: (501) 683-4006

CALIFORNIA
Hon. Tani Cantil-Sakauye
Chief Justice
Supreme Court
350 McAllister Court
San Francisco, CA 94102
P: (415) 865-7015

COLORADO
Hon. Nancy E. Rice
Chief Justice
Supreme Court
2 East 14th Avenue, Fourth
Floor
Denver, CO 80203
P: (303) 867-1111 Ext. 266

CONNECTICUT
Hon. Chase T. Rogers
Chief Justice
Supreme Court
231 Capitol Avenue
Hartford, CT 06106
P: (860) 757-2200
F: (860) 757-2217

DELAWARE
Hon. Leo E. Strine Jr.
Chief Justice
Supreme Court
New Castle Courthouse
500 North King Street, Suite
11400
Wilmington, DE 19801
P: (302) 255-0511
F: (302) 255-2276

DISTRICT OF COLUMBIA
Hon. Eric T. Washington
Chief Judge
Court of Appeals
Moultrie Courthouse
500 Indiana Avenue, Northwest,
6th Floor
Washington, DC 20001
P: (202) 879-2771

FLORIDA
Hon. Jorge Labarga
Chief Justice
Supreme Court
500 South Duval Street
Tallahassee, FL 32399
P: (850) 488-2281
F: (850) 488-6130

GEORGIA
Hon. Hugh P. Thompson
Chief Justice
Supreme Court
244 Washington Street,
Southwest
Room 572, State Office Annex
Atlanta, GA 30334
P: (404) 656-3470
F: (404) 656-2253

GUAM
Hon. Robert J. Torres Jr.
Chief Justice
Supreme Court
Suite 300, Guam Judicial Center
120 West O'Brien Drive
Hagatna, GU 96910
P: (671) 475-3162
F: (671) 475-3140

HAWAII
Hon. Mark E. Recktenwald
Chief Justice
Supreme Court
Aliiolani Hale
417 South King Street
Honolulu, HI 96813
P: (808) 539-4919
F: (808) 539-4928

IDAHO
Hon. Roger S. Burdick
Chief Justice
Supreme Court
P.O. Box 83720
451 West State Street
Boise, ID 83720
P: (208) 334-3464
F: (208) 947-7590

ILLINOIS
Hon. Rita B. Garman
Chief Justice
Supreme Court
Supreme Court Building
200 East Capitol Avenue
Springfield, IL 62701
P: (217) 782-2035

INDIANA
Hon. Loretta H. Rush
Chief Justice
Supreme Court
200 West Washington Street
315 State House
Indianapolis, IN 46204
P: (317) 242-2540

IOWA
Hon. Mark S. Cady
Chief Justice
Supreme Court
Iowa Judicial Branch Building
111 East Court Avenue
Des Moines, IA 50319
P: (515) 281-5174

KANSAS
Hon. Lawton R. Nuss
Chief Justice
Supreme Court
Judicial Center
301 West 10th Street
Topeka, KS 66612
P: (785) 296-3229
F: (785) 296-1028
E: nussl@kscourts.org

KENTUCKY
Hon. John D. Minton Jr.
Chief Justice
Supreme Court
1001 Center Street, 2nd Floor
Room 204
Bowling Green, KY 42101
P: (270) 746-7867

LOUISIANA
Hon. Bernette J. Johnson
Chief Justice
Supreme Court
400 Royal Street
New Orleans, LA 70130
P: (504) 310-2300

MAINE
Hon. Leigh I. Saufley
Chief Justice
Supreme Judicial Court
142 Federal Street
P.O. Box 368
Portland, ME 04112
P: (207) 822-4286

MARYLAND
Hon. Mary Ellen Barbera
Chief Judge
Court of Appeals
Judicial Center
50 Maryland Avenue
Rockville, MD 20850
P: (240) 777-9320

MASSACHUSETTS
Hon. Ralph D. Gants
Chief Justice
Supreme Judicial Court
John Adams Courthouse, Suite
1-400
One Pemberton Square
Boston, MA 02108
P: (617) 557-1020
F: (617) 557-1145

MICHIGAN
Hon. Robert P. Young Jr.
Chief Justice
Supreme Court
P.O. Box 30052
Lansing, MI 48909
P: (517) 373-0120

MINNESOTA
Hon. Lorie Skjerven Gildea
Chief Justice
Supreme Court
Minnesota Judicial Center
25 Rev. Martin Luther King Jr.
Boulevard
St. Paul, MN 55155

MISSISSIPPI
Hon. William L. Waller Jr.
Chief Justice
Supreme Court
Gartin Building, 3rd Floor
P.O. Box 249
Jackson, MS 39205
P: (601) 359-3694
F: (601) 359-2407

MISSOURI
Hon. Mary Russell
Chief Justice
Supreme Court
P.O. Box 150
Jefferson City, MO 65102
E: mary.russell
   @courts.mo.gov

MONTANA
Hon. Mike McGrath (D)
Chief Justice
Supreme Court
215 North Sanders
P.O. Box 203001
Helena, MT 59620
P: (406) 444-5490
F: (404) 444-3274

NEBRASKA
Hon. Michael G. Heavican
Chief Justice
Supreme Court
State Capitol, Room 2214
Lincoln, NE 68509
P: (402) 471-3738
F: (402) 471-2197
E: mike.heavican
   @nebraska.gov

NEVADA
Hon. James W. Hardesty
Chief Justice
Supreme Court
201 South Carson Street, Suite 201
Carson City, NV 89701
P: (775) 684-1600
F: (775) 684-1601

NEW HAMPSHIRE
Hon. Linda S. Dalianis
Chief Justice
Supreme Court
Supreme Court Building
One Charles Doe Drive
Concord, NH 03301
P: (603) 271-2646

NEW JERSEY
Hon. Stuart Rabner (D)
Chief Justice
Supreme Court
Richard J. Hughes Justice Complex
P.O. Box 970
Trenton, NJ 08625
P: (609) 292-4837

NEW MEXICO
Hon. Barbara J. Vigil
Chief Justice
Supreme Court
P.O. Box 848
Santa Fe, NM 87504
P: (505) 827-4886

NEW YORK
Hon. Sheila Abdus-Salaam
Chief Judge
Court of Appeals
20 Eagle Street
Albany, NY 12207
P: (518) 455-7700
F: (518) 463-6869

NORTH CAROLINA
Hon. Mark D. Martin
Chief Justice
Supreme Court
P.O. Box 2170
Raleigh, NC 27602
P: (919) 733-3723

NORTH DAKOTA
Hon. Gerald W. VandeWalle
Chief Justice
Supreme Court
State Capitol Building
600 East Boulevard Avenue, Dept. 180
Bismark, ND 58505
P: (701) 328-2221
F: (701) 328-4480
E: GVandeWalle
   @ndcourts.gov

NORTHERN MARIANA ISLANDS
Hon. Alexandro C. Castro
Chief Justice
Supreme Court
P.O. Box 502165
Saipan, MP 96950
P: (670) 236-9700
F: (670) 236-9702

OHIO
Hon. Maureen O'Connor (R)
Chief Justice
Supreme Court
65 South Front Street, 9th Floor
Columbus, OH 43215
P: (614) 466-5201
F: (614) 752-4418

OKLAHOMA
Hon. John F. Reif
Chief Justice
Supreme Court
State Capitol, Room B
2300 North Lincoln Boulevard
Oklahoma City, OK 73105
P: (405) 521-2163

OREGON
Hon. Thomas A. Balmer
Chief Justice
Supreme Court
1163 State Street
Salem, OR 97301
P: (503) 986-5717
F: (503) 986-5730

PENNSYLVANIA
Hon. Thomas G. Saylor
Chief Justice
Supreme Court
434 Main Capitol
P.O. Box 624
Harrisburg, PA 17108
P: (717) 787-6181

PUERTO RICO
Hon. Liana Fiol-Matta
Chief Justice
Supreme Court
P.O. Box 9022392
San Juan, PR 00902
P: (787) 723-6033
F: (787) 722-9177

RHODE ISLAND
Hon. Paul A. Suttell
Chief Justice
Supreme Court
250 Benefit Street, 7th Floor
Providence, RI 02903
P: (401) 222-3272
F: (401) 222-3599

SOUTH CAROLINA
Hon. Jean Hoefer Toal
Chief Justice
Supreme Court
P.O. Box 11330
Columbia, SC 29211
P: (803) 734-1080
F: (803) 734-1499

SOUTH DAKOTA
Hon. David Gilbertson
Chief Justice
Supreme Court
500 East Capitol Avenue
Pierre, SD 57501
P: (605) 773-3511
F: (605) 773-6128

TENNESSEE
Hon. Sharon G. Lee
Chief Justice
Supreme Court
401 7th Avenue North
Nashville, TN 37219
P: (615) 253-1470

TEXAS
Hon. Nathan L. Hecht
Chief Justice
Supreme Court
P.O. Box 12248
Austin, TX 78711
P: (512) 463-1312
F: (512) 463-1365

U.S. VIRGIN ISLANDS
Hon. Rhys S. Hodge
Chief Justice
Supreme Court
P.O. Box 590
St. Thomas, VI 00804
P: (340) 774-2237
F: (340) 774-2258

UTAH
Hon. Matthew B. Durrant
Chief Justice
Supreme Court
450 South State Street
P.O. Box 140210
Salt Lake City, UT 84114
P: (801) 238-7937
F: (801) 238-7980

VERMONT
Hon. Paul L. Reiber
Chief Justice
Supreme Court
109 State Street
Montpelier, VT 05609
P: (802) 828-3278
F: (802) 828-4750

VIRGINIA
Hon. Donald W. Lemons
Chief Justice
Supreme Court
100 North 9th Street
P.O. Box 1315
Richmond, VA 23218
P: (804) 786-2251
F: (804) 786-6249

WASHINGTON
Hon. Barbara A. Madsen
Chief Justice
Supreme Court
415 12th Avenue, Southwest
P.O. Box 40929
Olympia, WA 98504
P: (360) 357-2037
F: (360) 357-2102

Chief Justice

WEST VIRGINIA
Hon. Margaret L.
  Workman (D)
Chief Justice
Supreme Court
State Capitol, Room E-317
Charleston, WV 25305
P: (304) 558-2601
F: (304) 558-3815

WISCONSIN
Hon. Shirley S. Abrahamson
Chief Justice
Supreme Court
16 East State Capitol
P.O. Box 1688
Madison, WI 53701
P: (608) 266-1885
F: (608) 261-8299

WYOMING
Hon. E. James Burke
Chief Justice
Supreme Court
Supreme Court Building
2301 Capitol Avenue
Cheyenne, WY 82001
P: (307) 777-7316
F: (307) 777-6129

Child Support Enforcement

Processes child support cases and implements required provisions of child support enforcement program.

ALABAMA
Ms. Faye Nelson
Director
Child Support Enforcement
Division
Department of Human
Resources
P.O. Box 304000
Montgomery, AL 36130
P: (334) 242-9300
F: (334) 242-0606
E: fnelson@dhr.alabama.gov

ALASKA
Mr. Randall Hoffbeck
Commissioner
Department of Revenue
P.O. Box 110400
Juneau, AK 99501
P: (907) 465-2300
F: (907) 465-2389
E: randall.hoffbeck
    @alaska.gov

AMERICAN SAMOA
Dr. Taeaoafua Meki Solomona
Director
Department of Human & Social
Services
P.O. Box 997534
Pago Pago, AS 96799
P: (684) 633-1664
F: (684) 633-7449
E: mtsolomona@dhss.as

ARIZONA
Ms. Veronica Hart Ragland
Director
Division of Child Support
Enforcement
Department of Economic
Security
1717 West Jefferson Street
Phoenix, AZ 85007
P: (602) 771-8190

ARKANSAS
Mr. Dan McDonald
Administrator
Office of Child Support
Enforcement
Department of Finance &
Administration
322 South Main Street
Little Rock, AR 72201
P: (501) 682-6169
F: (501) 682-6002
E: Dan.McDonald
    @ocse.arkansas.gov

COLORADO
Ms. Paulette St. James
Director
Division of Child Support
Services
Department of Human Services
1575 Sherman Street, 5th Floor
Denver, CO 80203
P: (303) 866-4300
F: (303) 866-4360
E: paulette.stjames
    @state.co.us

CONNECTICUT
Asha Stead
Bureau of Child Support
Enforcement
Department of Social Services
55 Farmington Avenue
Hartford, CT 06105
P: (860) 424-5255
E: asha.stead@ct.gov

DELAWARE
Mr. Charles E. Hayward
Director
Division of Child Support
Enforcement
P.O. Box 11223
Wilmington, DE 19850
P: (302) 395-6520
F: (302) 395-6735
E: chayward@state.de.us

DISTRICT OF COLUMBIA
Ms. Benidia A. Rice
Deputy
Child Support Services Division
One Judiciary Square
441 4th Street, Northwest, N550
Washington, DC 20001
P: (202) 442-9900
E: cssd.oag@dc.gov

FLORIDA
Ms. Ann Coffin
Program Director
Child Support Enforcement
Program
Department of Revenue
P.O. Box 8030
Tallahassee, FL 32314
P: (850) 717-7000
E: CoffinA@dor.state.fl.us

GEORGIA
Mr. Keith Horton
Commissioner
Division of Child Support
Services
2 Peachtree Street, Northwest
Suite 29-250
Atlanta, GA 30303
P: (404) 656-5680
F: (404) 651-8669

GUAM
Ms. Barbara P. Cepeda
Deputy Attorney General
Child Support Enforcement
Division
590 South Marine Corps Drive
Suite 704, ITC Building
Tamuning, GU 96913
P: (671) 475-3360
F: (671) 477-2159
E: child.support
    @guamcse.net

HAWAII
Mr. Garry L. Kemp
Administrator
Child Support Enforcement
Agency
Kakuhihewa Building
601 Kamokila Boulevard, Suite
251
Kapolei, HI 96707
P: (808) 692-8265
F: (808) 692-7060

IDAHO
Mr. M. Scott Keim
Deputy Attorney General
Human Services/Child Support
Office of the Attorney General
450 West State Street, 10th Floor
Boise, ID 83720
P: (208) 334-5537
F: (208) 334-5548
E: keims@dhw.idaho.gov

ILLINOIS
Ms. Pam Compton Lowry
Administrator
Division of Child Support
Enforcement
509 South 6th Street, Floor 1
Springfield, IL 62701
P: (217) 782-2624
F: (217) 524-4608

INDIANA
Ms. Mary Beth Bonaventura
Director
Department of Child Services
302 West Washington Street,
Room E306
Indianapolis, IN 46204
P: (317) 234-1391
F: (317) 232-4490
E: MaryBeth.Bonaventura
    @dcs.IN.gov

IOWA
Mr. Charles M. Palmer
Director
Department of Human Services
Hoover State Office Building
1305 East Walnut Street
Des Moines, IA 50319
P: (515) 281-5452
F: (515) 281-4980
E: cpalmer1@dhs.state.ia.us

KANSAS
Ms. Trisha Thomas
Director
Child Support Services
915 Southwest Harrison Street,
6th Floor
Topeka, KS 66612
P: (785) 296-3237
F: (785) 296-5206

KENTUCKY
Mr. Steven P. Veno
Deputy Commissioner
Division of Child Support
Department for Income Support
P.O. Box 2150
Frankfort, KY 40601
P: (502) 564-2285
F: (502) 564-5988
E: steven.veno@ky.gov

LOUISIANA
Ms. Lisa Andry
Executive Director
Child Support Enforcement
Department of Children &
Family Services
P.O. Box 94065
Baton Rouge, LA 70802
P: (225) 342-4780
F: (225) 342-7397
E: lisa.Andry@la.gov

MAINE
Mr. Jerry Joy
Division Director, Child Support
Office for Family Independence
11 State House Station
19 Union Street
Augusta, ME 04333
P: (207) 624-4168
F: (207) 287-5096
E: jerry.joy@maine.gov

Child Support Enforcement

MARYLAND
Mr. Sam Malhotra
Secretary
Department of Human
Resources
311 West Saratoga Street
Baltimore, MD 21201
P: (410) 767-7109
F: (410) 333-0099
E: sam.malhotra
     @maryland.gov

MASSACHUSETTS
Ms. Laurie McGrath
Deputy Commissioner
Child Support Enforcement
Division
Department of Revenue
100 Cambridge Street
Boston, MA 02114
P: (617) 660-1234

MICHIGAN
Ms. Erin Frisch
Director
Bureau of Child Support
Department of Human Services
P.O. Box 30037
Lansing, MI 48909
P: (517) 241-7460
F: (517) 335-6236
E: FrischE@michigan.gov

MINNESOTA
Mr. Wayland Campbell
Director
Child Support Enforcement
Division
Department of Human Services
P.O. Box 64946
St. Paul, MN 55164
P: (651) 431-4400
F: (651) 431-7517
E: wayland.campbell
     @state.mn.us

MISSISSIPPI
Mr. Walley Naylor
Director
Division of Child Support
Enforcement
Department of Human Services
750 North State Street
Jackson, MS 39202
P: (601) 359-4105

MISSOURI
Ms. Janel Luck
Director
Family Support Division
Department of Social Services
P.O. Box 2320
Jefferson City, MO 65102
P: (573) 751-3221
F: (573) 751-3091

MONTANA
Mr. Chad Dexter
Administrator
Child Support Enforcement
Division
3075 North Montana Avenue
P.O. Box 202943
Helena, MT 59620
P: (406) 444-6856
F: (406) 444-1370

NEBRASKA
Mr. Tony Green
Acting Director
Division of Children & Family
Services
P.O. Box 95026
Lincoln, NE 60509
P: (402) 471-9272
E: Tony.Green@nebraska.gov

NEW HAMPSHIRE
Ms. Mary S. Weatherill
System Specialist
Division of Child Support
Services
Department of Health & Human
Services
129 Pleasant Street
Concord, NH 03301
P: (603) 271-4427
F: (603) 271-4787
E: mweather
     @dhhs.state.nh.us

NEW JERSEY
Ms. Jeanette Page-Hawkins
Director
Division of Family
Development
P.O. Box 716
Trenton, NJ 08625
P: (609) 588-2400
F: (609) 584-4404

NEW MEXICO
Mr. Steven Smith
Director
Child Support Enforcement
Division
Human Services Department
P.O. Box 2348
Santa Fe, NM 87504
P: (800) 585-7631

NEW YORK
Ms. Eileen Stack
Deputy Commissioner
Center for Child Well-Being
40 North Pearl Street
Albany, NY 12243
P: (888) 208-4485

NORTH CAROLINA
Mr. Wayne E. Black
Director
Division of Social Services
McBryde Building, 820 South
Boylan Ave.
2401 Mail Service Center
Raleigh, NC 27699
P: (919) 527-6335
F: (919) 334-1018
E: wayne.black@dhhs.nc.gov

NORTH DAKOTA
Mr. James Fleming
Director
Child Support Enforcement
Division
Department of Human Services
P.O. Box 7190
Bismarck, ND 58507
P: (701) 328-3582
F: (701) 328-5425
E: jfleming@nd.gov

OHIO
Mr. Michael McCreight
Assistant Director, Health &
Human Services
Department of Job & Family
Services
30 East Broad Street, 32nd Floor
Columbus, OH 43215
P: (614) 466-9195
F: (614) 466-2815

OKLAHOMA
Mr. Gary Dart
Director
Child Support Enforcement
Division
Department of Human Services
P.O. Box 248822
Oklahoma City, OK 73124
P: (405) 522-2273
E: OCSS.Director@OKDHS.org

RHODE ISLAND
Ms. Sharon A. Santilli
Associate Director
Office of Child Support
Services
Department of Human Services
77 Dorrance Street
Providence, RI 02903
P: (401) 458-4404
E: richildsupport
     @cse.state.ri.us

SOUTH CAROLINA
Ms. V. Susan Alford
Director
Department of Social Services
1535 Confederate Avenue
Extension
P.O. Box 1520
Columbia, SC 29202
P: (803) 898-7360
F: (803) 898-7277

SOUTH DAKOTA
Ms. Gail Stoltenburg
Director
Division of Child Support
Department of Social Services
700 Governors Drive
Pierre, SD 57501
P: (605) 773-3641
F: (605) 773-7295
E: DCS@state.sd.us

TENNESSEE
Mr. David Sanchez
Assistant Commissioner
Child Support Services
Department of Human Services
400 Deaderick Street, 15th Floor
Nashville, TN 37243
P: (615) 313-4712
F: (615) 741-4165
E: david.sanchez@tn.gov

TEXAS
Mr. Charles Smith
Deputy Attorney General for
Child Support
Office of the Attorney General
209 West 14th Street
P.O. Box 12548
Austin, TX 78711
P: (512) 460-6000
F: (512) 463-2063
E: child.support
     @texasattorneygeneral.gov

U.S. VIRGIN ISLANDS
Ms. Regina De Chabert
Director
Paternity & Child Support
Division
8000 Nisky Shopping Center,
Suite 500
2nd Floor
St. Thomas, VI 00802
P: (340) 775-3070
F: (340) 775-3808

UTAH
Ms. Liesa Stockdale
Director
Office of Recovery Services
Department of Human Services
515 East 100 South
Salt Lake City, UT 84102
P: (801) 536-8901
F: (801) 536-8509
E: lcorbri2@utah.gov

VERMONT
Mr. Jeffrey P. Cohen
Director
Office of Child Support
103 South Main Street
Waterbury, VT 05671
P: (802) 769-6478
F: (802) 769-6429
E: Jeff.Cohen@state.vt.us

VIRGINIA
Mr. Craig Burshem
Deputy Commissioner &
Director
Division of Child Support
Enforcement
Department of Social Services
7 North 8th Street
Richmond, VA 23219
P: (804) 726-7000
E: craig.burshem
   @dss.virginia.gov

WASHINGTON
Mr. David Stillman
Assistant Secretary
Division of Child Support
Department of Social & Health
Services
P.O. Box 11520
Tacoma, WA 98411
P: (360) 664-5321
F: (360) 664-5303

WEST VIRGINIA
Mr. Garrett M. Jacobs
Commissioner
Bureau for Child Support
Enforcement
350 Capitol Street, Room 147
Charleston, WV 25301
P: (304) 558-3780
F: (304) 558-4092
E: garrett.m.jacobs@wv.gov

WISCONSIN
Ms. Eloise Anderson
Secretary
Department of Children &
Families
201 East Washington Avenue,
2nd Floor
P.O. Box 8916
Madison, WI 53708
P: (608) 267-3905
F: (608) 266-6836
E: dcfweb@wisconsin.gov

Children and Youth Services

Implements programs designed to protect children and youth against abuse, neglect and exploitation.

ALABAMA
Ms. Jeana Ross
Commissioner
Department of Children's Affairs
135 South Union Street, Suite 215
P.O. Box 302755
Montgomery, AL 36130
P: (334) 353-2702
F: (334) 353-2701
E: jeana.ross
   @dca.alabama.gov

ALASKA
Ms. Christy Lawton
Director
Office of Children's Services
Department of Health & Social Services
P.O. Box 110630
Juneau, AK 99811
P: (907) 465-3191
F: (907) 465-3397
E: christy.lawton
   @alaska.gov

AMERICAN SAMOA
Dr. Taeaoafua Meki Solomona
Director
Department of Human & Social Services
P.O. Box 997534
Pago Pago, AS 96799
P: (684) 633-1664
F: (684) 633-7449
E: mtsolomona@dhss.as

ARIZONA
Ms. Debbie Moak
Director
Governor's Office for Children, Youth & Families
1700 West Washington, Suite 230
Phoenix, AZ 85007
P: (602) 542-4043
F: (602) 542-3423
E: dmoak@az.gov

ARKANSAS
Ms. Cecile Blucker
Director
Division of Children & Family Services
P.O. Box 1437, Slot S560
Little Rock, AR 72203
P: (501) 682-8772
F: (501) 682-6968
E: Cecile.Blucker
   @dhs.arkansas.gov

CALIFORNIA
Mr. Will Lightbourne
Director
Department of Social Services
744 P Street
Sacramento, CA 95814
P: (916) 657-2598
F: (916) 651-6569

COLORADO
Ms. Ann Rosales
Director
Division of Child Welfare
Department of Human Services
1575 Sherman Street
Denver, CO 80203
P: (303) 866-5414
E: ann.rosales@state.co.us

CONNECTICUT
Ms. Joette Katz
Commissioner
Department of Children & Families
505 Hudson Street
Hartford, CT 06106
P: (860) 550-6300
E: commissioner.dcf@ct.gov

DELAWARE
Ms. Jennifer Ranji
Cabinet Secretary
Department of Services for Children, Youth & Their Families
1825 Faulkland Road
Wilmington, DE 19805
P: (302) 633-2500
F: (302) 995-8290
E: info.dscyf@state.de.us

FLORIDA
Mr. Mike Carroll
Secretary
Department of Children & Families
1317 Winewood Boulevard
Building 1, Room 202
Tallahassee, FL 32399
P: (850) 487-1111
F: (850) 922-2993
E: mike_carroll
   @dcf.state.fl.us

GEORGIA
Ms. Sharon Hill
Division Director
Division of Family & Children Services
Two Peachtree Street, Northwest
Suite 18-486
Atlanta, GA 30303
P: (404) 657-3433
F: (404) 657-5105

HAWAII
Mr. David Hipp
Executive Director
Office of Youth Services
Department of Human Services
P.O. Box 339
Honolulu, HI 96809
P: (808) 587-5706
F: (808) 587-5734

IDAHO
Mr. Robert B. Luce
Administrator
Division of Family & Community Services
450 West State Street, 5th Floor
Cenarrusa Building, P.O. Box 83720
Boise, ID 83720
P: (208) 334-0641
F: (208) 332-7331
E: brownd3@dhw.idaho.gov

ILLINOIS
Mr. Richard Calica
Director
Department of Children & Family Services
406 East Monroe Street
Springfield, IL 62701
P: (217) 785-2509
F: (217) 785-1052

INDIANA
Ms. Adrienne Shields
Director of Family Resources
Family & Social Services Administration
402 West Washington Street, Room W392
Indianapolis, IN 46204
P: (317) 234-2373
F: (317) 232-4490
E: Adrienne.Shields
   @fssa.IN.gov

IOWA
Ms. Wendy Rickman
Administrator
Division of Adult, Children & Family Services
Department of Human Services
1305 East Walnut
Des Moines, IA 50319
P: (515) 281-5521
F: (515) 242-6036
E: wrickma@dhs.state.ia.us

KENTUCKY
Ms. Teresa James
Commissioner
Department for Community Based Services
275 East Main Street
Mail Stop 3W-A
Frankfort, KY 40621
P: (502) 564-3703
F: (502) 564-6907

LOUISIANA
Ms. Suzy Sonnier
Secretary
Department of Children & Family Services
P.O. Box 3776
Baton Rouge, LA 70821
P: (225) 342-0286
F: (225) 342-8636
E: Suzy.Sonnier@dcfs.la.gov

MAINE
Ms. Therese Cahill-Low
Director
Office of Child & Family Services
2 Anthony Avenue
Augusta, ME 04333
P: (207) 624-7900
F: (207) 287-5282

MARYLAND
Ms. Arlene Lee
Executive Director
Governor's Office for Children
301 West Preston Street, Suite 1502
Baltimore, MD 21201
P: (410) 767-4160
F: (410) 333-5248
E: arlene.lee@maryland.gov

Mr. Sam Malhotra
Secretary
Department of Human Resources
311 West Saratoga Street
Baltimore, MD 21201
P: (410) 767-7109
F: (410) 333-0099
E: sam.malhotra
   @maryland.gov

Children and Youth Services

MASSACHUSETTS
Mr. Peter Forbes
Commissioner
Department of Youth Services
600 Washington Street, 4th
Floor
Boston, MA 02111
P: (617) 727-7575
F: (617) 727-0696

MICHIGAN
Mr. Steve Yager
Director
Children's Services
Administration
235 South Grand Avenue
P.O. Box 30037
Lansing, MI 48909
P: (517) 241-9859
E: YagerS@michigan.gov

MISSISSIPPI
Ms. Jill Dent
Director
Division of Early Childhood
Care & Development
750 North State Street
P.O. Box 352
Jackson, MS 39205
P: (601) 359-4555
F: (601) 359-4422

MISSOURI
Mr. Tim Decker
Director
Division of Youth Services
3418 Knipp, Suite A-1
P.O. Box 447
Jefferson City, MO 65102
P: (573) 751-3324
F: (573) 526-4494
E: tim.decker@dss.mo.gov

NEBRASKA
Mr. Tony Green
Acting Director
Division of Children & Family
Services
P.O. Box 95026
Lincoln, NE 60509
P: (402) 471-9272
E: Tony.Green@nebraska.gov

NEVADA
Ms. Amber Howell
Administrator
Division of Child & Family
Services
Department of Health & Human
Services
4126 Technology Way, Suite 100
Carson City, NV 89706
P: (775) 684-4000
F: (775) 684-4010
E: ahowell@dcfs.nv.gov

NEW HAMPSHIRE
Ms. Maggie Bishop
Director
Division for Children, Youth &
Families
Department of Health & Human
Services
129 Pleasant Street
Concord, NH 03301
P: (603) 271-4440
F: (603) 271-5058
E: mbishop@dhhs.state.nh.us

NEW JERSEY
Dr. Allison Blake
Commissioner
Department of Children &
Families
222 South Warren Street
P.O. Box 729, 3rd Floor
Trenton, NJ 08625
P: (609) 984-4500
E: dcf_commissioner
   @dcf.state.nj.us

NEW MEXICO
Ms. Monique Jacobson
Cabinet Secretary
Children, Youth & Families
Department
P.O. Drawer 5160
Santa Fe, NM 87502
P: (505) 827-7602
F: (505) 827-4053
E: monique.jacobson
   @state.nm.us

NEW YORK
Ms. Sheila Poole
Acting Commissioner
Office of Children & Family
Services
Capitol View Office Park
52 Washington Street
Rensselaer, NY 12144
P: (518) 473-7793
F: (518) 486-7550

NORTH CAROLINA
Mr. Wayne E. Black
Director
Division of Social Services
McBryde Building, 820 South
Boylan Ave.
2401 Mail Service Center
Raleigh, NC 27699
P: (919) 527-6335
F: (919) 334-1018
E: wayne.black@dhhs.nc.gov

NORTH DAKOTA
Ms. Shari Doe
Director
Children & Family Services
600 East Boulevard Avenue
Department 325
Bismarck, ND 58505
P: (701) 328-2316
F: (701) 328-3538
E: sedoe@nd.gov

**NORTHERN MARIANA
ISLANDS**
Ms. Laura T. Ogumoro
Secretary
Department of Community &
Cultural Affairs
1341 Ascension Court
Caller Box 10007
Saipan, MP 96950
P: (670) 664-2120
F: (670) 664-2139
E: laura.ogumoro@gov.mp

OHIO
Ms. Cynthia J. Dungey
Director
Department of Job & Family
Services
30 East Broad Street, 32nd Floor
Columbus, OH 43215
P: (614) 466-9195
F: (614) 466-2815

Mr. Michael McCreight
Assistant Director, Health &
Human Services
Department of Job & Family
Services
30 East Broad Street, 32nd Floor
Columbus, OH 43215
P: (614) 466-9195
F: (614) 466-2815

OKLAHOMA
Ms. Deborah G. Smith
Director
Child Welfare Services
Department of Human Services
P.O. Box 25352
Oklahoma City, OK 73125
P: (405) 521-3777
F: (405) 521-4373
E: Deborahg.smith@okdhs.org

OREGON
Ms. Iris Bell
Interim Transition Director
Commission on Children &
Families
530 Center Street, Northeast,
Suite 405
Salem, OR 97301
P: (503) 373-1283
F: (503) 378-8395
E: iris.bell@state.or.us

Ms. Erinn L. Kelley-Siel
Director
Department of Human Services
500 Summer Street, Northeast,
E-15
Salem, OR 97301
P: (503) 945-7001
F: (503) 378-2897
E: erinn.kelley-siel
   @state.or.us

PENNSYLVANIA
Ms. Cathy Utz
Acting Secretary
Office of Children, Youth &
Families
Dept. of Public Welfare
P.O. Box 2675
Harrisburg, PA 17105
P: 1-800-692-7462

PUERTO RICO
Ms. Idalia Columbus Rondon
Secretary
Department of the Family
P.O. Box 11398
Hato Rey, PR 00917
P: (787) 294-4900
F: (787) 294-0732

RHODE ISLAND
Mr. Kevin J. Aucoin
Deputy Director
Department of Children, Youth
& Families
101 Friendship Street
Providence, RI 02903
P: (401) 528-3502
F: (401) 528-3580
E: Kevin.Aucoin@dcyf.ri.gov

SOUTH CAROLINA
Ms. V. Susan Alford
Director
Department of Social Services
1535 Confederate Avenue
Extension
P.O. Box 1520
Columbia, SC 29202
P: (803) 898-7360
F: (803) 898-7277

Children and Youth Services

SOUTH DAKOTA
Ms. Virgena Wieseler
Division Director
Department of Social Services
Division of Child Protection
Services
700 Governors Drive
Pierre, SD 57501
P: (605) 773-3227
F: (605) 773-6834
E: CPS@state.sd.us

TENNESSEE
Mr. James M. Henry
Commissioner
Department of Children's
Services
Andrew Jackson Office Building
500 Deadrick Street, 15th Floor
Nashville, TN 37243
P: (615) 253-6885
F: (615) 253-4089
E: jim.henry@tn.gov

TEXAS
Mr. John J. Specia Jr.
Commissioner
Department of Family &
Protective Services
701 West 51st Street
P.O. Box 149030
Austin, TX 78714
P: (512) 438-4870

U.S. VIRGIN ISLANDS
Mr. Christopher E. Finch
Commissioner
Department of Human Services
Knud Hansen Complex,
Building A
1303 Hospital Ground
St. Thomas, VI 00802
P: (340) 774-0930
F: (340) 773-2980

UTAH
Mr. Brent Platt
Director
Division of Child & Family
Services
Department of Human Services
195 North 1950 West
Salt Lake City, UT 84116
P: (801) 538-4100
F: (801) 538-3993
E: bplatt@utah.gov

VERMONT
Mr. Ken Schatz
Commissioner
Department for Children &
Families
103 South Main Street
2nd Floor, 5 North
Waterbury, VT 05671
P: (802) 871-3385
E: ken.schatz@state.vt.us

VIRGINIA
Ms. Margaret Schultze
Commissioner
Department of Social Services
801 East Main Street
Richmond, VA 23219
P: (804) 726-7000
E: margaret.schultze
@dss.virginia.gov

WASHINGTON
Ms. Jennifer Strus
Assistant Secretary
Children's Administration
Department of Social & Health
Services
P.O. Box 45130
Olympia, WA 98504
P: (360) 902-7820

WEST VIRGINIA
Ms. Nancy Exline
Commissioner
Bureau for Children & Families
350 Capitol Street, Room 730
Charleston, WV 25301
P: (304) 558-0628
F: (304) 558-4194

WISCONSIN
Ms. Eloise Anderson
Secretary
Department of Children &
Families
201 East Washington Avenue,
2nd Floor
P.O. Box 8916
Madison, WI 53708
P: (608) 267-3905
F: (608) 266-6836
E: dcfweb@wisconsin.gov

WYOMING
Dr. Steve Corsi
Director
Department of Family Services
Hathaway Building, 3rd Floor
2300 Capitol Avenue
Cheyenne, WY 82002
P: (307) 777-7561
F: (307) 777-7747
E: steve.corsi@wyo.gov

Civil Rights

Overall responsibility for preventing and redressing discrimination in employment, education, housing, public accommodations and credit (because of race, color, sex, age, national origin, religion or disability.)

ALABAMA
Ms. Desiree Jackson
Director
Civil Rights/Equal Employment
Opportunity Division
Gordon Persons Building, Suite 2104
50 North Ripley Street
Montgomery, AL 36130
P: (334) 242-1550
E: Desiree.Jackson
@dhr.alabama.gov

ALASKA
Ms. Paula M. Haley
Executive Director
Commission for Human Rights
Office of the Governor
800 A Street, Suite 204
Anchorage, AK 99501
P: (907) 276-7474
F: (907) 278-8588
E: paula.haley@alaska.gov

ARIZONA
Mr. Thomas Chenal
Division Chief Counsel
Public Advocacy & Civil Rights
Division
Office of the Attorney General
1275 West Washington Street
Phoenix, AZ 85007
P: (602) 542-8323
F: (602) 542-8885
E: civilrightsinfo@azag.gov

CALIFORNIA
Mr. Jim Tashima
Acting Bureau Chief
Civil Rights Bureau
744 P Street
Sacramento, CA 95814
P: (916) 654-2107
F: (916) 653-9332
E: jim.tashima@dss.ca.gov

COLORADO
Ms. Rufina Hernandez
Director
Civil Rights Division
1560 Broadway, Suite 1050
Denver, CO 80202
P: (303) 894-2997
F: (303) 894-7830
E: dora_CCRD@state.co.us

CONNECTICUT
Ms. Tanya Hughes
Executive Director
Commission on Human Rights
& Opportunities
25 Sigourney Street
Hartford, CT 06106
P: (860) 541-3421
F: (860) 241-4875
E: tanya.hughes@ct.gov

DELAWARE
Ms. Romona S. Fullman
Director
Division of Human Relations
820 North French Street, 8th
Floor
Wilmington, DE 19801
P: (302) 577-5287
F: (302) 577-3486

DISTRICT OF COLUMBIA
Ms. Monica Palacio
Director
Office of Human Rights
441 4th Street, Northwest
Suite 570 North
Washington, DC 20001
P: (202) 727-4559
F: (202) 727-9589
E: ohr@dc.gov

FLORIDA
Hon. Pam Bondi (R)
Attorney General
Office of the Attorney General
The Capitol, PL 01
Tallahassee, FL 32399
P: (850) 414-3300
F: (954) 712-4826

GEORGIA
Mr. Melvin J. Everson
Executive Director &
Administrator
Commission on Equal
Opportunity
Suite 1002, West Tower
2 Martin Luther King Jr. Drive
Southeast
Atlanta, GA 30334
P: (404) 232-1776
F: (404) 656-4399
E: meverson
@gceo.state.ga.us

GUAM
Mr. Manuel Q. Cruz
Director
Department of Labor
Government of Guam
P.O. Box 9970
Tamuning, GU 96931
P: (671) 647-6510
F: (671) 674-6517

Mr. Tony A. Lamorena V
Director
Civil Service Commission
P.O. Box 3156
Hagatna, GU 96932
P: (671) 647-1855
F: (671) 647-1867

HAWAII
Mr. William D. Hoshijo
Executive Director
Civil Rights Commission
830 Punchbowl Street, Room 411
Honolulu, HI 96813
P: (808) 586-8636
F: (808) 586-8655
E: dlir.hcrc.infor
@hawaii.gov

IDAHO
Ms. Pamela Parks
Administrator
Human Rights Commission
317 West Main Street, Second
Floor
Boise, ID 83735
P: (208) 334-2873
F: (208) 334-2664
E: Pamela.Parks
@ihrc.idaho.gov

ILLINOIS
Mr. Rocco J. Claps
Director
Department of Human Rights
100 West Randolph Street, 10th
Floor
Intake Unit
Chicago, IL 60601
P: (312) 814-6200
F: (312) 814-1436

INDIANA
Mr. Jamal L. Smith
Executive Director
Civil Rights Commission
100 North Senate Avenue
IGCN, Room N103
Indianapolis, IN 46204
P: (317) 232-2600
F: (317) 232-6580
E: JSmith@gov.IN.gov

IOWA
Ms. Beth Townsend
Agency Director
Civil Rights Commission
1000 East Grand Avenue
Des Moines, IA 50319
P: (515) 281-5364
E: beth.townsend
@iwd.iowa.gov

KANSAS
Ms. Ruth Glover
Executive Director
Human Rights Commission
900 Southwest Jackson Street
Suite 568-S
Topeka, KS 66612
P: (785) 296-3206
F: (785) 296-0589

KENTUCKY
Mr. John J. Johnson
Executive Director
Commission on Human Rights
332 West Broadway, 7th Floor
Louisville, KY 40202
P: (502) 595-4024
F: (502) 595-4801
E: john.johnson@ky.gov

LOUISIANA
Hon. James D. Caldwell (R)
Attorney General
Office of the Attorney General
P.O. Box 94095
Baton Rouge, LA 70804
P: (225) 326-6000
F: (225) 326-6797
E: executive@ag.state.la.us

MAINE
Ms. Amy Sneirson
Executive Director
Human Rights Commission
51 State House Station
Augusta, ME 04333
P: (207) 624-6290
F: (207) 624-8729
E: amy.sneirson
@mhrc.maine.gov

MARYLAND
Mr. Alvin O. Gillard
Executive Director
Commission on Human
Relations
6 St. Paul Street
Baltimore, MD 21202
P: (410) 767-8563
F: (410) 333-1841
E: alvin.gillard
@maryland.gov

MASSACHUSETTS
Ms. Sunila Thomas-George
Commissioner
Commission Against
Discrimination
One Ashburton Place
Sixth Floor, Room 601
Boston, MA 02108
P: (617) 994-6000
F: (617) 994-6024

Civil Rights

Ms. Jamie R. Williamson
Chair
Commission Against
Discrimination
One Ashburton Place
Sixth Floor, Room 601
Boston, MA 02108
P: (617) 994-6000
F: (617) 994-6024

MINNESOTA
Mr. Kevin Lindsey
Commissioner
Department of Human Rights
Freeman Building
625 Robert Street, North
St. Paul, MN 55155
P: (651) 296-5675
F: (651) 296-9042
E: Kevin.Lindsey
    @state.mn.us

MISSISSIPPI
Hon. Jim Hood (D)
Attorney General
Office of the Attorney General
Department of Justice
P.O. Box 220
Jackson, MS 39205
P: (601) 359-3680
E: msag05@ago.state.ms.us

MISSOURI
Dr. Alisa Warren
Executive Director
Commission on Human Rights
3315 West Truman Boulevard,
Room 212
P.O. Box 1129
Jefferson City, MO 65102
P: (573) 751-3325
F: (573) 751-2905
E: mchr@labor.mo.gov

MONTANA
Marieke Beck
Bureau Chief
Human Rights Bureau
1625 11th Avenue
P.O. Box 1728
Helena, MT 59624
P: (406) 444-4344
F: (406) 444-2798
E: kcobos@mt.gov

NEBRASKA
Ms. Barbara Albers
Executive Director
Equal Opportunity Commission
301 Centennial Mall South, 5th
Floor
P.O. Box 94934
Lincoln, NE 68509
P: (402) 471-2024
F: (402) 471-4059
E: barbara.albers
    @nebraska.gov

NEVADA
Ms. Kara Jenkins
Commission Administrator
Equal Rights Commission
Employment, Training &
Rehabilitation
1820 East Sahara Avenue, Suite
314
Las Vegas, NV 89104
P: (702) 486-7161
F: (702) 486-7054

NEW HAMPSHIRE
Ms. Joni N. Esperian
Executive Director
Commission for Human Rights
2 Chennell Drive, Unit 2
Concord, NH 03301
P: (603) 271-2767
F: (603) 271-6339
E: humanrights
    @nhsa.state.nh.us

NEW JERSEY
Mr. Craig Sashihara
Director
Division on Civil Rights
P.O. Box 090
Trenton, NJ 08625
P: (609) 292-4605
F: (609) 984-3812

NEW MEXICO
Ms. Francie Cordova
Labor Relations Division
Director
Human Rights Bureau
Department of Workforce
Solutions
1596 Pacheco Street, Suite103
Santa Fe, NM 87505
P: (505) 827-6838
F: (505) 827-6878

NEW YORK
Ms. Helen Diane Foster
Acting Commissioner
Division of Human Rights
One Fordham Plaza, 4th Floor
Bronx, NY 10458
P: (718) 741-8400

NORTH DAKOTA
Ms. Bonnie Storbakken
Commissioner of Labor
Department of Labor
600 East Boulevard Avenue
Department 406
Bismarck, ND 58505
P: (701) 328-2660
F: (701) 328-2031
E: bstorbakken@nd.gov

OHIO
Mr. G. Michael Payton
Executive Director
Civil Rights Commission
Rhodes State Office Tower
30 East Broad Street, 5th Floor
Columbus, OH 43215
P: (614) 466-2785
F: (614) 466-7742
E: paytonm@ocrc.state.oh.us

OKLAHOMA
Hon. Scott Pruitt (R)
Attorney General
Office of the Attorney General
313 Northeast 21st Street
Oklahoma City, OK 73105
P: (405) 521-3921

OREGON
Ms. Amy K. Klare
Administrator
Civil Rights Division
800 Northeast Oregon Street
Suite 1045
Portland, OR 97232
P: (971) 673-0792
F: (971) 673-0765
E: Amy.K.Klare@state.or.us

PENNSYLVANIA
Ms. JoAnn L. Edwards
Executive Director
Human Relations Commission
333 Market Street, 8th Floor
Harrisburg, PA 17101
P: (717) 787-4410
E: phrc@pa.gov

PUERTO RICO
Ms. Rosa M.
    Rodriguez Gancitano
Executive Director
Civil Rights Commission
P.O. Box 192338
San Juan, PR 00919
P: (787) 764-8686
F: (787) 250-1756

RHODE ISLAND
Mr. Michael D. Evora
Executive Director
Commission for Human Rights
180 Westminster Street, 3rd
Floor
Providence, RI 02903
P: (401) 222-2661
F: (401) 222-2616

SOUTH CAROLINA
Mr. Raymond Buxton
Commissioner
Human Affairs Commission
2611 Forest Drive, Suite 200
P.O. Box 4490
Columbia, SC 29204
P: (803) 737-7825
E: rbuxton@schac.sc.gov

SOUTH DAKOTA
Ms. Marcia Hultman
Secretary
Department of Labor &
Regulation
700 Governors Drive
Pierre, SD 57501
P: (605) 773-3101
F: (605) 773-6184
E: marcia.hultman
    @state.sd.us

Mr. James E. Marsh
Director
Division of Labor &
Management
Department of Labor &
Regulation
700 Governors Drive
Pierre, SD 57501
P: (605) 773-3101
F: (605) 773-6184
E: james.marsh@state.sd.us

TENNESSEE
Ms. Beverly L. Watts
Executive Director
Human Rights Commission
710 James Robertson Parkway,
Suite 100
Corner of Rosa Parks Boulevard
Nashville, TN 37243
P: (615) 741-5825
F: (615) 253-1886

TEXAS
Mr. Kim Vickers
Executive Director
Commission on Law
Enforcement
6330 East Highway 290, Suite 200
Austin, TX 78723
P: (512) 936-7700 Ext. 7713
F: (512) 936-7766
E: kim.vickers
   @tcole.texas.gov

U.S. VIRGIN ISLANDS
Mr. Lunsford A. Williams
Executive Director
Civil Rights Commission
P.O. Box 6645
St. Thomas, VI 00804
P: (340) 774-5666 Ext. 176
F: (340) 776-3494

UTAH
Kerry Chlarson
Director
Antidiscrimination & Labor
Division
160 East 300 South, 3rd Floor
P.O. Box 146630
Salt Lake City, UT 84114
P: (801) 530-6801
F: (801) 530-7609
E: kchlarson@utah.gov

VERMONT
Ms. Karen Richards
Executive Director
Human Rights Commission
14-16 Baldwin Street
Montpelier, VT 05633
P: (802) 828-2482
F: (802) 828-2481
E: karen.richards
   @state.vt.us

VIRGINIA
Hon. Mark R. Herring (D)
Attorney General
Office of the Attorney General
900 East Main Street
Richmond, VA 23219
P: (804) 786-2071

WEST VIRGINIA
Dr. Darrell Cummings
Chair
Human Rights Commission
1321 Plaza East, Room 108A
Charleston, WV 25301
P: (304) 558-2616
F: (304) 558-0085

WISCONSIN
Ms. Jeanette Johnson
Administrator
Division of Affirmative Action
101 East Wilson Street
P.O. Box 7855
Madison, WI 53707
P: (608) 266-3017
F: (608) 267-1020
E: oserdaa@wi.gov

Clerk of the State's Highest Court

Individual who keeps records of the state's highest court.

ALABAMA
Ms. Julia Jordan Weller
Clerk
Supreme Court
300 Dexter Avenue
Montgomery, AL 36104
P: (334) 229-0700

ALASKA
Ms. Marilyn May
Clerk of the Appellate Courts
Appellate Courts
303 K Street
Anchorage, AK 99501
P: (907) 264-0612
F: (907) 264-0878
E: mmay
@appellate.courts.state.ak.us

AMERICAN SAMOA
Mr. Robert Gorniak
Chief Clerk
High Court of American Samoa
American Samoa Government
Pago Pago, AS 96799
P: (684) 633-4131
F: (684) 633-1318

ARIZONA
Ms. Janet Johnson
Clerk of the Court
Supreme Court
1501 West Washington, Suite 402
Phoenix, AZ 85007
P: (602) 452-3396
E: scclerk@courts.az.gov

ARKANSAS
Ms. Stacy Pectol
Clerk of the Courts
Supreme Court
1320 Justice Building
625 Marshall Street
Little Rock, AR 72201
P: (501) 682-6849

CALIFORNIA
Mr. Frank A. McGuire
Clerk of the Court
Supreme Court
350 McAllister Street
San Francisco, CA 94102
P: (415) 865-7000

COLORADO
Mr. Christopher T. Ryan
Clerk of the Supreme Court
Supreme Court
2 East 14th Avenue
Denver, CO 80203
P: (720) 625-5150
E: Christopher.Ryan
@judicial.state.co.us

CONNECTICUT
Ms. Michele T. Angers
Chief Clerk
Supreme Court
231 Capitol Avenue
Hartford, CT 06106
P: (860) 757-2200
F: (860) 757-2217

DELAWARE
Ms. Cathy L. Howard
Clerk of the Court
Supreme Court
Carvel State Office Building
820 North French Street, 11th Floor
Wilmington, DE 19801
P: (302) 739-4187
F: (302) 577-3702

DISTRICT OF COLUMBIA
Mr. Julio A. Castillo
Clerk of the Court of Appeals
Court of Appeals
Historic Courthouse
430 E Street, Northwest
Washington, DC 20001
P: (202) 879-2700

FLORIDA
Mr. John A. Tomasino
Clerk
Supreme Court
500 South Duval Street
Tallahassee, FL 32399
P: (850) 488-0125
E: supremecourt
@flcourts.org

GEORGIA
Ms. Therese S. Barnes
Clerk
Supreme Court
244 Washington Street
Room 572, State Office Annex Building
Atlanta, GA 30334
P: (404) 656-3470
F: (404) 656-2253

GUAM
Ms. Hannah M. Gutierrez-Arroyo
Clerk of Court
Supreme Court
Guam Judicial Center
120 West O'Brien Drive
Hagatna, GU 96910
P: (671) 475-3162
E: hgutierrezarroyo
@guamsupremecourt.com

HAWAII
Ms. Rochelle Hasuko
Chief Clerk
Supreme Court
Aliiolani Hale
417 South King Street
Honolulu, HI 96813
P: (808) 539-4919
F: (808) 539-4928

IDAHO
Mr. Stephen W. Kenyon
Clerk of the Supreme Court
Supreme Court
P.O. Box 83720
Boise, ID 83720
P: (208) 334-2210
F: (208) 947-7590

ILLINOIS
Ms. Carolyn Taft Grosboll
Clerk of the Supreme Court
Supreme Court
Supreme Court Building
200 East Capitol
Springfield, IL 62701
P: (217) 782-2035

INDIANA
Mr. Kevin Smith
Clerk/Administrator
State Courts
200 West Washington Street
315 State House
Indianapolis, IN 46204
P: (317) 232-2540
F: (317) 232-8372
E: Kevin.Smith
@courts.in.gov

IOWA
Ms. Donna Humpal
Clerk
Supreme Court
Iowa Judicial Branch Building
1111 East Court Avenue
Des Moines, IA 50319
P: (515) 281-5911
E: Donna.Humpal
@iowacourts.gov

KANSAS
Ms. Heather L. Smith
Clerk of the Appellate Courts
Supreme Court
Judicial Center
301 Southwest 10th Avenue, Room 374
Topeka, KS 66612
P: (785) 296-3229
F: (785) 296-1028
E: appellateclerk
@kscourts.org

KENTUCKY
Ms. Susan Stokley Clary
Clerk of the Supreme Court
Supreme Court
State Capitol
700 Capitol Avenue, Room 235
Frankfort, KY 40601
P: (502) 564-5444
F: (502) 564-2665

LOUISIANA
Mr. John Tarlton Olivier
Clerk of Court
Supreme Court
400 Royal Street, Suite 4200
New Orleans, LA 70130
P: (504) 310-2300

MAINE
Mr. Matthew Pollack
Clerk of the Law Court
Supreme Judicial Court
205 Newbury Street, Room 139
Portland, ME 04101
P: (207) 822-4146

MARYLAND
Ms. Bessie M. Decker
Clerk of Court of Appeals
Judiciary of Maryland
Robert Murphy Courts of Appeal Building
361 Rowe Boulevard
Annapolis, MD 21401
P: (410) 260-1500

MASSACHUSETTS
Mr. Francis V. Kenneally
Clerk
Supreme Judicial Court
John Adams Courthouse, Suite 1-400
One Pemberton Square
Boston, MA 02108
P: (617) 557-1020
F: (617) 557-1145
E: SJCCommClerk
@sjc.state.ma.us

MICHIGAN
Mr. Larry Royster
Clerk
Supreme Court
P.O. Box 30052
Lansing, MI 48909
P: (517) 373-0120
E: MSC_Clerk@courts.mi.gov

MINNESOTA
Ms. AnnMarie O'Neill
Clerk of Appellate Courts
Supreme Court
305 Minnesota Judicial Center
25 Martin Luther King Jr.
Boulevard
St. Paul, MN 55155
P: (651) 296-2581

MISSISSIPPI
Ms. Muriel B. Ellis
Clerk
Supreme Court
450 High Street
P.O. Box 117
Jackson, MS 39201
P: (601) 359-3694
F: (601) 359-2407
E: sctclerk
    @mssc.state.ms.us

MISSOURI
Mr. Bill Thompson
Supreme Court Clerk
Supreme Court
P.O. Box 150
Jefferson City, MO 65102
P: (573) 751-4144

MONTANA
Mr. Ed Smith
Clerk
Supreme Court
215 North Sanders, Room 323
P.O. Box 203003
Helena, MT 59620
P: (406) 444-3858
F: (406) 444-5705

NEBRASKA
Ms. Teresa Brown
Clerk
Supreme Court
2413 State Capitol
P.O. Box 98910
Lincoln, NE 68509
P: (402) 471-3731
F: (402) 471-3480
E: terri.a.brown
    @nebraska.gov

NEVADA
Ms. Tracie K. Lindeman
Chief Clerk
Supreme Court
201 South Carson Street
Carson City, NV 89701
P: (775) 684-1600
F: (775) 684-1601
E: nvscclerk
    @nvcourts.nv.gov

NEW HAMPSHIRE
Ms. Eileen Fox
Clerk of Court
Supreme Court
Supreme Court Building
One Charles Doe Drive
Concord, NH 03301
P: (603) 271-2646
F: (603) 271-6630

NEW JERSEY
Mr. Mark Neary
Clerk
Supreme Court
Richard J. Hughes Justice
Complex
P.O. Box 970
Trenton, NJ 08625
P: (609) 292-4837

NEW MEXICO
Mr. Joey D. Moya
Chief Clerk
Supreme Court
237 Don Gaspar Avenue, Room
104
P.O. Box 848
Santa Fe, NM 87504
P: (505) 827-4860
F: (505) 827-4837

NEW YORK
Mr. Andrew W. Klein
Clerk of the Court
Court of Appeals
20 Eagle Street
Albany, NY 12207
P: (518) 455-7700
F: (518) 463-6869

NORTH CAROLINA
Ms. Christie S.
    Cameron Roeder
Clerk
Supreme Court
2 East Morgan Street
P.O. Box 2170
Raleigh, NC 27602
P: (919) 831-5700

NORTH DAKOTA
Ms. Penny Miller
Clerk of Supreme Court
Supreme Court
Judicial Wing, 1st Floor
600 East Boulevard Avenue
Bismarck, ND 58505
P: (701) 328-2221
F: (701) 328-4480
E: PMiller@ndcourts.gov

**NORTHERN MARIANA
ISLANDS**
Ms. Deanna Ogo
Clerk
Supreme Court
P.O. Box 502165
Saipan, MP 96950
P: (670) 236-9800
F: (670) 236-9702
E: supreme.court@saipan.com

OHIO
Ms. Sandra Huth Grosko
Clerk of Court
Supreme Court
65 South Front Street, 8th Floor
Columbus, OH 43215
P: (614) 387-9530

OKLAHOMA
Mr. Michael S. Richie
Supreme Court Clerk
Supreme Court
P.O. Box 53126
Oklahoma City, OK 73152
P: (405) 521-2163

OREGON
Ms. Kingsley W. Click
State Court Administrator
Judicial Department
Supreme Court Building
1163 State Street
Salem, OR 97301
P: (503) 986-5500
F: (503) 986-5503
E: kingsley.w.click
    @state.or.us

PENNSYLVANIA
Ms. Patricia Johnson
Chief Clerk
Supreme Court
468 City Hall
Philadelphia, PA 19107
P: (215) 560-6370

Ms. Patricia A. Nicola
Chief Clerk
Supreme Court
801 City-County Building
Pittsburgh, PA 15219
P: (412) 565-2816

Ms. Elizabeth Zisk
Chief Clerk
Supreme Court
601 Commonwealth Avenue,
Suite 4500
P.O. Box 62575
Harrisburg, PA 17106
P: (717) 787-6181

PUERTO RICO
Ms. Patricia Oton Oliveri
Secretary of Supreme Court
Supreme Court
P.O. Box 9022392
San Juan, PR 00902
P: (787) 723-6033
F: (787) 723-9199

RHODE ISLAND
Ms. Debra A. Saunders
Supreme Court Clerk
Supreme Court
Frank Licht Judicial Complex
250 Benefit Street
Providence, RI 02903
P: (401) 222-3272
E: dsaunders@courts.ri.gov

SOUTH CAROLINA
Mr. Daniel E. Shearouse
Clerk of Court
Supreme Court
1231 Gervais Street
P.O. Box 11330
Columbia, SC 29211
P: (803) 734-1080
F: (803) 734-1499

SOUTH DAKOTA
Ms. Shirley A.
    Jameson-Fergel
Clerk
Supreme Court
500 East Capitol Avenue
Pierre, SD 57501
P: (605) 773-3511
F: (605) 773-6128

TENNESSEE
Mr. James Hivner
Appellate Court Clerk
Supreme Court
Supreme Court Building
401 7th Avenue, North
Nashville, TN 37219
P: (615) 741-2681
F: (615) 532-8757

Clerk of the State's Highest Court

TEXAS
Mr. Blake A. Hawthorne
Clerk of the Court
Supreme Court
201 West 14th Street, Room 104
P.O. Box 12248
Austin, TX 78711
P: (512) 463-1312
F: (512) 463-1365

U.S. VIRGIN ISLANDS
Ms. Veronica J. Handy
Clerk of the Court
Supreme Court
P.O. Box 590
St. Thomas, VI 00804
P: (340) 774-2237
F: (340) 774-2258

UTAH
Ms. Andrea Martinez
Clerk of the Supreme Court
Supreme Court
450 South State Street, 5th Floor
P.O. Box 140210
Salt Lake City, UT 84114
P: (801) 238-7974
F: (801) 578-3999
E: andrearm@utcourts.gov

VERMONT
Ms. Patricia Gabel
Court Administrator & Clerk
Supreme Court
109 State Street
Montpelier, VT 05609
P: (802) 828-3278
F: (802) 828-4750

VIRGINIA
Ms. Patricia L. Harrington
Clerk
Supreme Court
100 North 9th Street, 5th Floor
P.O. Box 1315
Richmond, VA 23219
P: (804) 786-2251

WASHINGTON
Mr. Ronald R. Carpenter
Clerk
Supreme Court
415 12th Avenue, Southwest
P.O. Box 40929
Olympia, WA 98504
P: (360) 357-2077
F: (360) 357-2102
E: supreme@courts.wa.gov

WEST VIRGINIA
Mr. Rory L. Perry II
Clerk of Court
Supreme Court of Appeals
State Capitol, Room E-317
1900 Kanawha Boulevard, East
Charleston, WV 25305
P: (304) 558-2601
F: (304) 558-3815

WISCONSIN
Ms. Diane M. Fremgen
Clerk of the Supreme Court
Supreme Court
100 East Main Street, Suite 215
P.O. Box 1688
Madison, WI 53701
P: (608) 261-4300
F: (608) 267-0640
E: Diane.Fremgen
    @courts.state.wi.us

WYOMING
Ms. Carol Thompson
Clerk of Court
Supreme Court
2301 Capitol Avenue
Cheyenne, WY 82002
P: (307) 777-7316
F: (307) 777-6129
E: cthompson
    @courts.state.wy.us

Commerce

Umbrella agency of commerce responsible for the overall regulation and growth of the state's economy.

ALABAMA
Mr. Greg Canfield
Secretary
Department of Commerce
P.O. Box 304106
Montgomery, AL 36130
P: (334) 242-0421
F: (334) 242-5669
E: greg.canfield
@commerce.alabama.gov

ALASKA
Ms. Britteny Cioni-Haywood
Division Director
Division of Economic
Development
P.O. Box 110804
Juneau, AK 99811
P: (907) 465-2510
F: (907) 465-3767
E: britteny.cioni-haywood
@alaska.gov

AMERICAN SAMOA
Mr. Keniseli Lafaele
Director
Department of Commerce
American Samoa Government
Executive Office Building,
Utulei
Pago Pago, AS 96799
P: (684) 633-5155
F: (684) 633-4195
E: keniseli.lafaele@doc.as

ARIZONA
Ms. Sandra Watson
President & CEO
Commerce Authority
333 North Central Avenue, Suite
1900
Phoenix, AZ 85004
P: (602) 845-1200
F: (602) 845-1201
E: commerce@azcommerce.com

ARKANSAS
Mr. Mike Preston
Exeuctive Director
Economic Development
Commission
900 West Capitol Avenue, Suite
400
Little Rock, AR 72201
P: (501) 682-7351
F: (501) 682-7394
E: mpreston@arkansasedc.com

CALIFORNIA
Ms. Panorea Avdis
Deputy Director
Governor's Office of Business &
Economic Development
1400 10th Street, 2nd Floor
Sacramento, CA 95814
P: (916) 322-0694

COLORADO
Ms. Fiona Arnold
Executive Director
Office of Economic
Development & International
Trade
1625 Broadway, Suite 2700
Denver, CO 80202
P: (303) 892-3840
F: (303) 892-3848
E: fiona.arnold@state.co.us

CONNECTICUT
Ms. Catherine H. Smith
Commissioner
Department of Economic &
Community Development
505 Hudson Street
Hartford, CT 06106
P: (860) 270-8000
E: catherine.smith@ct.gov

DISTRICT OF COLUMBIA
Mr. Brian Kenner
Deputy Mayor for Planning and
Economic Development
Office of the Deputy Mayor for
Planning & Economic
Development
John A. Wilson Building, Suite
317
1350 Pennsylvania Avenue,
Northwest
Washington, DC 20004
P: (202) 727-6365
F: (202) 727-6703
E: dmped.eom@dc.gov

FLORIDA
Mr. Karl Blischke
Director
Division of Strategic Business
Development
Department of Economic
Opportunity
107 East Madison St., Caldwell
Building
Tallahassee, FL 32399
P: (850) 245-7105
F: (850) 921-3223
E: karl.blischke
@deo.myflorida.com

GEORGIA
Mr. Chris Carr
Commissioner
Department of Economic
Development
75 Fifth Street, Northwest
Suite 1200
Atlanta, GA 30308
P: (404) 962-4000
F: (404) 962-4009

HAWAII
Ms. Catherine P.
Awakuni Colon
Director
Department of Commerce &
Consumer Affairs
King Kalakaua Building
335 Merchant Street
Honolulu, HI 96813
P: (808) 586-2850
F: (808) 586-2856
E: dcca@dcca.hawaii.gov

IDAHO
Mr. Jeffery Sayer
Director
Department of Commerce
700 West State Street
P.O. Box 83720
Boise, ID 83720
P: (208) 334-2470
F: (208) 334-2631
E: jeffery.sayer
@commerce.idaho.gov

ILLINOIS
Mr. Jim Schultz
Director
Department of Commerce &
Economic Opportunity
100 West Randolph Street, Suite
3-400
Chicago, IL 60601
P: (312) 814-2811
E: Jim.Schultz@Illinois.gov

INDIANA
Mr. Victor Smith
Secretary of Commerce
Economic Development
Corporation
One North Capitol, Suite 700
Indianapolis, IN 46204
P: (317) 234-1359
F: (317) 232-4146
E: VSmith@iedc.IN.gov

IOWA
Mr. James M. Schipper
Superintendent
Division of Banking
200 East Grand Avenue, Suite
300
Des Moines, IA 50309
P: (515) 281-4014
F: (515) 281-4862
E: jschipper
@idob.state.ia.us

KANSAS
Mr. Pat George
Secretary
Department of Commerce
1000 Southwest Jackson Street,
Suite 100
Topeka, KS 66612
P: (785) 296-2741
F: (785) 296-5055
E: pgeorge
@kansascommerce.com

KENTUCKY
Mr. Bob Stewart
Secretary
Tourism, Arts & Heritage
Cabinet
24th Floor, Capital Plaza Tower
500 Mero Street
Frankfort, KY 40601
P: (502) 564-4270
F: (502) 564-1512

LOUISIANA
Mr. Stephen Grissom
Secretary
Economic Development
1051 North Third Street
Baton Rouge, LA 70802
P: (225) 342-5478
F: (225) 342-9095
E: sgrissom@la.gov

MAINE
Mr. George C. Gervais
Commissioner
Department of Economic &
Community Development
59 State House Station
Augusta, ME 04333
P: (207) 624-9800

MARYLAND
Mr. R. Michael Gill
Secretary
Department of Business &
Economic Development
World Trade Center
401 East Pratt Street
Baltimore, MD 21202
P: (410) 767-6301
F: (410) 333-8628
E: Mike.Gill@maryland.gov

Commerce

MICHIGAN
Mr. Mike Zimmer
Director
Department of Licensing &
Regulatory Affairs
P.O. Box 30004
Lansing, MI 48909
P: (517) 373-1820
F: (517) 373-2129
E: zimmerm@michigan.gov

MINNESOTA
Mr. Mike Rothman
Commissioner
Department of Commerce
85 East 7th Place, Suite 500
St. Paul, MN 55101
P: (651) 539-1638
F: (651) 296-4328
E: commerce.commissioner
   @state.mn.us

MISSISSIPPI
Hon. Cindy Hyde-Smith (R)
Commissioner
Department of Agriculture &
Commerce
121 North Jefferson Street
Jackson, MS 39201
P: (601) 359-1100
F: (601) 354-7710

MISSOURI
Mr. Mike Downing
Director
Department of Economic
Development
301 West High Street
P.O. Box 1157
Jefferson City, MO 65102
P: (573) 751-4962
F: (573) 526-7700
E: ecodev@ded.mo.gov

MONTANA
Ms. Meg O'Leary
Director
Department of Commerce
301 South Park Avenue
P.O. Box 200501
Helena, MT 59620
P: (406) 841-2700
F: (406) 841-2701

NEBRASKA
Ms. Brenda Hicks-Sorensen
Director
Department of Economic
Development
550 South 16th Street
Lincoln, NE 68508
P: (402) 471-3125
E: brenda.hicks-sorensen
   @nebraska.gov

NEVADA
Mr. Bruce H. Breslow
Director
Department of Business &
Industry
555 East Washington Avenue,
Suite 4900
Las Vegas, NV 89101
P: (702) 486-2750
F: (702) 486-2758
E: breslow@business.nv.gov

NEW HAMPSHIRE
Ms. Carmen Lorentz
Director
Division of Economic
Development
72 Pembroke Road
Concord, NH 03301
P: (603) 271-2341
E: Carmen.Lorentz
   @dred.nh.gov

NEW JERSEY
Ms. Melissa Orsen
Chief Executive Officer
Economic Development
Authority
36 West State Street
P.O. Box 990
Trenton, NJ 08625
P: (609) 292-1800
F: (609) 292-0885
E: njeda@njeda.com

NEW MEXICO
Mr. Jon Barela
Secretary
Economic Development
Department
1100 South Saint Francis Drive
P.O. Box 20003
Santa Fe, NM 87504
P: (505) 827-0305
F: (505) 827-0328
E: Jon.Barela@state.nm.us

NEW YORK
Mr. Howard Zemsky
President & CEO
Empire State Development
633 Third Avenue
New York, NY 10017
P: (212) 803-3700
F: (212) 803-3715

NORTH CAROLINA
Mr. John Skvarla
Secretary
Department of Commerce
301 North Wilmington Street
4301 Mail Service Center
Raleigh, NC 27699
P: (919) 733-4151
E: john.skvarla
   @nccommerce.com

NORTH DAKOTA
Mr. Al Anderson
Commissioner
Department of Commerce
1600 East Century Avenue,
Suite 2
P.O. Box 2057
Bismarck, ND 58503
P: (701) 328-7284
F: (701) 328-5320
E: alrandeson@nd.gov

OHIO
Ms. Jacqueline Williams
Director
Department of Commerce
77 South High Street, 23rd Floor
Columbus, OH 43215
P: (614) 466-4100

OKLAHOMA
Mr. Deby Snodgrass
Secretary
Department of Commerce
900 North Stiles Avenue
Oklahoma City, OK 73104
P: (405) 815-6552
E: deby_snodgrass
   @okcommerce.gov

OREGON
Mr. Sean Robbins
Director
Business Oregon
775 Summer Street, Northeast,
Suite 200
Salem, OR 97301
P: (503) 986-0110
F: (503) 581-5115
E: sean.robbins@state.or.us

PENNSYLVANIA
Mr. Dennis Davin
Secretary
Department of Community &
Economic Development
Commonwealth Keystone
Building
400 North Street, 4th Floor
Harrisburg, PA 17120
P: (866) 466-3972
F: (717) 783-4662

PUERTO RICO
Mr. Antonio Medina Comas
Executive Director
Industrial Development
Company
P.O. Box 362350
San Juan, PR 00936
P: (787) 764-1175
E: antonio.medina
   @pridco.pr.gov

RHODE ISLAND
Mr. Mackey McCleary
Director
Department of Business
Regulation
1511 Pontiac Avenue
Cranston, RI 02920
P: (401) 462-9551
F: (401) 462-9532
E: mackey.mccleary
   @dbr.ri.gov

SOUTH CAROLINA
Mr. Robert M. Hitt III
Secretary
Department of Commerce
1201 Main Street, Suite 1600
Columbia, SC 29201
P: (803) 737-0400
F: (803) 737-0418

SOUTH DAKOTA
Mr. Pat Costello
Commissioner
Governor's Office of Economic
Development
711 East Wells Avenue
Pierre, SD 57501
P: (800) 872-6190
F: (605) 773-3256
E: goedinfo@state.sd.us

TENNESSEE
Ms. Julie Mix McPeak
Commissioner
Department of Commerce &
Insurance
Davy Crockett Tower, Twelfth
Floor
500 James Robertson Parkway
Nashville, TN 37243
P: (615) 741-6007
F: (615) 532-6934
E: ask.tdci@tn.gov

U.S. VIRGIN ISLANDS
Ms. Beverly Nicholson Doty
Commissioner
Department of Tourism
Elainco Building
78 Contant 1-2-3
St. Thomas, VI 00802
P: (340) 774-8784
F: (340) 773-0495

UTAH
Ms. Francine A. Giani
Executive Director
Department of Commerce
160 East 300 South, 2nd Floor
P.O. Box 146701
Salt Lake City, UT 84114
P: (801) 530-6431
F: (801) 530-6446
E: fgiani@utah.gov

VERMONT
Ms. Patricia Moulton
Secretary
Agency of Commerce &
Community Development
1 National Life Drive, 6th Floor
Montpelier, VT 05620
P: (802) 828-5204
F: (802) 828-3383
E: pat.moulton@state.vt.us

VIRGINIA
Mr. Maurice A. Jones
Secretary of Commerce & Trade
Office of Commerce & Trade
P.O. Box 1475
Richmond, VA 23218
P: (804) 786-7831
F: (804) 371-0250
E: maurice.jones
     @governor.virginia.gov

WASHINGTON
Mr. Brian Bonlender
Director
Department of Commerce
1011 Plum Street, Southeast
P.O. Box 42525
Olympia, WA 98504
P: (360) 725-4000

WEST VIRGINIA
Mr. J. Keith Burdette
Cabinet Secretary
Department of Commerce
Capitol Complex Building 6,
Room 525
1900 Kanawha Boulevard East
Charleston, WV 25305
P: (304) 558-2234
F: (304) 558-1189
E: J.Keith.Burdette@wv.gov

WISCONSIN
Mr. Reed Hall
CEO & Secretary
Economic Development
Corporation
201 West Washington Avenue
P.O. Box 1687
Madison, WI 53701
P: (608) 267-4417
E: Reed.Hall@wedc.org

WYOMING
Mr. Shawn Reese
Chief Executive Officer
Business Council
214 West 15th Street
Cheyenne, WY 82002
P: (307) 777-2862
F: (307) 777-2837
E: shawn.reese@wyo.gov

Comptroller

The principal accounting and dispersing officer of the state.

Information provided by:

National Association of State Auditors, Comptrollers & Treasurers
Kinney Poynter
Executive Director
449 Lewis Hargett Circle
Suite 290
Lexington, KY 40503
P: (859) 276-1147
F: (859) 278-0507
kpoynter@nasact.org
www.nasact.org

ALABAMA
Mr. Thomas L. White Jr.
State Comptroller
Office of the State Comptroller
100 North Union Street, Suite 220
Montgomery, AL 36104
P: (334) 242-7063
F: (334) 242-2440
E: tom.white
    @comptroller.alabama.gov

ALASKA
Mr. Scot Arehart
Director
Division of Finance
Department of Administration
P.O. Box 110204
Juneau, AK 99811
P: (907) 465-5601
F: (907) 465-2169
E: scot.arehart@alaska.gov

ARIZONA
Mr. D. Clark Partridge
State Comptroller
General Accounting Office
100 North 15th Avenue, Suite 302
Phoenix, AZ 85007
P: (602) 542-5405
F: (602) 542-5749
E: clark.partridge
    @azdoa.gov

ARKANSAS
Hon. Andrea Lea (R)
Auditor of State
Office of the State Auditor
State Capitol Building, Room 230
Little Rock, AR 72201
P: (501) 682-6030
F: (501) 682-2521

Mr. Larry Walther
Director
Department of Finance & Administration
1509 West 7th Street
DFA Building, Room 401
Little Rock, AR 72201
P: (501) 682-2242
F: (501) 682-1029
E: larry.walther
    @dfa.arkansas.gov

CALIFORNIA
Mr. Todd Jerue
Chief Operating Officer
Department of Finance
State Capitol, Room 1145
915 L Street
Sacramento, CA 95814
P: (916) 445-4923
F: (916) 445-7997

Hon. Betty T. Yee (D)
State Controller
Office of the State Controller
300 Capitol Mall, Suite 1850
P.O. Box 942805
Sacramento, CA 94250
P: (916) 445-2636
F: (916) 445-6379

COLORADO
Mr. Bob Jaros
State Controller
Department of Personnel & Administration
1525 Sherman Street, 5th Floor
Denver, CO 80202
P: (303) 866-2739
F: (303) 866-3569
E: bob.jaros@state.co.us

CONNECTICUT
Mr. Kevin Lembo
State Comptroller
Office of the Comptroller
55 Elm Street, Suite 307
Hartford, CT 06106
P: (860) 702-3301
F: (860) 702-3319
E: Kevin.Lembo@ct.gov

DELAWARE
Mr. Kristopher Knight
Director
Division of Accounting
820 Silver Lake Boulevard, Suite 200
Dover, DE 19904
P: (302) 672-5500
F: (302) 736-7969

DISTRICT OF COLUMBIA
Mr. Bill Slack
    (appointed)
Office of Financial Operations & Systems
1100 4th Street, Southwest
8th Floor
Washington, DC 20024
P: (202) 442-8200
F: (202) 442-8201

FLORIDA
Hon. Jeffrey H. Atwater (R)
Chief Financial Officer
Department of Financial Services
200 East Gaines Street
Tallahassee, FL 32399
P: (850) 413-2850
F: (850) 413-2950
E: allison@jeffatwater.com

GEORGIA
Mr. Alan Skelton
State Accounting Officer
State Accounting Office
200 Piedmont Avenue
Suite 1604, West Tower
Atlanta, GA 30334
P: (404) 656-2133
F: (404) 463-5089

GUAM
Ms. Benita A. Manglona
Director
Department of Administration
P.O. Box 884
Hagatna, GU 96932
P: (671) 475-1101
F: (671) 477-6788

HAWAII
Mr. Douglas Murdock
Comptroller
Department of Accounting & General Services
1151 Punchbowl Street, Room 412
Honolulu, HI 96813
P: (808) 586-0400
F: (808) 586-0775
E: dags@hawaii.gov

IDAHO
Hon. Brandon Woolf
State Controller
Office of the State Controller
700 West State Street
Boise, ID 83720
P: (208) 334-3100
F: (208) 334-3338
E: bwoolf@sco.idaho.gov

ILLINOIS
Hon. Leslie Geissler Munger
State Comptroller
Office of the State Comptroller
201 State Capitol Building
Springfield, IL 62706
P: (217) 782-6000
F: (217) 782-7561

INDIANA
Hon. Suzanne Crouch (R)
Auditor of State
Office of the Auditor of State
State House, Room 240
200 West Washington Street
Indianapolis, IN 46204
P: (317) 232-3300
F: (317) 234-1916

IOWA
Mr. Calvin McKelvogue
Chief Operating Officer
Department of Administrative Services
State Accounting Enterprise
Hoover State Office Building, 3rd Floor
Des Moines, IA 50319
P: (515) 281-4877
F: (515) 281-5255
E: calvin.mckelvogue
    @iowa.gov

KANSAS
Ms. DeAnn Hill
Chief Financial Officer
Office of the Chief Financial Officer
700 Southwest Harrison Street
Suite 300
Topeka, KS 66603
P: (785) 368-7390
F: (785) 296-6841

KENTUCKY
Mr. Edgar C. Ross
Controller
Office of the Controller
Capitol Annex, Room 484
702 Capitol Avenue
Frankfort, KY 40601
P: (502) 564-2998
F: (502) 564-6597
E: edc.ross@ky.gov

LOUISIANA
Mr. John McLean
Interim Director
Office of Statewide Reporting &
Accounting Policy
Division of Administration
P.O. Box 94095
Baton Rouge, LA 70804
P: (225) 342-0708
F: (225) 342-1053

MAINE
Mr. Douglas Cotnoir
State Controller
Office of the State Controller
Cross Office Building, 4th Floor
14 State House Station
Augusta, ME 04353
P: (207) 626-8420
F: (207) 626-8422
E: douglas.cotnoir
@maine.gov

MARYLAND
Hon. Peter Franchot (D)
Comptroller
Office of the Comptroller
L.L. Goldstein Treasury
Building
P.O. Box 466
Annapolis, MD 21404
P: (410) 260-7801
F: (410) 974-3808
E: mdcomptroller
@comp.state.md.us

MASSACHUSETTS
Mr. Thomas Shack III
Comptroller
Office of the State Comptroller
One Ashburton Place, 9th Floor
Boston, MA 02108
P: (617) 973-2315
F: (617) 727-2163

MICHIGAN
Mr. Michael J. Moody
Director
Office of Financial Management
Department of Management and
Budget
111 South Capitol Avenue
Lansing, MI 48913
P: (517) 335-1942
F: (517) 373-6458
E: moodym1@michigan.gov

MINNESOTA
Mr. Myron Frans
Commissioner
Management & Budget
658 Cedar Street, Suite 400
St. Paul, MN 55155
P: (651) 201-8011
F: (651) 797-1300
E: myron.frans@state.mn.us

MISSISSIPPI
Ms. Diane Langham
Fiscal Management Director
Department of Finance &
Administration
701 Woolfolk Building
501 North West Street
Jackson, MS 39201
P: (601) 359-3405
F: (601) 359-5525

MISSOURI
Ms. Stacy Neal
Director of Accounting
Office of Administration,
Division of Accounting
Truman State Office Building,
Room 570
P.O. Box 809
Jefferson City, MO 65102
P: (573) 751-4013
F: (573) 526-9810

MONTANA
Mr. Cody Pearce
Bureau Chief
State Accounting Division
Mitchell Building, Room 255
Helena, MT 59620
P: (406) 444-4609
F: (406) 444-2812

NEBRASKA
Mr. Weslie Mohling
Operations Manager
Department of Administrative
Services
Room 1309, State Capitol
P.O. Box 94664
Lincoln, NE 68509
P: (402) 471-2581
F: (402) 471-2583
E: weslie.mohling
@nebraska.gov

NEVADA
Hon. Ron Knecht (R)
State Controller
Office of the State Controller
State Capitol Building
101 North Carson Street, Suite 5
Carson City, NV 89701
P: (775) 684-5632
F: (775) 684-5696

NEW HAMPSHIRE
Mr. Gerard J. Murphy
Director
Department of Administrative
Services
25 Capitol Street
State House Annex, Room 310
Concord, NH 03301
P: (603) 271-1443
F: (603) 271-6666

NEW JERSEY
Ms. Charlene M. Holzbaur
Director
Office of Management &
Budget
Department of the Treasury
33 West State Street, P.O. Box
221
Trenton, NJ 08625
P: (609) 292-6746
F: (609) 633-8179
E: charlene.holzbaur
@treas.state.nj.us

NEW MEXICO
Mr. Ronald Spilman
State Controller/Division
Director
Department of Finance &
Administration
Bataan Memorial Building,
Suite 166
407 Galisteo Street
Santa Fe, NM 87501
P: (505) 827-3934
F: (505) 827-3692

NEW YORK
Hon. Thomas P. DiNapoli (D)
Comptroller
Office of the State Comptroller
110 State Street
Albany, NY 12236
P: (518) 474-4040
F: (518) 474-3004
E: tdinapoli
@osc.state.ny.us

Mr. Pete Grannis
Office of the State Comptroller -
Operations
110 State Street
Albany, NY 12236
P: (518) 474-2909
F: (518) 474-5220

NORTH CAROLINA
Ms. Linda Combs
State Controller
Office of the State Controller
3512 Bush Street
1410 Mail Service Center
Raleigh, NC 27699
P: (919) 707-0471
F: (919) 981-5567

NORTH DAKOTA
Ms. Pam Sharp
Director
Office of Management &
Budget
600 East Boulevard Avenue
Department 110
Bismarck, ND 58505
P: (701) 328-4606
F: (701) 328-3230
E: psharp@nd.gov

**NORTHERN MARIANA
ISLANDS**
Ms. Larissa Larson
Secretary
Department of Finance
P.O. Box 5234, CHRB
Saipan, MP 96950
P: (670) 664-1000
F: (670) 664-1115
E: revtax@gtepacifica.net

OHIO
Mr. Timothy S. Keen
Director
Office of Budget &
Management
30 East Broad Street, 34th Floor
Columbus, OH 43215
P: (614) 752-2579
F: (614) 485-1058
E: tim.keen@obm.state.oh.us

OKLAHOMA
Ms. Lynne Bajema
State Comptroller
Office of Management &
Enterprise Services
5005 North Lincoln Boulevard,
Suite 100
Oklahoma City, OK 73105
P: (405) 522-5577
F: (405) 521-3902
E: lynne.bajema@osf.ok.gov

Comptroller

OREGON
Mr. Robert Hamilton
SARS Manager
Department of Administrative
Services
155 Cottage Street, Northeast,
U-50
Salem, OR 97301
P: (503) 373-0265
F: (503) 378-3514

PENNSYLVANIA
Ms. Anna Maria Kiehl
State Comptroller/Chief
Accounting Officer
Office of the
Budget/Comptroller Operations
9th Floor Forum Place
555 Walnut Street
Harrisburg, PA 17101
P: (717) 787-6497
F: (717) 787-3376
E: akiehl@state.pa.us

RHODE ISLAND
Mr. Marc A. Leonetti
State Controller
Office of Accounts & Control
Department of Administration
One Capitol Hill
Providence, RI 02908
P: (401) 222-2271
F: (401) 222-6437
E: mleonetti@doa.ri.gov

SOUTH CAROLINA
Hon. Richard Eckstrom (R)
Comptroller General
Office of the Comptroller
General
305 Wade Hampton Office
Building
1200 Senate Street
Columbia, SC 29201
P: (803) 734-2588
F: (803) 734-1765
E: reckstrom@cg.sc.gov

SOUTH DAKOTA
Hon. Steve Barnett (R)
State Auditor
Office of the State Auditor
500 East Capitol Avenue
Pierre, SD 57501
P: (605) 773-3341
F: (605) 773-5929
E: steve.barnett
    @state.sd.us

Mr. Jason C. Dilges
Chief Financial Officer &
Commissioner
Bureau of Finance &
Management
500 East Capitol Avenue
Pierre, SD 57501
P: (605) 773-3411
F: (605) 773-4711
E: jason.dilges@state.sd.us

TENNESSEE
Mr. Mike Corricelli
Department of Finance &
Administration
W.R.S. Tennessee Tower, 21st
Floor
312 Rosa L. Parks Avenue
Nashville, TN 37243
P: (615) 253-3048
F: (615) 782-6633

TEXAS
Hon. Glenn Hegar (R)
Comptroller of Public Accounts
Office of the Comptroller of
Public Accounts
LBJ State Office Building, 1st
Floor
111 East 17th Street
Austin, TX 78774
P: (512) 463-4444
F: (512) 463-4902
E: glenn.hegar
    @cpa.state.tx.us

U.S. VIRGIN ISLANDS
Ms. Debra Gottlieb
    (appointed)
Director
Office of Management &
Budget
#41 Norre Gade
Emancipation Garden Station,
2nd Floor
St. Thomas, VI 00802
P: (340) 776-0750
F: (340) 776-0069
E: debra.gottlieb
    @omb.vi.gov

UTAH
Mr. John C. Reidhead
Director
Division of Finance
2110 State Office Building
Salt Lake City, UT 84114
P: (801) 538-3095
F: (801) 538-3244
E: jreidhead@utah.gov

VERMONT
Mr. James B. Reardon
Commissioner
Department of Finance &
Management
109 State Street
Montpelier, VT 05609
P: (802) 828-2376
F: (802) 828-2428
E: jim.reardon@state.vt.us

VIRGINIA
Mr. David A. Von Moll
State Comptroller
Department of Accounts
101 North 14th Street
P.O. Box 1971
Richmond, VA 23219
P: (804) 225-2109
F: (804) 786-8587
E: david.vonmoll
    @doa.virginia.gov

WASHINGTON
Mr. David Schumacher
Director
Office of Financial Management
P.O. Box 43113
Olympia, WA 98504
P: (360) 902-0555
F: (360) 664-2832
E: ofm.administration
    @ofm.wa.gov

WEST VIRGINIA
Hon. Glen B. Gainer III
State Auditor
Office of the State Auditor
State Capitol Complex
Building 1, Room W-100
Charleston, WV 25305
P: (304) 558-2251 Ext. 116
F: (304) 558-5200

Mr. Ross Taylor
Director of Finance
Finance Division, Department
of Administration
2101 Washington Street, East
Building 17
Charleston, WV 25305
P: (304) 558-6181 Ext. 105
F: (304) 558-1950
E: ross.a.taylor@wv.gov

WISCONSIN
Mr. Jeffrey Anderson
Department of Administration
101 East Wilson Street, 5th
Floor
P.O. Box 7932
Madison, WI 53593
P: (608) 266-8158
F: (608) 266-7734

WYOMING
Hon. Cynthia I. Cloud (R)
State Auditor
Office of the State Auditor
State Capitol, Suite 114
200 West 24th Street
Cheyenne, WY 82002
P: (307) 777-7831
F: (307) 777-6983
E: SAOAdmin@wyo.gov

Consumer Protection

Investigates consumer complaints, develops consumer education programs and alerts citizens to current consumer concerns within the state.

ALABAMA
Hon. Luther Strange (R)
Attorney General
Office of the Attorney General
501 Washington Avenue
P.O. Box 300152
Montgomery, AL 36130
P: (334) 242-7300

ALASKA
Ms. Signe Andersen
Chief Assistant Attorney
General, Section Supervisor
Commercial & Fair Business
Practices
Department of Law
1031 West 4th Avenue, Suite 200
Anchorage, AK 99501
P: (907) 269-5200
F: (907) 276-8554
E: signe.andersen
   @alaska.gov

AMERICAN SAMOA
Hon. Talauega Eleasalo V.
   Ale
Attorney General
Office of the Attorney General
American Samoa Government
Exeutive Office Building,
Utulei
Pago Pago, AS 96799
P: (684) 633-4163

Mr. Keniseli Lafaele
Director
Department of Commerce
American Samoa Government
Executive Office Building,
Utulei
Pago Pago, AS 96799
P: (684) 633-5155
F: (684) 633-4195
E: keniseli.lafaele@doc.as

ARIZONA
Mr. Dena Benjamin
Section Chief
Consumer Protection &
Advocacy
Office of the Attorney General
1275 West Washington Street
Phoenix, AZ 85007
P: (602) 542-7717
E: consumerinfo@azag.gov

ARKANSAS
Hon. Leslie Rutledge (R)
Attorney General
Office of the Attorney General
323 Center Street, Suite 200
Little Rock, AR 72201
P: (800) 482-8982
F: (501) 682-8084

CALIFORNIA
Ms. Melissa Wiekel
Manager
Public Inquiry Unit
P.O. Box 944255
Sacramento, CA 94244
P: (916) 322-3360
F: (916) 323-5341

COLORADO
Ms. Janet Zavislan
Director
Department of Law
Ralph L. Carr Judicial Center
1300 Broadway, 10th Floor
Denver, CO 80203
P: (720) 508-6000
F: (720) 508-6030
E: jan.zavislan@state.co.us

CONNECTICUT
Mr. Jonathan A. Harris
Commissioner
Department of Consumer
Protection
165 Capitol Avenue
Hartford, CT 06106
P: (860) 713-6050
F: (860) 713-7243
E: jonathan.harris@ct.gov

DELAWARE
Mr. Timothy M. Mullaney Sr.
Director
Fraud & Consumer Protection
Division
Carvel State Office Building
820 North French Street
Wilmington, DE 19801
P: (302) 577-8341
F: (302) 577-6499
E: consumer.protection
   @state.de.us

DISTRICT OF COLUMBIA
Mr. Rabbiah Sabbakhan
Director
Department of Consumer &
Regulatory Affairs
1100 4th Street, Southwest
Washington, DC 20024
P: (202) 442-4400
F: (202) 442-9445
E: dcra@dc.gov

FLORIDA
Hon. Pam Bondi (R)
Attorney General
Office of the Attorney General
The Capitol, PL 01
Tallahassee, FL 32399
P: (850) 414-3300
F: (954) 712-4826

GEORGIA
Mr. John Sours
Administrator
Governor's Office of Consumer
Protection
2 Martin Luther King Jr. Drive
Suite 356
Atlanta, GA 30334
P: (404) 651-8600
F: (404) 651-9018
E: john.sours@ocp.ga.gov

GUAM
Mr. J. Patrick Mason
Deputy Attorney General
Civil Litigation & Solicitor
Division
590 South Marine Corps Drive
Suite 706, ITC Building
Tamuning, GU 96913
P: (671) 475-3324
F: (671) 472-2493
E: law@guamag.org

HAWAII
Mr. Stephen H. Levins
Executive Director
Office of Consumer Protection
Leiopapa A. Kamehameha
Building
235 South Beretania Street, Suite
801
Honolulu, HI 96813
P: (808) 586-2630
F: (808) 586-2640
E: ocp@dcca.hawaii.gov

IDAHO
Hon. Lawrence Wasden (R)
Attorney General
Office of the Attorney General
Statehouse
Boise, ID 83720
P: (208) 334-2400
F: (208) 854-8071

ILLINOIS
Ms. Deborah Hagan
Chief
Division of Consumer
Protection
Office of the Attorney General
500 South Second Street
Springfield, IL 62706
P: (312) 814-3749

IOWA
Mr. William Brauch
Director
Consumer Protection Division
Office of the Attorney General
1305 East Walnut Street
Des Moines, IA 50319
P: (515) 281-5926
F: (515) 281-6771
E: william.brauch@iowa.gov

KANSAS
Hon. Derek Schmidt (R)
Attorney General
Office of the Attorney General
120 Southwest 10th Avenue, 2nd
Floor
Topeka, KS 66612
P: (785) 296-2215
F: (785) 296-6296

KENTUCKY
Mr. Todd Leatherman
Executive Director
Office of Consumer Protection
Office of the Attorney General
1024 Capital Center Drive, Suite
200
Frankfort, KY 40601
P: (502) 696-5389
F: (502) 564-2894
E: consumer.protection
   @ag.ky.gov

LOUISIANA
Hon. James D. Caldwell (R)
Attorney General
Office of the Attorney General
P.O. Box 94095
Baton Rouge, LA 70804
P: (225) 326-6000
F: (225) 326-6797
E: executive@ag.state.la.us

MAINE
Mr. William N. Lund
Superintendent
Bureau of Consumer Credit
Protection
Professional & Financial
Regulation
35 State House Station
Augusta, ME 04333
P: (207) 624-8527
F: (207) 582-7699
E: william.n.lund@maine.gov

MARYLAND
Mr. William D. Gruhn
Chief
Consumer Protection Division
Office of the Attorney General
200 Saint Paul Place
Baltimore, MD 21202
P: (410) 576-6558
F: (410) 576-6566
E: wgruhn@oag.state.md.us

Consumer Protection

MASSACHUSETTS
Mr. John Chapman
Office of Consumer Affairs &
Business Regulation
Ten Park Plaza, Suite 5170
Boston, MA 02116
P: (617) 973-8700
F: (617) 973-8799

MICHIGAN
Mr. Steve Arwood
CEO
Department of Licensing &
Regulatory Affairs
300 North Washington Square
Lansing, MI 48913
P: (517) 241-1400
F: (517) 241-3683
E: arwoods1@michigan.org

Hon. Bill Schuette (R)
Attorney General
Office of the Attorney General
525 West Ottawa Street
P.O. Box 30212
Lansing, MI 48909
P: (517) 373-1110

MINNESOTA
Hon. Lori Swanson (DFL)
Attorney General
Office of the Attorney General
State Capitol, Suite 102
St. Paul, MN 55155
P: (651) 296-3353
F: (651) 297-4193
E: attorney.general
    @state.mn.us

MISSISSIPPI
Ms. Meredith Aldridge
Special Assistant Attorney
Consumer Protection Division
P.O. Box 22947
Jackson, MS 39225
P: (601) 359-4230
F: (601) 359-4231

MONTANA
Mr. Matthew Dale
Executive Director
Office of Victim Services
2225 11th Avenue
P.O. Box 201410
Helena, MT 59620
P: (406) 444-1907
F: (406) 444-9680
E: dojovs@mt.gov

NEBRASKA
Hon. Doug Peterson (R)
Attorney General
Office of the Attorney General
State Capitol
P.O. Box 98920
Lincoln, NE 68509
P: (402) 471-2682
F: (402) 471-3297

NEVADA
Mr. Eric P. Witkoski
Chief Deputy Attorney General
Bureau of Consumer Protection
Office of the Attorney General
10791 West Twain Avenue
Las Vegas, NV 89135
P: (702) 486-3129
F: (775) 684-1108
E: ewitkoski@ag.nv.gov

NEW HAMPSHIRE
Ms. Lauren J. Noether
Assistant Attorney General
Office of the Attorney General
Department of Justice
33 Capitol Street
Concord, NH 03301
P: (603) 271-3679
F: (603) 271-2110
E: lauren.noether
    @doj.nh.gov

NEW JERSEY
Mr. Steve C. Lee
Acting Director
Division of Consumer Affairs
124 Halsey Street
Newark, NJ 07102
P: (973) 504-6200
F: (973) 273-8035
E: askconsumeraffairs
    @lps.state.nj.us

NEW MEXICO
Hon. Hector H. Balderas (D)
Attorney General
Office of the Attorney General
P.O. Drawer 1508
Santa Fe, NM 87504
P: (505) 827-6000
F: (505) 827-5826

NEW YORK
Hon. Cesar A. Perales
Secretary of State
Office of the Secretary of State
One Commerce Plaza
99 Washington Avenue, Suite
1100
Albany, NY 12231
P: (518) 486-9846
F: (518) 474-4797
E: info@dos.ny.gov

NORTH CAROLINA
Hon. Roy A. Cooper III (D)
Attorney General
Office of the Attorney General
Department of Justice
P.O.Box 629
Raleigh, NC 27602
P: (919) 716-6400
F: (919) 716-6750
E: rcooper@ncdoj.gov

NORTH DAKOTA
Mr. Parrell Grossman
Director
Consumer Protection &
Antitrust Division
Gateway Professional Center
1050 East Interstate Avenue,
Suite 200
Bismarck, ND 58503
P: (701) 328-3404
F: (701) 328-3535
E: pgrossman@nd.gov

OHIO
Hon. Mike DeWine (R)
Attorney General
Office of the Attorney General
State Office Tower
30 East Broad Street
Columbus, OH 43266
P: (614) 466-4320

OKLAHOMA
Mr. Scott Lesher
Administrator
Department of Consumer Credit
3613 Northwest 56th Street,
Suite 240
Oklahoma City, OK 73112
P: (405) 521-3653
F: (405) 521-6740
E: slesher@okdocc.ok.gov

PENNSYLVANIA
Ms. Linda J. Williams
Director & Chief Deputy
Attorney General
Bureau of Consumer Protection
Office of the Attorney General
16th Floor, Strawberry Square
Harrisburg, PA 17120
P: (717) 787-3391
F: (717) 787-8242

PUERTO RICO
Mr. Luis Rivera-Marin
Secretary
Department of Consumer
Affairs
P.O. Box 41059
Minillas Station
Santurce, PR 00940
P: (787) 722-7555
F: (787) 726-5707

RHODE ISLAND
Hon. Peter F. Kilmartin (D)
Attorney General
Office of the Attorney General
150 South Main Street
Providence, RI 02903
P: (401) 274-4400

SOUTH CAROLINA
Ms. Carri Grube Lybarker
Administrator
Department of Consumer
Affairs
2221 Devine Street, 2nd Floor
P.O. Box 5757
Columbia, SC 29250
P: (803) 734-4233
F: (803) 734-4060

SOUTH DAKOTA
Ms. Delane Smith
Director
Division of Consumer
Protection
Office of the Attorney General
1302 East Highway 14, Suite 3
Pierre, SD 57501
P: (605) 773-4400
F: (605) 773-7163
E: consumerhelp@state.sd.us

TENNESSEE
Mr. E. Ross White
Assistant Director
Division of Consumer Affairs
Department of Commerce &
Insurance
500 James Robertson Parkway,
12th Floor
Nashville, TN 37243
P: (615) 741-4737
F: (615) 532-4994
E: Ross.White@tn.gov

TEXAS
Mr. Rudy Aguilar
Consumer Protection Director
Office of Consumer Credit
Commissioner
2601 North Lamar Boulevard
Austin, TX 78705
P: (512) 936-7627
F: (512) 936-7610
E: rudy.aguilar
    @occc.state.tx.us

U.S. VIRGIN ISLANDS
Mr. Wayne L. Biggs Jr.
Acting Chief Executive Officer
Department of Licensing &
Consumer Affairs
8000 Nisky Shopping Center,
Suite 620
P.O. Box 305038
St. Thomas, VI 00802
P: (340) 714-1700
F: (340) 773-6499

UTAH
Mr. Daniel O'Bannon
Director
Division of Consumer
Protection
Department of Commerce
P.O. Box 146704
Salt Lake City, UT 84114
P: (801) 530-6601
F: (801) 530-6001
E: dobannon@utah.gov

WASHINGTON
Hon. Bob Ferguson (D)
Attorney General
Office of the Attorney General
1125 Washington Street,
Southeast
P.O. Box 40100
Olympia, WA 98504
P: (360) 753-6200
F: (360) 664-0228
E: bob.ferguson@atg.wa.gov

WEST VIRGINIA
Mr. Doug Davis
Assistant Attorney General
Consumer Protection &
Antitrust Division
Office of the Attorney General
P.O. Box 1789
Charleston, WV 25326
P: (304) 558-8986
F: (304) 558-0184
E: douglas.l.davis
    @wvago.gov

WISCONSIN
Mr. Frank Frassetto
Department of Agriculture,
Trade & Consumer Protection
P.O. Box 8911
Madison, WI 53708
P: (608) 224-4949
F: (608) 224-4939
E: Frank.Frassetto
    @wisconsin.gov

Corporate Records

Maintains a variety of corporate filings, records and documents.

ALABAMA
Ms. Rebecca Morris
Director of Business Services
Business Services Division
RSA Union Building , Suite 770
100 North Union Street
Montgomery, AL 36130
P: (334) 242-7221
F: (334) 240-3138
E: Rebecca.Morris
   @sos.alabama.gov

ALASKA
Mr. Don Habeger
Division Director
Division of Corporations,
Business & Professional
Licensing
P.O. Box 110806
Juneau, AK 99811
P: (907) 465-2550
F: (907) 465-2974
E: don.habeger@alaska.gov

AMERICAN SAMOA
Hon. Talauega Eleasalo V.
   Ale
Attorney General
Office of the Attorney General
American Samoa Government
Exeutive Office Building,
Utulei
Pago Pago, AS 96799
P: (684) 633-4163

Mr. Keniseli Lafaele
Director
Department of Commerce
American Samoa Government
Executive Office Building,
Utulei
Pago Pago, AS 96799
P: (684) 633-5155
F: (684) 633-4195
E: keniseli.lafaele@doc.as

ARIZONA
Ms. Patricia L. Barfield
Director
Corporations Division
Corporation Commission
1300 West Washington Street
Phoenix, AZ 85007
P: (602) 542-3026
F: (602) 542-0900
E: director.corp@azcc.gov

ARKANSAS
Hon. Mark Martin (R)
Secretary of State
Office of the Secretary of State
256 State Capitol Building
Little Rock, AR 72201
P: (501) 682-1010
F: (501) 682-3510
E: info@sos.arkansas.gov

Hon. Leslie Rutledge (R)
Attorney General
Office of the Attorney General
323 Center Street, Suite 200
Little Rock, AR 72201
P: (800) 482-8982
F: (501) 682-8084

CALIFORNIA
Ms. Betsy Bogart
Chief
Business Programs Division
1500 11th Street
Sacramento, CA 95814
P: (916) 651-6973
E: bbogart@sos.ca.gov

COLORADO
Mr. Michael Hardin
Director of Business &
Licensing
Department of State, Licensing
Programs
1700 Broadway, Suite 200
Denver, CO 80290
P: (303) 894-2200
F: (303) 869-4864
E: mike.hardin
   @sos.state.co.us

CONNECTICUT
Hon. Denise W. Merrill (D)
Secretary of State
Office of the Secretary of State
State Capitol Building, Room
104
Hartford, CT 06106
P: (860) 509-6200
F: (860) 509-6209
E: denise.merrill@ct.gov

DELAWARE
Mr. Robert Mathers
Administrator
Division of Corporations
401 Federal Street, Suite 4
P.O. Box 898
Dover, DE 19903
P: (302) 739-3073
F: (302) 739-3812

DISTRICT OF COLUMBIA
Mr. Rabbiah Sabbakhan
Director
Department of Consumer &
Regulatory Affairs
1100 4th Street, Southwest
Washington, DC 20024
P: (202) 442-4400
F: (202) 442-9445
E: dcra@dc.gov

FLORIDA
Ms. Brenda Tadlock
Director
Division of Corporations
Clifton Building
2661 Executive Center Circle
Tallahassee, FL 32301
P: (850) 245-6000
E: Brenda.Tadlock
   @DOS.MyFlorida.com

GEORGIA
Mr. Chauncey Newsome
Director
Corporations Division
2 Martin Luther King Jr. Drive
Suite 313, Floyd West Tower
Atlanta, GA 30334
P: (404) 656-2817
F: (404) 657-6380

GUAM
Mr. John Q. Carlos
Administrator
Department of Revenue &
Taxation
Regulatory Division
P.O. Box 23607
GMF, GU 96921
P: (671) 635-1846
F: (671) 633-2643
E: john.carlos
   @revtax.guam.gov

HAWAII
Ms. Catherine P.
   Awakuni Colon
Director
Department of Commerce &
Consumer Affairs
King Kalakaua Building
335 Merchant Street
Honolulu, HI 96813
P: (808) 586-2850
F: (808) 586-2856
E: dcca@dcca.hawaii.gov

IDAHO
Kim Hunter
Supervisor
Business Entity Division
450 North 4th Street
P.O. Box 83720
Boise, ID 83720
P: (208) 334-2301
F: (208) 334-2080
E: khunter@sos.idaho.gov

ILLINOIS
Mr. Ray Cachares
Director
Business Services
Howlett Building, Room 350
501 South 2nd Street
Springfield, IL 62756
P: (217) 782-4909

INDIANA
Hon. Connie Lawson (R)
Secretary of State
Office of the Secretary of State
201 State House
Indianapolis, IN 46204
P: (317) 232-6536
F: (317) 233-3283
E: sos@sos.in.gov

IOWA
Hon. Paul Pate (R)
Secretary of State
Office of the Secretary of State
Lucas Building, 1st Floor
321 East 12th Street
Des Moines, IA 50319
P: (515) 281-8993
F: (515) 242-5952
E: sos@sos.iowa.gov

KENTUCKY
Ms. Dala Cornish
Corporate Filings Manager
Corporations Division
Office of the Secretary of State
P.O. Box 718
Frankfort, KY 40601
P: (502) 564-3490
F: (502) 564-5687

LOUISIANA
Hon. Tom Schedler (R)
Secretary of State
Office of the Secretary of State
P.O. Box 94125
Baton Rouge, LA 70804
P: (225) 922-2880
F: (225) 922-2003
E: admin@sos.la.gov

Corporate Records

MAINE
Ms. Julie L. Flynn
Deputy Secretary of State
Bureau of Corporation,
Elections & Commissions
101 State House Station
Augusta, ME 04333
P: (207) 624-7736
F: (207) 287-5428
E: Julie.Flynn@maine.gov

MARYLAND
Mr. Sean Powell
Director
Department of Assessments &
Taxation
301 West Preston Street, Room
605
Baltimore, MD 21201
P: (410) 767-1191
F: (410) 333-5873
E: spowell@dat.state.md.us

MASSACHUSETTS
Hon. William Francis
   Galvin (D)
Secretary of the Commonwealth
Office of the Secretary of the
Commonwealth
220 Morrissey Blvd.
Boston, MA 02125
P: (617) 727-2816
F: (617) 288-8429
E: cis@sec.state.ma.us

MICHIGAN
Mr. Steve Arwood
CEO
Department of Licensing &
Regulatory Affairs
300 North Washington Square
Lansing, MI 48913
P: (517) 241-1400
F: (517) 241-3683
E: arwoods1@michigan.org

MINNESOTA
Hon. Steve Simon (DFL)
Secretary of State
Office of the Secretary of State
180 State Office Building
100 Martin Luther King Jr.
Boulevard
St. Paul, MN 55155
P: (651) 201-1328
F: (651) 269-9073
E: secretary.state
   @state.mn.us

MISSISSIPPI
Mr. Thomas H. Riley III
Assistant Secretary of State
Business Services Division
125 South Congress Street
P.O. Box 136
Jackson, MS 39205
P: (601) 359-1633
F: (601) 359-1499

MISSOURI
Ms. Carol Fischer
Deputy Secretary of State for
Business Services
Business Services
Kirkpatrick State Information
Center
P.O. Box 778
Jefferson City, MO 65102
P: (573) 751-4153
F: (573) 526-3124
E: corporations@sos.mo.gov

MONTANA
Hon. Linda McCulloch (D)
Secretary of State
Office of the Secretary of State
P.O. Box 202801
Helena, MT 59620
P: (406) 444-2034
F: (406) 444-4249
E: sos@mt.gov

NEBRASKA
Hon. John A. Gale (R)
Secretary of State
Office of the Secretary of State
P.O. Box 94608
Lincoln, NE 68509
P: (402) 471-2554
F: (402) 471-3237
E: Sos.info@nebraska.gov

NEVADA
Hon. Barbara Cegavske (R)
Secretary of State
Office of the Secretary of State
101 North Carson Stree, Suite 3
Carson City, NV 89701
P: (775) 684-5708
F: (775) 684-5724
E: sosexec@sos.nv.gov

NEW HAMPSHIRE
Hon. William M. Gardner (D)
Secretary of State
Office of the Secretary of State
State House, Room 204
Concord, NH 03301
P: (603) 271-3242
F: (603) 271-6316
E: kladd@sos.state.nh.us

NEW JERSEY
Mr. James J. Fruscione
Director
Division of Revenue
P.O. Box 628
Trenton, NJ 08646
P: (609) 984-3997

NEW MEXICO
Hon. Dianna J. Duran (R)
Secretary of State
Office of the Secretary of State
325 Don Gaspar, Suite 300
Capitol Annex
Santa Fe, NM 87501
P: (505) 827-3600
F: (505) 827-8081
E: diannaj.duran
   @state.nm.us

Ms. Stacy Starr-Garcia
Bureau Chief
Corporations Bureau
Office of the Secretary of State
325 Don Gaspar, Suite 300
Santa Fe, NM 87501
P: (505) 827-4508
F: (505) 827-4387
E: stacy.starr-garcia
   @state.nm.us

NEW YORK
Ms. Sandra J. Tallman
Director
Division of Corporations, State
Records & Uniform
Commercial Code
99 Washington Avenue, 6th
Floor
Albany, NY 12231
P: (518) 473-2281
F: (518) 474-1418
E: corporations@dos.ny.gov

NORTH CAROLINA
Ms. Cheri L. Myers
Director
Department of the Secretary of
State
Corporations Division
P.O. Box 29622
Raleigh, NC 27626
P: (919) 807-2225
F: (919) 807-2039
E: cmyers@sosnc.com

NORTH DAKOTA
Ms. Clara Jenkins
Director, Central Indexing
Office of the Secretary of State
600 East Boulevard Avenue
Department 108, 1st Floor
Bismarck, ND 58505
P: (701) 328-3662
F: (701) 328-4214
E: cjenkins@nd.gov

OHIO
Hon. Jon Husted (R)
Secretary of State
Office of the Secretary of State
180 East Broad Street
Columbus, OH 43215
P: (614) 466-2655
F: (614) 644-0649
E: jhusted
   @ohiosecretaryofstate.gov

OKLAHOMA
Hon. Chris Benge (R)
Secretary of State
Office of the Secretary of State
2300 North Lincoln Boulevard,
Suite 101
Oklahoma City, OK 73105
P: (405) 521-3912
F: (405) 521-2031
E: webmaster@sos.ok.gov

OREGON
Mr. Peter Threlkel
Director
Secretary of State, Corporation
Division
Public Service Building, Suite
151
Salem, OR 97310
P: (503) 986-2205
F: (503) 986-1616
E: peter.threlkel
   @state.or.us

PENNSYLVANIA
Mr. Richard K. House
Director
Corporation Bureau
401 North Street, Room 206
Harrisburg, PA 17120
P: (717) 787-1057
F: (717) 783-2244
E: RA-CORPS@pa.gov

Corporate Records

RHODE ISLAND
Hon. Nellie Gorbea (D)
Secretary of State
Office of the Secretary of State
82 Smith Street
217 State House
Providence, RI 02903
P: (401) 222-2357
F: (401) 222-1356
E: nmgorbea@sos.ri.gov

SOUTH CAROLINA
Hon. Mark Hammond (R)
Secretary of State
Office of the Secretary of State
1205 Pendleton Street, Suite 525
Columbia, SC 29201
P: (803) 734-2170
F: (803) 734-1661
E: rdaggerhart@sos.sc.gov

TENNESSEE
Mr. Nathan Burton
Director
Division of Business Services
312 Rosa L. Parks Avenue
Snodgrass Tower, 6th Floor
Nashville, TN 37243
P: (615) 741-2286
F: (615) 741-7310
E: business.services
  @state.tn.us

TEXAS
Ms. Carmen Flores
Division Director
Business & Public Filings
Division
Office of the Secretary of State
P.O.Box 12697
Austin, TX 78711
P: (512) 463-5588
F: (512) 463-5709

UTAH
Ms. Kathy Berg
Director
Division of Corporations &
Commericial Code
Department of Commerce
P.O. Box 146705
Salt Lake City, UT 84114
P: (801) 530-6024
F: (801) 530-6438
E: kberg@utah.gov

VERMONT
Ms. Marlene Betit
Director
Corporations Division
Office of the Secretary of State
128 State Street
Montpelier, VT 05633
P: (802) 828-2371
F: (802) 828-2853
E: marlene.betit
  @sec.state.vt.us

VIRGINIA
Mr. Joel Peck
Clerk
State Corporation Commission
State Corporation Commission
Tyler Building, 1300 East Main
Street
Richmond, VA 23219
P: (804) 371-9733
F: (804) 371-9521
E: joel.peck
  @scc.virginia.gov

WASHINGTON
Hon. Kim Wyman (R)
Secretary of State
Office of the Secretary of State
P.O. Box 40220
Olympia, WA 98504
P: (360) 902-4151
F: (360) 586-5629
E: kim.wyman@sos.wa.gov

WYOMING
Hon. Ed Murray (R)
Secretary of State
Office of the Secretary of State
State Capitol Building, Room
106
200 West 24th Street
Cheyenne, WY 82002
P: (307) 777-7378
F: (307) 777-6217
E: secofstate@wyo.gov

Corrections

Manages the state's corrections systems.

ALABAMA
Mr. Jefferson Dunn
Commissioner
Department of Corrections
P.O. Box 301501
101 South Union Street
Montgomery, AL 36130
P: (334) 353-3883

ALASKA
Mr. Ronald Taylor
Commissioner
Department of Corrections
550 West 7th Avenue, Suite 1800
550 West Seventh Avenue, Suite 601
Anchorage, AK 99501
P: (907) 465-4652
E: ronald.taylor@alaska.gov

AMERICAN SAMOA
Mr. William E. Haleck
Commissioner
Public Safety
American Samoa Government
P.O. Box 1086
Pato Pato, AS 96799
P: (684) 633-1111
F: (684) 633-7296
E: commissioner@dps.as.gov

ARIZONA
Mr. Charles L. Ryan
Director
Department of Corrections
1601 West Jefferson, MC 445
Phoenix, AZ 85007
P: (602) 542-5497
F: (602) 364-0159

ARKANSAS
Ms. Wendy Kelley
Director
Department of Correction
P.O. Box 8707
Pine Bluff, AR 71611
P: (870) 267-6999
F: (870) 267-6244

CALIFORNIA
Mr. Jeffrey Beard
Secretary
Department of Corrections & Rehabilitation
1515 S Street, Suite 502 South
P.O. Box 942883
Sacramento, CA 95811
P: (916) 323-6001

COLORADO
Mr. Rick Raemisch
Executive Director
Department of Corrections
2862 South Circle Drive, Suite 455
Colorado Springs, CO 80906
P: (719) 579-9580

CONNECTICUT
Mr. Scott Semple
Commissioner
Department of Correction
24 Wolcott Hill Road
Wethersfield, CT 06109
P: (860) 692-7480

DELAWARE
Colonel Robert M. Coupe
Commissioner
Department of Correction
245 McKee Road
Dover, DE 19904
P: (302) 739-5601

DISTRICT OF COLUMBIA
Mr. Thomas Faust
Director
Department of Corrections
2000 14th Street, Northwest
Washington, DC 20009
P: (202) 673-7316
F: (202) 332-1470

FLORIDA
Ms. Julie Jones
Secretary
Department of Corrections
501 South Calhoun Street
Tallahassee, FL 32399
P: (850) 488-5021

GEORGIA
Mr. Homer Bryson
Commissioner
Department of Corrections
300 Patrol Road
Forsyth, GA 31029
P: (478) 992-5253
F: (478) 992-5259
E: gdccommish
   @dcor.state.ga.us

GUAM
Mr. Jose San Agustin
Director
Department of Corrections
P.O. Box 3236
Agana, GU 96932
P: (671) 734-3981

HAWAII
Mr. Nolan Espinda
Director
Department of Public Safety
919 Ala Moana Boulevard, Room 400
Honolulu, HI 96814
P: (808) 587-1350
F: (808) 587-1282
E: psd.
   office.of.the.director
   @hawaii.gov

IDAHO
Mr. Kevin Kempf
Director
Department of Correction
1299 North Orchard Street, Suite 110
Boise, ID 83706
P: (208) 658-2000

INDIANA
Mr. Bruce Lemmon
Commissioner
Department of Correction
Government Center South, Room E334
302 West Washington Street
Indianapolis, IN 46204
P: (317) 232-5711
F: (317) 232-6798
E: blemmon@idoc.in.gov

IOWA
Mr. Jerry Bartruff
Director
Department of Corrections
510 East 12th Street
Des Moines, IA 50319
P: (515) 725-5701

KANSAS
Mr. Ray Roberts
Secretary
Department of Corrections
714 Southwest Jackson Street, Suite 300
Topeka, KS 66603
P: (785) 296-3317
F: (785) 296-0014

KENTUCKY
Ms. LaDonna H. Thompson
Commissioner
Department of Corrections
P.O. Box 2400
Frankfort, KY 40602
P: (502) 564-4726
F: (502) 564-5037
E: lthompson@asca.net

LOUISIANA
Mr. James M. LeBlanc
Secretary
Department of Public Safety & Corrections
Capitol Station
P.O. Box 94304
Baton Rouge, LA 70804
P: (225) 342-6740
F: (225) 342-3095
E: jleblanc@asca.net

MAINE
Dr. Joseph Fitzpatrick
Commissioner
Department of Corrections
State House Station 111
Augusta, ME 04333
P: (207) 287-2711
F: (207) 287-4370
E: joseph.fitzpatrick
   @maine.gov

MARYLAND
Mr. Stephen Moyer
Secretary
Department of Public Safety & Correctional Services
300 East Joppa Road, Suite 1000
10th Floor
Towson, MD 21286
P: (410) 339-5000

MASSACHUSETTS
Ms. Carol Higgins O'Brien
Commissioner
Department of Correction
50 Maple Street, Suite 3
Milford, MA 01757
P: (508) 422-3300

MICHIGAN
Mr. Daniel Heyns
Director
Department of Corrections
P.O. Box 30003
Lansing, MI 48909
P: (517) 373-0720
F: (517) 373-6883

MINNESOTA
Mr. Tom Roy
Commissioner
Department of Corrections
1450 Energy Park Drive, Suite 200
St. Paul, MN 55108
P: (651) 361-7200
F: (651) 642-0414
E: tom.roy@state.mn.us

Corrections

MISSISSIPPI
Mr. Marshall Fisher
Commissioner
Department of Corrections
633 North State Street
Jackson, MS 39202
P: (601) 359-5600
F: (601) 359-5680

MISSOURI
Mr. George Lombardi
Director
Department of Corrections
2729 Plaza Drive
P.O. Box 236
Jefferson City, MO 65102
P: (573) 751-2389
F: (573) 751-4099

MONTANA
Mr. Mike Batista
Director
Department of Corrections
5 South Last Chance Gulch
P.O. Box 201301
Helena, MT 59620
P: (406) 444-3930
F: (406) 444-4920

NEBRASKA
Mr. Scott Frakes
Director
Department of Correctional
Services
Folsom & Prospector Place,
Building 1
P.O. Box 94661
Lincoln, NE 68509
P: (402) 471-2654

NEVADA
Mr. Greg Cox
Director
Department of Corrections
3955 West Russell Road
Las Vegas, NV 89118
P: (702) 486-9910
F: (775) 687-6715

NEW HAMPSHIRE
Mr. William Wrenn
Commissioner
Department of Corrections
P.O. Box 1806
Concord, NH 03302
P: (603) 271-5600
F: (603) 271-5643
E: wwrenn@nhdoc.state.nh.us

NEW JERSEY
Mr. Gary M. Lanigan
Commissioner
Department of Corrections
Whittlesey Road
P.O. Box 863
Trenton, NJ 08625
P: (609) 292-4036
F: (609) 777-0445

NEW MEXICO
Mr. Greg Marcantel
Secretary
Corrections Department
P.O. Box 27116
Santa Fe, NM 87502
P: (505) 827-8645
F: (505) 827-8533

NEW YORK
Mr. Anthony Annucci
Commissioner
Department of Corrections &
Community Supervision
1220 Washington Avenue,
Building 2
Albany, NY 12226
P: (518) 457-8126

Mr. Joseph Ponte
Commissioner
New York City Department of
Corrections
7520 Astoria Boulevard
East Elmhurst, NY 11370
P: (718) 546-0896

NORTH CAROLINA
Mr. W. David Guice
Commissioner
Adult Correction
Department of Public Safety
512 North Salisbury Street
Raleigh, NC 27604
P: (919) 716-3700

NORTH DAKOTA
Ms. Leann Bertsch
Director
Department of Corrections &
Rehabilitation
3100 Railroad Avenue
P.O. Box 1898
Bismarck, ND 58502
P: (701) 328-6390
F: (701) 328-6186
E: lbertsch@asca.net

OHIO
Mr. Gary C. Mohr
Director
Department of Rehabilitations
& Correction
70 West Broad Street
Columbus, OH 43222
P: (614) 387-0588
F: (614) 752-1171

OKLAHOMA
Mr. Robert Patton
Director
Department of Corrections
3400 North Martin Luther King
Avenue
P.O. Box 11400
Oklahoma City, OK 73136
P: (405) 425-2500

OREGON
Ms. Colette S. Peters
Director
Department of Corrections
2575 Center Street, Northeast
Salem, OR 97301
P: (503) 945-9090
F: (503) 373-1173
E: colette.peters
   @state.or.us

PENNSYLVANIA
Mr. Louis Giorla
Commissioner
Philadelphia Prison System
7901 State Road
Philadelphia, PA 19136
P: (215) 685-8201
F: (215) 685-8577

Mr. John E. Wetzel
Secretary
Department of Corrections
1920 Technology Parkway
Mechanicsburg, PA 17050
P: (717) 728-4109
F: (717) 731-0486

PUERTO RICO
Mr. Jose Aponte Carro
Secretary
Department of Correction
P.O. Box 71308
San Juan, PR 00936
P: (787) 674-6067

RHODE ISLAND
Mr. Ashbel T. Wall II
Director
Department of Corrections
40 Howard Avenue
Cranston, RI 02920
P: (401) 462-1000
F: (401) 462-2630
E: at.wall@doc.ri.gov

SOUTH CAROLINA
Mr. Bryan Stirling
Director
Department of Corrections
4444 Broad River Road, Room
300
P.O. Box 21787
Columbia, SC 29221
P: (803) 896-8500

SOUTH DAKOTA
Mr. Denny Kaemingk
Secretary
Department of Corrections
3200 East Highway #34
Pierre, SD 57501
P: (605) 773-3478
F: (605) 773-3194

TENNESSEE
Mr. Derrick Schofield
Commissioner
Department of Correction
Rachel Jackson State Office
Building
320 6th Avenue North, 6th Floor
Nashville, TN 37243
P: (615) 741-1000

TEXAS
Mr. Brad Livingston
Executive Director
Department of Criminal Justice
209 West 14th, Suite 500
P.O. Box 13084
Austin, TX 78711
P: (512) 463-9776
F: (512) 936-2169
E: blivingston@asca.net

U.S. VIRGIN ISLANDS
Mr. Julius Wilson
Director
Bureau of Corrections
6040 Castle Coakley
Christiansted, VI 00820
P: (340) 715-7550

UTAH
Mr. Rollin Cook
Executive Director
Department of Corrections
14717 South Minuteman Drive
Draper, UT 84020
P: (801) 545-5500

VERMONT
Mr. Andrew Pallito
Commissioner
Department of Corrections
103 South Main Street
Waterbury, VT 05671
P: (802) 241-2276
F: (802) 241-2565
E: Andrew.Pallito
   @ahs.state.vt.us

VIRGINIA
Mr. Harold Clarke
Director
Department of Corrections
6900 Atmore Drive
Richmond, VA 23225
P: (804) 674-3000
F: (804) 674-3509
E: harold.clarke
   @vadoc.virginia.gov

WASHINGTON
Mr. Bernie Warner
Secretary
Department of Corrections
P.O. Box 41101
Olympia, WA 98504
P: (360) 725-8213
F: (360) 664-4056
E: bewarner@doc1.wa.gov

WEST VIRGINIA
Mr. Jim Rubenstein
Commissioner
Division of Corrections
112 California Avenue, Room 302
Charleston, WV 25305
P: (304) 558-2036
F: (304) 558-5367
E: jrubens1@mail.wvnet.edu

WISCONSIN
Mr. Edward F. Wall
Secretary
Department of Corrections
P. O. Box 7925
3099 East Washington Avenue
Madison, WI 53707
P: (608) 240-5000
E: wallef@doj.state.wi.us

WYOMING
Mr. Bob Lampert
Director
Department of Corrections
1934 Wyott Drive, Suite 100
Cheyenne, WY 82002
P: (307) 777-7208
F: (307) 777-7479
E: rlampert@asca.net

Crime Victims Compensation

Provides compensation to victims of crime.

ALABAMA
Dr. Cassie T. Jones
Executive Director
Crime Victims Compensation
Commission
5845 Carmichael Road
P.O. Box 231267
Montgomery, AL 36123
P: (334) 290-4420
F: (334) 290-4455
E: cassie.jones
   @acvcc.alabama.gov

ALASKA
Ms. Kate Hudson
Administrator
Violent Crimes Compensation
Board
Department of Administration
P.O. Box 110230
Juneau, AK 99811
P: (907) 465-3040
F: (907) 465-2379
E: kate.hudson@alaska.gov

AMERICAN SAMOA
Hon. Talauega Eleasalo V.
   Ale
Attorney General
Office of the Attorney General
American Samoa Government
Exeutive Office Building,
Utulei
Pago Pago, AS 96799
P: (684) 633-4163

ARIZONA
Hon. Mark Brnovich (R)
Attorney General
Office of the Attorney General
1275 West Washington Street
Phoenix, AZ 85007
P: (602) 542-4266
F: (602) 542-4085

ARKANSAS
Ms. Avis Lane
Director
Community Relations Division
Office of the Attorney General
323 Center Street, Suite 200
Little Rock, AR 72201
P: (501) 682-3659
F: (501) 682-5313
E: avis.lane@arkansasag.gov

CALIFORNIA
Ms. Deborah Bain
Deputy Attorney General
Victims' Services Unit
P.O. Box 944255
Sacramento, CA 94244
P: (877) 433-9069

COLORADO
Ms. Nancy Feldman
Programs Manager
Office for Victims Programs
Division of Criminal Justice
700 Kipling Street, Suite 1000
Denver, CO 80215
P: (303) 239-4437
F: (303) 239-5743
E: NancyL.Feldman
   @state.co.us

DELAWARE
Ms. Lisa Borin Ogden
Executive Director
Victims Compensation
Assistance Program
900 North King Street, Suite 4
Wilmington, DE 19801
P: (302) 255-1770
F: (302) 577-1326
E: Lisa.Ogden@state.de.us

DISTRICT OF COLUMBIA
Ms. Laura B. Reed
Program Director
Crime Victims Compensation
Program
Court Building A
515 5th Street, Northwest, Room
109
Washington, DC 20001
P: (202) 879-4216
F: (202) 879-4230

FLORIDA
Hon. Pam Bondi (R)
Attorney General
Office of the Attorney General
The Capitol, PL 01
Tallahassee, FL 32399
P: (850) 414-3300
F: (954) 712-4826

Ms. Gwen Roache
Bureau Chief, Victim
Compensation
Bureau of Victim Compensation
Office of the Attorney General
The Capitol PL-01
Tallahassee, FL 32399
P: (850) 414-3300
F: (850) 487-1595

GUAM
Hon. Elizabeth
   Barrett-Anderson
Attorney General
Office of the Attorney General
590 South Marine Corps Drive
ITC Building, Suite 706
Tamuning, GU 96913
P: (671) 475-3324
F: (671) 472-2493
E: law@guamag.org

HAWAII
Ms. Pamela Ferguson-Brey
Executive Director
Crime Victims Compensation
Commission
Department of Public Safety
1136 Union Mall, Room 600
Honolulu, HI 96813
P: (808) 587-1143
F: (808) 587-1146
E: cvcc@hawaii.rr.com

IDAHO
Mr. George Gutierrez
Crime Victims Bureau Chief
Crime Victims Compensation
Bureau
Industrial Commission, P.O.
Box 83720
700 South Clearwater Lane
Boise, ID 83720
P: (208) 334-6070
F: (208) 332-7559
E: george.gutierrez
   @iic.idaho.gov

ILLINOIS
Ms. Delores J. Martin
Director & Deputy Clerk
Court of Claims
630 South College Street
Springfield, IL 62756
P: (217) 782-7101

INDIANA
Ms. Sarah Davis
Senior Grant Manager
Victim Services Division
101 West Washington Street
Room 1170, East Tower
Indianapolis, IN 46204
P: (317) 232-3482
F: (317) 232-4979
E: sdavis@cji.in.gov

IOWA
Ms. Janelle Melohn
Director, Crime Victim
Assistance
Crime Victim Assistance
Division
Lucas State Office Building
321 East 12th Street
Des Moines, IA 50319
P: (515) 281-5044
F: (515) 281-8199
E: Janelle.Melohn@iowa.gov

KANSAS
Mr. Jeff Wagaman
Executive Director
Crime Victims Compensation
Board
120 Southwest 10th Avenue, 2nd
Floor
Topeka, KS
P: (785) 296-2539
F: (785) 296-0652

KENTUCKY
Ms. Virginia L. Woodward
Executive Director
Crime Victims Compensation
Board
130 Brighton Park Boulevard
Frankfort, KY 40601
P: (502) 573-2290
F: (502) 573-4817
E: virginia.woodward@ky.gov

LOUISIANA
Mr. Joey Watson
Executive Director
Commission on Law
Enforcement & Administration
of Criminal Justice
602 North Fifth Street
P.O. Box 3133
Baton Rouge, LA 70821
P: (225) 342-1500
F: (225) 342-1847
E: Joey.Watson@lcle.la.gov

MAINE
Ms. Tessa Mosher
Director of Victims Services
Department of Corrections
25 Tyson Drive, 3rd Floor
State House Station 111
Augusta, ME 04333
P: (207) 287-2711
F: (207) 287-4370
E: Tessa.Mosher@maine.gov

MARYLAND
Mr. Robin Woolford
Executive Director
Criminal Injuries Compensation
Board
Public Safety & Correctional
Services
6776 Reisterstown Road, Suite
200
Baltimore, MD 21215
P: (410) 585-3010
F: (410) 764-3815
E: rwoolford
@dpscs.state.md.us

MASSACHUSETTS
Ms. Deborah Fogarty
Director
Office of the Attorney General
One Ashburton Place, 19th Floor
Boston, MA 02108
P: (617) 727-2200 Ext. 2160
F: (617) 742-6262

Mr. Liam Lowney
Executive Director
Office for Victim Assistance
One Ashburton Place, Suite
1101
Boston, MA 02108
P: (617) 586-1340
F: (617) 727-6552
E: mova@state.ma.us

MINNESOTA
Raeone Loscalzo
Executive Director
Crime Victims Services
Bremer Tower, Suite 2300
445 Minnesota Street
St. Paul, MN 55101
P: (651) 201-7305
F: (651) 296-5787
E: raeone.loscalzo
@state.mn.us

MISSISSIPPI
Ms. Janet Kennedy
Director
Crime Victims Compensation
Program
P.O. Box 220
Jackson, MS 39205
P: (601) 359-3680
F: (601) 359-3262

MISSOURI
Mr. Tyler Rieke
Program Manager
Crime Victims Services Unit
Department of Public Safety
P.O. Box 749
Jefferson City, MO 65102
P: (573) 526-1464
E: Tyler.Rieke@dps.mo.gov

MONTANA
Mr. Mike Batista
Director
Department of Corrections
5 South Last Chance Gulch
P.O. Box 201301
Helena, MT 59620
P: (406) 444-3930
F: (406) 444-4920

NEBRASKA
Ms. Lisa Stamm
Chief, Grants Division
Commission on Law
Enforcement & Criminal Justice
301 Centennial Mall South
P.O. Box 94946
Lincoln, NE 68509
P: (402) 471-3687
F: (402) 471-2837
E: lisa.stamm@nebraska.gov

NEVADA
Ms. Rebecca Salazar
Program Manager
Victims of Crime Program
Department of Administration
2200 South Rancho Drive, Suite
210-A
Las Vegas, NV 89102
P: (702) 486-2740
F: (702) 486-2879
E: salazar@admin.nv.gov

NEW HAMPSHIRE
Ms. Sandra Matheson Cochran
Director
Office of Victim/Witness
Assistance
Office of the Attorney General
33 Capitol Street
Concord, NH 03301
P: (603) 271-3671
F: (603) 271-2110
E: sandi.matheson
@doj.nh.gov

NEW JERSEY
Ms. Marsetta Lee
Director
Victims of Crime Compensation
Office
50 Park Place
Newark, NJ 07102
P: (976) 648-2107
F: (976) 648-3937

NEW MEXICO
Mr. Frank Zubia
Director
Crime Victims Reparation
Commission
8100 Mountain Road Northeast,
Suite 106
Albuquerque, NM 87110
P: (505) 841-9432
F: (505) 841-9437
E: Frank.Zubia@state.nm.us

NEW YORK
Ms. Elizabeth Cronin
Director
Office of Victim Services
1 Columbia Circle, Suite 200
Albany, NY 12203
P: (518) 485-5719
F: (518) 457-8658

NORTH CAROLINA
Ms. Debbie Allen
Administrator
Department of Public Safety
Victims Compensation Services
4232 Mail Service Center
Raleigh, NC 27699
P: (919) 733-7974
F: (919) 715-4209

NORTH DAKOTA
Ms. Lori Steele
Administrator, Crime Victims
Compensation
Department of Corrections &
Rehabilitation, Division of
Adult Services
Crime Victims Compensation
P.O. Box 5521
Bismarck, ND 58506
P: (701) 328-6195
F: (701) 328-6186
E: loristeele@nd.gov

**NORTHERN MARIANA
ISLANDS**
Mr. James C.
Deleon Guerrero
Commissioner
Department of Public Safety
Jose M. Sablan Building
Caller Box 10007
Saipan, MP 96950
P: (670) 664-9022
F: (670) 664-9070

OHIO
Hon. Mike DeWine (R)
Attorney General
Office of the Attorney General
State Office Tower
30 East Broad Street
Columbus, OH 43266
P: (614) 466-4320

OKLAHOMA
Ms. Suzanne Breedlove
Director of Victims Services
Crime Victims' Compensation
Board
District Attorneys Council
421 Northwest 13th, Suite 290
Oklahoma City, OK 73103
P: (405) 264-5006
E: victimsservices
@dac.state.ok.us

OREGON
Ms. Shannon Sivell
Director
Crime Victims Services
Division
Promotory Plaza
4035 12th Street, Southeast
Salem, OR 97302
P: (503) 378-5348
F: (503) 378-5738
E: shannon.l.sivell
@state.or.us

PENNSYLVANIA
Ms. Linda Rosenberg
Executive Director
Commission on Crime &
Delinquency
3101 North Front Street
P.O. Box 1167
Harrisburg, PA 17108
P: (717) 705-0888
F: (717) 705-0891

PUERTO RICO
Ms. Mariana S.
Perez Cordero
Director
Office of Crime Victims
Compensation
Department of Justice
P.O. Box 9020192
San Juan, PR 00902
P: (787) 721-2900
F: (787) 723-8675
E: msperez@justicia.pr.gov

RHODE ISLAND
Ms. Melba Depena
Program Administrator
Crime Victims Compensation
Program
50 Service Avenue, 2nd Floor
Warwick, RI 02886
P: (401) 462-7655
F: (401) 462-7694

Crime Victims Compensation

SOUTH CAROLINA
Dr. Larry Barker
Director
State Office of Victim
Assistance
1205 Pendleton Street, Room
401
Columbia, SC 29201
P: (803) 734-1900
F: (803) 734-1708
E: sova@oepp.sc.gov

SOUTH DAKOTA
Ms. Emily Paulsen
Administrator
Department of Social Services
Crime Victims' Compensation
Program
700 Governors Drive
Pierre, SD 57501
P: (605) 773-6317
F: (605) 773-4085
E: VictimsServices
    @state.sd.us

TENNESSEE
Hon. David H. Lillard Jr.
State Treasurer
Department of Treasury
State Capitol, First Floor
600 Charlotte Avenue
Nashville, TN 37243
P: (615) 741-2956
F: (615) 253-1591
E: david.lillard@tn.gov

TEXAS
Ms. Angie McCown
Director
Victim Services Division
Department of Criminal Justice
P.O. Box 13401, Capital Station
Austin, TX 78711
P: (512) 406-5900
F: (512) 452-0825
E: victim.svc
    @tdcj.state.tx.us

U.S. VIRGIN ISLANDS
Mr. Christopher E. Finch
Commissioner
Department of Human Services
Knud Hansen Complex,
Building A
1303 Hospital Ground
St. Thomas, VI 00802
P: (340) 774-0930
F: (340) 773-2980

UTAH
Mr. Gary Scheller
Director
Office for Victims of Crime
350 East 500 South, Suite 200
Salt Lake City, UT 84111
P: (801) 238-2360
F: (801) 533-4127
E: garys@utah.gov

VERMONT
Ms. Judy Rex
Executive Director
Center for Crime Victim
Services
58 South Main Street, Suite 1
Waterbury, VT 05676
P: (802) 241-1250 Ext. 106
F: (802) 241-4337

VIRGINIA
Ms. Francine Ecker
Director
Department of Criminal Justice
Services
1100 Bank Street
Richmond, VA 23219
P: (804) 786-8718
F: (804) 371-8981
E: francine.ecker
    @dcjs.virginia.gov

WASHINGTON
Ms. Rena Shawver
Crime Victims Compensation
Program
Department of Labor &
Industries
P.O. Box 44520
Olympia, WA 98504
P: (360) 902-5189
F: (360) 902-5333
E: rena.shawver@lni.wa.gov

WEST VIRGINIA
Hon. Patrick Morrisey (R)
Attorney General
Office of the Attorney General
State Capitol
1900 Kanawha Boulevard, East
Charleston, WV 25305
P: (304) 558-2021
F: (304) 558-0140

WISCONSIN
Ms. Jill Karofsky
Director
Office of Crime Victims
Services
P.O. Box 7951
Madison, WI 53707
P: (608) 264-9497
F: (608) 264-6368
E: karofskyjj
    @doj.state.wi.us

Criminal Justice

Oversees the administration of justice by providing public safety, assisting victims of crime, analyzing criminal data, administering funds, and providing training and guidance to law enforcement officials.

ALABAMA
Mr. William Babington
Division Chief
Law Enforcement & Traffic
Safety Division
Dept. of Economic &
Community Affairs
P.O. Box 5690
Montgomery, AL 36101
P: (334) 242-5897
F: (334) 242-5099
E: bill.babington
    @adeca.alabama.gov

ALASKA
Mr. Gary Folger
Commissioner
Department of Public Safety
5700 East Tudor Road
Anchorage, AK 99507
P: (907) 269-5086
F: (907) 269-4543
E: gary.folger@alaska.gov

AMERICAN SAMOA
Mr. Keith Gebauer
Acting Director
Criminal Justice Planning
Agency
Executive Office Building,
Utulei
Territory of American Samoa
Pago Pago, AS 96799
P: (684) 633-5221
F: (684) 633-7552

ARIZONA
Mr. John A. Blackburn Jr.
Executive Director
Criminal Justice Commission
1110 West Washington, Suite 230
Phoenix, AZ 85007
P: (602) 364-1146
F: (602) 364-1175
E: JRBlackburn@azcjc.gov

ARKANSAS
Colonel Bill Bryant
Director
State Police
1 State Police Plaza Drive
Little Rock, AR 72209
P: (501) 618-8299
F: (501) 618-8710
E: info@asp.arkansas.gov

COLORADO
Ms. Jeanne Smith
Director
Division of Criminal Justice
Department of Public Safety
700 Kipling Street, Suite 1000
Denver, CO 80215
P: (303) 239-4451
F: (303) 239-4491
E: jeanne.smith@state.co.us

CONNECTICUT
Mr. Kevin T. Kane
Chief State's Attorney
Division of Criminal Justice
300 Corporate Place
Rocky Hill, CT 06067
P: (860) 258-5800
F: (860) 258-5858
E: conndcj@ct.gov

DELAWARE
Mr. Christian Kervick
Acting Executive Director
Criminal Justice Council
Carvel State Office Building
820 North French Street, 10th Floor
Wilmington, DE 19801
P: (302) 577-8699
F: (302) 577-7056
E: Christian.Kervick
    @state.de.us

DISTRICT OF COLUMBIA
Ms. Cathy L. Lanier
Chief of Police
Metropolitan Police Department
300 Indiana Avenue, Northwest
Room 5059
Washington, DC 20001
P: (202) 727-9099
F: (202) 727-4106
E: mpd@dc.gov

FLORIDA
Mr. Rick Swearingen
Commissioner
Department of Law
Enforcement
2331 Phillips Road
P.O. Box 1489
Tallahassee, FL 32302
P: (850) 410-7001
E: RickSwearingen
    @fdle.state.fl.us

GEORGIA
Ms. Jacqueline Bunn
Executive Director
Criminal Justice Coordinating
Council
104 Marietta Street, Suite 440
Atlanta, GA 30303
P: (404) 657-1956
F: (404) 657-1957
E: jbunn@cjcc.ga.gov

GUAM
Mr. Fred E. Bordallo Jr.
Chief of Police
Police Department
#13-16A Mariner Avenue
P.O. Box 23909
Tiyan, GU 96913
P: (671) 475-8508
F: (671) 472-4036
E: chief@gpd.guam.gov

HAWAII
Hon. Doug Chin (D)
Attorney General
Office of the Attorney General
425 Queen Street
Honolulu, HI 96813
P: (808) 586-1500

ILLINOIS
Mr. Jack Maki
Exeuctive Director
Criminal Justice Information
Authority
300 West Adams Street, Suite 200
Chicago, IL 60606
P: (312) 793-8550
F: (312) 793-8422

INDIANA
Ms. Devon McDonald
Acting Director/Chief Counsel
Criminal Justice Institute
101 West Washington Street
Suite 1170, East Tower
Indianapolis, IN 46204
P: (317) 232-7611
F: (317) 232-4979
E: DeMcdonald@cji.IN.gov

IOWA
Mr. Steve Lukan
Director
Governor's Office of Drug
Control Policy
502 East 9th Street
Des Moines, IA 50319
P: (515) 725-0305
F: (515) 242-6390
E: steven.lukan@iowa.gov

KANSAS
Hon. Derek Schmidt (R)
Attorney General
Office of the Attorney General
120 Southwest 10th Avenue, 2nd Floor
Topeka, KS 66612
P: (785) 296-2215
F: (785) 296-6296

KENTUCKY
Mr. J. Michael Brown
Secretary
Justice & Public Safety Cabinet
125 Holmes Street
Frankfort, KY 40601
P: (502) 564-7554
F: (502) 564-4840

LOUISIANA
Mr. Joey Watson
Executive Director
Commission on Law
Enforcement & Administration
of Criminal Justice
602 North Fifth Street
P.O. Box 3133
Baton Rouge, LA 70821
P: (225) 342-1500
F: (225) 342-1847
E: Joey.Watson@lcle.la.gov

MAINE
Mr. John E. Morris
Commissioner
Department of Public Safety
45 Commerce Drive, Suite 1
104 State House Station
Augusta, ME 04333
P: (207) 626-3800
F: (207) 287-3042
E: john.e.morris@maine.gov

MARYLAND
Sen. Christopher B.
    Shank (R)
Governor's Office of Crime
Control & Prevention Office
300 East Joppa Road
Baltimore, MD 21286
P: (410) 281-2828
E: christopher.shank
    @senate.state.md.us

MASSACHUSETTS
Mr. Daniel Bennett
Secretary
Executive Office of Public
Safety & Security
One Ashburton Place, Suite 2133
Boston, MA 02108
P: (617) 727-7775
F: (617) 727-4764

Criminal Justice

MICHIGAN
Colonel Kriste Kibbey Etue
Director
State Police
333 South Grand Avenue
P.O. Box 30634
Lansing, MI 48909
P: (517) 332-2521
F: (517) 241-0409
E: EtueK@michigan.gov

MINNESOTA
Ms. Ramona Dohman
Commissioner
Department of Public Safety
445 Minnesota Street, Suite 1000
St. Paul, MN 55101
P: (651) 201-7160
F: (651) 297-5728
E: Mona.Dohman@state.mn.us

MISSISSIPPI
Ms. Joyce Word
Director
Office of Justice Programs
Department of Public Safety
1025 Northpark Drive
Ridgeland, MS 39157
P: (601) 987-3700
F: (601) 987-3764
E: jword@dps.ms.gov

MISSOURI
Mr. Lane Roberts
Director
Department of Public Safety
Office of the Director
P.O. Box 749
Jefferson City, MO 65102
P: (573) 751-4905
F: (573) 751-5399

MONTANA
Ms. Brooke Marshall
Executive Director
Board of Crime Control
5 South Last Chance Gulch
P.O. Box 201408
Helena, MT 59620
P: (406) 444-3615
F: (406) 444-4722
E: brookemarshall@mt.gov

NEBRASKA
Mr. Darrell Fischer
Executive Director
Commission on Law
Enforcement & Criminal Justice
301 Centennial Mall South
P.O. Box 94946
Lincoln, NE 68509
P: (402) 471-2194
F: (402) 471-2837
E: darrell.fisher
  @nebraska.gov

NEVADA
Mr. James Wright
Director
Department of Public Safety
555 Wright Way
Carson City, NV 89711
P: (775) 684-4808
F: (775) 684-4809

NEW HAMPSHIRE
Ms. Rosemary Faretra
Director of Administration
Office of the Attorney General
Department of Justice
33 Capitol Street
Concord, NH 03301
P: (603) 271-1234
F: (603) 271-2110
E: rosemary.faretra
  @doj.nh.gov

NEW JERSEY
Mr. Elie Honig
Director
Division of Criminal Justice
Richard J. Hughes Justice
Complex
25 Market Street, P.O. Box 80
Trenton, NJ 08625
P: (609) 984-6500
F: (609) 292-3508

NEW MEXICO
Mr. Gregory J. Fouratt Jr.
Cabinet Secretary
Department of Public Safety
4491 Cerrillos Road
P.O. Box 1628
Santa Fe, NM 87504
P: (505) 827-3370
F: (505) 827-3434

NEW YORK
Mr. Michael C. Green
Executive Deputy Commissioner
Division of Criminal Justice
Services
4 Tower Place, 10th Floor
Albany, NY 12203
P: (518) 457-5837
F: (518) 473-1271

NORTH CAROLINA
Mr. David Huffman
Executive Director
Governor's Crime Commission
1201 Front Street
Suite 200
Raleigh, NC 27609
P: (919) 733-4564
F: (919) 733-4625

NORTH DAKOTA
Hon. Wayne Stenehjem (R)
Attorney General
Office of the Attorney General
State Capitol
600 East Boulevard Avenue
Bismarck, ND 58505
P: (701) 328-2210
F: (701) 328-2226
E: wstenehjem@nd.gov

NORTHERN MARIANA ISLANDS
Mr. John Cruz
Executive Director
Criminal Justice Planning
Agency
P.O. Box 501133
Saipan, MP 96950
P: (670) 664-4557
F: (670) 664-4560
E: john.cruz@cjpa.gov.mp

OHIO
Mr. Karhlton F. Moore
Executive Director
Office of Criminal Justice
Services
1970 West Broad Street
P.O. Box 182081
Columbus, OH 43218
P: (614) 466-8360
F: (614) 644-7731

OKLAHOMA
Ms. Suzanne McClain Atwood
Executive Administrator
District Attorneys Council
421 Northwest 13th, Suite 290
Oklahoma City, OK 73103
P: (405) 264-5000
F: (405) 264-5099

OREGON
Mr. Michael Schmidt
Executive Director
Criminal Justice Commission
885 Summer Street, Northeast
Salem, OR 97301
P: (503) 378-4858
F: (503) 378-4830

PENNSYLVANIA
Ms. Linda Rosenberg
Executive Director
Commission on Crime &
Delinquency
3101 North Front Street
P.O. Box 1167
Harrisburg, PA 17108
P: (717) 705-0888
F: (717) 705-0891

RHODE ISLAND
Mr. Thomas H. Mongeau
Administrative Manager
Public Safety Grant
Administration Office
1 Capitol Hill
Providence, RI 02908
P: (401) 222-4493
F: (401) 222-1294
E: Thomas.Mongeau
  @psga.dps.ri.gov

SOUTH CAROLINA
Mr. Hubert F. Harrell
Director
Criminal Justice Academy
5400 Broad River Road
Columbia, SC 29212
P: (803) 896-7779
F: (803) 896-7776
E: HFHarrell@sccja.sc.gov

SOUTH DAKOTA
Mr. Trevor Jones
Secretary
Department of Public Safety
118 West Capitol Avenue
Pierre, SD 57501
P: (605) 773-3178
F: (605) 773-3018
E: DPSInfo@state.sd.us

TENNESSEE
Mr. Bill Scollon
Director
Office of Criminal Justice
Programs
William R. Snodgrass Tennessee
Tower
312 Rosa L. Parks Avenue, 12th
Floor
Nashville, TN 37243
P: (615) 532-2983
E: bill.scollon@tn.gov

TEXAS
Mr. Brad Livingston
Executive Director
Department of Criminal Justice
209 West 14th, Suite 500
P.O. Box 13084
Austin, TX 78711
P: (512) 463-9776
F: (512) 936-2169
E: blivingston@asca.net

U.S. VIRGIN ISLANDS
Mr. Renaldo Rivera
Adjutant General
National Guard
4031 La Grande Princess, Lot
1B
Christiansted, VI 00820
P: (340) 712-7710
F: (340) 712-7709
E: renaldo.rivera
    @us.army.mil

UTAH
Mr. Ronald Gordon
Executive Director
Commission on Criminal &
Juvenile Justice
Senate Building, Suite 330
P.O. Box 142330
Salt Lake City, UT 84114
P: (801) 538-1432
F: (801) 538-1024
E: rbgordon@utah.gov

VIRGINIA
Ms. Francine Ecker
Director
Department of Criminal Justice
Services
1100 Bank Street
Richmond, VA 23219
P: (804) 786-8718
F: (804) 371-8981
E: francine.ecker
    @dcjs.virginia.gov

WEST VIRGINIA
Mr. W. Richard Staton
Director
Division of Justice &
Community Services
1204 Kanawha Boulevard, East
Charleston, WV 25301
P: (304) 558-8814 Ext. 53335
F: (304) 558-0391
E: Rick.W.Staton@wv.gov

Debt Management

Responsible for structuring debt issues.

ALABAMA
Ms. Patricia Haigler
State Debt Manager
Division of Debt Management
Department of Finance
100 N. Union Street, Room 224
Montgomery, AL 36130
P: (334) 353-3328
F: (334) 353-3466
E: patricia.haigler
@finance.alabama.gov

ALASKA
Mr. Deven Mitchell
Debt Manager
Treasury Division
Department of Revenue
P.O. Box 110405
Juneau, AK 99811
P: (907) 465-3409
F: (907) 465-2902
E: deven.mitchell
@alaska.gov

AMERICAN SAMOA
Hon. Falema'o M. Pili
Treasurer
Office of the Treasurer
American Samoa Government
Pago Pago, AS 96799
P: (684) 633-4155
F: (684) 633-4100

ARKANSAS
Mr. Aaron Burkes
President
Development Finance Authority
900 West Capitol, Suite 310
P.O. Box 8023
Little Rock, AR 72203
P: (501) 682-3339
F: (501) 682-5939
E: aaron.burkes
@adfa.arkansas.gov

CALIFORNIA
Mr. Michael Cohen
Director
Department of Finance
915 L Street
Sacramento, CA 95814
P: (916) 445-4141
E: michael.cohen@dof.ca.gov

CONNECTICUT
Hon. Denise L. Nappier (D)
State Treasurer
Office of State Treasurer
55 Elm Street, 7th Floor
Hartford, CT 06106
P: (860) 702-3010
F: (860) 702-3043
E: denise.nappier@ct.gov

FLORIDA
Mr. J. Ben Watkins III
Director
Division of Bond Finance
State Board of Administration
1801 Hermitage Centre, Suite
200
Tallahassee, FL 32308
P: (850) 488-4782
F: (850) 413-1315
E: watkins_ben
@fsba.state.fl.us

IDAHO
Hon. Ron G. Crane (R)
State Treasurer
State Treasurer's Office
304 North 8th Street
Boise, ID 83720
P: (208) 334-3200
F: (208) 332-2959
E: ron.crane@sto.idaho.gov

ILLINOIS
Mr. Tim Nuding
Director
Governor's Office of
Management & Budget
401 South Spring
603 Stratton Building
Springfield, IL 62706
P: (217) 782-4520
F: (217) 524-4876

INDIANA
Mr. Dennis L. Bassett
Public Finance Director
Finance Authority
One North Capitol, Suite 900
Indianapolis, IN 46204
P: (317) 233-4332
F: (317) 232-6786
E: DeBassett@ifa.IN.gov

IOWA
Hon. Michael L.
Fitzgerald (D)
State Treasurer
State Treasurer's Office
State Capitol Building
Des Moines, IA 50319
P: (515) 281-5368
F: (515) 281-7562
E: mike.fitzgerald@iowa.gov

KENTUCKY
Mr. Ryan Barrow
Executive Director
Office of Financial Management
702 Capitol Avenue
Capitol Annex, Room 076
Frankfort, KY 40601
P: (502) 564-2924
F: (502) 564-7416

LOUISIANA
Ms. Lela M. Folse
Director
State Bond Commission
P.O. Box 44154
Baton Rouge, LA 70804
P: (225) 342-0040
F: (225) 342-0064
E: lfolse
@treasury.state.la.us

MARYLAND
Hon. Nancy K. Kopp (D)
State Treasurer
State Treasurer's Office
80 Calvert Street
Annapolis, MD 21401
P: (410) 260-7160
F: (410) 260-6056
E: nkopp
@treasurer.state.md.us

MASSACHUSETTS
Mr. Colin McNaught
Deputy Treasurer for Debt
Management
Department of State Treasury
C/o Debt Management
Department
One Ashburton Place, 12th Floor
Boston, MA 02108
P: (617) 367-9333 Ext. 226
E: massbondholder
@tre.state.ma.us

MINNESOTA
Mr. Myron Frans
Commissioner
Management & Budget
658 Cedar Street, Suite 400
St. Paul, MN 55155
P: (651) 201-8011
F: (651) 797-1300
E: myron.frans@state.mn.us

MISSISSIPPI
Ms. Mitzi Munroe Preziosi
Director
Investment & Cash
Management Division
P.O. Box 138
Jackson, MS 39205
P: (601) 359-3536
F: (601) 359-2001

MONTANA
Ms. Cheryl Grey
Administrator
State Accounting Division
125 North Roberts Street, Room
270
P.O. Box 200102
Helena, MT 59620
P: (406) 444-7334
F: (406) 444-2812
E: chgrey@mt.gov

NEBRASKA
Mr. Byron L. Diamond
Director
Department of Administrative
Services
State Capitol, Room 1315
Lincoln, NE 68509
P: (402) 471-2331
E: byron.diamond
@nebraska.gov

NEW HAMPSHIRE
Hon. Catherine Provencher
State Treasurer
State Treasury
25 Capitol Street, Room 121
Concord, NH 03301
P: (603) 271-2621
F: (603) 271-3922
E: cprovencher
@treasury.state.nh.us

NEW JERSEY
Mr. James M. Petrino
Director
Office of Public Finance
P.O. Box 002
Trenton, NJ 08625
P: (609) 633-6447
E: james.petrino
@treas.state.nj.us

NEW MEXICO
Mr. Jeff Primm
Acting Director
Board of Finance Division
181 Bataan Memorial Building
407 Galisteo Street
Santa Fe, NM 87501
P: (505) 827-3936
F: (505) 827-3985
E: Jeff.Primm@state.nm.us

NORTH DAKOTA
Ms. Pam Sharp
Director
Office of Management &
Budget
600 East Boulevard Avenue
Department 110
Bismarck, ND 58505
P: (701) 328-4606
F: (701) 328-3230
E: psharp@nd.gov

Debt Management

OHIO
Mr. Kurt J. Kauffman
Debt Manager
Office of Budget &
Management
30 East Broad Street, 34th Floor
Columbus, OH 43215
P: (614) 466-0691
F: (614) 728-9295

OKLAHOMA
Mr. James C. Joseph
State Bond Advisor
State Bond Advisor's Office
5900 North Classen Court
Oklahoma City, OK 73118
P: (405) 602-3100
F: (405) 848-3314
E: jjoseph@oksba.org

OREGON
Ms. Laura Lockwood-McCall
Director
Debt Management Division
Office of the State Treasurer
350 Winter Street, Northeast,
Suite 100
Salem, OR 97301
P: (503) 378-4930
F: (503) 378-2237
E: laura.lockwood-mccall
    @state.or.us

PENNSYLVANIA
Ms. Eileen McNulty
Secretary
Department of Revenue
Strawberry Square
Harrisburg, PA 17128
P: (717) 783-3683
F: (717) 787-3990

PUERTO RICO
Mr. Jose V. Pagan-Beauchamp
Interim President
Government Development Bank
for Puerto Rico
P.O. Box 42001
San Juan, PR 00940
P: (787) 722-2525
F: (787) 721-1443

SOUTH CAROLINA
Mr. Rick Harmon
Senior Assistant State Treasurer,
Debt Management
Office of the State Treasurer
1200 Senate St., Wade Hampton
Bldg.
P.O. Box 11778
Columbia, SC 29211
P: (803) 734-2114
F: (803) 734-2690
E: rick.harmon@sto.sc.gov

TENNESSEE
Mr. Larry Martin
Commissioner
Department of Finance &
Administration
312 Rosa Parks Avenue, 21st
Floor
Nashville, TN 37243
P: (615) 741-2401
E: Larry.Martin@tn.gov

U.S. VIRGIN ISLANDS
Ms. Debra Gottlieb
Director
Office of Management &
Budget
#41 Norre Gade
Emancipation Garden Station,
2nd Floor
St. Thomas, VI 00802
P: (340) 776-0750
F: (340) 776-0069
E: debra.gottlieb
    @omb.vi.gov

VERMONT
Hon. Elizabeth Pearce
State Treasurer
Office of the State Treasurer
109 State Street
Montpelier, VT 05609
P: (802) 828-3322
F: (802) 828-2772
E: Beth.Pearce@state.vt.us

VIRGINIA
Ms. Evelyn R. Whitley
Director of Debt Management
Debt Management Division
Department of Treasury
101 North 14th Street
Richmond, VA 23219
P: (804) 371-6006
F: (804) 225-3187
E: evie.whitley
    @trs.virginia.gov

WASHINGTON
Hon. James L. McIntire (D)
State Treasurer
Office of the State Treasurer
Legislative Building
P.O. Box 40200
Olympia, WA 98504
P: (360) 902-9001
F: (360) 902-9044
E: watreas@tre.wa.gov

WEST VIRGINIA
Mr. H. Craig Slaughter
Executive Director
Investment Management Board
500 Virginia Street, East, Suite
200
Charleston, WV 25301
P: (304) 345-2672
F: (304) 345-5939
E: info@wvimb.org

WYOMING
Hon. Mark Gordon
State Treasurer
Office of the State Treasurer
200 West 24th Street
Cheyenne, WY 82002
P: (307) 777-7408
F: (307) 777-5411
E: treasurer@wyo.gov

Develop-mentally Disabled

Oversees the care, treatment and future service needs of the developmentally disabled.

ALABAMA
Ms. Courtney Tarver
Associate Commissioner
Division of Developmental
Disabilities
Department of Mental Health
100 North Union Street, P.O.
Box 301410
Montgomery, AL 36130
P: (334) 242-3701
E: courtney.tarver
@mh.alabama.gov

ALASKA
Mr. Duane Mayes
Director
Senior & Disabilities Services
Department of Health & Social
Services
550 West 8th Street
Anchorage, AK 99501
P: (907) 269-2083
F: (907) 269-3688
E: duane.mayes@alaska.gov

ARIZONA
Dr. Larry L. Latham
Assistant Director
Division of Developmental
Disabilities
Department of Economic
Security
P.O. Box 6123, Site Code 791A
Phoenix, AZ 85005
P: (602) 542-6857
E: llatham@azdes.gov

ARKANSAS
Mr. Jim Brader
Interim Director
Division of Developmental
Disabilities Services
Donaghey Plaza North
P.O. Box 1437, N505
Little Rock, AR 72203
P: (501) 682-4747
E: james.brader
@dhs.arkansas.gov

CALIFORNIA
Mr. Santi Rogers
Director
Department of Developmental
Services
P.O. Box 944202
Sacramento, CA 94244
P: (916) 654-1897
F: (916) 654-2167
E: santi.rogers@dds.ca.gov

COLORADO
Ms. Barbara Ramsey
Director
Division for Intellectual &
Developmental Disabilities
Health Care Policy and
Financing
1570 Grant Street
Denver, CO 80203
P: (303) 866-2773
E: barbara.ramsey
@state.co.us

CONNECTICUT
Ms. Morna A. Murray
Commissioner
Department of Developmental
Services
460 Capitol Avenue
Hartford, CT 06106
P: (860) 418-6011
E: morna.murray@ct.gov

DELAWARE
Ms. Jane J. Gallivan
Director
Division of Developmental
Disabilities Services, Health &
Social Services
Woodbrook Professional Center
1056 South Governor's Avenue,
Suite 101
Dover, DE 19904
P: (302) 744-9600
E: jane.gallivan
@state.de.us

DISTRICT OF COLUMBIA
Ms. Laura Nuss
Director
Department on Disability
Services
1125 15th Street, Northwest, 8th
Floor
Washington, DC 20005
P: (202) 730-1607
F: (202) 730-1843
E: laura.nuss@dc.gov

FLORIDA
Ms. Barbara Palmer
Director
Agency for Persons with
Disabilities
4030 Esplanade Way, Suite 380
Tallahassee, FL 32399
P: (850) 488-4257
E: barbara.palmer
@apdcares.org

GEORGIA
Mr. Dan Howell
Director
Department of Behavioral
Health & Developmental
Disabilities
Department of Developmental
Disabilities
Two Peachtree Street,
Southwest, 22-210
Atlanta, GA 30303
P: (404) 657-2680
E: dlhowell1
@dhr.state.ga.us

HAWAII
Ms. Mary Brogan
Chief
Developmental Disabilities
Division
Department of Health
P.O. Box 3378
Honolulu, HI 96801
P: (808) 586-5842
E: mary.brogan
@doh.hawaii.gov

IDAHO
Mr. Arthur Evans
Developmentally Disabled
Services Bureau Chief
Developmental Disabilities
Program
Department of Health & Welfare
3232 Elder Street
Boise, ID 83705
P: (208) 364-1896
E: evansa@dhw.idaho.gov

ILLINOIS
Mr. Gregory A. Fenton
Acting Director
Division of Developmental
Disabilities
Department of Human Services
319 East Madison, Suite 4N
Springfield, IL 62701
P: (217) 782-6803
E: greg.fenton@illinois.gov

INDIANA
Ms. Nicole Norvell
Director, Disability &
Rehabilitative Services
Family & Social Services
Administration
402 West Washington Street,
W451
P.O. Box 7083
Indianapolis, IN 46207
P: (317) 232-1147
E: nicole.norvell
@fssa.in.gov

IOWA
Mr. Rick Shults
Division Administrator
Division of Mental Health &
Disability Services
Department of Human Services
Hoover Building 5SE, 1305 East
Walnut
Des Moines, IA 50319
P: (515) 281-8580
F: (515) 242-6036
E: rshults@dhs.state.ia.us

KANSAS
Ms. Kari Bruffett
Acting Secretary
Department for Aging &
Disability Services
New England Building
503 South Kansas Avenue
Topeka, KS 66603
P: (785) 296-4986
F: (785) 296-0256
E: kari.bruffett
@kdads.ks.gov

KENTUCKY
Ms. Mary Reinle Begley
Commissioner
Department for Behavioral
Health, Developmental &
Intellectual Disabilities
Cabinet for Health & Family
Services
100 Fair Oaks Lane, 4E-E
Frankfort, KY 40621
P: (502) 564-4527
E: mary.begley@ky.gov

LOUISIANA
Mr. Mark Thomas
Assistant Secretary
Office for Citizens with
Developmental Disabilities
Department of Health &
Hospitals
628 North Fourth Street
Baton Rouge, LA 70821
P: (225) 342-0095
E: mark.thomas@la.gov

Developmentally Disabled

MAINE
Mr. Gary Wolcott
Acting Director
Office of Aging & Disability
Services
Health & Human Services, 32
Blossom Lane
SHS #11- 2nd Floor Marquart
Augusta, ME 04333
P: (207) 287-4242
E: gary.wolcott@maine.gov

MARYLAND
Mr. Bernard Simons
Deputy Secretary for
Developmental Disabilities
Developmental Disabilities
Administration
Department of Health & Mental
Hygiene
201 West Preston Street
Baltimore, MD 21201
P: (410) 767-5600
E: bernard.simons
@maryland.gov

MASSACHUSETTS
Ms. Elin Howe
Commissioner
Department of Developmental
Services
500 Harrison Avenue
Boston, MA 02118
P: (617) 624-7723
E: elin.howe@state.ma.us

MICHIGAN
Ms. Lynda Zeller
Deputy Director
Behavioral Health &
Developmental Disabilities
Administration
Department of Community
Health
320 South Walnut Street
Lansing, MI 48913
P: (517) 335-0196
F: (517) 335-4798
E: zellerl2@michigan.gov

MINNESOTA
Mr. Alex Bartolic
Director
Disability Services Division
Department of Human Services
P.O. Box 64967
St. Paul, MN 55164
P: (651) 431-2381
F: (651) 431-7412
E: alex.e.bartolic
@state.mn.us

MISSISSIPPI
Mr. Matt Armstrong
Director
Bureau of Intellectual &
Developmental Disabilities
Department of Mental Health
239 North Lamar Street, Suite
1101
Jackson, MS 39201
P: (601) 359-1288
E: matt.armstrong
@dmh.state.ms.us

MISSOURI
Ms. Valerie Huhn
Director
Division of Developmental
Disabilities
Department of Mental Health
1706 East Elm Street
Jefferson City, MO 65101
P: (573) 751-8676
E: valerie.huhn@dmh.mo.gov

MONTANA
Ms. Novelene Martin
Bureau Chief
Department of Public Health &
Human Services
Developmental Disabilities
Program
P.O. Box 4210
Helena, MT 59604
P: (406) 444-5662
E: nomartin@mt.gov

NEBRASKA
Ms. Jodi Fenner
Director
Division of Developmental
Disabilities
Department of Health & Human
Services
P.O. Box 95026
Lincoln, NE 68509
P: (402) 471-6038
F: (402) 471-9449
E: jodi.fenner@nebraska.gov

NEVADA
Ms. Jane Gruner
Administrator
Aging & Disability Services
Division
3416 Goni Road, Building
D-132
Carson City, NV 89706
P: (775) 687-4210
F: (775) 687-4264
E: jgruner@adsd.nv.gov

NEW HAMPSHIRE
Ms. Lorene Reagan
Bureau Chief
Bureau of Developmental
Services
Department of Health & Human
Services
105 Pleasant Street
Concord, NH 03301
P: (603) 271-5034
E: Lorene.reagan
@dhhs.state.nh.us

NEW JERSEY
Ms. Elizabeth Shea
Assistant Commissioner
Division of Developmental
Disabilities
Department of Human Services
P.O. Box 726
Trenton, NJ 08625
P: (609) 631-6500
E: liz.shea@dhs.state.nj.us

NEW MEXICO
Ms. Cathy Stevenson
Director
Developmental Disabilities
Supports Division
Department of Health
P.O. Box 26110
Santa Fe, NM 87502
P: (505) 476-8913
E: cathy.stevenson
@state.nm.us

NEW YORK
Kerry A. Delaney
Acting Commissioner
Office for People With
Developmental Disabilities
44 Holland Avenue
Albany, NY 12229
P: (518) 473-1997
E: kerry.a.delaney
@opwdd.ny.gov

NORTH CAROLINA
Dr. Courtney M. Cantrell
Director
Division of Mental Health,
Developmental Disabilities &
Substance Abuse Services
Department of Health & Human
Services
3001 Mail Service Center
Raleigh, NC 27699
P: (919) 733-7011
F: (919) 508-0951
E: courtney.m.cantrell
@dhhs.nc.gov

NORTH DAKOTA
Ms. Tina Bay
Director
Developmental Disabilities
Division
Department of Human Services
1237 West Divide Avenue, Suite
1A
Bismarck, ND 58501
P: (701) 328-8966
E: tbay@nd.gov

OHIO
Mr. John L. Martin
Director
Department of Developmental
Disabilities
30 East Broad Street, 12th Floor
Columbus, OH 43215
P: (614) 466-0129
F: (614) 644-5013
E: john.martin
@dodd.ohio.gov

OKLAHOMA
Ms. JoAnne Goin
Division Director
Developmental Disabilities
Services
Department of Human Services
P.O. Box 25352
Oklahoma City, OK 73125
P: (405) 521-6267
E: joanne.goin@okdhs.org

OREGON
Ms. Lilia Teninty
Director
Developmental Disability
Services
Department of Human Services
500 Summer Street Northeast,
E09
Salem, OR 97301
P: (503) 945-6918
E: lilia.teninty
@state.or.us

PENNSYLVANIA
Mr. Stephen H. Suroviec
Deputy Secretary
Office of Developmental
Programs
Department of Public Welfare
625 Forster Street
Harrisburg, PA 17120
P: (717) 787-3700
E: stsuroviec@pa.gov

Developmentally Disabled

RHODE ISLAND
Ms. Maria Montanaro
Director
Department of Behavioral
Healthcare, Developmental
Disabilities & Hospitals
Barry Hall
14 Harrington Road
Cranston, RI 02920
P: (401) 462-2339
F: (401) 462-3204
E: maria.montanaro
    @bhddh.ri.gov

SOUTH CAROLINA
Dr. Beverly A. H. Buscemi
Director
Department of Disabilities &
Special Needs
P.O. Box 4706
Columbia, SC 29240
P: (803) 898-9769
F: (803) 898-9653
E: bbuscemi@ddsn.sc.gov

SOUTH DAKOTA
Mr. Dan Lusk
Director
Division of Developmental
Disabilities, Department of
Human Services
3800 East Highway 34,
Hillsview Plaza
C/o 500 East Capitol Avenue
Pierre, SD 57501
P: (605) 773-3438
E: dan.lusk@state.sd.us

TENNESSEE
Ms. Debbie Payne
Commissioner
Department of Intellectual &
Developmental Disabilities
Citizens Plaza, 10th Floor
400 Deaderick Street
Nashville, TN 37243
P: (615) 532-5970
E: debbie.payne@tn.gov

TEXAS
Mr. Chris Adams
Deputy Commissioner
Department of Aging &
Disability Services
Mail Code W-619
P.O. Box 149030
Austin, TX 78714
P: (512) 438-3030
E: chris.adams
    @dads.state.tx.us

UTAH
Mr. Paul Smith
Director
Division of Services for People
with Disabilities
Department of Human Services
195 North 1950 West
Salt Lake City, UT 84116
P: (801) 538-4135
E: ptsmith@utah.gov

VERMONT
Camille George
Director, Developmental
Disabilities Services Division
Department of Disabilities,
Aging & Independent Living
103 South Main Street, Weeks
Building
Waterbury, VT 05671
P: (802) 871-3386
E: camille.george
    @state.vt.us

VIRGINIA
Ms. Connie Cochran
Assistant Commissioner for
Developmental Services
Department of Behavioral
Health & Developmental
Services
P.O. Box 1797
Richmond, VA 23218
P: (804) 370-5990
E: connie.cochran
    @dbhds.virginia.gov

WASHINGTON
Ms. Evelyn Perez
Assistant Secretary
Developmental Disabilities
Administration
Department of Social & Health
Services
P.O. Box 45310
Olympia, WA 98504
P: (360) 725-3461
E: pereze@dshs.wa.gov

WEST VIRGINIA
Ms. Beth Morrison
Director
Division of Intellectual &
Developmental Disabilities
Behavioral Health and Health
Facilities
350 Capitol Street, Room 350
Charleston, WV 25301
P: (304) 356-4976
E: beth.j.morrison@wv.gov

WISCONSIN
Ms. Camille Rodriguez
Chief, Developmental
Disabilities Services
Long Term Care & Policy
Initiatives, Division of Long
Term Care
Department of Health Services
1 West Wilson, Room 418
Madison, WI 53707
P: (608) 266-9366
E: camille.rodriguez
    @wisconsin.gov

WYOMING
Ms. Chris Newman
Senior Administrator
Behavioral Health Division
Department of Health
6101 Yellowstone Road, Suite
220
Cheyenne, WY 82002
P: (307) 777-6494
F: (307) 777-5849
E: chris.newman@wyo.gov

Economic Development

Responsible for efforts designed to encourage industry to locate, develop and expand in the state.

ALABAMA
Mr. Greg Canfield
Secretary
Department of Commerce
P.O. Box 304106
Montgomery, AL 36130
P: (334) 242-0421
F: (334) 242-5669
E: greg.canfield
@commerce.alabama.gov

ALASKA
Ms. Britteny Cioni-Haywood
Division Director
Division of Economic
Development
P.O. Box 110804
Juneau, AK 99811
P: (907) 465-2510
F: (907) 465-3767
E: britteny.cioni-haywood
@alaska.gov

AMERICAN SAMOA
Mr. Keniseli Lafaele
Director
Department of Commerce
American Samoa Government
Executive Office Building,
Utulei
Pago Pago, AS 96799
P: (684) 633-5155
F: (684) 633-4195
E: keniseli.lafaele@doc.as

ARIZONA
Ms. Sandra Watson
President & CEO
Commerce Authority
333 North Central Avenue, Suite 1900
Phoenix, AZ 85004
P: (602) 845-1200
F: (602) 845-1201
E: commerce@azcommerce.com

ARKANSAS
Mr. Mike Preston
Exeuctive Director
Economic Development
Commission
900 West Capitol Avenue, Suite 400
Little Rock, AR 72201
P: (501) 682-7351
F: (501) 682-7394
E: mpreston@arkansasedc.com

CALIFORNIA
Ms. Panorea Avdis
Deputy Director
Governor's Office of Business &
Economic Development
1400 10th Street, 2nd Floor
Sacramento, CA 95814
P: (916) 322-0694

COLORADO
Ms. Fiona Arnold
Executive Director
Office of Economic
Development & International
Trade
1625 Broadway, Suite 2700
Denver, CO 80202
P: (303) 892-3840
F: (303) 892-3848
E: fiona.arnold@state.co.us

CONNECTICUT
Ms. Catherine H. Smith
Commissioner
Department of Economic &
Community Development
505 Hudson Street
Hartford, CT 06106
P: (860) 270-8000
E: catherine.smith@ct.gov

DELAWARE
Mr. Alan B. Levin
Cabinet Secretary
Economic Development Office
99 Kings Highway
Dover, DE 19901
P: (302) 672-6808
F: (302) 739-5749
E: Alan.Levin@state.de.us

DISTRICT OF COLUMBIA
Mr. Brian Kenner
Deputy Mayor for Planning and
Economic Development
Office of the Deputy Mayor for
Planning & Economic
Development
John A. Wilson Building, Suite 317
1350 Pennsylvania Avenue,
Northwest
Washington, DC 20004
P: (202) 727-6365
F: (202) 727-6703
E: dmped.eom@dc.gov

FLORIDA
Mr. Karl Blischke
Director
Division of Strategic Business
Development
Department of Economic
Opportunity
107 East Madison St., Caldwell
Building
Tallahassee, FL 32399
P: (850) 245-7105
F: (850) 921-3223
E: karl.blischke
@deo.myflorida.com

GEORGIA
Mr. Chris Carr
Commissioner
Department of Economic
Development
75 Fifth Street, Northwest
Suite 1200
Atlanta, GA 30308
P: (404) 962-4000
F: (404) 962-4009

HAWAII
Mr. Luis P. Salaveria
Director
Department of Business,
Economic Development &
Tourism
250 South Hotel Street
P.O. Box 2359
Honolulu, HI 96804
P: (808) 586-2355
F: (808) 586-2377
E: director
@dbedt.hawaii.gov

IDAHO
Mr. Jeffery Sayer
Director
Department of Commerce
700 West State Street
P.O. Box 83720
Boise, ID 83720
P: (208) 334-2470
F: (208) 334-2631
E: jeffery.sayer
@commerce.idaho.gov

ILLINOIS
Mr. Jim Schultz
Director
Department of Commerce &
Economic Opportunity
100 West Randolph Street, Suite 3-400
Chicago, IL 60601
P: (312) 814-2811
E: Jim.Schultz@Illinois.gov

INDIANA
Mr. Victor Smith
Secretary of Commerce
Economic Development
Corporation
One North Capitol, Suite 700
Indianapolis, IN 46204
P: (317) 234-1359
F: (317) 232-4146
E: VSmith@iedc.IN.gov

IOWA
Ms. Debi Durham
Director
Economic Development
Authority
200 East Grand Avenue
Des Moines, IA 50309
P: (515) 725-3022
F: (515) 725-3010
E: debi.durham@iowa.gov

KANSAS
Mr. Pat George
Secretary
Department of Commerce
1000 Southwest Jackson Street,
Suite 100
Topeka, KS 66612
P: (785) 296-2741
F: (785) 296-5055
E: pgeorge
@kansascommerce.com

KENTUCKY
Mr. Larry Hayes
Secretary
Cabinet for Economic
Development
Old Capitol Annex
300 West Broadway
Frankfort, KY 40601
P: (502) 564-7140
F: (502) 564-3256
E: Larry.Hayes@ky.gov

LOUISIANA
Mr. Stephen Grissom
Secretary
Economic Development
1051 North Third Street
Baton Rouge, LA 70802
P: (225) 342-5478
F: (225) 342-9095
E: sgrissom@la.gov

MAINE
Mr. George C. Gervais
Commissioner
Department of Economic &
Community Development
59 State House Station
Augusta, ME 04333
P: (207) 624-9800

Economic Development

MARYLAND
Mr. R. Michael Gill
Secretary
Department of Business &
Economic Development
World Trade Center
401 East Pratt Street
Baltimore, MD 21202
P: (410) 767-6301
F: (410) 333-8628
E: Mike.Gill@maryland.gov

MASSACHUSETTS
Mr. Jay Ash
Secretary
Executive Office of Housing &
Economic Development
One Ashburton Place, Room
2101
Boston, MA 02108
P: (617) 788-3610
F: (617) 788-3605

MICHIGAN
Mr. Steve Arwood
CEO
Economic Development
Corporation
300 North Washington Square
Lansing, MI 48913
P: (517) 241-1400
F: (517) 241-3683
E: arwoods1@michigan.org

MINNESOTA
Ms. Katie Clark Sieben
Commissioner
Department of Employment &
Economic Development
1st National Bank Building
332 Minnesota Street, Suite
E200
St. Paul, MN 55101
P: (651) 259-7119
F: (651) 296-4772
E: katie.clark.sieben
    @state.mn.us

MISSISSIPPI
Mr. Glenn McCullough Jr.
Chief Executive Officer
Development Authority
501 North West Street
P.O. Box 849
Jackson, MS 39205
P: (601) 359-3449
F: (601) 359-3832
E: gmccullough
    @mississippi.org

MISSOURI
Mr. Mike Downing
Director
Department of Economic
Development
301 West High Street
P.O. Box 1157
Jefferson City, MO 65102
P: (573) 751-4962
F: (573) 526-7700
E: ecodev@ded.mo.gov

MONTANA
Mr. John Rogers
Chief Business Officer
Governor's Office of Economic
Development
State Capitol
Helena, MT 59620
P: (406) 444-5470
F: (406) 444-3674
E: business@mt.gov

NEBRASKA
Ms. Brenda Hicks-Sorensen
Director
Department of Economic
Development
550 South 16th Street
Lincoln, NE 68508
P: (402) 471-3125
E: brenda.hicks-sorensen
    @nebraska.gov

NEVADA
Mr. Steve Hill
Executive Director
Governor's Office of Economic
Development
555 East Washington Avenue,
Suite 5400
Las Vegas, NV 89101
P: (702) 486-2700
F: (702) 486-2701
E: ltaylor
    @diversifynevada.com

NEW HAMPSHIRE
Ms. Carmen Lorentz
Director
Division of Economic
Development
72 Pembroke Road
Concord, NH 03301
P: (603) 271-2341
E: Carmen.Lorentz
    @dred.nh.gov

NEW JERSEY
Ms. Melissa Orsen
Chief Executive Officer
Economic Development
Authority
36 West State Street
P.O. Box 990
Trenton, NJ 08625
P: (609) 292-1800
F: (609) 292-0885
E: njeda@njeda.com

NEW MEXICO
Mr. Jon Barela
Secretary
Economic Development
Department
1100 South Saint Francis Drive
P.O. Box 20003
Santa Fe, NM 87504
P: (505) 827-0305
F: (505) 827-0328
E: Jon.Barela@state.nm.us

NEW YORK
Mr. Howard Zemsky
President & CEO
Empire State Development
633 Third Avenue
New York, NY 10017
P: (212) 803-3700
F: (212) 803-3715

NORTH CAROLINA
Mr. John Skvarla
Secretary
Department of Commerce
301 North Wilmington Street
4301 Mail Service Center
Raleigh, NC 27699
P: (919) 733-4151
E: john.skvarla
    @nccommerce.com

NORTH DAKOTA
Mr. Paul Lucy
Director
Economic Development &
Finance Division
Department of Commerce
1600 East Century Avenue, Suite
2
Bismark, ND 58503
P: (701) 328-5388
F: (701) 328-5320
E: plucy@nd.gov

**NORTHERN MARIANA
ISLANDS**
Mr. Manuel A. Sablan
Executive Director
Commonwealth Development
Authority
P.O. Box 502149
Saipan, MP 96950
P: (670) 234-6245
F: (670) 235-7147
E: administration
    @cda.gov.mp

OKLAHOMA
Mr. Deby Snodgrass
Secretary
Department of Commerce
900 North Stiles Avenue
Oklahoma City, OK 73104
P: (405) 815-6552
E: deby_snodgrass
    @okcommerce.gov

OREGON
Mr. Sean Robbins
Director
Business Oregon
775 Summer Street, Northeast,
Suite 200
Salem, OR 97301
P: (503) 986-0110
F: (503) 581-5115
E: sean.robbins@state.or.us

PENNSYLVANIA
Mr. Dennis Davin
Secretary
Department of Community &
Economic Development
Commonwealth Keystone
Building
400 North Street, 4th Floor
Harrisburg, PA 17120
P: (866) 466-3972
F: (717) 783-4662

PUERTO RICO
Mr. Antonio Medina Comas
Executive Director
Industrial Development
Company
P.O. Box 362350
San Juan, PR 00936
P: (787) 764-1175
E: antonio.medina
    @pridco.pr.gov

RHODE ISLAND
Mr. Marcel A. Valois
Executive Director
Economic Development
Corporation
315 Iron Horse Way, Suite 101
Providence, RI 02908
P: (401) 278-9100
F: (401) 273-8270
E: executivedirector
    @riedc.com

SOUTH CAROLINA
Mr. Robert M. Hitt III
Secretary
Department of Commerce
1201 Main Street, Suite 1600
Columbia, SC 29201
P: (803) 737-0400
F: (803) 737-0418

SOUTH DAKOTA
Mr. Pat Costello
Commissioner
Governor's Office of Economic
Development
711 East Wells Avenue
Pierre, SD 57501
P: (800) 872-6190
F: (605) 773-3256
E: goedinfo@state.sd.us

TENNESSEE
Mr. Randy Boyd
Commissioner
Department of Economic &
Community Development
312 Rosa L. Parks Avenue, 11th
Floor
Nashville, TN 37243
P: (615) 741-1888
F: (615) 741-7306
E: Randy.Boyd@tn.gov

TEXAS
Mr. Bryan Daniel
Director
Economic Development &
Tourism Division
Office of the Governor
P.O. Box 12428
Austin, TX 78711
P: (512) 936-0101
F: (512) 936-0303
E: bdaniel@gov.texas.gov

U.S. VIRGIN ISLANDS
Mr. Wayne L. Biggs Jr.
Acting Chief Executive Officer
Economic Development
Authority
8000 Nisky Shopping Center,
Suite 620
P.O. Box 305038
St. Thomas, VI 00802
P: (340) 714-1700
F: (340) 773-6499

UTAH
Mr. Q. Val Hale
Executive Director
Governor's Office of Economic
Development
60 East South Temple, 3rd Floor
Salt Lake City, UT 84111
P: (801) 538-8769
F: (801) 538-8888

VERMONT
Ms. Joan Goldstein
Commissioner
Department of Economic
Development
1 National Life Drive, 6th Floor
Montpelier, VT 05620
P: (802) 727-2399
E: joan.goldstein
    @state.vt.us

VIRGINIA
Mr. Martin Briley
President & CEO
Economic Development
Partnership
901 East Byrd Street
P.O. Box 798
Richmond, VA 23218
P: (804) 545-5612
F: (804) 371-6524
E: mbriley@yesvirginia.org

WASHINGTON
Mr. Brian Bonlender
Director
Department of Commerce
1011 Plum Street, Southeast
P.O. Box 42525
Olympia, WA 98504
P: (360) 725-4000

WEST VIRGINIA
Mr. J. Keith Burdette
Cabinet Secretary
Department of Commerce
Capitol Complex Building 6,
Room 525
1900 Kanawha Boulevard East
Charleston, WV 25305
P: (304) 558-2234
F: (304) 558-1189
E: J.Keith.Burdette@wv.gov

WISCONSIN
Mr. Reed Hall
CEO & Secretary
Economic Development
Corporation
201 West Washington Avenue
P.O. Box 1687
Madison, WI 53701
P: (608) 267-4417
E: Reed.Hall@wedc.org

WYOMING
Mr. Shawn Reese
Chief Executive Officer
Business Council
214 West 15th Street
Cheyenne, WY 82002
P: (307) 777-2862
F: (307) 777-2837
E: shawn.reese@wyo.gov

Education (Chief State School Officer)

Overall responsibility for public elementary and secondary school systems.

ALABAMA
Dr. Thomas Bice
State Superintendent of Education
Department of Education
50 North Ripley Street
Montgomery, AL 36104
P: (334) 242-9700
F: (334) 242-9708
E: tbice@alsde.edu

ALASKA
Mr. Mike Hanley
Commissioner of Education
Department of Education &
Early Development
801 West 10th Street, Suite 200
Juneau, AK 99811
P: (907) 465-2800
F: (907) 465-4156

AMERICAN SAMOA
Dr. Salu S. Hunkin-Finau
Director of Education
Department of Education
P.O. Box DOE
Pago Pago, AS 96799
P: (684) 633-5237
F: (684) 633-4240

ARIZONA
Hon. Diane Douglas (R)
Superintendent of Public
Instruction
Department of Education
1535 West Jefferson Street
Phoenix, AZ 85007
P: (602) 542-5393
E: adeinbox@azed.gov

ARKANSAS
Mr. Johnny Key
Commissioner
Department of Education
Four Capitol Mall
Little Rock, AR 72201
P: (501) 682-4203
E: Johnny.Key@arkansas.gov

CALIFORNIA
Hon. Tom Torlakson (D)
State Superintendent of Public
Instruction
Department of Education
1430 N Street
Sacramento, CA 95814
P: (916) 319-0800
F: (916) 319-0175
E: superintendent
   @cde.ca.gov

COLORADO
Mr. Robert Hammond
Commissioner of Education
Department of Education
201 East Colfax Avenue
Denver, CO 80203
P: (303) 866-6646
F: (303) 830-0793
E: commissioner
   @cde.state.co.us

CONNECTICUT
Dr. Dianna R. Wentzell
Interim Commissioner
Department of Education
165 Capitol Avenue
Hartford, CT 06106
P: (860) 713-6500
F: (860) 713-7001
E: dianna.roberge-wentzell
   @ct.gov

DELAWARE
Mr. Mark Murphy
Secretary of Education
Department of Education
John G. Townsend Building
Dover, DE 19901
P: (302) 735-4000
F: (302) 739-4654
E: mark.murphy
   @doe.k12.de.us

DISTRICT OF COLUMBIA
Ms. Hanseul Kang
Superintendent of Education
Office of the State
Superintendent of Education
810 First Street Northeast, 9th
Floor
Washington, DC 20002
P: (202) 727-6436
E: osse@dc.gov

FLORIDA
Ms. Pam Stewart
Commissioner of Education
Department of Education
Turlington Building, Suite 1514
Tallahassee, FL 32399
P: (850) 245-0505
F: (850) 245-9667
E: pam.stewart@fldoe.org

GEORGIA
Hon. Richard L. Woods (R)
State School Superintendent
Department of Education
2066 Twin Towers East
Atlanta, GA 30334
P: (404) 657-1175
F: (404) 651-8737
E: state.superintendent
   @doe.k12.ga.us

GUAM
Mr. Jon Fernandez
Superintendent of Public School
System
Department of Education
P.O. Box DE
Hagatna, GU 96932
P: (671) 475-0457
F: (671) 472-5001

HAWAII
Ms. Kathryn Matayoshi
Superintendent of Education
Department of Education
P.O. Box 2360
Honolulu, HI 96804
P: (808) 586-3313
F: (808) 586-3314

IDAHO
Hon. Sherri Ybarra (R)
Superintendent of Public
Instruction
State Department of Educaiton
650 West State Street
Boise, ID 83720
P: (208) 332-6800
F: (208) 334-2228

ILLINOIS
Dr. Tony Smith
Superintendent of Education
State Board of Education
100 North First Street
Springfield, IL 62777
P: (866) 262-6663

INDIANA
Ms. Glenda Ritz
Superintendent of Public
Instruction
Department of Education
151 West Ohio Street
Indianapolis, IN 46204
P: (317) 232-6613
F: (317) 232-8004
E: superintendent
   @doe.in.gov

IOWA
Dr. Brad Buck
Director
Department of Education
Grimes State Office Building
Des Moines, IA 50319
P: (515) 281-3436
F: (515) 242-5988
E: brad.buck@iowa.gov

KANSAS
Mr. Brad Neuenswander
Interim Commissioner of
Education
State Department of Education
900 Southwest Jackson Street,
Room 600
Topeka, KS 66612
P: (785) 296-3202
E: bneuenswander@ksde.org

KENTUCKY
Dr. Terry Holliday
Commissioner of Education
Department of Education
500 Mero Street
Frankfort, KY 40601
P: (502) 564-4770
F: (502) 564-5680

LOUISIANA
Mr. John White
State Superintendent of
Education
Department of Education
P.O. Box 94064
Baton Rouge, LA 70804
P: (877) 453-2721
F: (225) 342-0193

MAINE
Mr. Tom Desjardin
Commissioner of Education
Department of Education
23 State House Station
Augusta, ME 04333
P: (207) 624-6620
E: commish.doe@maine.gov

MARYLAND
Dr. Lillian Lowery
Superintendent of Schools
Department of Education
200 West Baltimore Street
Baltimore, MD 21201
P: (410) 767-0462

MASSACHUSETTS
Mr. Mitchell D. Chester
Commissioner of Education
Department of Elementary &
Secondary Education
75 Pleasant Street
Malden, MA 02148
P: (781) 338-3100
F: (781) 338-3770
E: www@doe.mass.edu

Education (Chief State School Officer)

MICHIGAN
Mr. Michael P. Flanagan
Superindendent of Public
Instruction
Department of Education
608 West Allegan Street
Lansing, MI 48909
P: (517) 373-3324
F: (517) 375-4565

MINNESOTA
Ms. Brenda Cassellius
Commissioner
Department of Education
1500 Highway 36 West
Roseville, MN 55113
P: (651) 582-8204
F: (651) 582-8724
E: Brenda.Cassellius
  @state.mn.us

MISSISSIPPI
Dr. Carey Wright
Superintendent of Education
Department of Education
P.O. Box 771
Jackson, MS 39205
P: (601) 359-3513

MISSOURI
Dr. Margie Vandeven
Commissioner
Department of Elementary &
Secondary Education
P.O. Box 480
Jefferson City, MO 65102
P: (573) 751-4212
F: (573) 751-8613
E: commissioner@dese.mo.gov

MONTANA
Hon. Denise Juneau (D)
Superintendent of Public
Instruction
Office of Public Instruction
P.O. Box 202501
Helena, MT 59620
P: (406) 444-3095
F: (406) 444-9299
E: OPISupt@mt.gov

NEBRASKA
Dr. Matthew Blomstedt
Commissioner of Education
Department of Education
301 Centennial Mall South
Lincoln, NE 68509
P: (402) 471-2295
F: (402) 471-0117

NEVADA
Mr. Dale Erquiaga
Superintendent of Public
Instruction
Department of Education
700 East Fifth Street
Carson City, NV 89701
P: (775) 687-9200
F: (775) 687-9101

NEW HAMPSHIRE
Dr. Virginia M. Barry
Commissioner of Education
Department of Education
101 Pleasant Street
Concord, NH 03301
P: (603) 271-3144
E: Virginia.Barry
  @doe.nh.gov

NEW JERSEY
Mr. David Hespe
Education Commissioner
Department of Education
P.O. Box 500
Trenton, NJ 08625
P: (609) 292-4450
F: (609) 777-4099

NEW MEXICO
Ms. Hanna Skandera
Secretary of Education
Public Education Department
Jerry Apodaca Education
Building
Santa Fe, NM 87501
P: (505) 827-5800
F: (505) 827-6520

NEW YORK
Ms. Elizabeth Berlin
Acting Commissioner
State Education Department
89 Washington Avenue
Albany, NY 12234
P: (518) 474-3852

NORTH CAROLINA
Dr. June Atkinson
Superintendent of Public
Instruction
Department of Public
Instruction
Education Building
Raleigh, NC 27699
P: (919) 807-3300
F: (919) 807-3445
E: jatkinson
  @dpi.state.nc.us

NORTH DAKOTA
Hon. Kirsten Baesler
Superintendent of Public
Instruction
Department of Public
Instruction
600 East Boulevard Avenue
Department 201
Bismarck, ND 58505
P: (701) 328-4570
F: (701) 328-2461
E: kbaesler@nd.gov

**NORTHERN MARIANA
ISLANDS**
Ms. Rita Sablan
Commissioner of Education
CNMI Public School System
P.O. Box 501370
Saipan, MP 96950
P: (670) 237-3001
F: (670) 664-3798

OHIO
Dr. Richard Ross
Superintendent of Public
Instruction
Department of Education
25 South Front Street
Columbus, OH 43215
P: (877) 644-6338

OKLAHOMA
Hon. Joy Hofmeister (R)
Superintendent of Public
Instruction
State Department of Education
2500 North Lincoln Boulevard
Oklahoma City, OK 73105
P: (405) 521-3301
F: (405) 521-6205
E: Joy.Hofmeister
  @sde.ok.gov

OREGON
Mr. Rob Saxton
Deputy Superintendent of Public
Instruction
Department of Education
255 Capitol Street, Northeast
Salem, OR 97310
P: (503) 947-5740
F: (503) 378-5156
E: rob.saxton@state.or.us

PENNSYLVANIA
Mr. Pedro A. Rivera
Acting Secretary of Education
Department of Education
333 Market Street
Harrisburg, PA 17126
P: (717) 783-6788

PUERTO RICO
Hon. Rafael Román-Meléndez
Secretary of Education
Department of Education
P.O. Box 190759
San Juan, PR 00919
P: (787) 766-2911
E: romanmr@de.pr.gov

RHODE ISLAND
Dr. Deborah A. Gist
Commissioner of Education
Department of Education
255 Westminster Street
Providence, RI 02903
P: (401) 222-8700
F: (202) 727-2019
E: deborah.gist@ride.ri.gov

SOUTH CAROLINA
Hon. Molly Mitchell
  Spearman (R)
Superintendent of Education
Department of Education
1429 Senate Street
Columbia, SC 29201
P: (803) 734-8500
F: (803) 734-3389

SOUTH DAKOTA
Dr. Melody Schopp
Secretary of Education
Department of Education
800 Governors Drive
Pierre, SD 57501
P: (605) 773-5669
F: (605) 773-6139
E: melody.schopp
  @state.sd.us

TENNESSEE
Dr. Candice McQueen
Commissioner of Education
Department of Education
710 James Robertson Parkway
Nashville, TN 37243
P: (615) 741-5158
F: (615) 532-4791
E: Commissioner.McQueen
  @tn.gov

TEXAS
Hon. Michael L.
  Williams (R)
Commissioner of Education
State Education Agency
William B. Travis Building
Austin, TX 78701
P: (512) 463-8985

Education (Chief State School Officer)

U.S. VIRGIN ISLANDS
Ms. Donna Frett-Gregory
Commissioner
Department of Education
1834 Kongens Gade
St. Thomas, VI 00802
P: (340) 774-0100
F: (340) 779-7153

UTAH
Mr. Brad Smith
State Superintendent
State Office of Education
250 East 500, South
P.O. Box 144200
Salt Lake City, UT 84114
P: (801) 538 7500

VERMONT
Ms. Rebecca Holcombe
Superintendent of Education
Agency of Education
219 North Main Street, Suite 402
Barre, VT 05641
P: (802) 479-1030
E: rebecca.holcombe
   @state.vt.us

VIRGINIA
Dr. Steven Staples
Superintendent of Public
Instruction
Department of Education
P.O. Box 2120
Richmond, VA 23218
P: (804) 225-2023
F: (804) 371-2099
E: steven.staples
   @doe.virginia.gov

WASHINGTON
Hon. Randy Dorn
Superintendent of Public
Instruction
Office of the Superintendent of
Public Instruction
Old Capitol Building
Olympia, WA 98504
P: (360) 725-6115
F: (360) 753-6712
E: randy.dorn@k12.wa.us

WEST VIRGINIA
Dr. Michael Martirano
State Superintendent
Department of Education
1900 Kanawha Boulevard, East
Charleston, WV 25305
P: (304) 558-2681
F: (304) 558-0048
E: superintendent
   @wvde.state.wv.us

WISCONSIN
Hon. Anthony Evers
Superintendent of Public
Instruction
Department of Public
Instruction
125 South Webster Street
Madison, WI 53707
P: (608) 266-3390
E: anthony.evers@dpi.wi.gov

WYOMING
Hon. Jillian Balow (R)
Superintendent of Public
Instruction
Office of the Superintendent of
Public Instruction
2300 Capitol Avenue
Cheyenne, WY 82002
P: (307) 777-7675
F: (307) 777-6234

Elections Administration

Administers state election laws and supervises the printing and distribution of ballots.

ALABAMA
Mr. Ed Packard
Director of Elections
Office of the Secretary of State
P.O. Box 5616
Montgomery, AL 36103
P: (334) 242-4845
F: (334) 244-2444
E: ed.packard
    @sos.alabama.gov

ALASKA
Ms. Gail Fenumiai
Director
Division of Elections
P.O. Box 110017
Juneau, AK 99811
P: (907) 465-4611
F: (907) 465-3203
E: gail.fenumiai@alaska.gov

AMERICAN SAMOA
Mr. Soliai T. Fuimaono
Chief Election Officer
Territorial Election Office
P.O. Box 3790
Pago Pago, AS 96799
P: (684) 699-3570
F: (684) 699-3574
E: Asgelect@samoatelco.com

ARIZONA
Ms. Christina Estes-Werther
Election Director
Secretary of State's Office
1700 West Washington, 7th Floor
Phoenix, AZ 85007
P: (602) 542-8683
F: (602) 542-6172
E: cwerther@azsos.gov

Mr. Eric Spencer
Election Director
Secretary of State's Office
1700 West Washington, 7th Floor
Phoenix, AZ 85007
P: (602) 542-8683
F: (602) 542-6172
E: espencer@azsos.gov

ARKANSAS
Mr. Rob Hammons
Director of Elections
Office of the Secretary of State
State Capitol, Room 062
Little Rock, AR 72201
P: (501) 683-3733
F: (501) 683-3732
E: Rob.Hammons
    @sos.arkansas.gov

CALIFORNIA
Ms. Jana Lean
Chief of Elections
Elections Division
1500 11th Street, 5th Floor
Sacramento, CA 95814
P: (916) 657-2166
F: (916) 653-3214
E: jana.lean@sos.ca.gov

COLORADO
Mr. Judd Choate
Director of Elections
Secretary of State's Office
Department of State
1700 Broadway, Suite 200
Denver, CO 80290
P: (303) 894-2200
F: (303) 869-4861
E: judd.choate
    @sos.state.co.us

CONNECTICUT
Ms. Peggy Reeves
Director of Elections
Office of the Secretary of State
30 Trinity Street
Hartford, CT 06106
P: (860) 509-6123
F: (860) 509-6127
E: peggy.reeves@ct.gov

DELAWARE
Ms. M. Elaine Manlove
State Election Commissioner
Office of the State Election Commissioner
905 South Governors Avenue, Suite 170
Dover, DE 19904
P: (302) 739-4277
F: (302) 739-6794
E: elaine.manlove
    @state.de.us

DISTRICT OF COLUMBIA
Mr. Cliff Tatum
Executive Director
Board of Elections & Ethics
441 Fourth Street, Northwest, Suite 250N
Washington, DC 20001
P: (202) 727-2525
F: (202) 347-2648
E: ctatum@dcboee.org

FLORIDA
Mr. Gary J. Holland
Assistant Director, Division of Elections
Department of State
R.A. Gray Building, Room 316
500 South Bronough Street
Tallahassee, FL 32399
P: (850) 245-6268
F: (850) 245-6217
E: Gary.Holland
    @DOS.MyFlorida.com

Ms. Maria Matthews
Director, Division of Elections
Department of State
R.A. Gray Building, Room 316
500 South Bronough Street
Tallahassee, FL 32399
P: (850) 245-6268
F: (850) 245-6217
E: Maria.Matthews
    @DOS.MyFlorida.com

GEORGIA
Ms. Ann Hicks
Acting Director of Elections
Office of the Secretary of State
2 Martin Luther King Jr. Drive Southeast
Suite 802, West Tower
Atlanta, GA 30334
P: (404) 656-2871
F: (404) 651-9531
E: ahicks@sos.ga.gov

GUAM
Ms. Maria I.D. Pangelinan
Executive Director
Election Commission
414 West Soledad Avenue
GCIC Building, Suite 200
Hagatna, GU 96910
P: (671) 477-9791
F: (671) 477-1895
E: vote@gec.guam.gov

HAWAII
Mr. Scott Nago
Chief Election Officer
Office of Elections
802 Lehua Avenue
Pearl City, HI 96782
P: (808) 453-8683
F: (808) 453-6006
E: elections@hawaii.gov

IDAHO
Ms. Betsie Kimbrough
Election Director
Office of the Secretary of State
304 North 8th, Suite 149
P.O. Box 83720
Boise, ID 83720
P: (208) 334-2852
F: (208) 334-2282
E: bkimbrough@sos.idaho.gov

ILLINOIS
Mr. Steve Sandvoss
Executive Director
State Board of Elections
2329 South Macarthur Boulevard
Springfield, IL 62704
P: (217) 782-4141
F: (217) 524-5574
E: ssandvoss
    @elections.il.gov

INDIANA
Mr. Trent Deckard
Co-Director
Election Division
Office of the Secretary of State
302 West Washington Street, Room E-204
Indianapolis, IN 46204
P: (317) 232-3940
F: (317) 233-6793
E: tdeckard@iec.in.gov

Mr. J. Bradley King
Co-Director
Election Division
Office of the Secretary of State
302 West Washington Street, Room E-204
Indianapolis, IN 46204
P: (317) 233-0929
F: (317) 233-6793
E: bking@iec.in.gov

IOWA
Ms. Carol Olson
Deputy Secretary of State
Secretary of State Office
Lucas Building
321 East 12th Street
Des Moines, IA 50319
P: (515) 242-5071
F: (515) 242-5953
E: carol.olson
    @sos.state.ia.us

KANSAS
Mr. Bryan Caskey
Election Director
Office of the Secretary of State
120 Southwest 10th Avenue
Memorial Hall, 1st Floor
Topeka, KS 66612
P: (785) 296-4561
F: (785) 291-3051
E: Bryan.Caskey@sos.ks.gov

KENTUCKY
Ms. Maryellen Allen
Executive Director
State Board of Elections
140 Walnut Street
Frankfort, KY 40601
P: (502) 573-7100
F: (502) 573-4369
E: maryellen.allen@ky.gov

Elections Administration

LOUISIANA
Ms. Angie Rogers
Commissioner of Elections
Secretary of State's Office
8549 United Plaza Boulevard
P.O. Box 94125
Baton Rouge, LA 70802
P: (225) 922-0900
F: (225) 922-0945
E: Angie.rogers
   @sos.louisiana.gov

MAINE
Ms. Julie L. Flynn
Deputy Secretary of State
Office of the Secretary of State
101 State House Station
Augusta, ME 04333
P: (207) 624-7736
F: (207) 287-5428
E: Julie.Flynn@maine.gov

MARYLAND
Ms. Linda H. Lamone
Administrator of Elections
State Board of Elections
P.O. Box 6486
Annapolis, MD 21401
P: (410) 269-2840
F: (410) 974-2019
E: Linda.Lamone
   @Maryland.gov

MASSACHUSETTS
Ms. Michelle Tassinari
Director of Elections & Legal
Counsel
Election Division
One Ashburton Place, Room
1705
Boston, MA 02108
P: (617) 727-2828
F: (617) 742-3238
E: Michelle.Tassinari
   @sec.state.ma.us

MICHIGAN
Mr. Christopher M. Thomas
Director
Bureau of Elections
Richard H. Austin Building,
First Floor
430 West Allegan Street
Lansing, MI 48918
P: (517) 335-2789
F: (517) 373-0941
E: ChristopherT
   @michigan.gov

MINNESOTA
Mr. Gary Poser
Director of Elections
Office of the Secretary of State
174 State Office Building
100 Martin Luther King Jr.
Boulevard
St. Paul, MN 55155
P: (651) 556-0612
F: (651) 296-9073
E: Gary.Poser@state.mn.us

MISSISSIPPI
Ms. Kim Turner
Senior Attorney
Elections Division
Secretary of State's Office
401 Mississippi Street
Jackson, MS 39201
P: (601) 359-5137
F: (601) 359-1499
E: Kim.Turner@sos.ms.gov

MISSOURI
Ms. Julie A. Allen
Executive Director
Secretary of State's Office
3411A Knipp Drive
Jefferson City, MO 65109
P: (573) 751-2020
F: (573) 526-4506
E: julie.allen@sos.mo.gov

Ms. Waylene Hiles
Interim Deputy Secretary of
State for Elections
Secretary of State's Office
P.O. Box 1767
Jefferson City, MO 65102
P: (573) 751-1869
F: (573) 526-3242
E: Waylene.hiles@sos.mo.gov

MONTANA
Ms. Lisa Kimmet
Deputy for Elections
Office of the Secretary of State
P.O. Box 202801
Helena, MT 59620
P: (406) 444-5376
F: (406) 444-2023
E: lkimmet@mt.gov

NEBRASKA
Mr. Neal Erickson
Deputy Secretary of State
Election Administration
State Capitol, Room 345
Lincoln, NE 68509
P: (402) 471-4127
F: (402) 471-7834
E: neal.erickson
   @nebraska.gov

NEVADA
Mr. Richard Hy
Deputy Secretary of State
Office of the Secretary of State
101 North Carson Street, Suite 3
Carson City, NV 89701
P: (775) 684-5705
E: HyR@sos.nv.gov

NEW HAMPSHIRE
Mr. Anthony B. Stevens
Assistant Secretary of State
Office of the Secretary of State
State House, Room 204
Concord, NH 03301
P: (603) 271-8238
F: (603) 271-7933
E: Anthony.Stevens
   @sos.nh.gov

NEW JERSEY
Mr. Robert F. Giles
Director
Division of Elections
225 West State Street, 3rd Floor
P.O. Box 304
Trenton, NJ 08625
P: (609) 292-3760
F: (609) 777-1280
E: Robert.Giles
   @sos.state.nj.us

NEW MEXICO
Ms. Kari Fresquez
Interim Elections Director
Bureau of Elections
Secretary of State's Office
325 Don Gaspar, Suite 300
Santa Fe, NM 87501
P: (505) 827-3600
F: (505) 827-8403
E: kari.fresquez
   @state.nm.us

NEW YORK
Mr. Robert A. Brehm
Co-Director
State Board of Elections
40 North Pearl Street, Suite 5
Albany, NY 12207
P: (518) 474-8100
F: (518) 486-4068
E: Robert.Brehm
   @elections.ny.gov

Mr. Todd D. Valentine
Co-Director
State Board of Elections
40 North Pearl Street, Suite 5
Albany, NY 12207
P: (518) 474-8100
F: (518) 486-4068
E: Todd.Valentine
   @elections.ny.gov

NORTH CAROLINA
Ms. Kim Westbrook Strach
Executive Director
Board of Elections
441 North Harrington Street
P.O. Box 27255
Raleigh, NC 27611
P: (919) 733-7173
F: (919) 715-0135
E: kim.strach@ncsbe.gov

NORTH DAKOTA
Mr. Jim Silrum
Deputy Secretary of State
Office of the Secretary of State
600 East Boulevard Avenue
Department 108
Bismarck, ND 58505
P: (701) 328-3660
F: (701) 328-1690
E: jsilrum@nd.gov

OHIO
Mr. Matthew Damschroder
Deputy Assistant Secretary of
State
Office of the Secretary of State
180 East Broad Street, 15th
Floor
Columbus, OH 43215
P: (614) 466-5515
F: (614) 485-7526
E: mdamschroder
   @ohiosecretaryofstate.gov

OKLAHOMA
Mr. Paul Ziriax
Secretary
State Election Board
Room 6, State Capitol
Oklahoma City, OK 73105
P: (405) 522-6615
F: (405) 521-6457
E: pziriax@elections.ok.gov

OREGON
Mr. Jim Williams
Director of Elections
Office of the Secretary of State
Public Service Building, Suite
501
Salem, OR 97301
P: (503) 986-1518
F: (503) 373-7414
E: James.R.Williams
   @state.or.us

PENNSYLVANIA

Mr. Jonathan M. Marks
Commissioner
Bureau of Commissions,
Elections & Legislation
Department of State
210 North Office Building
Harrisburg, PA 17120
P: (717) 787-5280
F: (717) 705-0721
E: RA-BCEL@pa.gov

PUERTO RICO

Hon. Angel A.
  Gonzalez Roman
Election Commission
P.O. Box 195552
San Juan, PR 00919
P: (787) 777-8675
F: (787) 296-0173
E: aagonzalez
  @cee.gobierno.pr

RHODE ISLAND

Mr. Robert Kando
Executive Director
State Board of Elections
50 Branch Avenue
Providence, RI 02904
P: (401) 222-2345
F: (401) 222-3135
E: campaignfinance
  @elections.ri.gov

SOUTH CAROLINA

Ms. Marci Andino
Executive Director
State Election Commission
P.O. Box 5987
Columbia, SC 29250
P: (803) 734-9060
F: (803) 734-9366
E: marci@elections.sc.gov

SOUTH DAKOTA

Ms. Kea Warner
Deputy Secretary of State,
Elections Division
Office of the Secretary of State
500 East Capitol Avenue, Suite
204
Pierre, SD 57501
P: (605) 773-5003
F: (605) 773-6580
E: Kea.Warner@state.sd.us

TENNESSEE

Mr. Mark K. Goins
Coordinator of Elections
Secretary of State's Office
312 Rosa L. Parks Avenue
Snodgrass Tower, 9th Floor
Nashville, TN 37243
P: (615) 741-7956
F: (615) 741-1278
E: Mark.Goins@tn.gov

TEXAS

Mr. Keith Ingram
Director of Elections
Elections Division
Office of the Secretary of State
P.O.Box 12697
Austin, TX 78711
P: (512) 463-9871
F: (512) 475-2811
E: kingram@sos.state.tx.us

U.S. VIRGIN ISLANDS

Ms. Caroline Fawkes
Supervisor of Elections
Election System
P.O. Box 1499, Kingshill
St. Croix, VI 00851
P: (340) 773-1021
F: (340) 773-4523
E: caroline.fawkes@vi.gov

UTAH

Mr. Mark Thomas
Director of Elections
Office of the Lieutenant
Governor
Utah State Capitol Suite 220
P.O. Box 142325
Salt Lake City, UT 84114
P: (801) 538-1041
F: (801) 538-1133
E: mjthomas@utah.gov

VERMONT

Mr. Will Senning
Director of Elections &
Campaign Finance
Office of the Secretary of State
26 Terrace Street, Drawer 09
Montpelier, VT 05609
P: (802) 828-2363
F: (802) 828-5171
E: will.senning
  @sec.state.vt.us

VIRGINIA

Mr. Edgardo Cortes
Commissioner
Department of Elections
Washington Building
1100 Bank Street, First Floor
Richmond, VA 23219
P: (804) 864-8903
F: (804) 371-0194
E: edgardo.cortes
  @elections.virginia.gov

WASHINGTON

Ms. Lori Augino
Director of Elections
Elections Division
Office of Secretary of State
Legislative Building, P.O. Box
40220
Olympia, WA 98504
P: (360) 725-5771
F: (360) 664-4619
E: lori.augino@sos.wa.gov

WEST VIRGINIA

Ms. Layna Valentine Brown
Manager of Elections
Office of the Secretary of State
State Capitol, Room 157-K
1900 Kanawha Boulevard, East
Charleston, WV 25305
P: (304) 558-6000
F: (304) 558-0900

WISCONSIN

Mr. Michael Haas
Elections Division Administrator
Government Accountability
Board
212 East Washington Avenue,
3rd Floor
P.O. Box 7984
Madison, WI 53707
P: (608) 266-0136
F: (608) 267-0500
E: Michael.Haas@wi.gov

Mr. Kevin J. Kennedy
Executive Director & General
Counsel
Government Accountability
Board
P.O. Box 7984
Madison, WI 53707
P: (608) 266-8005
F: (608) 267-0500
E: gab@wi.gov

WYOMING

Ms. Peggy Nighswonger
Director of Elections
Secretary of State's Office
200 West 24th Street
Cheyenne, WY 82002
P: (307) 777-3573
F: (307) 777-7640
E: peggy.nighswonger
  @wyo.gov

Emergency Management

Prepares, maintains and/or implements state disasters plans and coordinates emergency activities.

Information provided by:

National Emergency Management Association
Trina Sheets
Executive Director
P.O. Box 11910
Lexington, KY 40578
P: (859) 244-8000
F: (859) 244-8239
tsheets@csg.org
www.nemaweb.org

ALABAMA
Mr. Art Faulkner
Director
Emergency Management Agency
5898 County Road 41
P.O. Box 2160
Clanton, AL 35046
P: (205) 280-2201
F: (205) 280-2410
E: art.faulkner
   @ema.alabama.gov

ALASKA
Mr. Mike O'Hare
Director
Division of Homeland Security & Emergency Management
Military & Veterans Affairs
P.O. Box 5750
Joint Base Elemendorf
Richardson, AK 99505
P: (907) 428-7066
E: mike.ohare@alaska.gov

AMERICAN SAMOA
Iuniasolua Savusa
Director
State Department of Homeland Security
P.O. Box 4567
Pago Pago, AS 96799
P: (684) 699-0411
E: i.savusa@asdhs.as.gov

ARIZONA
Ms. Wendy Smith-Reeve
Director
State Division of Emergency Management
5636 East McDowell Road
Phoenix, AZ 85008
P: (602) 464-6203
F: (602) 464-6356
E: wendy.smith-reeve
   @azdema.gov

ARKANSAS
Mr. David Maxwell
Director
Department of Emergency Management
Building 9501
Camp Joseph T. Robinson
North Little Rock, AR 72199
P: (501) 683-7834
F: (501) 683-7890
E: david.maxwell
   @adem.arkansas.gov

CALIFORNIA
Mr. Mark Ghilarducci
Director
Governor's Office of Emergency Services
3650 Schriever Avenue
Mather, CA 95655
P: (916) 845-8506
F: (916) 845-8511
E: mark.ghilarducci
   @caloes.ca.gov

COLORADO
Mr. Dave Hard
Director
Division of Homeland Security & Emergency Management
9195 East Mineral Avenue
Centennial, CO 80112
P: (720) 852-6611
F: (720) 852-6750
E: dave.hard@state.co.us

CONNECTICUT
Mr. William J. Hackett
Director
State Division of Emergency Management & Homeland Security
25 Sigourney Street, 6th Floor
Hartford, CT 06106
P: (860) 256-0801
F: (860) 256-0855
E: william.j.hackett@ct.gov

DELAWARE
Mr. James E. Turner III
Director
State Emergency Management Agency
165 Brick Store Landing Road
Smyrna, DE 19977
P: (302) 659-2240
F: (302) 659-6855
E: jamie.turner@state.de.us

DISTRICT OF COLUMBIA
Mr. Chris Geldart
Director
Homeland Security & Emergency Management Agency
2720 Martin Luther King Jr. Avenue,
Southeast, 2nd Floor
Washington, DC 20032
P: (202) 481-3180
F: (202) 715-7288
E: Chris.Geldart@dc.gov

FLORIDA
Mr. Bryan Koon
Director
Division of Emergency Management
2555 Shumard Oak Boulevard
Tallahassee, FL 32399
P: (850) 413-9930
F: (850) 488-1016
E: bryan.koon
   @em.myflorida.com

GEORGIA
Mr. James B. Butterworth
Director
Emergency Management Agency/Office of Homeland Security
935 East Confederate Avenue, Southeast
Atlanta, GA 30316
P: (404) 635-7008
E: jim.butterworth
   @gema.ga.gov

GUAM
Mr. James T. McDonald
Director
Office of Homeland Security & Civil Defense
221-B Chalan Palasyo
Agana Heights, GU 96910
P: (671) 475-9600
F: (671) 477-3727
E: jim.mcdonald
   @ghs.guam.gov

HAWAII
Mr. Doug Mayne
CEM, Director
State Emergency Management Agency
3949 Diamond Head Road
Honolulu, HI 96816
P: (808) 733-4300 Ext. 501
F: (808) 733-4287
E: dmayne@scd.hawaii.gov

IDAHO
Colonel Brad Richy
Director
State Bureau of Homeland Security
4040 West Guard Street,
Building 600
Boise, ID 83705
P: (208) 258-6591
F: (208) 422-3044
E: brichy@bhs.idaho.gov

ILLINOIS
Mr. James Joseph
Director
State Emergency Management Agency
2200 South Dirksen Parkway
Springfield, IL 62703
P: (217) 782-2700
E: james.joseph
   @illinois.gov

INDIANA
Mr. David Kane
Director
State Department of Homeland Security
302 West Washington Street,
Room E-208
Indianapolis, IN 46204
P: (317) 232-6139
E: dkane@dhs.in.gov

IOWA
Mr. Mark J. Schouten
Director
Homeland Security & Emergency Management Department
7900 Hickmand Road, Suite 500
Windsor Heights, IA 50324
P: (515) 725-3223
F: (515) 725-3260
E: mark.schouten@iowa.gov

KANSAS
Ms. Angee Morgan
Director
Division of Emergency
Management
2800 Southwest Topeka
Boulevard
Topeka, KS 66611
P: (785) 274-1403
F: (785) 274-1426
E: angelynn.t.morgan.nfg
  @mail.mil

KENTUCKY
Mr. Michael Dossett
Director
State Division of Emergency
Management
Boone National Guard Center
100 Minuteman Parkway, EOC
Room 106
Frankfort, KY 40601
P: (502) 607-1682
E: michael.e.dossett.nfg
  @mail.mil

LOUISIANA
Mr. Kevin Davis
Director
Governor's Office of Homeland
Security & Emergency
Preparedness
7667 Independence Boulevard
Baton Rouge, LA 70608
P: (225) 922-1503
F: (225) 925-7501
E: kevin.davis@la.gov

MAINE
Mr. Bruce Fitzgerald
Director
State Emergency Management
Agency
45 Commerce Drive, Suite #2
Augusta, ME 04333
P: (207) 624-4400
F: (207) 287-3178
E: Bruce.F.Fitzgerald
  @maine.gov

MARYLAND
Mr. Clay Stamp
Director
State Emergency Management
Agency
5401 Rue Saint Lo Drive
Reisterstown, MD 21136
P: (410) 517-3625
E: clay.stamp@maryland.gov

MASSACHUSETTS
Mr. Kurt Schwartz
Director
State Emergency Management
Agency
Executive Office of Public
Safety
400 Worcester Road
Framingham, MA 01702
P: (508) 820-2014
F: (508) 820-2015
E: kurt.schwartz
  @state.ma.us

MICHIGAN
Captain Chris A. Kelenske
Director
State Police Emergency
Management & Homeland
Security
State Police
4000 Collins Road
Lansing, MI 48910
P: (517) 333-5043
F: (517) 333-4987
E: kelenskec@michigan.gov

MINNESOTA
Mr. Joseph Kelly
Director
State Division of Homeland
Security & Emergency
Management
Department of Public Safety
445 Minnesota Street, Suite 223
St. Paul, MN 55101
P: (651) 201-7404
E: joseph.kelly@state.mn.us

MISSISSIPPI
Mr. Robert Latham
Director
State Emergency Management
Agency
#1 MEMA Drive
P.O. Box 5644
Pearl, MS 39288
P: (601) 933-6882
F: (601) 933-6810
E: rlatham@mema.ms.gov

MISSOURI
Mr. Ron Walker
Director
State Emergency Management
Agency
P.O. Box 116
Jefferson City, MO 65102
P: (573) 526-9101
F: (573) 634-7966
E: ron.walker
  @sema.dps.mo.gov

MONTANA
Mr. Brad Livingston
Director
State Disaster & Emergency
Services
P.O. Box 4789
Fort Harrison, MT 59636
P: (406) 324-4766
E: blivingston@mt.gov

NEBRASKA
Mr. Bryan Tuma
Director
State Emergency Management
Agency
2433 Northwest 24th Street
Lincoln, NE 68524
P: (402) 471-7410
E: Bryan.Tuma@nebraska.gov

NEVADA
Mr. Christopher B. Smith
Director
Division of Emergency
Management/Homeland
Security
Public Safety
2478 Fairview Drive
Carson City, NV 89701
P: (775) 687-0300
F: (775) 687-0322
E: cbsmith@dps.state.nv.us

NEW HAMPSHIRE
Mr. Perry Plummer
Director
Homeland Security &
Emergency Management
Department of Safety
33 Hazen Drive
Concord, NH 03305
P: (603) 271-2231
F: (603) 271-6336
E: perry.plummer@dos.nh.gov

NEW JERSEY
Lt. Col. Christian Schulz
Director
State Police, Emergency
Management & Homeland
Security
P.O. Box 7068
West Trenton, NJ 08628
P: (609) 882-2000 Ext. 6161
E: lpp4657@gw.njsp.org

NEW MEXICO
Mr. Jay Mitchell
Director
State Department of Homeland
Security & Emergency
Management
P.O. Box 27111
Santa Fe, NM 87502
P: (505) 476-9655
E: jay.mitchell@state.nm.us

NEW YORK
Mr. Kevin Wisely
Director
State Office of Emergency
Management
1220 Washington Avenue
Building 22, Suite 101
Albany, NY 12226
P: (518) 292-2301
E: kevin.wisely
  @dhses.ny.gov

NORTH CAROLINA
Mr. Michael Sprayberry
Director
State Division of Emergency
Management
1636 Gold Star Drive
Raleigh, NC 27607
P: (919) 825-2291
F: (919) 733-5406
E: mike.sprayberry
  @ncdps.gov

NORTH DAKOTA
Mr. Greg Wilz
Director
Department of Emergency
Services
Building 35, Fraine Barracks
Road
Bismarck, ND 58506
P: (701) 328-8100 Ext. 8101
F: (701) 328-8181
E: gwilz@nd.gov

NORTHERN MARIANA
ISLANDS
Mr. Marvin P. Seman
Director
Homeland Security &
Emergency Management
Office of the Governor
Caller Box 10007
Saipan, MP 95950
P: (670) 664-2216
F: (670) 664-2211
E: marvin.seman@gmail.com

Emergency Management

OHIO
Mr. Evan Schumann
Director
State Emergency Management
Agency
2855 West Dublin-Granville
Road
Columbus, OH 43235
P: (614) 889-7180
E: ewschumann@dps.ohio.gov

OKLAHOMA
Mr. Albert Ashwood
Director
Department of Emergency
Management
P.O. Box 53365
Oklahoma City, OK 73105
P: (405) 521-2481
F: (405) 521-4053
E: albert.ashwood
   @oem.ok.gov

OREGON
Mr. Andrew Phelps
Director
State Office of Emergency
Management
P.O. Box 14370
Salem, OR 97309
P: (503) 373-2911 Ext 22292
E: andrew.phelps
   @oem.state.or.us

PENNSYLVANIA
Mr. Richard Flinn Jr.
Director
State Emergency Management
Agency
2605 Interstate Drive
Harrisburg, PA 17110
P: (717) 651-2007
E: rflinn@pa.gov

PUERTO RICO
Mr. Miguel Rios Torres
Director
Emergency Management
Agency
P.O. Box 194140
San Juan, PR 00919
P: (787) 724-0124 Ext. 1167
F: (787) 725-4244
E: mrios@prema.pr.gov

RHODE ISLAND
Mr. Peter Gaynor
Director
State Emergency Management
Agency
645 New London Avenue
Cranston, RI 02920
P: (401) 946-9996
E: peter.gaynor@ema.ri.gov

SOUTH CAROLINA
Kim Stenson
Director
State Emergency Management
Division
2779 Fish Hatchery Road
West Columbia, SC 29172
P: (803) 737-8566
F: (803) 737-8570
E: kstenson@emd.sc.gov

SOUTH DAKOTA
Ms. Tina Titze
Director
State Office of Emergency
Management
118 West Capitol Avenue
Pierre, SD 57501
P: (605) 773-3231
E: tina.titze@state.sd.us

TENNESSEE
Mr. David Purkey
Director
State Emergency Management
Agency
3041 Sidco Drive
Nashville, TN 37204
P: (615) 741-4332
E: David.Purkey@tn.gov

TEXAS
Nim Kidd
Director
State Department of Public
Safety
5805 North Lamar Boulevard
P.O. Box 4087
Austin, TX 78752
P: (512) 424-2443
F: (512) 424-2444
E: nim.kidd
   @txdps.state.tx.us

U.S. VIRGIN ISLANDS
Ms. Mona Barnes
Director
Territorial Emergency
Management Agency
St. Thomas, VI 00802
P: (340) 773-2244
E: Mona.Barnes
   @vitema.vi.gov

UTAH
Mr. Kris J. Hamlet
Director
Division of Emergency
Management
1110 State Office Building
Salt Lake City, UT 84114
P: (801) 538-9553
F: (801) 965-4608
E: krishamlet@utah.gov

VERMONT
Mr. Joe Flynn
Director
Division of Emergency
Management
103 South Main Street
Waterbury, VT 05671
P: (802) 241-5376
F: (802) 244-5556
E: joe.flynn@state.vt.us

VIRGINIA
Mr. Jeffrey Stern
Director
State Department of Emergency
Management
10501 Trade Court
Richmond, VA 23236
P: (804) 897-6501
E: jeff.stern
   @vdem.virginia.gov

WASHINGTON
Mr. Robert Ezelle
Director
State Emergency Management
Division
20 Aviation Drive
Building 20
Camp Murray, WA 98430
P: (253) 512-7003
F: (253) 512-7207
E: Robert.ezelle@mil.wa.gov

WEST VIRGINIA
Mr. Jimmy Gianato
Director
Division of Homeland Security
& Emergency Management
1900 Kanawha Boulevard
Building 1, Room EB-80
Charleston, WV 25305
P: (304) 558-5380
F: (304) 344-4538
E: jimmy.j.gianato@wv.gov

WISCONSIN
Mr. Brian M. Satula
Director
State Division of Emergency
Management
2400 Wright Street
P.O. Box 7865
Madison, WI 53704
P: (608) 242-3210
F: (608) 242-3247
E: brian.satula
   @wisconsin.gov

WYOMING
Mr. Guy Cameron
Director
Office of Homeland Security
5500 Bishop Boulevard
East Door
Cheyenne, WY 82002
P: (307) 777-8511
F: (307) 635-6017
E: guy.cameron@wyo.gov

Employment Services

Provides job counseling, testing and placement services in the state.

ALABAMA
Mr. Fitzgerald Washington
Commissioner
Department of Labor
649 Monroe Street
Montgomery, AL 36131
P: (334) 242-8990

ALASKA
Mr. James Harvey
Director
Division of Employment
Security
P.O. Box 115509
Juneau, AK 99811
P: (907) 465-2712
F: (907) 465-4537
E: james.harvey@alaska.gov

AMERICAN SAMOA
Mr. Le'i S. Thompson
Director
Department of Human
Resources
Executive Office Building
AP Lutali, 2nd Floor
Pago Pago, AS 96799
P: (684) 644-4485
F: (684) 633-1139
E: sonnythompson
   @samoatelco.com

ARIZONA
Mr. James Apperson
Assistant Director
Division of Employment &
Rehabilitation Services
Department of Economic
Security
1717 West Jefferson Street
Phoenix, AZ 85007
P: (602) 542-4910
E: japperson@azdes.gov

ARKANSAS
Mr. Daryl Bassett
Director
Department of Workforce
Services
#2 Capitol Mall
Little Rock, AR 72201
P: (501) 682-2121
F: (501) 682-8845
E: daryl.bassett
   @arkansas.gov

COLORADO
Ms. Ellen Golombek
Executive Director
Department of Labor &
Employment
633 17th Street, Suite 201
Denver, CO 80202
P: (303) 318-8020
F: (303) 318-8047
E: Ellen.Golombek
   @state.co.us

CONNECTICUT
Ms. Sharon Palmer
Commissioner
Department of Labor
200 Folly Brook Boulevard
Westerfield, CT 06109
P: (860) 263-6505
F: (850) 263-6529
E: sharon.palmer@ct.gov

DELAWARE
Ms. Lori Reeder
Director
Department of Labor
Division of Employment &
Training
4425 North Market Street
Wilmington, DE 19802
P: (302) 761-8085
E: lori.reeder@state.de.us

DISTRICT OF COLUMBIA
Mr. F. Thomas Luparello
Acting Director
Department of Employment
Services
4058 Minnesota Avenue,
Northeast
Washington, DC 20019
P: (202) 724-7000
F: (202) 673-6993
E: does@dc.gov

GEORGIA
Hon. Mark Butler (R)
Commissioner
Department of Labor
148 International Boulevard
Northeast
Atlanta, GA 30303
P: (404) 232-7300
F: (404) 656-2683
E: commissioner@gdol.ga.gov

GUAM
Mr. Manuel Q. Cruz
Director
Department of Labor
Government of Guam
P.O. Box 9970
Tamuning, GU 96931
P: (671) 647-6510
F: (671) 674-6517

HAWAII
Ms. Elaine Young
Acting Director
Workforce Development
Division
Ke'elikolani Building
830 Punchbowl Street
Honolulu, HI 96813
P: (808) 586-8844
F: (808) 586-9099
E: dlir.director@hawaii.gov

IDAHO
Mr. Kenneth D. Edmunds
Director
Department of Labor
317 West Main Street
Boise, ID 83735
P: (208) 334-6110
F: (208) 334-6430
E: kenneth.edmunds
   @labor.idaho.gov

INDIANA
Mr. Steve Braun
Commissioner
Department of Workforce
Development
Government Center South
10 North Senate Avenue
Indianapolis, IN 46204
P: (317) 232-7676
E: SBraun@dwd.IN.gov

IOWA
Ms. Teresa Wahlert
Agency Director
Workforce Development
1000 East Grand Avenue
Des Moines, IA 50319
P: (515) 281-5364
E: teresa.wahlert
   @iwd.iowa.gov

KANSAS
Mr. Pat George
Secretary
Department of Commerce
1000 Southwest Jackson Street,
Suite 100
Topeka, KS 66612
P: (785) 296-2741
F: (785) 296-5055
E: pgeorge
   @kansascommerce.com

LOUISIANA
Ms. Shannon Templet
Director
Department of State Civil
Service
1201 North Third Street, Suite
3-280
P.O. Box 94111
Baton Rouge, LA 70804
P: (225) 342-8272
F: (225) 342-0966
E: shannon.templet@la.gov

MAINE
Ms. Jeanne Paquette
Commissioner
Department of Labor
54 State House Station
Augusta, ME 04333
P: (207) 623-7900
F: (207) 623-7934
E: jeanne.paquette
   @maine.gov

MARYLAND
Ms. Cynthia Kollner
Executive Director
Office of Personnel Services &
Benefits
Department of Budget &
Management
301 West Preston Street, Room
609
Baltimore, MD 21201
P: (410) 767-4715
F: (410) 333-5262
E: ckollner@dbm.state.md.us

MASSACHUSETTS
Mr. Ronald L. Walker II
Secretary
Executive Office of Labor &
Workforce Development
One Ashburton Place, Suite
2112
Boston, MA 02108
P: (617) 626-7122
F: (617) 727-1090

MINNESOTA
Ms. Katie Clark Sieben
Commissioner
Department of Employment &
Economic Development
1st National Bank Building
332 Minnesota Street, Suite
E200
St. Paul, MN 55101
P: (651) 259-7119
F: (651) 296-4772
E: katie.clark.sieben
   @state.mn.us

Employment Services

MISSISSIPPI
Mr. Mark Henry
Executive Director
Department of Employment
Security
1235 Echelon Parkway
P.O. Box 1699
Jackson, MS 39215
P: (601) 321-6000
F: (601) 321-6104
E: mhenry@mdes.ms.gov

MISSOURI
Mr. Mike Downing
Director
Department of Economic
Development
301 West High Street
P.O. Box 1157
Jefferson City, MO 65102
P: (573) 751-4962
F: (573) 526-7700
E: ecodev@ded.mo.gov

MONTANA
Ms. Pam Bucy
Commissioner
Department of Labor & Industry
P.O. Box 1728
Helena, MT 59624
P: (406) 444-2840
F: (406) 444-1419
E: pbucy@mt.gov

NEBRASKA
Ms. Brenda Hicks-Sorensen
Director
Department of Economic
Development
550 South 16th Street
Lincoln, NE 68508
P: (402) 471-3125
E: brenda.hicks-sorensen
    @nebraska.gov

NEVADA
Ms. Renee Olson
Administrator
Department of Employment,
Training & Rehabilitation
Employment Security Division
500 East Third Street
Carson City, NV 89713
P: (775) 684-3909
F: (775) 684-3850
E: rlolson@nvdetr.org

NEW JERSEY
Mr. Harold Wirths
Commissioner
Department of Labor &
Workforce Development
P.O. Box 110
Trenton, NJ 08625
P: (609) 292-2323
F: (609) 633-9271
E: hal.wirths
    @dol.state.nj.us

NEW MEXICO
Ms. Celina Bussey
Secretary
Department of Workforce
Solutions
401 Broadway, Northeast
P.O. Box 1928
Albuquerque, NM 87103
P: (505) 841-8405
F: (505) 841-8491
E: celina.bussey
    @state.nm.us

NEW YORK
Mr. Peter M. Rivera
Commissioner
Department of Labor
W. Averell Harriman State
Office Campus
Building 12
Albany, NY 12240
P: (518) 457-9000
F: (518) 485-6297

NORTH CAROLINA
Mr. Dale R. Folwell
Assistant Secretary
Division of Employment
Security
700 Wade Avenue
P.O. Box 25903
Raleigh, NC 27611
P: (919) 707-1600
E: assistantsecretary
    @nccommerce.com

NORTH DAKOTA
Mr. Darren Brostrom
Interim Executive Director
Job Service North Dakota
P.O. Box 5507
Bismarck, ND 58506
P: (701) 328-2825
F: (701) 328-4000
E: dbrostro@nd.gov

**NORTHERN MARIANA
ISLANDS**
Mr. Alfred A. Pangelinan
Director of Employment
Services
Department of Labor
Capitol Hill
Saipan, MP 96950
P: (670) 664-3190
F: (670) 236-0994

OHIO
Mr. Bruce Madson
Assistant Director, Employment
Services
Department of Job & Family
Services
30 East Broad Street, 32nd Floor
Columbus, OH 43215
P: (614) 466-9195
F: (614) 466-2815

OKLAHOMA
Mr. Richard McPherson
Executive Director
Employment Security
Commission
2401 North Lincoln Boulevard
P.O. Box 52003
Oklahoma City, OK 73152
P: (405) 557-7201

Ms. Lucinda Meltabarger
Administrator
Human Capital Management
Division
2101 North Lincoln Boulevard,
Room G-80
Oklahoma City, OK 73105
P: (405) 521-3928
F: (405) 522-0694
E: lucinda.meltabarger
    @omes.ok.gov

OREGON
Ms. Lisa Nisenfeld
Director
Employment Department
875 Union Street, Northeast
Salem, OR 97311
P: (503) 947-1477
F: (503) 947-1472
E: lisa.nisenfeld
    @oregon.gov

PENNSYLVANIA
Ms. Sharon Minnich
Secretary
Governor's Office of
Administration
207 Finance Building
Harrisburg, PA 17102
P: (717) 772-5174
E: sminnich@pa.gov

PUERTO RICO
Mr. Vance Thomas
Secretary
Department of Labor & Human
Resources
P.O. Box 195540
Hato Rey, PR 00918
P: (787) 754-2119
F: (787) 753-9550

RHODE ISLAND
Mr. Scott Jensen
Director
Department of Labor & Training
Center General Complex
1511 Pontiac Avenue
Cranston, RI 02920
P: (401) 462-8000
F: (401) 462-8872
E: director-dlt@dlt.ri.gov

SOUTH CAROLINA
Ms. Cheryl M. Stanton
Executive Director
Department of Employment &
Workforce
1550 Gadsden Street
P.O. Box 995
Columbia, SC 29202
P: (803) 737-2617
E: cstanton@dew.sc.gov

SOUTH DAKOTA
Ms. Marcia Hultman
Secretary
Department of Labor &
Regulation
700 Governors Drive
Pierre, SD 57501
P: (605) 773-3101
F: (605) 773-6184
E: marcia.hultman
    @state.sd.us

TENNESSEE
Mr. Burns Phillips
Commissioner
Department of Labor &
Workforce Development
220 French Landing Drive
Nashville, TN 37243
P: (615) 741-6642
F: (615) 741-5078
E: burns.phillips@tn.gov

TEXAS
Mr. Larry E. Temple
Executive Director
Workforce Commission
101 East 15th Street
Austin, TX 78778
P: (512) 463-0735
F: (512) 475-2321
E: larry.temple
    @twc.state.tx.us

U.S. VIRGIN ISLANDS
Mr. Albert Bryan Jr.
Commissioner of Labor
Department of Labor
4401 Sion Farm
Christiansted, VI 00820
P: (340) 773-1994
F: (340) 773-0094
E: abryan@vidol.gov

UTAH
Mr. John Pierpont
Executive Director
Department of Workforce
Service
P.O. Box 45249
Salt Lake City, UT 84145
P: (801) 526-9210
F: (801) 526-9211
E: jpierpo@utah.gov

VERMONT
Ms. Annie Noonan
Commissioner
Department of Labor
5 Green Mountain Drive
P.O. Box 488
Montpelier, VT 05601
P: (802) 828-4301
F: (802) 828-4022
E: annie.noonan@state.vt.us

VIRGINIA
Ms. Ellen Marie Hess
Commissioner
Employment Commission
703 East Main Street
Richmond, VA 23219
E: ellen.hess
    @vec.virginia.gov

WASHINGTON
Mr. Glen Christopherson
Director
State Human Resources
Division
128 10th Avenue, Southeast
P.O. Box 43113
Olympia, WA 98504
P: (360) 407-4104
F: (360) 753-1003
E: glen.christopherson
    @ofm.wa.gov

Mr. Dale Peinecke
Commissioner
Employment Security
Department
212 Maple Park Avenue,
Southeast
P.O. Box 9046
Olympia, WA 98507
P: (360) 902-9500
E: dpeinecke@esd.wa.gov

WEST VIRGINIA
Mr. J. Keith Burdette
Cabinet Secretary
Department of Commerce
Capitol Complex Building 6,
Room 525
1900 Kanawha Boulevard East
Charleston, WV 25305
P: (304) 558-2234
F: (304) 558-1189
E: J.Keith.Burdette@wv.gov

WYOMING
Ms. Joan K. Evans
Director
Department of Workforce
Services
122 West 25th Street
Herschler Building, 2nd Floor
East
Cheyenne, WY 82002
P: (307) 777-8728
F: (307) 777-5857
E: joan.evans@wyo.gov

Energy

Develops and administers programs relating to energy conservation, alternative energy research and development, and energy information.

Information provided by:

National Association of State Energy Officials
David Terry
Executive Director
1414 Prince Street, Suite 200
Alexandria, VA 22314
P: (703) 299-8800
F: (703) 299-6208
dterry@naseo.org
www.naseo.org

ALABAMA
Ms. Terri L. Adams
Division Director
Energy Division
Economic & Community Affairs
401 Adams Avenue, P.O. Box 5690
Montgomery, AL 36103
P: (334) 242-5292
F: (334) 242-0552
E: terri.adams
    @adeca.alabama.gov

ALASKA
Ms. Rebecca Garrett
Project Development Specialist
State Energy Authority
813 West Northern Lights Boulevard
Anchorage, AK 99503
P: (907) 771-3042
F: (907) 771-3044
E: rgarrett@aidea.org

AMERICAN SAMOA
Taliga Vaiolo
WAP Program Assistant III
Territorial Energy Office
American Samoa Government
Samoa Energy House, Tauna
Pago Pago, AS 96799
P: (684) 699-1101
F: (684) 699-2835
E: t.vaiolo@asgteo.com

ARIZONA
Mr. Chris McIsaac
Policy Advisor for Energy & Environment
Governor's Office of Energy Policy
1700 West Washington, Suite 220
Phoenix, AZ 85007
P: (602) 542-3424
F: (602) 771-1203
E: cmcisaac@az.gov

ARKANSAS
Mr. Mitchell Simpson
Deputy Director
State Energy Office
Economic Development Commission
900 West Capitol, Suite 400
Little Rock, AR 72201
P: (501) 682-7346
F: (501) 682-7499
E: msimpson@arkansasedc.com

CALIFORNIA
Mr. Rob Oglesby
Executive Director
State Energy Commission
1516 9th Street, MS #39
Sacramento, CA 95814
P: (916) 654-4996
F: (916) 654-4423
E: rob.oglesby
    @energy.ca.gov

COLORADO
Mr. Jeff Ackermann
Director
State Energy Office
1580 Logan Street, Suite 100
Denver, CO 80203
P: (303) 866-2100
F: (303) 866-2930
E: jeffrey.ackermann
    @state.co.us

CONNECTICUT
Ms. Katie Scharf Dykes
Deputy Commissioner
Department of Energy & Environmental Protection
79 Elm Street
Hartford, CT 06106
P: (860) 424-3000
F: (860) 418-6495
E: katie.dykes@ct.gov

DELAWARE
Mr. Philip J. Cherry
Division Director
Division of Clean Energy & Climate
1203 College Park Drive, Suite 101
Dover, DE 19904
P: (302) 735-3480
F: (302) 739-1840
E: philip.cherry
    @state.de.us

DISTRICT OF COLUMBIA
Mr. Tommy Wells
Acting Director
Energy Office, Department of the Environment
1200 First Street, Northeast
Fifth Floor
Washington, DC 20002
P: (202) 535-2600
F: (202) 535-1359
E: tommy.wells@dc.gov

FLORIDA
Ms. Kelley Smith Burk
Acting Director
Department of Agriculture & Consumer Services
600 South Calhoun Street, Suite 251
Tallahassee, FL 32399
P: (850) 617-7484
E: kelley.smithburk
    @freshfromflorida.com

GEORGIA
Mr. David Gipson
Director, Energy Resources Division
State Environmental Finance Authority
233 Peachtree Street, Northeast
Harris Tower, Suite 900
Atlanta, GA 30303
P: (404) 584-1007
F: (404) 584-1008
E: dgipson@gefa.ga.gov

GUAM
Ms. Lorilee T. Crisostomo
Administrator
Energy Office
548 North Marine Corps Drive
Tamuning, GU 96913
P: (671) 646-4361
F: (671) 477-9402
E: lorilee.crisostomo
    @epa.guam.gov

HAWAII
Ms. Mark Glick
Energy Administrator
Department of Business, Economic Development & Tourism
235 South Beretania Street, 5th Floor
P.O. Box 2359
Honolulu, HI 96813
P: (808) 587-3807
F: (808) 586-2536
E: mark.b.glick
    @dbedt.hawaii.gov

IDAHO
Mr. John Chatburn
Administrator
State Office of Energy Resources
304 North 8th Street, Suite 250
P.O. Box 83720
Boise, ID 83720
P: (208) 332-1660
F: (208) 332-1661
E: John.Chatburn
    @oer.idaho.gov

ILLINOIS
Ms. Molly Lunn
Assistant Deputy Director
Energy & Recycling Office
Commerce & Economic Opportunity
500 East Monroe
Springfield, IL 62701
P: (217) 785-3416
F: (217) 558-2647
E: marion.lunn@illinois.gov

INDIANA
Mr. Tristan Vance
Director
State Office of Energy Development
1 North Capitol, Suite 600
Indianapolis, IN 46204
P: (317) 232-8939
F: (317) 233-6887
E: TVance1@oed.IN.gov

IOWA
Mr. Brian Selinger
Team Lead
State Energy Division
Economic Development Authority
200 East Grand Avenue
Des Moines, IA 50309
P: (515) 725-3000
F: (515) 725-3010
E: brian.selinger@iowa.gov

KANSAS
Mr. Terry Steuber
Manager of Commercial &
Industrial Programs
State Energy Office
State Corporation Commission
1500 Southwest Arrowhead
Road
Topeka, KS 66604
P: (785) 271-3152
F: (785) 271-3268
E: t.steuber@kcc.ks.gov

KENTUCKY
Mr. John H. Davies
Deputy Commissioner
Department for Energy
Development & Independence
500 Mero Street
12th Floor, Capital Plaza Tower
Frankfort, KY 40601
P: (502) 564-7192
F: (502) 564-7484
E: John.Davies@ky.gov

MAINE
Mr. Michael Stoddard
Executive Director
Efficiency Maine
151 Capitol Street, Suite 1
Augusta, ME 04330
P: (207) 626-8273
F: (207) 287-1039
E: Michael.stoddard
   @efficiencymaine.com

MARYLAND
Mr. Devon L. Dodson
Acting Director
Energy Administration
60 West Street, Suite 300
Annapolis, MD 21401
P: (410) 260-7257
F: (410) 974-2250
E: devon.dodson
   @maryland.gov

MASSACHUSETTS
Ms. Judith F. Judson
Commissioner
Department of Energy
Resources
Office of Energy &
Environmental Affairs
100 Cambridge Street, Suite
1020
Boston, MA 02114
P: (617) 626-7285
F: (617) 727-0030
E: judith.judson
   @state.ma.us

MICHIGAN
Mr. Robert Jackson
Director
State Agency for Energy
Economic Development
Corporation
300 North Washington Square
Lansing, MI 48933
P: (517) 373-2731
F: (517) 373-6734
E: jacksonr16@michigan.org

MISSISSIPPI
Mr. Blake Kelly
Project Manager, Energy Policy,
Planning, & Research
Energy & Natural Resources
Division
State Development Authority
501 North West Street, P.O. Box
849
Jackson, MS 39205
P: (601) 359-6645
F: (601) 359-6642
E: bkelly@mississippi.org

MISSOURI
Ms. Llona C. Weiss
Deputy Director for
Administration
Division of Energy
P.O. Box 1766
Jefferson City, MO 65102
P: (573) 751-2254
F: (573) 526-7553
E: llona.weiss@ded.mo.gov

MONTANA
Ms. Laura Andersen
Energy Pollution & Prevention
Bureau Chief
Department of Environmental
Quality
1520 East Sixth Avenue
P.O. Box 200901
Helena, MT 59620
P: (406) 444-6588
E: landersen3@mt.gov

NEBRASKA
Mr. David Bracht
Director
State Energy Office
P.O. Box 95085
Lincoln, NE 68509
P: (402) 471-2867
F: (402) 471-3064
E: david.bracht
   @nebraska.gov

NEVADA
Mr. Paul Thomsen
Director
State Office of Energy
755 North Roop Street, Suite
202
Carson City, NV 89701
P: (775) 687-1850 Ext. 7310
F: (775) 687-1869
E: pthomsen@energy.nv.gov

NEW HAMPSHIRE
Ms. Meredith Hatfield
Director
Office of Energy & Planning
107 Pleasant Street
Johnson Hall, 3rd Floor
Concord, NH 03301
P: (603) 271-2155
F: (603) 271-2615
E: meredith.hatfield@nh.gov

NEW JERSEY
Mr. Michael Winka
Director
Office of Clean Energy
Board of Public Utilities
44 South Clinton Avenue, P.O.
Box 350
Trenton, NJ 08625
P: (609) 777-3335
F: (609) 777-3320
E: michael.winka
   @bpu.state.nj.us

NEW MEXICO
Ms. Louise Martinez
Director, Energy Conservation
and Management Division
State Energy, Minerals &
Natural Resources Department
1220 South St. Francis Drive
P.O. Box 6429
Santa Fe, NM 87505
P: (505) 476-3315
F: (505) 476-3322
E: Louise.n.martinez
   @state.nm.us

NEW YORK
Mr. John B. Rhodes
President & CEO
State Energy Research &
Development Authority
17 Columbia Circle
Albany, NY 12203
P: (518) 862-1090
F: (518) 862-1091
E: jbr@nyserda.ny.gov

NORTH CAROLINA
Ms. Starlette Hodge
Section Chief
Division of Energy, Mineral &
Land Resources
Environment & Natural
Resources
512 North Salisbury Street
Raleigh, NC 27604
P: (919) 707-9240
F: (919) 733-2953
E: star.hodge@ncdenr.gov

NORTH DAKOTA
Ms. Bonnie Malo
Director, Office of Renewable
Energy & Energy Efficiency
Department of Commerce
1600 East Century Avenue,
Suite 2
P.O. Box 2057
Bismarck, ND 58502
P: (701) 328-4499
F: (701) 328-2308
E: bmalo@nd.gov

**NORTHERN MARIANA
ISLANDS**
Ms. Thelma B. Inos
Energy Director
Commonwealth of the Northern
Mariana Islands
Energy Division
P.O. Box 500340
Saipan, MP 96950
P: (670) 664-4480
F: (670) 664-4483
E: cnmienergy@gmail.com

OHIO
Mr. Randall Hunt
Development Services Agency
77 South High Street, 26th Floor
P.O. Box 1001
Columbus, OH 43216
P: (614) 466-6797
F: (614) 466-1864
E: randall.hunt
   @development.ohio.gov

Mr. Mike Kaplan
Director
Department of Energy
625 Marion Street, Northeast
Salem, OH 97301
P: (503) 378-4040
F: (503) 373-7806
E: mike.kaplan@state.or.us

Energy

OKLAHOMA
Mr. Vaughn Clark
Director
Office of Community
Development
Department of Commerce
900 North Stiles Street
Oklahoma City, OK 73104
P: (405) 815-5370
F: (405) 605-2870
E: vaughn_clark
    @odoc.state.ok.us

PENNSYLVANIA
Mr. Dave A. Althoff Jr.
Alternative Energy &
Transportation Programs
Office of Pollution Prevention
& Energy Assistance
Rachel Carson State Office
Building
400 Market Street, 16th Floor
Harrisburg, PA 17101
P: (717) 783-0542
F: (717) 783-2703
E: dalthoff@pa.gov

PUERTO RICO
Mr. Jose Maeso Gonzalez
Executive Director
Energy Affairs Administration
P.O. Box 41314
San Juan, PR 00940
P: (787) 999-2200 Ext. 2888
F: (787) 999-2246
E: jose.maeso@aae.pr.gov

RHODE ISLAND
Ms. Marion Gold
Commissioner of Energy
Resources
State Office of Energy
Resources
1 Capitol Hill, 2nd Floor
Providence, RI 02908
P: (401) 574-9105
F: (401) 574-9125
E: marion.gold
    @energy.ri.gov

SOUTH CAROLINA
Ms. Ashlie Lancaster
Deputy Director
State Energy Office
1201 Main Street, Suite 430
Columbia, SC 29201
P: (803) 737-9822
F: (803) 737-9846
E: alancaster@energy.sc.gov

SOUTH DAKOTA
Ms. Michele Farris
State Energy Manager
Energy Management Office
Bureau of Administration
523 East Capitol Avenue
Pierre, SD 57501
P: (605) 773-3899
F: (605) 773-5980
E: Michele.Farris
    @state.sd.us

TENNESSEE
Ms. Molly Cripps
Director
Office of Energy Programs
Department of Environment &
Conservation
312 Rosa L. Parks Avenue, 2nd
Floor
Nashville, TN 37243
P: (615) 741-2994
F: (615) 741-5070
E: molly.cripps@tn.gov

TEXAS
Mr. William E. Taylor
Director
State Energy Conservation
Office
Comptroller of Public Accounts
111 East 17th Street, 11th Floor
Austin, TX 78701
P: (512) 463-8352
F: (512) 475-2569
E: dub.taylor
    @cpa.state.tx.us

U.S. VIRGIN ISLANDS
Mr. Elmo Roebuck Jr.
Energy Office
Office of the Governor
No. 4101, Estate Mars Hill
Frederiksted, VI 00840
P: (340) 713-8436 Ext. 3605
F: (340) 772-2133
E: elmo.roebuck@eo.vi.gov

UTAH
Ms. Laura Nelson
Director
State Office of Energy
Development
60 East South Temple, 3rd Floor
Salt Lake City, UT 84111
P: (801) 538-8732
F: (801) 538-4795
E: lnelson@utah.gov

VERMONT
Mr. Christopher Recchia
Commissioner
Planning & Energy Resources
Division
Department of Public Service
112 State Street
Montpelier, VT 05620
P: (802) 828-2321
F: (802) 828-2342
E: chris.recchia
    @state.vt.us

VIRGINIA
Mr. Al Christopher
Director
Division of Energy
Department of Mines, Minerals
and Energy
1100 Bank Street, 8th Floor
Richmond, VA 23219
P: (804) 692-3216
F: (804) 692-3238
E: al.chistopher
    @dmme.virginia.gov

WASHINGTON
Mr. Tony Usibelli
Division Director, State Energy
Office
Department of Commerce
1011 Plum Street, Southeast
P.O. Box 42525
Olympia, WA 98504
P: (360) 725-3110
F: (360) 586-8440
E: tony.usibelli
    @commerce.wa.gov

WEST VIRGINIA
Mr. Jeff F. Herholdt Jr.
Director
State Division of Energy
State Capitol Complex, Building
6
Room 620
Charleston, WV 25305
P: (304) 558-2234
F: (304) 558-0362
E: Jeff.F.Herholdt@wv.gov

WISCONSIN
Mr. Kevin Vesperman
Administrator
State Energy Office
101 East Wilson Street, 6th
Floor
P.O. Box 7868
Madison, WI 53707
P: (608) 266-9770
F: (608) 261-8427
E: Kevin.Vesperman
    @wisconsin.gov

WYOMING
Mr. Ben Avery
Director, Business and Industry
Division
State Energy Office
Wyoming Business Council
214 West 15th Street
Cheyenne, WY 82002
P: (307) 777-2800
F: (307) 777-2837
E: ben.avery@wyo.gov

Environmental Protection

Oversees the overall quality of the environment by coordinating and managing the state's pollution control programs and planning, permit granting and regulation of standards.

ALABAMA
Mr. Lance R. LeFleur
Director
Department of Environmental Management
P.O. Box 301463
Montgomery, AL 36130
P: (334) 271-7710
F: (334) 279-3043

ALASKA
Mr. Larry Hartig
Commissioner
Department of Environmental Conservation
410 Willoughby Avenue, Suite 105
Juneau, AK 99801
P: (907) 465-5065
F: (907) 465-5070
E: larry.hartig@alaska.gov

ARIZONA
Mr. Henry Darwin
Director
Deaprtment of Environmental Quality
1110 West Washington Street
Phoenix, AZ 85007
P: (602) 771-2203
F: (602) 771-2218
E: hrd@azdeq.gov

ARKANSAS
Ms. Becky Keogh
Director
Department of Environmental Quality
8001 National Drive
Little Rock, AR 72209
P: (501) 682-0959
F: (501) 682-0798
E: keogh@adeq.state.ar.us

CALIFORNIA
Mr. Matthew Rodriquez
Secretary
Environmental Protection Agency
1001 I Street
P.O. Box 2815
Sacramento, CA 95812
P: (916) 445-3846
F: (916) 445-6401

COLORADO
Ms. Martha Rudolph
Director of Environmental Programs
Department of Public Health & Environment
4300 Cherry Creek Drive, South
Denver, CO 80246
P: (303) 692-3397
F: (303) 691-7702
E: martha.rudolph
   @state.co.us

CONNECTICUT
Mr. Robert J. Klee
Commissioner
Department of Energy & Environmental Protection
79 Elm Street
Hartford, CT 06106
P: (860) 424-3001
F: (860) 424-4051
E: deep.commissioner@ct.gov

DELAWARE
Mr. David Small
Secretary
Department of Natural Resources & Environmental Control
89 Kings Highway
Dover, DE 19901
P: (302) 739-9000
F: (302) 739-6242

DISTRICT OF COLUMBIA
Mr. Tommy Wells
Acting Director
Department of the Environment
1200 First Street, Northeast
Fifth Floor
Washington, DC 20002
P: (202) 535-2600
F: (202) 535-1359
E: tommy.wells@dc.gov

FLORIDA
Mr. Jon Steverson
Secretary
Department of Environmental Protection
3900 Commonwealth Boulevard
Tallahassee, FL 32399
P: (850) 245-2011
F: (850) 245-2128
E: jon.steverson
   @dep.state.fl.us

GEORGIA
Mr. Judson H. Turner
Director
Environmental Protection Division
2 Martin Luther King Jr. Drive Southeast
Suite 1152, East Tower
Atlanta, GA 30334
P: (404) 656-4713
F: (404) 651-5778

Mr. Mark Williams
Commissioner
Department of Natural Resources
2 Martin Luther King Jr. Drive Southeast
Suite 1252, East Tower
Atlanta, GA 30334
P: (404) 656-3500
F: (404) 656-0770

HAWAII
Mr. Gary L. Gill
Deputy Director for Environmental Health
Department of Health
1250 Punchbowl Street
Honolulu, HI 96813
P: (808) 586-4424
F: (808) 586-4444
E: gary.gill@doh.hawaii.gov

IDAHO
Mr. Curt Fransen
Director
Department of Environmental Quality
1410 North Hilton
Boise, ID 83706
P: (208) 373-0240
F: (208) 373-0417
E: curt.fransen
   @deq.idaho.gov

ILLINOIS
Ms. Lisa Bonnett
Director
Environmental Protection Agency
1021 North Grand Avenue, East
Springfield, IL 62706
P: (217) 782-9540
F: (217) 782-9039

INDIANA
Mr. Thomas Easterly
Commissioner
Department of Environmental Management
100 North Senate Avenue, MC 50-01
Indianapolis, IN 46206
P: (317) 232-8611
F: (317) 233-6647
E: teasterl@idem.in.gov

IOWA
Mr. Bill Ehm
Administrator of Environmental Services Division
Department of Natural Resources
4th Floor, Wallace Building
502 East 9th Street
Des Moines, IA 50319
P: (515) 281-5817
F: (515) 281-8895
E: william.ehm@dnr.iowa.gov

Mr. Chuck Gipp
Director
Department of Natural Resources
4th Floor, Wallace Building
502 East 9th Street
Des Moines, IA 50319
P: (515) 281-5817
F: (515) 281-8895
E: chuck.gipp@dnr.iowa.gov

KANSAS
Mr. John Mitchell
Director
Division of Environment
Department of Health & Environment
1000 Southwest Jackson, Suite 400
Topeka, KS 66612
P: (785) 296-1535
F: (785) 296-8464
E: jmitchell@kdheks.gov

KENTUCKY
Mr. Bruce Scott
Commissioner
Department of Environmental Protection
300 Fair Oaks Lane
Frankfort, KY 40601
P: (502) 564-2150
F: (502) 564-4245
E: bruce.scott@ky.gov

Environmental Protection

LOUISIANA
Ms. Peggy Hatch
Secretary
Department of Environmental
Quality
602 North Fifth Street
Baton Rouge, LA 70802
P: (225) 219-3950
F: (225) 219-3970
E: peggy.hatch@la.gov

MAINE
Ms. Patricia Aho
Commissioner
Department of Environmental
Protection
17 State House Station
Augusta, ME 04333
P: (207) 287-2812
F: (207) 287-2814
E: patricia.aho@maine.gov

MARYLAND
Mr. Ben Grumbles
Secretary
Department of the Environment
1800 Washington Boulevard
Baltimore, MD 21230
P: (410) 537-3084
F: (410) 537-3888

MASSACHUSETTS
Mr. Matthew A. Beaton
Secretary of Energy and
Environmental Affairs
Department of Environmental
Protection
100 Cambridge Street, Suite 900
Boston, MA 02114
P: (614) 626-1000
F: (614) 626-1181

Mr. Douglas Fine
Assistant Commissioner
Department of Environmental
Protection
One Winter Street
Boston, MA 02108
P: (617) 292-5792
F: (617) 574-6880

Mr. Martin Suuberg
Commissioner
Department of Environmental
Protection
One Winter Street
Boston, MA 02108
P: (617) 292-5856
F: (617) 574-6880

MICHIGAN
Mr. Jim Sygo
Deputy Director
Department of Environmental
Quality
P.O. Box 30473, 525 West
Allegan Street
Constitution Hall, 6th Floor
South
Lansing, MI 48909
P: (517) 373-7917
F: (517) 241-7401

Mr. Dan Wyant
Director
Department of Environmental
Quality
Constitution Hall, 6th Floor
South
525 West Allegan Street
Lansing, MI 48909
P: (517) 373-7917
F: (517) 241-7401

MINNESOTA
Mr. John Linc Stine
Commissioner
Pollution Control Agency
520 Lafayette Road North, Sixth
Floor
St. Paul, MN 55155
P: (651) 757-2016
F: (651) 296-6334
E: john.stine@state.mn.us

MISSISSIPPI
Mr. Gary Rikard
Executive Director
Department of Environmental
Quality
515 East Amite Street
Jackson, MS 39201
P: (601) 961-5001
F: (601) 961-5093
E: gary_rikard
    @deq.state.ms.us

MISSOURI
Ms. Sara Parker Pauley
Director
Department of Natural
Resources
P.O. Box 176
Jefferson City, MO 65102
P: (573) 751-3443
F: (573) 751-7627
E: sara.pauley@ded.mo.gov

NEBRASKA
Mr. Jim Macy
Director
Department of Environmental
Quality
1200 N Street, Suite 400
Lincoln, NE 68508
P: (402) 471-3585
F: (402) 471-2909
E: Jim.Macy@nebraska.gov

NEVADA
Ms. Colleen Cripps
Administrator
Division of Environmental
Protection, Department of
Conservation & Natural
Resources
901 South Stewart Street, Suite
4001
Carson City, NV 89701
P: (775) 687-9302
F: (775) 687-5856
E: cripps@ndep.nv.gov

Mr. Leo Drozdoff
Director
Department of Conservation &
Natural Resources
901 South Stewart Street, Suite
5001
Carson City, NV 89701
P: (775) 687-9301
F: (775) 687-5856
E: ldrozdoff@dcnr.nv.gov

NEW HAMPSHIRE
Mr. Thomas S. Burack
Commissioner
Department of Environmental
Services
Six Hazen Drive
Concord, NH 03301
P: (603) 271-2958
F: (603) 271-2867
E: thomas.burack@des.nh.gov

NEW JERSEY
Mr. Bob Martin
Commissioner
Department of Environmental
Protection
401 East State Street
P.O. Box 402
Trenton, NJ 08625
P: (609) 292-2885
F: (609) 292-7695

NEW MEXICO
Mr. Ryan Flynn
Cabinet Secretary
Environment Department
1190 Saint Francis Drive
Harold Runnels Building, Room
North 4050
Santa Fe, NM 87505
P: (505) 827-2855
F: (505) 827-2836

NEW YORK
Mr. Joe Martens
Commissioner
Department of Environmental
Conservation
625 Broadway, 14th Floor
Albany, NY 12233
P: (518) 402-8540
F: (518) 402-8541
E: joemartens
    @gw.dec.state.ny.us

NORTH DAKOTA
Mr. L. David Glatt
Chief
Environmental Health Section
Department of Health
1200 Missouri Avenue, P.O. Box
5520
Bismarck, ND 58506
P: (701) 328-5152
F: (701) 328-5200
E: dglatt@nd.gov

OHIO
Mr. Craig Butler
Interim Director
Environmental Protection
Agency
Lazarus Government Center
122 South Front Street, 6th Floor
Columbus, OH 43215
P: (614) 644-2782
F: (614) 644-3184
E: scott.nally
    @epa.state.oh.us

OKLAHOMA
Mr. Scott Thompson
Executive Director
Department of Environmental
Quality
707 North Robinson, Suite 7100
Oklahoma City, OK 73102
P: (405) 702-7163
F: (405) 702-7101

OREGON
Mr. Dick Pedersen
Director
Department of Environmental
Quality
811 Southwest 6th Avenue
Portland, OR 97204
P: (503) 229-5300
F: (503) 229-5850
E: pedersen.dick
@deq.state.or.us

PENNSYLVANIA
Mr. John Quigley
Acting Secretary
Department of Environmental
Protection
Rachel Carson State Office
Building
400 Market Street, 16th Floor
Harrisburg, PA 17101
P: (717) 787-2814
F: (717) 705-4980

PUERTO RICO
Mr. Edwin Irizarry
Secretary of Governing Board
Environmental Quality Board
Apartado 11488 Santurce
San Juan, PR 00910
P: (787) 767-8056
F: (787) 767-4861

Ms. Laura Velez
Chairman
Environmental Quality Board
1375 Ponce De Leon Avenue
San Juan, PR 00926
P: (787) 767-8056
F: (787) 767-4861

Mr. Javier Velez-Arocho
Secretary
Department of Natural &
Environmental Resources
P.O. Box 366147
San Juan, PR 00936
P: (787) 999-2200
F: (787) 999-2303

RHODE ISLAND
Ms. Janet Coit
Director
Department of Environmental
Management
235 Promenade Street, 4th Floor
Providence, RI 02908
P: (401) 222-2771
F: (401) 222-6802
E: janet.coit@dem.ri.gov

SOUTH CAROLINA
Ms. Elizabeth Dieck
Commissioner
Department of Health &
Environmental Control
2600 Bull Street
Columbia, SC 29201
P: (803) 896-8940
F: (803) 896-8941

SOUTH DAKOTA
Mr. Steven M. Pirner
Secretary
Department of Environment &
Natural Resources
Joe Foss Building
523 East Capital Avenue
Pierre, SD 57501
P: (605) 773-5559
F: (605) 773-6035
E: steve.pirner@state.sd.us

TENNESSEE
Mr. Robert J. Martineau Jr.
Commissioner
Department of Environment &
Conservation
William R. Snodgrass Tennessee
Tower
312 Rosa L. Parks Avenue, 2nd
Floor
Nashville, TN 37243
P: (615) 532-0106
F: (615) 532-0120

Ms. Shari Meghreblian
Deputy Commissioner of
Environment
Department of Environment &
Conservation
William R. Snodgrass Tennessee
Tower
312 Rosa L. Parks Avenue, 2nd
Floor
Nashville, TN 37243
P: (615) 532-0106
F: (615) 532-0120

TEXAS
Mr. Toby Baker
Commissioner
Commission on Environmental
Quality
12100 Park 35 Circle (MC-100)
Austin, TX 78753
P: (512) 239-5515
F: (512) 239-5533

Dr. Bryan W. Shaw
Chair
Commission on Environmental
Quality
12100 Park 35 Circle
P.O. Box 13087
Austin, TX 78711
P: (512) 239-5510
F: (512) 239-5533
E: bryan.shaw
@tceq.texas.gov

UTAH
Ms. Amanda Smith
Executive Director
Department of Environmental
Quality
168 North 1950, West
Salt Lake City, UT 84116
P: (801) 536-4404
F: (801) 536-0061
E: amandasmith@utah.gov

VERMONT
Ms. Deborah L. Markowitz
Secretary
Agency of Natural Resources
103 South Main Street, Center
Building
Waterbury, VT 05671
P: (802) 241-3808
F: (802) 244-1102
E: deb.markowitz
@state.vt.us

Mr. Trey Martin
Deputy Secretary
Agency of Natural Resources
103 South Main Street, Center
Building
Waterbury, VT 05671
P: (802) 241-3808

VIRGINIA
Mr. David K. Paylor
Director
Department of Environmental
Quality
629 East Main Street
Richmond, VA 23219
P: (804) 698-4390
F: (804) 698-4019
E: david.paylor
@deq.virginia.gov

WASHINGTON
Ms. Maia Bellon
Director
Department of Ecology
300 Desmond Drive, Southeast
Lacey, WA 98503
P: (360) 407-7001
F: (360) 407-6989
E: maib461@ecy.wa.gov

WEST VIRGINIA
Mr. John Benedict
Director, Division of Air Quality
Department of Environmental
Protection
601 57th Street, Southeast
Charleston, WV 25304
P: (304) 926-3647
F: (304) 926-1713

Mr. Randy Huffman
Cabinet Secretary
Department of Environmental
Protection
1356 Hansford Street
Charleston, WV 25301
P: (304) 926-0440
F: (304) 926-0447
E: randy.c.huffman@wv.gov

WISCONSIN
Ms. Cathy Stepp
Secretary
Department of Natural
Resources
101 South Webster Street
Madison, WI 53703
P: (608) 266-0865
F: (608) 266-6983
E: DNRSecretary
@Wisconsin.gov

WYOMING
Mr. Todd Parfitt
Director
Department of Environmental
Quality
122 West 25th Street
Herschler Building
Cheyenne, WY 82002
P: (307) 777-7937
F: (307) 777-7682
E: todd.parfitt@wyo.gov

Equal Employment Opportunity

Enforces laws promoting equal employment opportunity in the state.

ALABAMA
Mr. Fitzgerald Washington
Commissioner
Department of Labor
649 Monroe Street
Montgomery, AL 36131
P: (334) 242-8990

ALASKA
Ms. Camille Brill
EEO Program Manager
Department of Administration
619 East Ship Creek Avenue,
Suite 309
Anchorage, AK 99501
P: (907) 375-7705
F: (907) 375-7719
E: camille.brill@alaska.gov

AMERICAN SAMOA
Mr. Le'i S. Thompson
Director
Department of Human
Resources
Executive Office Building
AP Lutali, 2nd Floor
Pago Pago, AS 96799
P: (684) 644-4485
F: (684) 633-1139
E: sonnythompson
    @samoatelco.com

ARIZONA
Ms. Dora Espinosa
Program Manager
Governor's Office of Equal
Opportunity
100 North Fifteenth Avenue,
Suite 261
Phoenix, AZ 85007
P: (602) 542-1384
F: (602) 542-3712
E: Dora.Espinosa@azdoa.gov

ARKANSAS
Ms. Gloria Johnson
Equal Opportunity Manager
Department of Workforce
Services
#2 Capitol Mall
Little Rock, AR 72201
P: (501) 682-2389
F: (501) 682-3748
E: gloria.johnson
    @arkansas.gov

CALIFORNIA
Ms. Joanne Bailey
Chief
Equal Employment Opportunity
Office
744 P Street
Sacramento, CA 95814
P: (916) 657-2326
F: (916) 657-2285

COLORADO
Ms. Rufina Hernandez
Director
Civil Rights Division
1560 Broadway, Suite 1050
Denver, CO 80202
P: (303) 894-2997
F: (303) 894-7830
E: dora_CCRD@state.co.us

CONNECTICUT
Ms. Tanya Hughes
Executive Director
Commission on Human Rights
& Opportunities
25 Sigourney Street
Hartford, CT 06106
P: (860) 541-3421
F: (860) 241-4875
E: tanya.hughes@ct.gov

DELAWARE
Ms. Sandy Reyes
Human Resource Administrator
Human Resource Operations
Office of Management and
Budget
122 Martin Luther King Jr.
Blvd., South
Dover, DE 19901
P: (302) 739-4195
F: (302) 739-3000
E: sandy.reyes@state.de.us

DISTRICT OF COLUMBIA
Ms. Monica Palacio
Director
Office of Human Rights
441 4th Street, Northwest
Suite 570 North
Washington, DC 20001
P: (202) 727-4559
F: (202) 727-9589
E: ohr@dc.gov

FLORIDA
Mr. Peter De Haan
EO Officer
Office for Civil Rights
110 Southeast 6th Street
Fort Lauderdale, FL 33301
P: (954) 712-4607
F: (954) 527-3704
E: peter.dehaan
    @awi.state.fl.us

GEORGIA
Mr. Melvin J. Everson
Executive Director &
Administrator
Commission on Equal
Opportunity
Suite 1002,West Tower
2 Martin Luther King Jr. Drive
Southeast
Atlanta, GA 30334
P: (404) 232-1776
F: (404) 656-4399
E: meverson
    @gceo.state.ga.us

GUAM
Mr. Manuel Q. Cruz
Director
Department of Labor
Government of Guam
P.O. Box 9970
Tamuning, GU 96931
P: (671) 647-6510
F: (671) 674-6517

HAWAII
Mr. William D. Hoshijo
Executive Director
Civil Rights Commission
830 Punchbowl Street, Room
411
Honolulu, HI 96813
P: (808) 586-8636
F: (808) 586-8655
E: dlir.hcrc.infor
    @hawaii.gov

IDAHO
Ms. Pamela Parks
Administrator
Human Rights Commission
317 West Main Street, Second
Floor
Boise, ID 83735
P: (208) 334-2873
F: (208) 334-2664
E: Pamela.Parks
    @ihrc.idaho.gov

ILLINOIS
Mr. Rocco J. Claps
Director
Department of Human Rights
100 West Randolph Street, 10th
Floor
Intake Unit
Chicago, IL 60601
P: (312) 814-6200
F: (312) 814-1436

INDIANA
Ms. Lavenia Haskett
Program Director
Employee Relations
Personnel Department
402 West Washington, Room
W161
Indianapolis, IN 46204
P: (317) 232-4555
F: (317) 232-3089
E: lhaskett@spd.in.gov

IOWA
Ms. Beth Townsend
Agency Director
Civil Rights Commission
1000 East Grand Avenue
Des Moines, IA 50319
P: (515) 281-5364
E: beth.townsend
    @iwd.iowa.gov

KANSAS
Ms. Ruth Glover
Executive Director
Human Rights Commission
900 Southwest Jackson Street
Suite 568-S
Topeka, KS 66612
P: (785) 296-3206
F: (785) 296-0589

Ms. Lana Gordon
Secretary of Labor
Department of Labor
401 Southwest Topeka
Boulevard
Topeka, KS 66603
P: (785) 296-5058
F: (785) 368-5289
E: lana.gordon@dol.ks.gov

KENTUCKY
Mr. Arthur B. Lucas Jr.
Executive Director
Office of Diversity & Equality
Personnel Cabinet
501 High Street, 3rd Floor
Frankfort, KY 40601
P: (502) 564-8000
F: (502) 564-0182
E: arthurb.lucas@ky.gov

LOUISIANA
Mr. Curt Eysink
Executive Director
Workforce Commission
1001 North 23rd Street
P.O. Box 94094
Baton Rouge, LA 70804
P: (225) 342-3111
F: (225) 342-3778
E: owd@lwc.la.gov

MAINE
Ms. Joyce Oreskovich
Director
Bureau of Human Resources
Administrative & Financial
Services
4 State House Station
Augusta, ME 04333
P: (207) 624-7761
F: (207) 287-4414
E: joyce.a.oreskovich
    @maine.gov

MARYLAND
Mr. Alvin O. Gillard
Executive Director
Commission on Human
Relations
6 St. Paul Street
Baltimore, MD 21202
P: (410) 767-8563
F: (410) 333-1841
E: alvin.gillard
    @maryland.gov

MASSACHUSETTS
Ms. Sandra E. Borders
Director
Office of Diversity & Equal
Opportunity
One Ashburton Place, Room 213
Boston, MA 02108
P: (617) 727-7441
F: (617) 878-9830

Ms. Linda Spears
Commissioner
Department of Children &
Families
600 Washington Street
Boston, MA 02111
P: (617) 748-2000

MINNESOTA
Mr. Kevin Lindsey
Commissioner
Department of Human Rights
Freeman Building
625 Robert Street, North
St. Paul, MN 55155
P: (651) 296-5675
F: (651) 296-9042
E: Kevin.Lindsey
    @state.mn.us

MISSOURI
Dr. Alisa Warren
Executive Director
Commission on Human Rights
3315 West Truman Boulevard,
Room 212
P.O. Box 1129
Jefferson City, MO 65102
P: (573) 751-3325
F: (573) 751-2905
E: mchr@labor.mo.gov

MONTANA
Ms. Anjenette Schafer
Administrator
Human Resources Division
125 North Roberts Street, Room
125
P.O. Box 200127
Helena, MT 59620
P: (406) 444-3885
F: (406) 444-0703
E: aschafer2@mt.gov

NEBRASKA
Ms. Barbara Albers
Executive Director
Equal Opportunity Commission
301 Centennial Mall South, 5th
Floor
P.O. Box 94934
Lincoln, NE 68509
P: (402) 471-2024
F: (402) 471-4059
E: barbara.albers
    @nebraska.gov

NEVADA
Ms. Kara Jenkins
Commission Administrator
Equal Rights Commission
Employment, Training &
Rehabilitation
1820 East Sahara Avenue, Suite
314
Las Vegas, NV 89104
P: (702) 486-7161
F: (702) 486-7054

NEW HAMPSHIRE
Ms. Joni N. Esperian
Executive Director
Commission for Human Rights
2 Chennell Drive, Unit 2
Concord, NH 03301
P: (603) 271-2767
F: (603) 271-6339
E: humanrights
    @nhsa.state.nh.us

NEW JERSEY
Ms. Parthenopy A. Bardis
EEO/AA Officer
Office of Equal Employment
Opportunity & Affirmative
Action
P.O. Box 317
Trenton, NJ 08625
P: (609) 292-6547
F: (609) 984-3800

NEW MEXICO
Ms. Francie Cordova
Labor Relations Division
Director
Human Rights Bureau
Department of Workforce
Solutions
1596 Pacheco Street, Suite103
Santa Fe, NM 87505
P: (505) 827-6838
F: (505) 827-6878

NEW YORK
Mr. Jerry Boone
Commissioner
Department of Civil Service
Alfred E. Smith State Office
Building
Albany, NY 12239
P: (518) 457-3701
F: (518) 473-5696
E: jerry.boone
    @cs.state.ny.us

NORTH CAROLINA
Ms. Nellie F. Riley
Director
Equal Employment
Opportunity, Diversity &
Inclusion
Office of State Human
Resources
116 West Jones Street
Raleigh, NC 27603
P: (919) 807-4800
F: (919) 733-0653
E: nellie.riley@nc.gov

NORTH DAKOTA
Ms. Bonnie Storbakken
Commissioner of Labor
Department of Labor
600 East Boulevard Avenue
Department 406
Bismarck, ND 58505
P: (701) 328-2660
F: (701) 328-2031
E: bstorbakken@nd.gov

NORTHERN MARIANA
ISLANDS
Mr. Sid Seman
Director
Office of Personnel
Management
Saipan, MP 96950
F: (670) 234-1013

OHIO
Mr. Robert Blair
Director
Department of Administrative
Services
30 East Broad Street, Suite 4040
Columbus, OH 43215
P: (614) 466-6511
F: (614) 644-8151
E: Robert.Blair
    @das.ohio.gov

OKLAHOMA
Mr. Ross Tripp
Organizational Planning &
Development Director
Workforce Diversity & Certified
Discrimination Complaint
Investigator
Human Capital Management
Division
2101 North Lincoln Boulevard,
Room G-80
Oklahoma City, OK 73105
P: (405) 521-6376
F: (405) 524-6942

OREGON
Hon. Brad Avakian (D)
Commissioner
Bureau of Labor & Industries
800 Northeast Oregon Street
Suite 1045
Portland, OR 97232
P: (971) 673-0781
F: (971) 673-0762
E: brad.avakian@state.or.us

PENNSYLVANIA
Ms. Kathy M. Manderino
Secretary
Department of Labor & Industry
651 Boas Street, Room 1700
Harrisburg, PA 17121
P: (717) 787-5279
F: (717) 787-8826

PUERTO RICO
Mr. Vance Thomas
Secretary
Department of Labor & Human
Resources
P.O. Box 195540
Hato Rey, PR 00918
P: (787) 754-2119
F: (787) 753-9550

Equal Employment Opportunity

RHODE ISLAND
Mr. Raymond Lambert
Administrator
State Equal Opportunity Office
State Equal Opportunity
Programs
1 Capitol Hill
Providence, RI 02908
P: (401) 222-3090
F: (401) 222-2490
E: rlambert
    @gw.doa.state.ri.us

SOUTH CAROLINA
Mr. Raymond Buxton
Commissioner
Human Affairs Commission
2611 Forest Drive, Suite 200
P.O. Box 4490
Columbia, SC 29204
P: (803) 737-7825
E: rbuxton@schac.sc.gov

SOUTH DAKOTA
Ms. Laurie R. Gill
Commissioner
Bureau of Human Resources
Capitol Building
500 East Capitol Avenue
Pierre, SD 57501
P: (605) 773-3148
F: (605) 773-4344
E: bhrinfo@state.sd.us

TENNESSEE
Ms. Rebecca R. Hunter
Commissioner
Department of Human
Resources
James K. Polk Building, 1st
Floor
505 Deaderick Street
Nashville, TN 37243
P: (615) 741-2958
F: (615) 741-7880
E: rebecca.hunter@tn.gov

TEXAS
Mr. Lowell A. Keig
Division Director
Civil Rights Division
Texas Workforce Commission
101 East 15th Street
Austin, TX 78778
P: (512) 463-4385
E: lowell.keig
    @twc.state.tx.us

U.S. VIRGIN ISLANDS
Mr. Albert Bryan Jr.
Commissioner of Labor
Department of Labor
4401 Sion Farm
Christiansted, VI 00820
P: (340) 773-1994
F: (340) 773-0094
E: abryan@vidol.gov

UTAH
Kerry Chlarson
Director
Antidiscrimination & Labor
Division
160 East 300 South, 3rd Floor
P.O. Box 146630
Salt Lake City, UT 84114
P: (801) 530-6801
F: (801) 530-7609
E: kchlarson@utah.gov

VIRGINIA
Mrs. Sara Redding Wilson
Director
Department of Human Resource
Management
101 North 14th Street, 12th
Floor
Richmond, VA 23219
P: (804) 225-2237
F: (804) 371-7401
E: sara.wilson
    @dhrm.virginia.gov

WASHINGTON
Mr. Glen Christopherson
Director
State Human Resources
Division
128 10th Avenue, Southeast
P.O. Box 43113
Olympia, WA 98504
P: (360) 407-4104
F: (360) 753-1003
E: glen.christopherson
    @ofm.wa.gov

WEST VIRGINIA
Ms. Jann Hoke
Director
Equal Employment Opportunity
Office
50 Dee Drive
Charleston, WV 25311
P: (304) 558-0400
F: (304) 558-3861
E: Jann.D.Hoke@wv.gov

WISCONSIN
Ms. Jeanette Johnson
Administrator
Division of Affirmative Action
101 East Wilson Street
P.O. Box 7855
Madison, WI 53707
P: (608) 266-3017
F: (608) 267-1020
E: oserdaa@wi.gov

WYOMING
Ms. Joan K. Evans
Director
Department of Workforce
Services
122 West 25th Street
Herschler Building, 2nd Floor
East
Cheyenne, WY 82002
P: (307) 777-8728
F: (307) 777-5857
E: joan.evans@wyo.gov

Ethics

Administers and enforces the state ethics laws applying to public officials.

ALABAMA
Mr. James L. Sumner Jr.
Director
Ethics Commission
100 North Union Street, Suite 104
P.O. Box 4840
Montgomery, AL 36103
P: (334) 242-2997
F: (334) 242-0248
E: info@ethics.alabama.gov

ALASKA
Ms. Joyce Anderson
Administrator
Select Committee on Legislative Ethics
P.O. Box 101468
Anchorage, AK 99510
P: (907) 269-0150
F: (907) 269-0152
E: joyce.anderson@akleg.gov

Mr. Reggie Drummond
Administrator
Select Committee on Legislative Ethics
P.O. Box 101468
Anchorage, AK 99510
P: (907) 269-0150
F: (907) 269-0152
E: reggie.drummond
    @akleg.gov

ARKANSAS
Mr. Graham Sloan
Director
State Ethics Commission
P.O. Box 1917
Little Rock, AR 72203
P: (501) 682-9600
F: (501) 682-9606
E: graham.sloan
    @arkansas.gov

CALIFORNIA
Ms. Erin Peth
Executive Director
Fair Political Practices Commission
428 J Street, Suite 800
Sacramento, CA 95814
P: (916) 322-5660
F: (916) 322-0886
E: executivedirector
    @fppc.ca.gov

COLORADO
Ms. Amy C. DeVan
Executive Director
Independent Ethics Commission
1300 Broadway, 12th Floor
Denver, CO 80203
P: (303) 625-5697
F: (303) 625-5696
E: amy.devan@state.co.us

CONNECTICUT
Ms. Carol Carson
Executive Director
Office of State Ethics
18-20 Trinity Street, Suite 205
Hartford, CT 06106
P: (860) 263-2384
F: (860) 263-2402
E: carol.carson@ct.gov

DELAWARE
Ms. Deborah Weaver
Commission Counsel
Public Integrity Commission
Margaret O'Neill Building
410 Federal Street, Suite 3
Dover, DE 19901
P: (302) 739-2399
F: (302) 739-2398
E: deborah.weaver
    @state.de.us

DISTRICT OF COLUMBIA
Mr. Cliff Tatum
Executive Director
Board of Elections
441 Fourth Street, Northwest, Suite 250N
Washington, DC 20001
P: (202) 727-2525
F: (202) 347-2648
E: ctatum@dcboee.org

FLORIDA
Ms. Virlindia Doss
Executive Director
Commission on Ethics
P.O. Drawer 15709
Tallahassee, FL 32317
P: (904) 488-7864
F: (904) 488-3077
E: doss.virlindia
    @leg.state.fl.us

GEORGIA
Mr. Stefan Ritter
Executive Director
Government Transparency & Campaign Finance Commission
200 Piedmont Avenue, Southeast
Suite 1402, West Tower
Atlanta, GA 30334
P: (404) 463-1980
F: (404) 463-1988
E: gaethics@ethics.ga.gov

HAWAII
Mr. Leslie H. Kondo
Executive Director
State Ethics Commission
1001 Bishop Street, Suite 970
P.O. Box 616
Honolulu, HI 96809
P: (808) 587-0460
F: (808) 587-0470
E: ethics@hawaiiethics.org

IDAHO
Hon. Lawrence Wasden (R)
Attorney General
Office of the Attorney General
Statehouse
Boise, ID 83720
P: (208) 334-2400
F: (208) 854-8071

ILLINOIS
Mr. Randy Erford
Executive Director
Legislative Ethics Commission
420 Stratton Building
Springfield, IL 62706
P: (217) 558-1561
F: (217) 557-0505
E: randye@ilga.gov

Mr. Chad Fornoff
Executive Director
Executive Ethics Commission
401 South Spring Street
513 William Stratton Building
Springfield, IL 62706
P: (217) 558-1393
F: (217) 558-1399
E: Chad.Fornoff
    @illinois.gov

INDIANA
Ms. Cynthia Carrasco
Ethics Director
Office of the Inspector General
315 West Ohio Street, Room 104
Indianapolis, IN 46202
P: (317) 232-3850
F: (317) 232-0707
E: ccarrasco@ig.IN.gov

IOWA
Ms. Megan Tooker
Executive Director
Ethics & Campaign Disclosure Board
510 East 12th, Suite 1A
Des Moines, IA 50319
P: (515) 281-3489
F: (510) 281-4073
E: megan.tooker@iowa.gov

KANSAS
Ms. Carol E. Williams
Executive Director
Governmental Ethics Commission
109 West 9th Street, Suite 504
Topeka, KS 66612
P: (785) 296-4219
F: (785) 296-2548
E: ethics@ethics.ks.gov

KENTUCKY
Mr. John R. Steffen
Executive Director
Executive Branch Ethics Commission
#3 Fountain Place
Frankfort, KY 40601
P: (502) 564-7954
E: john.steffen@ky.gov

Mr. Anthony M. Wilhoit
Executive Director
Legislative Ethics Commission
22 Mill Creek Park
Frankfort, KY 40601
P: (502) 573-2863
F: (502) 573-2929
E: tony.wilhoit@lrc.ky.gov

LOUISIANA
Ms. Kathleen Allen
Ethics Administrator
Ethics Administration
617 North Third Street, Suite 10-36
P.O. Box 4368
Baton Rouge, LA 70821
P: (225) 219-5600
F: (225) 381-7271
E: kathleen.allen@la.gov

MAINE
Mr. Jonathan Wayne
Executive Director
Commission on Governmental Ethics & Election Practices
135 State House Station
Augusta, ME 04333
P: (207) 287-4179
F: (207) 287-6775
E: Jonathan.Wayne@maine.gov

MARYLAND
Mr. Michael W. Lord
Executive Director
State Ethics Commission
45 Calvert Street, 3rd Floor
Annapolis, MD 21401
P: (410) 260-7770
F: (410) 260-7747
E: Michael.Lord
    @Maryland.gov

Ethics

MASSACHUSETTS
Ms. Karen L. Nober
Executive Director
Ethics Commission
One Ashburton Place, Room 619
Boston, MA 02108
P: (617) 727-0600
F: (617) 723-5851
E: knober@eth.state.ma.us

MICHIGAN
Mr. John Gnodtke
Executive Secretary
State Board of Ethics
400 South Pine Street
P.O. Box 30002
Lansing, MI 48909
P: (517) 373-3644
F: (517) 373-7690
E: ethicsboard@michigan.gov

MINNESOTA
Mr. Gary Goldsmith
Executive Director
Campaign Finance & Public
Disclosure Board
Centennial Office Building,
Suite 190
658 Cedar Street
St. Paul, MN 55155
P: (651) 539-1190
F: (651) 539-1196
E: gary.goldsmith
    @state.mn.us

MISSISSIPPI
Mr. Tom Hood
Executive Director
Ethics Commission
P.O. Box 22746
Jackson, MS 39225
P: (601) 359-1285
F: (601) 354-6253
E: info@ethics.state.ms.us

MISSOURI
Ms. Julie A. Allen
Executive Director
Ethics Commission
3411A Knipp Drive
Jefferson City, MO 65109
P: (573) 751-2020
F: (573) 526-4506
E: julie.allen@sos.mo.gov

MONTANA
Mr. Jonathan R. Motl
Commissioner
Commissioner of Political
Practices
P.O. Box 202401
Helena, MT 59620
P: (406) 444-2942
F: (406) 444-1643
E: jmotl@mt.gov

NEBRASKA
Mr. Frank Daley
Executive Director
Accountability & Disclosure
Commission
P.O. Box 95086
Lincoln, NE 68509
P: (402) 471-2522
F: (402) 471-6599
E: frank.daley@nebraska.gov

NEVADA
Ms. Yvonne Navarez-Goodson
Executive Director
Commission on Ethics
704 West Nye Lane, Suite 204
Carson City, NV 89703
P: (775) 687-5469
F: (775) 687-1279
E: ynevarez@ethics.nv.gov

NEW HAMPSHIRE
Mr. Joseph DiBrigida Jr.
Chair
Executive Branch Ethics
Committee
33 Capitol Street
Concord, NH 03301
P: (603) 271-3658
F: (603) 271-2110
E: ethics@doj.nh.gov

Mr. Richard M. Lambert
Executive Administrator
Legislative Ethics Committee
State House, Room 112
107 North Main Street
Concord, NH 03301
P: (603) 271-3326
F: (603) 271-6607
E: richard.lambert
    @leg.state.nh.us

NEW JERSEY
Mr. Peter J. Tober
Executive Director
State Ethics Commission
P.O. Box 082
Trenton, NJ 08625
P: (609) 292-1892
F: (609) 633-9252
E: peter.tober
    @ethics.state.nj.us

NEW MEXICO
Ms. Kari Fresquez
Interim Elections Director
Bureau of Elections
Secretary of State's Office
325 Don Gaspar, Suite 300
Santa Fe, NM 87501
P: (505) 827-3600
F: (505) 827-8403
E: kari.fresquez
    @state.nm.us

NEW YORK
Mr. Daniel J. Horowitz
Chair
Joint Commission on Public
Ethics
540 Broadway
Albany, NY 12207
P: (518) 408-3976

Ms. Lisa P. Reid
Executive Director/Counsel
Legislative Ethics Commission
Legislative Office Building
Box 75
Albany, NY 12247
P: (518) 432 7837
F: (518) 432-7838
E: lreid@nysenate.gov

NORTH CAROLINA
Mr. Perry Newson
Executive Director
State Ethics Commission
424 North Blount Street
1324 Mail Service Center
Raleigh, NC 27699
P: (919) 715-2071
F: (919) 715-1644
E: ethics.commission
    @doa.nc.gov

NORTH DAKOTA
Mr. Jerod Tufte
Legal Counsel
Governor's Office
600 East Boulevard Avenue
Bismark, ND 58505
P: (701) 328-1048
F: (701) 328-2205
E: jetufte@nd.gov

OHIO
Mr. Paul M. Nick
Executive Director
Ethics Commission
30 West Spring Street, L3
Columbus, OH 43215
P: (614) 466-7090
F: (614) 466-8368
E: ethics@ethics.ohio.gov

OKLAHOMA
Mr. Lee Slater
Executive Director
Ethics Commission
2300 North Lincoln Boulevard,
Room B-5
Oklahoma City, OK 73105
P: (405) 521-3451
F: (405) 521-4905
E: lee.slater@ethics.ok.gov

OREGON
Mr. Ronald A. Bersin
Executive Director
Government Ethics Commission
3218 Pringle Road, Southeast,
Suite 220
Salem, OR 97302
P: (503) 378-5105
F: (503) 373-1456
E: ron.a.bersin@state.or.us

PENNSYLVANIA
Mr. Robert Caruso
Executive Director
State Ethics Commission
P.O. Box 11470
Room 309, Finance Building
Harrisburg, PA 17108
P: (717) 783-1610
F: (717) 787-0806

PUERTO RICO
Ms. Zulma L. Rosario Vega
Executive Director
Office of Governmental Ethics
P.O. Box 194200
San Juan, PR 00919
P: (787) 722-0305
F: (787) 754-0977

RHODE ISLAND
Mr. Kent A. Willever
Executive Director/Chief
Prosecutor
Ethics Commission
40 Fountain Street, 8th Floor
Providence, RI 02903
P: (401) 222-3790
F: (401) 272-3382

SOUTH CAROLINA
Mr. Herbert R. Hayden Jr.
Executive Director
State Ethics Commission
5000 Thurmond Mall, Suite 250
Columbia, SC 29201
P: (803) 253-4192
F: (803) 253-7539
E: herb@ethics.state.sc.us

TENNESSEE
Mr. Drew Rawlins
Executive Director
Bureau of Ethics & Campaign
Finance
404 James Robertson Parkway,
Suite 104
Nashville, TN 37243
P: (615) 741-7959
F: (615) 532-8905
E: drew.ralins@tn.gov

TEXAS
Ms. Natalia Luna Ashley
Executive Director
Ethics Commission
201 East 14th Street, 10th Floor
P.O. Box 12070
Austin, TX 78711
P: (512) 463-5800
F: (512) 463-5777
E: natalia.ashley
   @ethics.state.tx.us

U.S. VIRGIN ISLANDS
Mr. Bernard M. VanSluytman
Solicitor General
Solicitor General's Office
34-38 Kron Prindsens Gade
GERS Building, 2nd Floor
St. Thomas, VI 00802
P: (340) 774-5666
F: (340) 776-3494

UTAH
Ms. Kim Jones Bouck
Executive Director
Independent Legislative Ethics
Commission
P.O. Box 141175
Salt Lake City, UT 84114
P: (801) 326-1422
E: kbouck@le.utah.gov

VERMONT
Hon. Jim Condos (D)
Secretary of State
Office of the Secretary of State
128 State Street
Montpelier, VT 05633
P: (802) 828-2148
F: (802) 828-2496
E: jim.condos
   @sec.state.vt.us

WASHINGTON
Ms. Andrea McNamara Doyle
Executive Director
Public Disclosure Commission
711 Capitol Way, #206
P.O. Box 40908
Olympia, WA 98504
P: (360) 753-1111
F: (360) 753-1112
E: Andrea.Doyle@pdc.wa.gov

Mr. Mike O'Connell
Counsel
Legislative Ethics Board
101 Legislative Building
P.O. Box 40600
Olympia, WA 98504
P: (360) 786-7540
F: (360) 786-1553
E: OConnell.Mike@leg.wa.gov

WEST VIRGINIA
Ms. C. Joan Parker
Executive Director
Ethics Commission
210 Brooks Street, Suite 300
Charleston, WV 25301
P: (304) 558-0664
F: (304) 558-2169
E: c.joan.parker@wv.gov

WISCONSIN
Mr. Kevin J. Kennedy
Executive Director & General
Counsel
Government Accountability
Board
P.O. Box 7984
Madison, WI 53707
P: (608) 266-8005
F: (608) 267-0500
E: gab@wi.gov

WYOMING
Hon. Ed Murray (R)
Secretary of State
Office of the Secretary of State
State Capitol Building, Room
106
200 West 24th Street
Cheyenne, WY 82002
P: (307) 777-7378
F: (307) 777-6217
E: secofstate@wyo.gov

Facilities Management

Maintains, constructs, designs, renovates and delivers basic services to state-owned facilities.

Information provided by:

National Association of State Facilities Administrators
Marcia Stone
Association Manager
2760 Research Park Drive
P.O. Box 11910
Lexington, KY 40578
P: (859) 244-8181
F: (859) 244-8001
nasfa@nasfa.net
www.nasfa.net

ALABAMA
Mr. Sean Cassidy
Chief of Services
State of Alabama
425 South Union Street
Montgomery, AL 36130
P: (334) 353-0371

ALASKA
Mr. Joel St. Aubin
Facilities Chief
Statewide Public Facilities
Transportation & Public Facilities
2200 East 42nd Avenue
Anchorage, AK 99508
P: (907) 269-0823
F: (907) 269-0805
E: joel.staubin@alaska.gov

ARIZONA
Mr. Matt Halstead
General Manager
Facilities Operations & Maintenance
Department of Administration
100 North 15th Avenue, Suite 202
Phoenix, AZ 85007
P: (602) 542-1579
E: matt.halstead@azdoa.gov

ARKANSAS
Mr. Floyd Farmer
State Engineer
Design Review Section
Building Authority
501 Woodlane, Suite 600
Little Rock, AR 72201
P: (501) 682-5563
E: ffarmer@aba.state.ar.us

CALIFORNIA
Mr. Dan Burgoyne
Sustainability Manager,
Executive Office, Green Team
Department of General Services
707 3rd Street, 4th Floor
P.O. Box 989052
West Sacramento, CA 95605
P: (916) 376-5010
E: Daniel.Burgoyne
   @dgs.ca.gov

COLORADO
Mr. Bradford T. Membel
Director
Division of Facilities
Management
Department of Human Services
4112 South Knox Court
Denver, CO 80236
P: (303) 866-7290
F: (303) 866-7299
E: bradford.membel
   @state.co.us

CONNECTICUT
Mr. David Barkin
Chief Architect
State of Connecticut
165 Capitol Avenue, Room 477
Hartford, CT 06106
P: (860) 713-5631

Mr. Allen Herring
Chief Engineer
State of Connecticut
165 Capitol Avenue, Room 469
Hartford, CT 06106
P: (860) 713-5691

DELAWARE
Mr. Mark Devore
Chief of Engineering & Operations
Division of Facilities
Management
Office of Management & Budget
540 South Dupont Highway, Suite 1
Dover, DE 19901
P: (302) 739-5644
E: mark.devore@state.de.us

Mr. Dennis M. Groom
Director
State of Delaware
540 South Dupont Highway, Suite 1
Dover, DE 19901
P: (302) 739-5644

DISTRICT OF COLUMBIA
Mr. Brian J. Hanlon
Director
Department of General Services
2000 14th Street Northwest, 8th Floor
Washington, DC 20009
P: (202) 727-2800

FLORIDA
Mr. Tom Berger
Director
Real Estate Development & Management
Department of Management Services
4050 Esplanade Way, Suite 315
Tallahassee, FL 32399
P: (850) 487-9921
E: tom.berger
   @dms.myflorida.com

GEORGIA
Mr. Steve Fanczi
Deputy Executive Director
State Building Authority
1 Martin Luther King Jr. Drive
Atlanta, GA 30334
P: (404) 463-4683
F: (404) 651-9595
E: sfanczi@doas.ga.gov

Mr. Steve Stancil
State Property Officer
State Building Authority
47 Trinity Avenue Southwest, Suite G02
Atlanta, GA 30334
P: (404) 656-3253
F: (404) 656-6006
E: sstancil@gsfic.ga.gov

HAWAII
Mr. Douglas Murdock
Comptroller
Department of Accounting & General Services
1151 Punchbowl Street, Room 412
Honolulu, HI 96813
P: (808) 586-0400
F: (808) 586-0775
E: dags@hawaii.gov

IDAHO
Mr. Tim Mason
Administrator
Division of Public Works
Department of Administration
502 North 4th Street
Boise, ID 83702
P: (208) 332-1900
F: (208) 334-4031
E: tim.mason@adm.idaho.gov

ILLINOIS
Mr. Josh Weger
Deputy Director of Construction
State of Illinois
W. G. Stratton Building, 364 North
401 South Spring Street
Springfield, IL 62706
P: (217) 782-8527

Mr. Michael A. Wilson II
Deputy Director of Operations
State Capital Development Board
W. G. Stratton Building
401 South Spring Street, Room 50
Springfield, IL 62706
P: (312) 814-4441

INDIANA
Mr. Brian Renner
Deputy Commissioner of Operations
Office of the Commissioner
Department of Administration
302 West Washington Street, Room E-024
Indianapolis, IN 46204
P: (317) 232-3125
E: brenner@idoa.in.gov

IOWA
Mr. Scott Gustafson
Facilities Engineer I
Support Services & Design
Department of Transportation
800 Lincoln Way
Ames, IA 50010
P: (515) 239-1443
E: scott.gustafson
   @dot.iowa.gov

KANSAS
Mr. Gary Grimes
Facilities Architect,
Management Operations
Disability & Behavioral Health Services
Aging & Disability Services
503 South Kansas Avenue
Topeka, KS 66603
P: (785) 296-3772
F: (785) 532-6363
E: gwg@ksu.edu

Facilities Management

KENTUCKY
Mr. Paul Gannoe
Deputy Commissioner,
Department for Facilities &
Support Services
Finance & Administration
Cabinet
403 Wapping Street
Frankfort, KY 40601
P: (502) 564-3590

LOUISIANA
Mr. Mark A. Moses
Assistant Director
State of Louisiana
P.O. Box 94095
Baton Rouge, LA 70804
P: (225) 342-0820

MAINE
Mr. Edward Dahl
Director
Bureau of General Services
77 State House Station
Augusta, ME 04333
P: (207) 624-7314
E: edward.dahl@maine.gov

MARYLAND
Ms. Gail Bassette
Secretary
Department of General Services
301 West Preston Street, Room
1401
Baltimore, MD 21201
P: (410) 767-4960

MASSACHUSETTS
Ms. Hope Davis
Director
Division of Capital Asset
Management
Facilities Maintenance &
Management
One Ashburton Place, 15th Floor
Boston, MA 02108
P: (617) 727-4030 Ext. 447
F: (617) 727-4043
E: hope.davis@state.ma.us

MICHIGAN
Mr. John E. Nixon
Director
State of Michigan
George W. Romney Building
111 South Capitol Avenue
Lansing, MI 48933
P: (517) 373-4978
E: dtmb@michigan.gov

MINNESOTA
Mr. Wayne Waslaski
Senior Director, Real Estate &
Construction Services
Department of Administration
309 Administration Building
50 Sherburne Avenue
St. Paul, MN 55155
P: (651) 201-2548
E: Wayne.Waslaski
   @state.mn.us

MISSISSIPPI
Mr. Glenn Kornbrek
Assistant Director
Bureau of Buildings, Grounds &
Real Property Management
Department of Finance &
Administration
501 North West Street, Suite
1401 B
Jackson, MS 39201
P: (601) 359-3894
E: kornbrg@dfa.state.ms.us

MISSOURI
Mr. Gary Claspill
Design Development Survey
Manager
State of Missouri
301 West High Street, Room
730
P.O. Box 809
Jefferson City, MO 65102
P: (573) 751-3740
F: (573) 751-7277
E: gary.claspill@oa.mo.gov

MONTANA
Mr. Russ Katherman
Engineering Manager
Architecture & Engineering
Division
Department of Administration
P.O. Box 200103
Helena, MT 59620
P: (406) 444-3332
F: (406) 444-3399
E: rkatherman@mt.gov

NEBRASKA
Mr. Rodney Anderson
Administrator
State Building Division
Department of Administrative
Services
521 South 14th Street, Suite 500
Lincoln, NE 68508
P: (402) 471-3191
E: rodney.anderson
   @nebraska.gov

NEVADA
Mr. Gustavo Nunez
Administrator
State Public Works Board
Department of Administration
515 East Musser Street, Room
102
Carson City, NV 89701
P: (775) 684-4141
E: gnunez@spwb.state.nv.us

NEW HAMPSHIRE
Ms. Michelle Juliano
Assistant Administrator
Public Works
Public Works, Design &
Construction
7 Hazen Drive
Concord, NH 03302
P: (603) 271-1645
E: mjuliano@dot.state.nh.us

NEW JERSEY
Mr. Guy Bocage
Deputy Director
Division of Property
Management & Construction
Department of the Treasury
33 West State Street, P.O. Box
230
Trenton, NJ 08625
P: (609) 292-5111
F: (609) 984-2575
E: guy.bocage
   @treas.state.nj.us

NEW MEXICO
Mr. George D. Morgan
Director
Building Services Division
General Services Department
2542 Cerrilos Road, P.O. Box
6850
Santa Fe, NM 87502
P: (505) 827-2141

NEW YORK
Mr. James Dirolf
Director, Division of Design &
Construction
Department of General Services
Corning Tower 32nd Floor
Empire State Plaza
Albany, NY 12242
P: (518) 474-0222

NORTH CAROLINA
Mr. Gregory Driver
Director
State Construction Office
Department of Administration
1301 Mail Service Center, 116
West Jones
Raleigh, NC 27699
P: (919) 807-4100
F: (919) 807-4110
E: gregory.driver
   @doa.nc.gov

NORTH DAKOTA
Mr. John Boyle
Director, Facilities Management
Office of Management &
Budget
State Capitol Building, 4th Floor
600 East Boulevard Avenue
Bismarck, ND 58505
P: (701) 328-4002
E: jaboyle@nd.gov

Mr. Joel Leapaldt
State Facility Planner, Division
of Facility Management
Office of Management &
Budget
State Capitol Building, 4th Floor
600 East Boulevard Avenue
Bismarck, ND 58505
P: (701) 328-1968
F: (701) 328-3230
E: jleapaldt@nd.gov

OHIO
Mr. Peter A.J. Gunnell
Chief Administrator
General Services
Division/Office of Properties &
Facilities
Department of Administrative
Services
4200 Surface Road
Columbus, OH 43228
P: (614) 752-0455
E: pete.gunnell
   @das.state.oh.us

OKLAHOMA
Mr. Mark Sauchuk
Director
Office of Facilities Management
Department of Central Services
2222 North Walnut
Oklahoma City, OK 73105
P: (405) 522-0084
E: mark_sauchuk
   @dcs.state.ok.us

Facilities Management

OREGON
Mr. Randy Gengler
Operations & Maintenance
Manager
Facilities Division
Department of Administrative
Services
1240 Ferry Street, Southeast,
U100
Salem, OR 97301
P: (503) 378-3664
E: randy.gengler
   @state.or.us

PENNSYLVANIA
Mr. Daniel Schiavoni
Deputy Secretary
Property & Asset Management
515 North Office Building
Harrisburg, PA 17125
P: (717) 783-5028
E: dschiavoni@state.pa.us

RHODE ISLAND
Mr. Marco Schiappa
Associate Director
Facilities Management
Department of Administration
One Capitol Hill, 2nd Floor
Providence, RI 02908
P: (401) 222-5717
E: MSchiappa
   @gw.doa.state.ri.us

SOUTH CAROLINA
Mr. John St. C. White
State Engineer
Materials Management Office
Budget & Control Board
1201 Main Street, Suite 600
Columbia, SC 29201
P: (803) 737-0768
E: jwhite@mmo.sc.gov

SOUTH DAKOTA
Ms. Kristi Honeywell
State Engineer
Bureau of Administration
Joe Foss Building
523 East Capitol
Pierre, SD 57501
P: (605) 773-3466
E: Kristi.Honeywell
   @state.sd.us

TENNESSEE
Mr. Bob Oglesby
Commissioner
Finance & Administration
22nd Floor, 312 8th Avenue,
North
Nashville, TN 37243
P: (615) 741-2081
E: bob.oglesby@tn.gov

Mr. J. Alan Robertson
Assistant State Architect
State of Tennessee
312 Rosa L. Parks Avenue
Snodgrass Tennessee Tower
Nashville, TN 37243
P: (615) 741-3259
E: alan.robertson@tn.gov

TEXAS
Ms. Robin E. De Rosa
Deputy Assistant Director
Infrastructure Support &
Administration Division
Department of Public Safety
5805 North Lamar Boulevard
Austin, TX 78773
P: (512) 424-7807

UTAH
Mr. Bruce Whittington
Assistant Director
Facilities, Construction &
Management
Administrative Services
4130 State Office Bulding
Salt Lake City, UT 84114
P: (801) 538-3547
F: (801) 538-3378
E: bwhittington@utah.gov

VERMONT
Mr. William Laferriere
Director of Property
Management
Department of Buildings &
Property Management
Four Governor Aiken Avenue
Montpelier, VT 05633
P: (802) 828-1115
F: (802) 828-6501
E: bill.laferriere
   @state.vt.us

VIRGINIA
Mr. Ed Gully
Director
Engineering & Buildings
Department of General Services
1100 Bank Street, Suite 506
Richmond, VA 23219
P: (804) 786-3263

WASHINGTON
Mr. Thomas R. Henderson
Assistant Director
State of Washington
P.O. Box 41011
Olympia, WA 98504
P: (360) 407-9311
E: Tom.Henderson@des.wa.gov

WEST VIRGINIA
Mr. Micheal Q. Evans
Architect
State of West Virginia
1900 Kanawha Boulevard, East
Charleston, WV 25305
P: (304) 957-7145
E: david.m.oliverio@wv.gov

WISCONSIN
Mr. Keith Beck
Director of Facilities
State of Wisconsin
101 East Wilson Street
P.O. Box 7866
Madison, WI 53703
P: (608) 266-2645
E: keith.beck@wisconsin.gov

Mr. Bill Napier
Architect & Professional
Engineer
State of Wisconsin
P.O. Box 7866
Madison, WI 53707
P: (608) 267-0422

Ms. Summer Shannon-Bradley
Administrator, Division of
Facilities Development
State Building Commission
State Building Commission
131 West Wilson Street, P.O.
Box 7866
Madison, WI 53707
P: (608) 266-1031

WYOMING
Mr. Raymond Vigil Jr.
Field Operations & Facilities
Program Manager, Facilities
Management
Department of Transportation
5300 Bishop Boulevard
Building 6101, Room B-25
Cheyenne, WY 82009
P: (307) 777-4474
F: (307) 777-3801
E: raymond.vigil
   @dot.state.wy.us

Federal Liaison

The individual, typically based in Washington D.C., who serves as the chief representative of state government in the nation's capital, and works to promote state-federal relations.

For more information contact:

National Governors Association
Dan Crippen
Executive Director
Hall of States
444 North Capitol Street
Washington, DC 20001
P: (202) 624-5300
F: (202) 624-5313
www.nga.org

ALABAMA
Ms. Jill Boxler
Federal Relations Director
Office of the Governor
444 North Capitol Street, Suite 328A
Washington, DC 20001
P: (202) 220-1379

ALASKA
Mr. Kip Knudson
Director
Office of the Governor
444 North Capitol Street, Suite 336
Washington, DC 20001
P: (202) 624-5858
F: (202) 624-5857

AMERICAN SAMOA
Ms. Minnie Tuia
Deputy Chief of Staff
Office of the Governor
Executive Office Building
Pago Pago, AS 96799
P: (684) 633-4116 Ext. 233

ARIZONA
Mr. Danny Seiden
Deputy Chief of Staff
Office of the Governor
State Capitol
1700 West Washington
Phoenix, AZ 85007
P: (602) 542-4331

ARKANSAS
Ms. Alison Williams
Director, Federal Government Relations
Washington Office of the Goverr
444 North Capitol Street, Suite 365
Washington, DC 20001
P: (501) 682-2345

CALIFORNIA
Ms. Katie Mathews
Director
Office of the Governor
444 North Capitol Street, Suite 134
Washington, DC 20014
P: (202) 624-5270
F: (202) 624-5280

COLORADO
Ms. Jena Griswold
Washington Director
Office of the Governor
444 North Capitol Street, Suite 134
Washington, DC 20013
P: (202) 624-5278

CONNECTICUT
Mr. Dan DeSimone
Director
Office of the Governor
444 North Capitol Street, Suite 317
Washington, DC 20001
P: (202) 347-4535
F: (202) 347-7151

DELAWARE
Mr. Garth Spencer
Director
Washington Office
444 North Capitol Street, Suite 230
Washington, DC 20001
P: (202) 624-7724

FLORIDA
Mr. Chris Hartline
D.C. Liaison
Washington Office
State of Florida
444 North Capitol Street, Suite 349
Washington, DC 20001
P: (202) 624-5885

GEORGIA
Mr. Todd Smith
Washington Representative
Office of the Governor
1455 Pennsylvania Avenue, Northwest
Suite 400
Washington, DC 20004
P: (202) 652-2299
F: (202) 347-1142

GUAM
Mr. Jay Rojas
Director
Washington Office
444 North Capitol Street, Suite 619
Washington, DC 20001
P: (202) 434-4855
F: (202) 434-4856

HAWAII
Ms. Elizabeth Kim
Special Advisor
Office of the Governor
State Capitol
Executive Chambers
Honolulu, HI 96813
P: (808) 586-0034

IDAHO
Mr. David Hensley
Chief of Staff
Office of the Governor
700 West Jefferson Street
2nd Floor, West Wing
Boise, ID 83702
P: (208) 854-3005
F: (208) 334-2175
E: dhensley@gov.idaho.gov

ILLINOIS
Ms. Kathy Lydon
Director
Washington Office
State of Illinois
444 North Capitol Street, Suite 400
Washington, DC 20001
P: (202) 624-7760

INDIANA
Mr. Josh Pitcock
Federal Representative
Office of the Governor
444 North Capitol Street, Suite 411
Washington, DC 20001
P: (202) 624-1474

IOWA
Mr. Doug Hoelscher
Director
Office for State-Federal Relation
400 North Capitol Street, Suite 359
Washington, DC 20001
P: (202) 624-5479
F: (202) 624-8189

KANSAS
Mr. Adam Nordstrom
Washington Representative for the Governor
Washington Office
500 New Jersey Avenue, Northwest
Suite 400
Washington, DC 20001
P: (202) 715-2923
F: (202) 638-1045

KENTUCKY
Ms. Rebecca Byers
Director
Office of the Governor
444 North Capitol Street, Suite 380
Washington, DC 20019
P: (202) 220-1350
F: (202) 220-1359

LOUISIANA
Ms. Melissa Mann
Director of Legislative Affairs
Office of the Governor
P.O. Box 94004
Baton Rouge, LA 70804
P: (225) 342-7188
E: melissa.mann@la.gov

MAINE
Mr. Lance Libby
Legislative Policy Coordinator
Office of the Governor
One State House Station
Augusta, ME 04333
P: (207) 287-3533

MARYLAND
Mr. Brad Peganoff
Director
Washington Office of the Goverr
State of Maryland
444 North Capitol Street, Suite 311
Washington, DC 20001
P: (202) 624-1430

Federal Liaison

MASSACHUSETTS
Ms. Tiffany Watkins Ahern
Director
Washington Office of the Goverr
Commonwealth of
Massachusetts
444 North Capitol Street, Suite
208
Washington, DC 20001
P: (202) 624-7713

MICHIGAN
Mr. Bill McBride
Director
Office of the Governor
444 North Capitol Street, Suite
411
Washington, DC 20001
P: (202) 624-5840
F: (202) 624-5841

MISSOURI
Mr. Dustin Allison
Deputy Chief of Staff
Office of the Governor
State Capitol Building
301 West Hight Street, Room
216
Jefferson City, MO 65101
P: (573) 751-3222

MONTANA
Mr. Adam Schafer
Director of Public Engagement
& Senior Advisor
Office of the Governor
P.O. Box 200801
Helena, MT 59620
P: (406) 444-3111

NEBRASKA
Ms. Lauren Kintner
Policy Director & General
Counsel
Office of the Governor
State Capitol, Room 1319
Lincoln, NE 68509
P: (402) 471-2244

NEVADA
Mr. Ryan McGinness
Director
Washington Office
444 North Capitol Street, Suite
209
Washington, DC 20001
P: (202) 624-5405
F: (202) 624-8181
E: ryan@nevadadc.org

NEW HAMPSHIRE
Ms. Pamela Walsh
Chief of Staff
Office of the Governor
State House
107 North Main Street, Room
208
Concord, NH 03301
P: (603) 271-2121
F: (603) 271-7640
E: pamela.walsh@nh.gov

NEW JERSEY
Ms. Dona De Leon
Director
Washington Office
The State House
P.O. Box 001
Trenton, NJ 08625
P: (609) 292-6000

NEW MEXICO
Mr. James Ross
Cabinet Director
Office of the Governor
State Capitol, Fourth Floor
Santa Fe, NM 87501
P: (505) 476-2200

NEW YORK
Mr. Alexander Cochran
Director
Office of the Governor
444 North Capitol Street, Suite
301
Washington, DC 20001
P: (202) 434-7112
F: (202) 434-7110

NORTH CAROLINA
Ms. Virginia Johnson
Director of Federal Relations
Washington Office
444 North Capitol Street,
Northwest
Suite 332
Washington, DC 20001
P: (202) 624-5833

NORTH DAKOTA
Ms. Krista Carman
Washington Representative
Washington Office
211 North Union Street, Suite
100
Alexandria, VA 22314
P: (703) 519-1207
F: (202) 478-0811

**NORTHERN MARIANA
ISLANDS**
Ms. Esther Fleming
Chief of Staff
Office of the Governor
Caller Box 10007, Capitol Hill
Saipan, MP 96950
P: (670) 664-2212
F: (670) 664-2211

OHIO
Ms. Jeanne Jacco
Assistant To the Chief of Staff
& Policy
Office of the Governor
77 South High Street, 30th
Floor
Columbus, OH 43215
P: (614) 466-3555

OKLAHOMA
Ms. Katie Altshuler
Policy Director
Office of the Governor
State of Oklahoma
2300 North Lincoln Boulevard,
Suite 212
Oklahoma City, OK 73105
P: (405) 521-2342

RHODE ISLAND
Mr. Matt Bucci
Director
Office of the Governor
State House
Providence, RI 02903

SOUTH CAROLINA
Mr. Josh Baker
Budget Director
Office of the Governor
Statehouse
1205 Pendleton Street
Columbia, SC 29201
P: (803) 734-2100

TENNESSEE
Ms. Beth Tipps
Deputy Director of Policy &
Research
Office of the Governor
State Capitol, First Floor
Nashville, TN 37243
P: (615) 741-2001

TEXAS
Mr. Jerry Strickland
Director
Office of State-Federal Relations
10 G Street Northeast, Suite
650
Washington, DC 20002

U.S. VIRGIN ISLANDS
Ms. Rochelle Corneiro
Deputy Chief of Staff
Office of the Governor
Government House
21-22 Kongens Gade,
Charlotte Amalie
St. Thomas, VI 00802
P: (340) 774-0001

UTAH
Mr. Wesley Smith
Director of State & Federal
Relations
Office of the Governor
500 New Jersey Avenue,
Northwest
Suite 400
Washington, DC 20002
P: (801) 538-1000

VERMONT
Ms. Alyson Richards
Deputy Chief of Staff &
Director of Intergovernmental
Affairs
Office of the Governor
Pavilion Office Building
109 State Street, Fifth Floor
Montpelier, VT 05609
P: (802) 828-3333

VIRGINIA
Ms. Maribel Ramos
Director
Office of Intergovernmental Affa
444 North Capitol Street,
Northwest
Suite 214
Washington, DC 20001
P: (202) 783-1769

WASHINGTON
Mr. Sam Ricketts
Director
Washington, D.C. Office
444 North Capitol Street, Suite
411
Washington, DC 20001
P: (202) 624-3691
F: (202) 624-5841

WISCONSIN
Ms. Wendy Riemann
Director
Office of the Governor
444 North Capitol Street, Suite
613
Washington, DC 20001
P: (202) 624-5870
F: (202) 624-5871

WYOMING
Mr. Tony Young
Deputy Chief of Staff
Office of the Governor
State Capitol
200 West 24th Street
Cheyenne, WY 82002
P: (307) 777-7434

Finance

Responsible for multiple financial functions (budget, payroll, accounting, revenue estimation.)

ALABAMA
Mr. Bill Newton
Acting Director
Department of Finance
State Capitol
600 Dexter Avenue, Suite N-105
Montgomery, AL 36130
P: (334) 242-7230
F: (334) 353-3300
E: bill.newton
    @budget.alabama.gov

ALASKA
Mr. Scot Arehart
Director
Division of Finance
Department of Administration
P.O. Box 110204
Juneau, AK 99811
P: (907) 465-5601
F: (907) 465-2169
E: scot.arehart@alaska.gov

AMERICAN SAMOA
Hon. Falema'o M. Pili
Treasurer
Office of the Treasurer
American Samoa Government
Pago Pago, AS 96799
P: (684) 633-4155
F: (684) 633-4100

ARIZONA
Mr. D. Clark Partridge
State Comptroller
General Accounting Office
100 North 15th Avenue, Suite 302
Phoenix, AZ 85007
P: (602) 542-5405
F: (602) 542-5749
E: clark.partridge
    @azdoa.gov

ARKANSAS
Mr. Larry Walther
Director
Department of Finance &
Administration
1509 West 7th Street
DFA Building, Room 401
Little Rock, AR 72201
P: (501) 682-2242
F: (501) 682-1029
E: larry.walther
    @dfa.arkansas.gov

CALIFORNIA
Mr. Michael Cohen
Director
Department of Finance
915 L Street
Sacramento, CA 95814
P: (916) 445-4141
E: michael.cohen@dof.ca.gov

CONNECTICUT
Mr. Benjamin Barnes
Secretary
Office of Policy & Management
450 Capitol Avenue
Hartford, CT 06106
P: (860) 418-6500
F: (860) 418-6487
E: Ben.Barnes@Ct.gov

DELAWARE
Mr. Thomas J. Cook
Secretary of Finance
Department of Finance
Carvel State Building, 8th Floor
820 North French Street
Wilmington, DE 19801
P: (302) 577-8987
F: (302) 577-8982
E: tom.cook@state.de.us

GUAM
Ms. Benita A. Manglona
Director
Department of Administration
P.O. Box 884
Hagatna, GU 96932
P: (671) 475-1101
F: (671) 477-6788

HAWAII
Hon. Wesley Machida
Director of Finance
Department of Budget &
Finance
P.O. Box 150
Honolulu, HI 96810
P: (808) 586-1518
F: (808) 586-1976
E: hi.budgetandfinance
    @hawaii.gov

IDAHO
Mr. Gavin M. Gee
Director
Department of Finance
800 Park Boulevard, Suite 200
P.O. Box 83720
Boise, ID 83720
P: (208) 332-8010
F: (208) 332-8097
E: gavin.gee
    @finance.idaho.gov

ILLINOIS
Mr. Tim Nuding
Director
Governor's Office of
Management & Budget
401 South Spring
603 Stratton Building
Springfield, IL 62706
P: (217) 782-4520
F: (217) 524-4876

INDIANA
Mr. Brian E. Bailey
Director
State Budget Agency
200 West Washington Street,
Room 212
Indianapolis, IN 46204
P: (317) 234-8538
F: (317) 233-3323
E: bbailey@gov.in.gov

IOWA
Ms. Courtney M. Kay-Decker
Director
Department of Revenue
Hoover State Office Building
1305 East Walnut Street
Des Moines, IA 50319
P: (515) 281-3204
E: courtney.decker@iowa.gov

KANSAS
Ms. Colleen Becker
Director
Office of Financial Management
900 Southwest Jackson Street
Suite 500
Topeka, KS 66612
P: (785) 296-7703
E: colleen.becker@da.ks.gov

KENTUCKY
Ms. Lori Hudson Flanery
Secretary
Finance & Administration
Cabinet
383 Capitol Annex
Frankfort, KY 40601
P: (502) 564-4240
F: (502) 564-5856
E: Lori.Flanery@ky.gov

LOUISIANA
Mr. Afranie Adomako
Assistant Commissioner,
Management & Finance
Office of Finance & Support
Services
Division of Administration
P.O. Box 94095
Baton Rouge, LA 70804
P: (225) 342-0708
F: (225) 342-1057
E: afranie.adomako@la.gov

MAINE
Mr. H. Sawin Millett Jr.
Commissioner
Department of Administrative &
Financial Services
78 State House Station
Augusta, ME 04333
P: (207) 624-7800
F: (207) 624-7804
E: sawin.millett@maine.gov

MARYLAND
Mr. David R. Brinkley
Secretary
Department of Budget &
Management
45 Calvert Street, 1st Floor
Annapolis, MD 21401
P: (410) 260-7041
F: (410) 974-2585
E: David.Brinkley
    @maryland.gov

MICHIGAN
Mr. John E. Nixon
Director
Department of Technology,
Management & Budget
George W. Romney Building
111 South Capitol Avenue
Lansing, MI 48933
P: (517) 373-4978
E: dtmb@michigan.gov

MINNESOTA
Mr. Myron Frans
Commissioner
Management & Budget
658 Cedar Street, Suite 400
St. Paul, MN 55155
P: (651) 201-8011
F: (651) 797-1300
E: myron.frans@state.mn.us

MISSISSIPPI
Mr. Kevin J. Upchurch
Executive Director
Department of Finance &
Administration
P.O. Box 267
Jackson, MS 39205
P: (601) 359-3402
F: (601) 359-2405
E: Kevin.Upchurch
    @dfa.ms.gov

MISSOURI
Ms. Debbie Hardman
Acting Commissioner of Finance
Division of Finance
Truman State Office Building,
Room 630
P.O. Box 716
Jefferson City, MO 65102
P: (573) 751-3242
F: (573) 751-9192
E: finance@dof.mo.gov

MONTANA

Ms. Cheryl Grey
Administrator
State Accounting Division
125 North Roberts Street, Room 270
P.O. Box 200102
Helena, MT 59620
P: (406) 444-7334
F: (406) 444-2812
E: chgrey@mt.gov

Mr. Dan Villa
Budget Director
Office of Budget & Program Planning
State Capitol, Room 277
P.O. Box 200802
Helena, MT 59620
P: (406) 444-3616
F: (406) 444-4670
E: dvilla@mt.gov

NEBRASKA

Mr. Byron L. Diamond
Director
Department of Administrative Services
State Capitol, Room 1315
Lincoln, NE 68509
P: (402) 471-2331
E: byron.diamond
@nebraska.gov

NEVADA

Mr. Jeff Mohlenkamp
Director
Department of Administration
209 East Musser Street, Room 200
Carson City, NV 89701
P: (775) 684-0222
F: (775) 684-0260
E: DeptAdmin@admin.nv.gov

NEW HAMPSHIRE

Ms. Linda M. Hodgdon
Commissioner
Department of Administrative Services
25 Capitol Street
State House Annex, Room 120
Concord, NH 03301
P: (603) 271-3201
F: (603) 271-6600
E: linda.hodgdon@nh.gov

NEW JERSEY

Ms. Charlene M. Holzbaur
Director
Office of Management & Budget
Department of the Treasury
33 West State Street, P.O. Box 221
Trenton, NJ 08625
P: (609) 292-6746
F: (609) 633-8179
E: charlene.holzbaur
@treas.state.nj.us

NEW MEXICO

Mr. Tom Clifford
Cabinet Secretary
Department of Finance & Administration
180 Bataan Memorial Building
407 Galisteo Street, Room 180
Santa Fe, NM 87501
P: (505) 827-4985
F: (505) 827-4984
E: Tom.Clifford@state.nm.us

NEW YORK

Mr. Thomas H. Mattox
Commissioner
Department of Taxation & Finance
W.A. Harriman Campus, Building 9
Albany, NY 12227

NORTH CAROLINA

Mr. Art Pope
State Budget Director
Office of State Budget & Management
116 West Jones Street
Raleigh, NC 27603
P: (919) 807-4700
E: art.pope@osbm.nc.gov

NORTH DAKOTA

Ms. Sheila Peterson
Director, Fiscal Management Division
Fiscal Management Division
600 East Boulevard Avenue
Department 110
Bismarck, ND 58505
P: (701) 328-2680
F: (701) 328-3230
E: speterson@nd.gov

Ms. Pam Sharp
Director
Office of Management & Budget
600 East Boulevard Avenue
Department 110
Bismarck, ND 58505
P: (701) 328-4606
F: (701) 328-3230
E: psharp@nd.gov

OKLAHOMA

Mr. Preston L. Doerflinger
Secretary & Director of Finance
Office of Management & Enterprise Services
2300 North Lincoln Boulevard, Room 122
Oklahoma City, OK 73105
P: (405) 521-2141
F: (405) 521-3902

OREGON

Mr. George M. Naughton
Chief Operating Officer
Chief Financial Office
155 Cottage Street, Northeast, U10
Salem, OR 97301
P: (503) 378-5460
F: (503) 373-7643
E: george.m.naughton
@oregon.gov

PENNSYLVANIA

Mr. Randy Albright
Secretary of the Budget
Office of the Budget
19th Floor, 333 Market Street
Harrisburg, PA 17101
P: (717) 787-2542
F: (717) 783-3368

PUERTO RICO

Mr. Carlos Quinones Rivas
Director
Office of Management & Budget
P.O. Box 9023228
San Juan, PR 00902
P: (787) 725-9420
F: (787) 722-0299

RHODE ISLAND

Mr. Thomas A. Mullaney
Director
Budget Office
Office of Management & Budget
One Capitol Hill, 4th Floor
Providence, RI 02908
P: (401) 222-6414
F: (401) 222-6436
E: thomas.mullaney
@budget.ri.gov

SOUTH DAKOTA

Mr. Jason C. Dilges
Chief Financial Officer & Commissioner
Bureau of Finance & Management
500 East Capitol Avenue
Pierre, SD 57501
P: (605) 773-3411
F: (605) 773-4711
E: jason.dilges@state.sd.us

TENNESSEE

Mr. Larry Martin
Commissioner
Department of Finance & Administration
312 Rosa Parks Avenue, 21st Floor
Nashville, TN 37243
P: (615) 741-2401
E: Larry.Martin@tn.gov

TEXAS

Hon. Glenn Hegar (R)
Comptroller of Public Accounts
Office of the Comptroller of Public Accounts
LBJ State Office Building, 1st Floor
111 East 17th Street
Austin, TX 78774
P: (512) 463-4444
F: (512) 463-4902
E: glenn.hegar
@cpa.state.tx.us

UTAH

Mr. John C. Reidhead
Director
Division of Finance
2110 State Office Building
Salt Lake City, UT 84114
P: (801) 538-3095
F: (801) 538-3244
E: jreidhead@utah.gov

VERMONT

Mr. James B. Reardon
Commissioner
Department of Finance & Management
109 State Street
Montpelier, VT 05609
P: (802) 828-2376
F: (802) 828-2428
E: jim.reardon@state.vt.us

Finance

VIRGINIA
Hon. Richard D. Brown
Secretary of Finance
Office of the Secretary of
Finance
1111 East Broad Street
Richmond, VA 23219
P: (804) 692-2551
F: (804) 692-0676
E: Ric.Brown
    @governor.virginia.gov

WASHINGTON
Mr. David Schumacher
Director
Office of Financial Management
P.O. Box 43113
Olympia, WA 98504
P: (360) 902-0555
F: (360) 664-2832
E: ofm.administration
    @ofm.wa.gov

WEST VIRGINIA
Mr. Robert S. Kiss
Cabinet Secretary
Department of Revenue
State Capitol
Building 1, W-300
Charleston, WV 25305
P: (304) 558-1017
F: (304) 558-2324
E: Robert.S.Kiss@wv.gov

WISCONSIN
Mr. Kevin Heifetz
Administrator
Division of Executive Budget &
Finance
P.O. Box 7864
Madison, WI 53703
P: (608) 266-1035
E: kevin.heifetz
    @wisconsin.gov

WYOMING
Hon. Cynthia I. Cloud (R)
State Auditor
Office of the State Auditor
State Capitol, Suite 114
200 West 24th Street
Cheyenne, WY 82002
P: (307) 777-7831
F: (307) 777-6983
E: SAOAdmin@wyo.gov

Firearms

Conducts background checks for firearm purchases, issues weapon permits, regulates firearm sales, and oversees all other matters relating to the buying and selling of firearms within the state.

ALABAMA
Hon. Luther Strange (R)
Attorney General
Office of the Attorney General
501 Washington Avenue
P.O. Box 300152
Montgomery, AL 36130
P: (334) 242-7300

ALASKA
Mr. Gary Folger
Commissioner
Department of Public Safety
5700 East Tudor Road
Anchorage, AK 99507
P: (907) 269-5086
F: (907) 269-4543
E: gary.folger@alaska.gov

AMERICAN SAMOA
Mr. William E. Haleck
Commissioner
Department of Public Safety
American Samoa Government
P.O. Box 1086
Pato Pato, AS 96799
P: (684) 633-1111
F: (684) 633-7296
E: commissioner@dps.as.gov

ARIZONA
Ms. Donna J. Street
Supervisor
Concealed Weapons Permit Unit
Department of Public Safety
P.O. Box 6488
Phoenix, AZ 85005
P: (602) 256-6280
F: (602) 223-2928

ARKANSAS
Colonel Bill Bryant
Director
State Police
1 State Police Plaza Drive
Little Rock, AR 72209
P: (501) 618-8299
F: (501) 618-8710
E: info@asp.arkansas.gov

CALIFORNIA
Mr. Stephen Lindley
Chief
Bureau of Firearms
P.O. Box 160487
Sacramento, CA 95816
P: (916) 227-4010
F: (916) 227-7480
E: stephen.lindley
   @doj.ca.gov

COLORADO
Mr. Ron Sloan
Director
Bureau of Investigation
690 Kipling Street, Suite 3000
Lakewood, CO 80215
P: (303) 239-4201
F: (303) 235-0568
E: ron.sloan@state.co.us

CONNECTICUT
Mr. Frank P. Blando
Chair
Board of Firearms Permit
Examiners
Office of Governmental
Accountability
20 Trinity Street, 5th Floor
Hartford, CT 06106
P: (860) 256-2947
F: (860) 256-2997
E: bfpe@ct.gov

DELAWARE
Hon. Matthew Denn (D)
Attorney General
Office of the Attorney General
Carvel State Office Building
820 North French Street
Wilmington, DE 19801
P: (302) 577-8338
E: matthew.denn@state.de.us

DISTRICT OF COLUMBIA
Ms. Cathy L. Lanier
Chief of Police
Metropolitan Police Department
300 Indiana Avenue, Northwest
Room 5059
Washington, DC 20001
P: (202) 727-9099
F: (202) 727-4106
E: mpd@dc.gov

FLORIDA
Mr. Rick Swearingen
Commissioner
Department of Law
Enforcement
2331 Phillips Road
P.O. Box 1489
Tallahassee, FL 32302
P: (850) 410-7001
E: RickSwearingen
   @fdle.state.fl.us

GEORGIA
Mr. Vernon M. Keenan
Director
Bureau of Investigation
3121 Panthersville Road
Decatur, GA 30034
P: (404) 244-2600
F: (404) 270-8352
E: vernon.keenan@gbi.ga.gov

IDAHO
Hon. Lawrence Wasden (R)
Attorney General
Office of the Attorney General
Statehouse
Boise, ID 83720
P: (208) 334-2400
F: (208) 854-8071

ILLINOIS
Mr. Hiram Grau
State Director
State Police
801 South 7th Street, Suite 1100
– S
Springfield, IL 62703
P: (217) 782-7263
E: hiram.grau@illinois.gov

INDIANA
Mr. Douglas G. Carter
Superintendent
State Police
Indiana Government Center
North
100 North Senate Avenue
Indianapolis, IN 46204
P: (317) 232-8248
E: ISP@isp.in.gov

KANSAS
Hon. Derek Schmidt (R)
Attorney General
Office of the Attorney General
120 Southwest 10th Avenue, 2nd
Floor
Topeka, KS 66612
P: (785) 296-2215
F: (785) 296-6296

Mr. Kirk D. Thompson
Director
Bureau of Investigation
1620 Southwest Tyler Street
Topeka, KS 66612
P: (785) 296-8200

KENTUCKY
Mr. Rodney Brewer
Commissioner
State Police
919 Versailles Road
Frankfort, KY 40601
P: (502) 782-1800
F: (502) 573-1479

LOUISIANA
Col. Michael D. Edmonson
Deputy Secretary
State Police
Public Safety Services
7919 Independence Boulevard
Baton Rouge, LA 70806
P: (225) 925-6118
F: (225) 925-6006

MAINE
Colonel Robert A. Williams
Chief
State Police
42 State House Station
45 Commerce Drive
Augusta, ME 04333
P: (207) 624-7200
E: robert.a.williams
   @maine.gov

MARYLAND
Colonel William Pallozzi
Superintendent
Department of State Police
1201 Reisterstown Road
Pikesville, MD 21208
P: (410) 653-4219
E: msp.superintendent
   @maryland.gov

MASSACHUSETTS
Colonel Richard D. McKeon
Superintendent
State Police
470 Worcester Road
Framingham, MA 01702
P: (508) 820-2300
F: (617) 727-6874

MICHIGAN
Colonel Kriste Kibbey Etue
Director
State Police
333 South Grand Avenue
P.O. Box 30634
Lansing, MI 48909
P: (517) 332-2521
F: (517) 241-0409
E: EtueK@michigan.gov

MINNESOTA
Ms. Ramona Dohman
Commissioner
Department of Public Safety
445 Minnesota Street, Suite
1000
St. Paul, MN 55101
P: (651) 201-7160
F: (651) 297-5728
E: Mona.Dohman@state.mn.us

Firearms

MISSISSIPPI
Lt. Eugene Williams Jr.
Director
Firearm Permits Unit
Department of Public Safety
P.O. Box 958
Jackson, MS 39205
P: (601) 987-1575
E: ewilliams@dps.ms.gov

MISSOURI
Hon. Chris Koster (D)
Attorney General
Office of the Attorney General
Supreme Court Building
207 West High Street
Jefferson City, MO 65101
P: (573) 751-3321
F: (573) 751-0774

MONTANA
Hon. Tim Fox (R)
Attorney General
Department of Justice
Justice Building
215 North Sanders
Helena, MT 59620
P: (406) 444-2026
F: (406) 444-3549
E: contactdoj@mt.gov

NEBRASKA
Colonel Bradley Rice
Superintendent of Law
Enforcement & Public Safety
State Patrol
P.O. Box 94907
Lincoln, NE 68509
P: (402) 471-4545
F: (402) 479-4002
E: bradley.rice
    @nebraska.gov

NEW HAMPSHIRE
Mr. John J. Barthelmes
Commissioner
Department of Safety
James H. Hayes Safety Building
33 Hazen Drive
Concord, NH 03305
P: (603) 223-3889
F: (603) 271-3903
E: john.barthelmes
    @dos.nh.gov

NEW JERSEY
Col. Rick Fuentes
Superintendent
State Police
P.O. Box 7068
West Trenton, NJ 08628
P: (609) 882-2000
F: (609) 530-4383

NEW MEXICO
Mr. Gregory J. Fouratt Jr.
Cabinet Secretary
Department of Public Safety
4491 Cerrillos Road
P.O. Box 1628
Santa Fe, NM 87504
P: (505) 827-3370
F: (505) 827-3434

NEW YORK
Mr. Joseph D'Amico
Superintendent
State Police
1220 Washington Avenue,
Building 22
Albany, NY 12226
P: (518) 457-6721

NORTHERN MARIANA ISLANDS
Mr. James C.
    Deleon Guerrero
Commissioner
Department of Public Safety
Jose M. Sablan Building
Caller Box 10007
Saipan, MP 96950
P: (670) 664-9022
F: (670) 664-9070

OHIO
Colonel John Born
Director
Department of Public Safety
1970 West Broad Street
P.O. Box 182081
Columbus, OH 43218
P: (614) 466-3383
F: (614) 466-0433

OKLAHOMA
Mr. Stan Florence
Director
State Bureau of Investigation
6600 North Harvey
Oklahoma City, OK 73116
P: (405) 848-6724

OREGON
Ms. Susan Hormman
Interim Director
Forensic Services Division
State Department of Police
255 Capitol Street, Northeast,
4th Floor
Salem, OR 97310
P: (503) 378-3720

PENNSYLVANIA
Colonel Marcus L. Brown
Acting Commissioner
State Police
1800 Elmerton Avenue
Harrisburg, PA 17110
P: (717) 783-5517
F: (717) 783-7690

SOUTH CAROLINA
Mr. Mark A. Keel
Chief
State Law Enforcement Division
4400 Broad River Road
P.O. Box 21398
Columbia, SC 29221
P: (803) 896-9223
F: (803) 896-7041

TENNESSEE
Ms. Lisa Knight
Program Director
Handgun Carry Permits
Department of Safety &
Homeland Security
1150 Foster Avenue
Nashville, TN 37243
P: (615) 251-8590

TEXAS
Mr. Steve McCraw
Director
Department of Public Safety
5805 North Lamar Boulevard
P.O. Box 4087
Austin, TX 78773
P: (512) 424-2000
F: (512) 483-5708

U.S. VIRGIN ISLANDS
Mr. Rodney F. Querrard
Commissioner
Police Department
Alexander Farrelly Criminal
Justice Ctr.
Charlotte Amalie
St. Thomas, VI 00802
P: (340) 715-5605
F: (340) 715-5517

UTAH
Ms. Alice Moffat
Bureau Chief
Department of Public Safety
Bureau of Criminal
Identification
3888 West 5400 South
Salt Lake City, UT 84118
P: (801) 965-4939
F: (801) 965-4749
E: AERICKSO@utah.gov

VIRGINIA
Col. W. Steven Flaherty
Superintendent
Department of State Police
7700 Midlothian Turnpike
P.O. Box 27472
Richmond, VA 23235
P: (804) 674-2087
F: (804) 674-2132
E: steve.flaherty
    @vsp.virginia.gov

WEST VIRGINIA
Colonel Jay Smithers
Superintendent
State Police
725 Jefferson Road
South Charleston, WV 25309
P: (304) 746-2115
F: (304) 746-2230
E: Jay.Smithers@wvsp.gov

WYOMING
Mr. Steve Woodson
Director
Division of Criminal
Investigation
208 South College Drive
Cheyenne, WY 82002
P: (307) 777-7181
F: (307) 777-7252

Fish and Wildlife

Protects and manages fish and wildlife resources and enforces the state's fish and game laws.

ALABAMA
Mr. Charles Sykes
Director
Division of Wildlife &
Freshwater Fisheries
Conservation & Natural
Resources
64 North Union Street
Montgomery, AL 36130
P: (334) 242-3465
F: (334) 242-3032
E: dcnr.wffdirector
    @dcnr.alabama.gov

ALASKA
Mr. Sam Cotten
Commissioner
Department of Fish & Game
P.O. Box 25526
Juneau, AK 99802
P: (907) 465-6141
F: (907) 465-2332
E: sam.cotten@alaska.gov

ARIZONA
Mr. Larry D. Voyles
Director
Game & Fish Department
5000 West Carefree Highway
Phoenix, AZ 85086
P: (623) 942-3000

ARKANSAS
Mr. Mike Knoedl
Director
Game & Fish Commission
#2 Natural Resources Drive
Little Rock, AR 72205
P: (501) 223-6383
F: (501) 223-6448
E: mwknoedl
    @agfc.state.ar.us

CALIFORNIA
Mr. Charlton H. Bonham
Director
Department of Fish & Wildlife
1416 Ninth Street, 12th Floor
P.O. Box 944209
Sacramento, CA 94244
P: (916) 653-7667
F: (916) 653-7387
E: director@wildlife.ca.gov

COLORADO
Mr. Bob Broscheid
Director
Division of Parks & Wildlife
1313 Sherman Street, 6th Floor
Denver, CO 80203
P: (303) 866-3203
F: (303) 866-3206
E: bob.broscheid
    @state.co.us

CONNECTICUT
Mr. William Hyatt
Chief
Bureau of Natural Resources
79 Elm Street
Hartford, CT 06106
P: (860) 424-3010
F: (860) 424-4070
E: william.hyatt@ct.gov

DELAWARE
Mr. Dave Saveikis
Director
Division of Fish & Wildlife
89 Kings Highway
Dover, DE 19901
P: (302) 739-9910
F: (302) 739-6157
E: David.Saveikis
    @state.de.us

DISTRICT OF COLUMBIA
Mr. Bryan King
Associate Director
Fisheries & Wildlife Division
Department of the Environment
51 N Street, Northeast, 5th Floor
Washington, DC 20002
P: (202) 997-9607
F: (202) 535-1373

FLORIDA
Mr. Nick Wiley
Executive Director
Fish & Wildlife Conservation
Commission
620 South Meridian Street
Tallahassee, FL 32399
P: (850) 487-3796
F: (850) 921-5786

GEORGIA
Mr. Dan Forster
Director
Wildlife Resources Division
2070 U.S. Highway 278,
Southeast
Social Circle, GA 30025
P: (770) 918-6401
F: (706) 557-3030

GUAM
Mr. Celestino Aguan
Acting Chief
Division of Aquatic & Wildlife
Resources
Department of Agriculture
192 Dairy Road
Mangilao, GU 96923
P: (671) 735-3979
F: (671) 734-6570
E: tino_aguon@hotmail.com

HAWAII
Ms. Suzanne D. Case
Chairperson
Department of Land & Natural
Resources
Kalanimoku Building
1151 Punchbowl Street
Honolulu, HI 96813
P: (808) 587-0400
F: (808) 587-0390
E: dlnr@hawaii.gov

IDAHO
Mr. Virgil Moore
Director
Fish & Game Department
Box 25, 600 South Walnut
Boise, ID 83707
P: (208) 334-3772
F: (208) 334-2148
E: virgil.moore
    @idfg.idaho.gov

ILLINOIS
Mr. Wayne Rosenthal
Director
Department of Natural
Resources
One Natural Resources Way
Springfield, IL 62702
P: (217) 785-0075
F: (217) 785-9236
E: wayne.rosenthal
    @illinois.gov

INDIANA
Mr. Mark Reiter
Fish & Wildlife - Central Office
Department of Natural
Resources
402 West Washington Street,
Room W-273
Indianapolis, IN 46204
P: (317) 232-8129
F: (317) 232-8150
E: MREITER@dnr.IN.gov

IOWA
Mr. Chuck Gipp
Director
Department of Natural
Resources
4th Floor, Wallace Building
502 East 9th Street
Des Moines, IA 50319
P: (515) 281-5817
F: (515) 281-8895
E: chuck.gipp@dnr.iowa.gov

KANSAS
Mr. Keith Sexson
Assistant Secretary, Wildlife
Operations
Department of Wildlife & Parks
512 Southeast 25th Avenue
Pratt, KS 67124
P: (316) 672-5911
F: (316) 672-6020

KENTUCKY
Mr. Benjy T. Kinman
Deputy Commissioner
Department of Fish & Wildlife
Resources
One Sportsman's Lane
Frankfort, KY 40601
P: (502) 564-3400
F: (502) 564-0506

LOUISIANA
Mr. Robert J. Barham
Secretary
Department of Wildlife &
Fisheries
2000 Quail Drive
P.O. Box 98000
Baton Rouge, LA 70898
P: (225) 765-2800
F: (225) 765-0948

MAINE
Mr. Chandler E. Woodcock
Commissioner
Department of Inland Fisheries
& Wildlife
41 State House Station
Augusta, ME 04333
P: (207) 287-8000
F: (207) 287-6395
E: chandler.woodcock
    @maine.gov

MARYLAND
Mr. Paul Peditto
Director
Wildlife & Heritage Service
Department of Natural
Resources
580 Taylor Avenue, E-1
Annapolis, MD 21401
P: (410) 260-8549
F: (410) 260-8595
E: ppeditto@dnr.state.md.us

Fish and Wildlife

MASSACHUSETTS
Mr. James Buckley
Director
Division of Fisheries & Widlife
100 Hartwell Street, Suite 230
West Boylan, MA
P: (508) 389-6300
E: masswildlife@state.ma.us

MICHIGAN
Mr. Keith Creagh
Director
Department of Natural
Resources
P.O. Box 30028
Lansing, MI 48909
P: (517) 373-2329
E: DNR-Director
    @michigan.gov

MINNESOTA
Mr. Ed Boggess
Director
Division of Fish & Wildlife
Department of Natural
Resources
500 Lafayette Road
St. Paul, MN 55155
P: (651) 259-5180
F: (651) 297-7272
E: ed.boggess@state.mn.us

MISSISSIPPI
Dr. Sam Polles
Executive Director
Department of Wildlife,
Fisheries & Parks
2906 Building
P.O. Box 451
Jackson, MS 39205
P: (601) 432-2001
F: (601) 432-2024

MISSOURI
Mr. Robert Ziehmer
Director
Department of Conservation
2901 West Truman Boulevard
Jefferson City, MO 65109
P: (573) 751-4115
F: (573) 751-4667

MONTANA
Mr. Jeff Hagener
Director
Department of Fish, Wildlife &
Parks
1420 East Sixth Avenue
P.O. Box 200701
Helena, MT 59620
P: (406) 444-3186
F: (406) 444-4952
E: fwpgen@mt.gov

NEBRASKA
Mr. James Douglas
Director
Game & Parks Commission
2200 North 33rd, Box 30370
Lincoln, NE 68510
P: (402) 471-5539
F: (402) 471-5528
E: jim.douglas@nebraska.gov

NEVADA
Mr. Tony Wasley
Director
Department of Wildlife
1100 Valley Road
Reno, NV 89512
P: (775) 688-1500
F: (775) 688-1207
E: twasley@ndow.org

NEW HAMPSHIRE
Mr. Glenn Normandeau
Executive Director
Fish & Game Department
11 Hazen Drive
Concord, NH 03301
P: (603) 271-3511
F: (603) 271-1438
E: glenn.normandeau
    @wildlife.nh.gov

NEW JERSEY
Mr. Dave Chanda
Director
Division of Fish & Wildlife
P.O. Box 400
Trenton, NJ 08625
P: (609) 292-9410
F: (609) 292-8207

NEW MEXICO
Ms. Alexa Sandoval
Director
Department of Game & Fish
One Wildlife Way
Santa Fe, NM 87507
P: (505) 476-8008
E: alexandra.sandoval
    @state.nm.us

NEW YORK
Ms. Patricia Riexinger
Director
Division of Fish, Wildlife &
Marine Resources
625 Broadway
Albany, NY 12233
P: (518) 402-8924
F: (518) 402-9027
E: fwinfo
    @gw.dec.state.ny.us

NORTH CAROLINA
Mr. Gordon Myers
Executive Director
Wildlife Resources Commission
1722 Mail Service Center
1751 Varsity Drive, Room 451
Raleigh, NC 27695
P: (919) 707-0151
F: (919) 707-0020
E: gordon.myers
    @ncwildlife.org

NORTH DAKOTA
Mr. Terry Steinwand
Director
Game & Fish Department
100 North Bismarck
Expressway
Bismarck, ND 58501
P: (701) 328-6305
F: (701) 328-6352
E: tsteinwa@nd.gov

OHIO
Mr. Scott Zody
Chief
Division of Wildlife
2045 Morse Road, Building G
Columbus, OH 43229
P: (614) 265-6304
F: (614) 262-1143

OKLAHOMA
Mr. Richard Hatcher
Director
Department of Wildlife
Conservation
P.O. Box 53465
Oklahoma City, OK 73152
P: (405) 522-6279
F: (405) 521-6505

OREGON
Mr. Curt Melcher
Director
Department of Fish & Wildlife
4034 Fairview Industrial Drive,
Southeas
Salem, OR 97302
P: (503) 947-6044

PENNSYLVANIA
Mr. John Arway
Executive Director
Fish & Boat Commission
P.O. Box 67000
Harrisburg, PA 17106
P: (717) 705-7801
F: (717) 705-7802

Mr. Matt Hough
Executive Director
Game Commission
2001 Elmerton Avenue
Harrisburg, PA 17110
P: (717) 787-3633
F: (717) 772-0502

PUERTO RICO
Mr. Miguel A. Garcia
Director, Terrestrial Resources
Division
Department of Natural &
Environmental Resources
Bureau of Fish & Wildlife
P.O. Box 366147
San Juan, PR 00936
P: (787) 723-3090
F: (787) 724-0365

Mr. Craig G. Lilyestrom
Director, Marine Resources
Division
Department of Natural &
Environmental Resources
P.O. Box 366147
San Juan, PR 00936
P: (787) 723-3090
F: (787) 724-0365

RHODE ISLAND
Ms. Catherine Sparks
Chief
Division of Fish & Wildlife
235 Promenade Street
Providence, RI 02908
P: (401) 222-4700
E: catherine.sparks
    @dem.ri.gov

SOUTH CAROLINA
Mr. Alvin A. Taylor
Director
Department of Natural
Resources
1000 Assembly Street
P.O. Box 167
Columbia, SC 29202
P: (803) 734-4020
F: (803) 734-6310
E: taylora@dnr.sc.gov

SOUTH DAKOTA
Mr. Jeff Vonk
Secretary
Game, Fish & Parks Department
523 East Capitol Avenue
Pierre, SD 57501
P: (605) 773-3718
F: (605) 773-6245

TENNESSEE
Mr. Ed Carter
Executive Director
Wildlife Resources Agency
P.O. Box 40747
Nashville, TN 37204
P: (615) 781-6552
F: (615) 781-6551

TEXAS
Mr. Carter P. Smith
Executive Director
Parks & Wildlife Department
4200 Smith School Road
Austin, TX 78744
P: (512) 389-4802
F: (512) 389-4960

U.S. VIRGIN ISLANDS
Mr. Roy Pemberton
Director
Division of Fish & Wildlife
6291 Estate Nazareth 101
St. Thomas, VI 00802
P: (340) 775-6762
F: (340) 775-3972
E: roy.pemberton
    @dpnr.gov.vi

UTAH
Mr. Greg Sheehan
Director
Division of Wildlife Resources
1594 West North Temple, Suite
2110
P.O. Box 146301
Salt Lake City, UT 84114
P: (801) 538-4702
F: (801) 538-4709
E: gregsheehan@utah.gov

VERMONT
Mr. Louis Porter
Commissioner
Department of Fish & Wildlife
103 South Main Street, 10 South
Waterbury, VT 05671
P: (802) 241-3700
E: louis.porter@state.vt.us

VIRGINIA
Mr. Bob Duncan
Director
Department of Game & Inland
Fisheries
4010 West Broad Street, Box
11104
Richmond, VA 23230
P: (804) 367-9231
F: (804) 367-0405
E: bob.duncan
    @dgif.virginia.gov

WASHINGTON
Mr. Jim Unsworth
Director
Department of Fish & Wildlife
600 Capitol Way North
Olympia, WA 98501
P: (360) 902-2200
F: (360) 902-2947
E: director@dfw.wa.gov

WEST VIRGINIA
Mr. Curtis Taylor
Chief
Wildlife Resources Section
Division of Natural Resources
324 4th Avenue
South Charleston, WV 25303
P: (304) 558-2771
F: (304) 558-3147
E: curtis.i.taylor@wv.gov

WISCONSIN
Ms. Cathy Stepp
Secretary
Department of Natural
Resources
101 South Webster Street
Madison, WI 53703
P: (608) 266-0865
F: (608) 266-6983
E: DNRSecretary
    @Wisconsin.gov

WYOMING
Mr. Scott Talbott
Director
Game & Fish Department
5400 Bishop Boulevard
Cheyenne, WY 82006
P: (307) 777-4600
F: (307) 777-4699

Gaming Officials

Head of the entity that administers and regulates state gaming laws.

ALASKA
Mr. Ken Alper
Oil & Gas Specialist
Tax Division
Department of Revenue
550 West 7th Avenue, Suite 500
Anchorage, AK 99501
P: (907) 269-6620
F: (907) 269-6644
E: ken.alper@alaska.gov

ARIZONA
Mr. Dan Bergin
Director
Department of Gaming
1110 West Washington Street,
Suite 450
Phoenix, AZ 85007
P: (602) 771-4263
F: (602) 255-3883

ARKANSAS
Mr. Cecil Alexander
Chair
Racing Commission
1515 West 7th Street, Suite 505
P.O. Box 3076
Little Rock, AR 72203
P: (501) 682-1467
F: (501) 682-5273

CALIFORNIA
Hon. Kamala Harris (D)
Attorney General
Office of the Attorney General
1300 I Street, Sutie 1740
Sacramento, CA 95814
P: (916) 445-9555

COLORADO
Mr. Flavio Quintana
Director
Division of Gaming
Department of Revenue
17301 West Colfax Avenue,
Suite 135
Golden, CO 80401
P: (303) 205-1300
F: (303) 205-1342
E: dor_gamingweb
    @state.co.us

CONNECTICUT
Mr. William Ryan
Director
Division of Gaming
Department of Consumer
Protection
165 Capitol Avenue
Hartford, CT 06106
P: (860) 713-6301
E: William.Ryan@ct.gov

DELAWARE
Mr. Vernon Kirk
Director
State Lottery
McKee Business Park
1575 McKee Road, Suite 102
Dover, DE 19904
P: (302) 739-5291
F: (302) 739-6706
E: brian.peters@state.de.us

FLORIDA
Mr. Ken Lawson
Secretary
Department of Business &
Professional Regulation
1940 North Monroe Street
Tallahassee, FL 32399
P: (850) 487-1395
F: (850) 488-1830
E: Call.Center
    @dbpr.state.fl.us

GEORGIA
Mr. Vernon M. Keenan
Director
Bureau of Investigation
3121 Panthersville Road
Decatur, GA 30034
P: (404) 244-2600
F: (404) 270-8352
E: vernon.keenan@gbi.ga.gov

GUAM
Mr. Artemio B. Ilagan
Banking & Insurance
Commissioner
Department of Revenue &
Taxation
Department of Revenue &
Taxation
P.O. Box 23607
GMF Barrigada, GU 96921
P: (671) 635-1817
F: (671) 633-2643
E: art.ilagan@revtax.gov.gu

IDAHO
Mr. Jeffrey R. Anderson
Director
State Liquor Division
1349 East Beechcraft Court
Boise, ID 83716
P: (208) 947-9402
F: (208) 947-9401
E: info@idaholottery.com

ILLINOIS
Mr. Mark Ostrowski
Administrator
Gaming Board
160 North LaSalle, Suite 300
Chicago, IL 60601
P: (312) 814-4700
F: (312) 814-4602

INDIANA
Ms. Sara Gonso Tait
Executive Director
Gaming Commission
East Tower, Suite 1600
101 West Washington Street
Indianapolis, IN 46204
P: (317) 233-0046
F: (317) 233-0047
E: STait@igc.IN.gov

IOWA
Mr. Brian J. Ohorilko
Administrator
Racing & Gaming Commission
717 East Court
Suite B
Des Moines, IA 50309
P: (515) 281-7352
F: (515) 242-6560
E: brian.ohorilko@iowa.gov

KANSAS
Mr. Mark Dodd
Executive Director
State Gaming Agency
420 Southwest 6th Street, Suite
3000
Topeka, KS 66607
P: (785) 368-6202
F: (785) 291-3798
E: ksga@ksgaming.org

KENTUCKY
Mr. Arch Gleason
President & CEO
State Lottery
1011 West Main Street
Louisville, KY 40202
P: (502) 560-1500
F: (502) 560-1532
E: custsrvs@kylottery.com

Mr. John T. Ward Jr.
Executive Director
Horse Racing Commission
4063 Ironworks Parkway,
Building B
Lexington, KY 40511
P: (859) 246-2040
F: (859) 246-2039
E: johnt.ward@ky.gov

LOUISIANA
Lt. Col. Murphy Paul
Deputy Superintendent
Bureau of Investigations
State Police
7919 Independence Boulevard
Baton Rouge, LA 70806
P: (800) 434-8007

MAINE
Mr. John E. Morris
Commissioner
Department of Public Safety
45 Commerce Drive, Suite 1
104 State House Station
Augusta, ME 04333
P: (207) 626-3800
F: (207) 287-3042
E: john.e.morris@maine.gov

MARYLAND
Mr. Michael J. Frenz
Executive Director
Stadium Authority
333 West Camden Street, Suite
500
Baltimore, MD 21201
P: (410) 333-1560
F: (410) 333-1888
E: mfrenz@mdstad.com

MASSACHUSETTS
Mr. John Chapman
Office of Consumer Affairs &
Business Regulation
Ten Park Plaza, Suite 5170
Boston, MA 02116
P: (617) 973-8700
F: (617) 973-8799

MICHIGAN
Mr. Richard S. Kalm
Executive Director
Gaming Control Board
3062 West Grand Boulevard,
Suite L-700
Detroit, MI 48202
P: (313) 456-4100
F: (313) 456-4200
E: KalmR@michigan.gov

MINNESOTA
Mr. Clint Harris
Executive Director
State Lottery
2645 Long Lake Road
Roseville, MN 55113
P: (651) 635-8273
F: (651) 297-7496
E: lottery@mnlottery.com

MISSISSIPPI
Mr. Allen Godfrey
Executive Director
Gaming Commission
620 North Street, Suite 200
P.O. Box 23577
Jackson, MS 39225
P: (601) 576-3800
F: (601) 576-3929
E: info@mgc.state.ms.us

MISSOURI
Mr. William K. Seibert Jr.
Executive Director
Gaming Commission
3417 Knipp Dirve
P.O. Box 1847
Jefferson City, MO 65102
P: (573) 526-4080
F: (573) 526-1999

MONTANA
Hon. Tim Fox (R)
Attorney General
Department of Justice
Justice Building
215 North Sanders
Helena, MT 59620
P: (406) 444-2026
F: (406) 444-3549
E: contactdoj@mt.gov

NEBRASKA
Mr. Leonard Sloup
Acting Tax Commissioner
Department of Revenue
P.O. Box 94818
Lincoln, NE 68509
P: (402) 471-5805
F: (402) 471-5608
E: len.sloup@nebraska.gov

NEVADA
Mr. A.G. Burnett
Chair
Gaming Control Board
1919 College Parkway
P.O. Box 8003
Carson City, NV 89702
P: (775) 684-7700
F: (775) 687-5817

NEW JERSEY
Mr. David L. Rebuck
Director
Division of Gaming
Enforcement
140 East Front Street
P.O. Box 047
Trenton, NJ 08625
P: (609) 292-9394
F: (609) 633-7355

NEW MEXICO
Mr. Donovan Lieurance
Acting Executive Director
Gaming Control Board
4900 Alameda Boulevard,
Northeast
Albuquerque, NM 87113
P: (505) 417-1079
F: (505) 841-9725
E: donovan.lieurance
   @state.nm.us

NEW YORK
Mr. Mark Gearan
Chair
Gaming Commission
P.O. Box 7500
Schenectady, NY 12301
P: (518) 395-5400
F: (518) 347-1250

NORTH CAROLINA
Ms. Alice Garland
Executive Director
Education Lottery
2100 Yonkers Road
Raleigh, NC 27604
P: (919) 715-6886
F: (919) 715-8833
E: playerinfo@lotterync.net

NORTH DAKOTA
Hon. Wayne Stenehjem (R)
Attorney General
Office of the Attorney General
State Capitol
600 East Boulevard Avenue
Bismarck, ND 58505
P: (701) 328-2210
F: (701) 328-2226
E: wstenehjem@nd.gov

OHIO
Mr. William Crawford
Executive Director
Racing Commission
77 South High Street, 18th Floor
Columbus, OH 43215
P: (614) 466-2757
F: (614) 466-1900
E: bill.crawford
   @rc.state.oh.us

OKLAHOMA
Mr. A. Keith Burt
Director
Alcoholic Beverage Laws
Enforcement Commission
3812 North Santa Fe
Suite 200
Oklahoma City, OK 73118
P: (405) 521-3484
F: (405) 521-6578
E: kburt@able.ok.gov

Mr. Constantin A. Rieger
Executive Director
State Horse Racing Commission
Shepherd Mall
2401 Northwest 23rd Street,
Suite 78
Oklahoma City, OK 73107
P: (405) 943-6472
F: (405) 943-6474
E: ohrc@socket.net

OREGON
Maj. Craig Durbin
Gaming Enforcement Division
State Department of Police
4190 Aumsville Highway,
Southeast
Salem, OR 97317
P: (503) 378-6999
E: ask.osp@state.or.us

PENNSYLVANIA
Hon. William H.
   Ryan Jr. (R)
Chairman
Gaming Control Board
P.O. Box 69060
Harrisburg, PA 17106
P: (717) 346-8300
F: (717) 346-8350

PUERTO RICO
Mr. Guillermo J. Cabret
Director
Gaming Division
P.O. Box 9023960
San Juan, PR 00902
P: (787) 721-2400
F: (787) 724-3009
E: logarcia@prtourism.com

RHODE ISLAND
Ms. Pauline M. Malec
Charitable Gaming Unit
Department of Public Safety
311 Danielson Pike
North Scituate, RI 02857
P: (401) 444-1147
F: (401) 444-1105

Colonel Steven G. O'Donnell
Commissioner & Superintendent
Department of Public Safety
311 Danielson Pike
North Scituate, RI 02857
P: (401) 444-1000
F: (401) 444-1105
E: sodonnell
   @risp.state.ri.us

SOUTH CAROLINA
Mr. Alvin A. Taylor
Director
Department of Natural
Resources
1000 Assembly Street
P.O. Box 167
Columbia, SC 29202
P: (803) 734-4020
F: (803) 734-6310
E: taylora@dnr.sc.gov

SOUTH DAKOTA
Mr. Larry Eliason
Executive Secretary
Gaming Commission
Department of Revenue
221 West Capitol Avenue, Suite
101
Pierre, SD 57501
P: (605) 773-6050
F: (605) 773-6053

TENNESSEE
Ms. Rebecca Paul Hargrove
President & CEO
Education Lottery Corporation
26 Century Boulevard, Suite 200
Nashville, TN 37214
P: (615) 324-6500
F: (615) 324-6512

TEXAS
Mr. Gary Grief
Executive Director
Lottery Commission
611 East Sixth Street
P.O.Box 16630
Austin, TX 78761
P: (512) 344-5160
F: (512) 478-3682
E: gary.grief
   @lottery.state.tx.us

Mr. Chuck Trout
Executive Director
State Racing Commission
8505 Cross Park Drive, Suite
110
P.O. Box 12080
Austin, TX 78711
P: (512) 833-6699
F: (512) 833-6907

U.S. VIRGIN ISLANDS
Mr. R. Oliver David
Director
Division of Gaming
Enforcement
5 Estate Orange Grove
Christiansted
St. Croix, VI 00820
P: (340) 773-9341
F: (340) 773-3442

Gaming Officials

WASHINGTON
Mr. David Trujillo
Director
Gambling Commission
P.O. Box 42400
Olympia, WA 98504
P: (360) 486-3440
F: (360) 486-3629

WEST VIRGINIA
Mr. Robert S. Kiss
Cabinet Secretary
Department of Revenue
State Capitol
Building 1, W-300
Charleston, WV 25305
P: (304) 558-1017
F: (304) 558-2324
E: Robert.S.Kiss@wv.gov

WISCONSIN
Mr. Steve Knudson
Administrator
Division of Gaming
3319 West Beltline Highway,
First Floor
P.O. Box 8979
Madison, WI 53713
P: (608) 270-2555
F: (608) 270-2564
E: Steven.Knudson
    @wisconsin.gov

WYOMING
Mr. Charles Moore
Executive Director/Simulcast
Steward
State Pari-Mutuel Commission
Energy II Building, Suite 335
951 Werner Court
Casper, WY 82601
P: (307) 265-4015
F: (307) 265-4279
E: charles.moore@wyo.gov

Geographic Information Systems

Coordinates geographic information systems within state government.

ALABAMA
Mr. Phillip Henderson
Director
Geographic Information
Program Office
201 South Union Street, Suite 300
Montgomery, AL 36130
P: (334) 517-2561
E: phillip.henderson
@alacop.gov

ALASKA
Mr. Chris Hamilton
IT Manager
Department of Natural
Resources
550 West 7th Avenue, Suite 706
Anchorage, AK 99501
P: (907) 269-8836
E: chris.hamilton
@alaska.gov

ARIZONA
Mr. Curtis Pulford
State Cartographer
State Land Department
1616 West Adams Street
Phoenix, AZ 85007
P: (602) 542-3190
F: (602) 542-2600
E: cpulford@azland.gov

ARKANSAS
Mr. Shelby Johnson
Geographic Information
Coordinator
Geographic Information Office
1 Capitol Mall, Suite 2B900
Little Rock, AR 72201
P: (501) 682-2767
F: (501) 682-4310
E: shelby.johnson
@arkansas.gov

CALIFORNIA
Mr. Scott Gregory
Geospatial Information Officer
Technology Agency
1325 J Street
Sacramento, CA 95814
P: (916) 431-5449
E: scott.gregory
@state.ca.gov

COLORADO
Mr. Jon Gottsegen
State GIS Coordinator
Department of Local Affairs
601 East 18th Avenue, Suite 250
Denver, CO 80203
P: (303) 764-7712
F: (303) 764-7725
E: jon.gottsegen
@state.co.us

DELAWARE
Ms. Miriam Pomilio
Planner/GIS Coordinator
Office of State Planning
Coordination
Office of Management &
Budget
122 Martin Luther King Jr.
Blvd., South
Dover, DE 19901
P: (302) 739-3090
E: miriam.pomilio
@state.de.us

DISTRICT OF COLUMBIA
Mr. Tim Abdella
GIS Program Manager
Office of the Chief Information
Officer
200 I Street Southeast, 5th Floor
Washington, DC 20003
P: (202) 727-0174
E: tim.abdella@dc.gov

FLORIDA
Mr. Richard Butgereit
Director
Division of Emergency
Management
2555 Shumard Oak
Tallahassee, FL 32399
P: (850) 413-9907
E: richard.butgereit
@em.myflorida.com

GEORGIA
Mr. Eric McRae
Associate Director
University of Georgia
1180 East Broad Street, Suite 2058
Athens, GA 30602
P: (706) 542-5308
F: (706) 542-6535
E: mcrae@cviog.itos.uga.edu

HAWAII
Ms. Joan Delos Santos
Acting Program Manager
Statewide GIS Program
Office of Planning
235 South Beretania Street, 6th Floor
Honolulu, HI 96813
P: (808) 587-2895
F: (808) 587-2824
E: jdelos_santos
@dbedt.hawaii.gov

IDAHO
Mr. Bill Farnsworth
GIO
Office of the CIO
650 West State Street
Boise, ID 83720
P: (208) 332-1878
F: (208) 332-1884
E: bill.farnsworth
@cio.idaho.gov

INDIANA
Mr. Jim Sparks
Geographic Information Officer
Geographic Information Council
100 North Senate Avenue
N551 Government Center North
Indianapolis, IN 46204
P: (317) 234-5889
F: (317) 234-0917
E: jsparks@iot.in.gov

Mr. Phillip Worrall
Geographic Information Council
777 Indiana Avenue, Suite 210
Indianapolis, IN 46202
P: (317) 489-0091
E: pworrall@igic.org

IOWA
Mr. Jonathan Paoli
Homeland Security &
Emergency Management
Joint Forces Headquarters
6100 Northwest 78th Avenue
Johnston, IA 50131
P: (515) 323-4384
F: (515) 323-4208
E: jonathan.paoli@iowa.gov

KANSAS
Mr. Kenneth A. Nelson
Data Access & Support Center
Geological Survey, University
of Kansas
1930 Constant Avenue
Lawrence, KS 66047
P: (785) 864-2164
F: (785) 864-5317
E: nelson@kgs.ku.edu

KENTUCKY
Mr. Thomas J. Rossman
Acting Director
Division of Geographic
Information
100 Fair Oaks Lane
Frankfort, KY 40601
P: (502) 564-6412
F: (502) 564-0427
E: thomas.rossman@ky.gov

LOUISIANA
Mr. Craig Johnson
Administrative & Programmatic
Support Manager
School of the Coast &
Environment
E-313 Howe-Russell Building
Louisiana State University
Baton Rouge, LA 70803
P: (225) 578-3479
F: (225) 578-7289
E: cjohnson@lsu.edu

MAINE
Mr. Joseph Young
Executive Director
State GeoLibrary
SHS 145
51 Commerce Drive
Augusta, ME 04333
P: (207) 624-2664
F: (207) 287-1131
E: Joseph.Young@maine.gov

MARYLAND
Mr. Barney Krucoff
Geographic Information Officer
Department of Information
Technology
45 Calvert Street
Annapolis, MD 21401
P: (443) 370-3008
E: Barney.Krucoff
@maryland.gov

Mr. Kenneth Miller
Deputy Geographic Information
Officer
Department of Information
Technology
45 Calvert Street
Annapolis, MD 21401
P: (410) 260-4044
E: ken.miller@maryland.gov

MASSACHUSETTS
Mr. Christian Jacqz
MassGIS Director
Executive Office of Energy &
Environmental Affairs
251 Causeway Street, 5th Floor
Boston, MA 02114
P: (617) 619-5639
F: (617) 626-1249
E: Christian.Jacqz
@state.ma.us

Geographic Information Systems

MICHIGAN
Mr. Rob Surber
Center for Geographic
Information
111 South Capitol Avenue, Floor
10
Lansing, MI 48933
P: (517) 373-7910
F: (517) 373-2939
E: surberr@michigan.gov

MINNESOTA
Mr. Will Craig
Center for Urban & Regional
Affairs
University of Minnesota
301 South 19th Avenue, Suite
330
Minneapolis, MN 55455
P: (612) 625-3321
F: (612) 626-0273
E: wcraig@umn.edu

Mr. Dan Ross
Geospatial Information Office
658 Cedar Street, Suite 300
St. Paul, MN 55155
E: dan.ross@state.mn.us

MISSISSIPPI
Dr. Scott Samson
Geospatial Extension Specialist
GeoResources Institute
2 Research Boulevard
HPCC 227 Mail Stop 9652
Starkville, MS 37959
P: (662) 325-9491
F: (662) 325-7692
E: scotts@gri.msstate.edu

MISSOURI
Mr. Tony Spicci
Central Regional Office &
Conservation Research Center
3500 East Grans Road
Columbia, MO 65201
P: (573) 882-8388
E: Tony.Spicci@mdc.mo.gov

Mr. Paul G. Wright
Director, Geographic
Information Systems
Information Technology
Services Division
Truman Building, Room 840
301 West High Street
Jefferson City, MO 65101
P: (573) 522-5034
E: Paul.Wright@oa.mo.gov

MONTANA
Mr. Stewart Kirkpatrick
State GIS Coordinator
Department of Administration
910 Helena Avenue
Helena, MT 59601
P: (406) 444-9013
F: (406) 444-1255
E: skirkpatrick@mt.gov

NEBRASKA
Mr. Nathan Watermeier
GIS Council Coordinator
GIS Council/NITC
Office of the Chief Information
Officer
P.O. Box 95045
Lincoln, NE 68509
P: (402) 471-3206
F: (402) 471-4864
E: Nathan.Watermeier
    @nebraska.gov

NEW JERSEY
Mr. Andrew Rowan
Geographic Information Officer
Office of Information
Technology
200 Riverview Plaza
P.O. Box 212
Trenton, NJ 08625
P: (609) 633-0276
F: (609) 633-0200
E: andrew.rowan@oit.nj.gov

NEW MEXICO
Gar Clarke
Broadband Program Manager
Department of Information
Technology
715 Alta Vista Street
Santa Fe, NM 87505
P: (505) 827-1663
E: george.clarke
    @state.nm.us

Mr. Leland Pierce
Department of Game & Fish
P.O. Box 25112
Santa Fe, NM 87505
P: (505) 476-8094
F: (505) 476-8128
E: leland.pierce
    @state.nm.us

NEW YORK
Mr. William F. Johnson
Geographic Information Officer,
Office of the CTO
Office of Information
Technology Services
1220 Washington Avenue, 4th
Floor
State Office Campus, Building
7A
Albany, NY 12242
P: (518) 549-8575
E: william.johnson
    @its.ny.gov

Mr. Frank Winters
Director, GIS Program Office
Office of Information
Technology Services
1220 Washington Avenue
State Office Campus, Building
7A
Albany, NY 12242
P: (518) 242-5036
E: francis.winters
    @its.ny.gov

NORTH CAROLINA
Mr. Tim Johnson
Director
Center for Geographic
Information & Analysis
20322 Mail Service Center
Raleigh, NC 27699
P: (919) 754-6588
F: (919) 715-8551
E: tim.johnson@its.nc.gov

NORTH DAKOTA
Mr. Bob Nutsch
GIS Coordinator
Information Technology
Department
600 East Boulevard Avenue
Department 112
Bismarck, ND 58505
P: (701) 328-3212
F: (701) 328-3000
E: bnutsch@nd.gov

OHIO
Mr. Stuart R. Davis
Chief Information Officer &
Assistant Director
Office of Information
Technology
Department of Administrative
Services
30 East Broad Street, 39th Floor
Columbus, OH 43215
P: (614) 644-6446
F: (614) 728-5297
E: Stu.Davis@das.ohio.gov

Mr. Jeff Smith
Spatial Data Infrastructure
Manager
Geographically Referenced
Information Program
Office of Information
Technology
77 South High Street, 19th Floor
Columbus, OH 43215
P: (614) 466-8862
E: Jeff.Smith@das.ohio.gov

OKLAHOMA
Mr. Mike Sharp
Director, State GIS Coordinator
Conservation Commission
2800 North Lincoln Boulevard
Suite 160
Oklahoma City, OK 73105
P: (405) 521-4813
F: (405) 521-6686
E: mike.sharp
    @conservation.ok.gov

OREGON
Mr. Cy Smith
Geospatial Information Officer
DAS/CIO Geospatial Enterprise
Office
155 Cottage Street, Northeast
4th Floor
Salem, OR 97301
P: (503) 378-6066
F: (503) 378-3795
E: cy.smith@state.or.us

PENNSYLVANIA
Ms. Mary Fulton
Manager, Geospatial Technology
Operations
Office of Information
Technology
Office of Administration
5 Technology Park
Harrisburg, PA 17110
P: (717) 787-7878
F: (717) 783-6955
E: mfulton@pa.gov

RHODE ISLAND
Mr. Shane White
GIS Coordinator
Division of Planning
Department of Administration
One Capitol Hill, 3rd Floor
Providence, RI 02908
P: (401) 222-6483
F: (401) 222-2083
E: shane.white@doa.ri.gov

SOUTH CAROLINA
Dr. Timothy M. De Troye
State GIS Coordinator
State Geographic Information
Systems
1000 Assembly Street, Suite 134
Columbia, SC 29201
P: (803) 734-3894
F: (803) 734-7001
E: detroyet@gic.sc.gov

TENNESSEE
Mr. Dennis Pedersen
Director of OIR-GIS Services
Office for Information
Resources
312 8th Avenue, North
Floor 16
Nashville, TN 37243
P: (615) 741-9356
F: (615) 532-0471
E: dennis.pedersen@tn.gov

TEXAS
Mr. Richard Wade
Geographic Information Officer
State of Texas
P.O. Box 13231
Room B40
Austin, TX 78711
P: (512) 463-4010
E: Richard.Wade
    @twdb.texas.gov

U.S. VIRGIN ISLANDS
Stevie Henry
Principal Investigator
University of Virgin Islands -
ECC
#2 John Brewer's Bay
St. Thomas, VI 00802
P: (340) 693-1033
F: (340) 693-1025
E: shenry@uvi.edu

UTAH
Mr. Bert Granberg
Director
Automated Geographic
Refererence Center
1 State Office Building, Room
5130
Salt Lake City, UT 84114
P: (801) 538-3072
F: (801) 538-3317
E: bgranberg@utah.gov

VERMONT
Mr. Stephen Sharp
Center for Geographic
Information
58 South Main Street, Suite 2
Waterbury, VT 05676
P: (802) 882-3006
F: (802) 882-3001
E: steve.sharp@state.vt.us

VIRGINIA
Mr. Dan Widner
Coordinator
Chesterfield Enterprise
Solutions Center
11751 Meadowville Lane
Chester, VA 23638
P: (804) 416-6198
F: (804) 416-6353
E: dan.widner
    @vita.virginia.gov

WASHINGTON
Ms. Joy Paulus
GIS Coordinator
Office of the Chief Information
Officer
P.O. Box 43113
Olympia, WA 98504
P: (360) 902-3447
E: joy.paulus@ofm.wa.gov

WEST VIRGINIA
Mr. Tony Simental
State GIS Coordinator
GIS Coordinator's Office
1124 Smith Street, Room LM-10
Charleston, WV 25301
P: (304) 558-4218
F: (304) 558-4963
E: Tony.A.Simental@wv.gov

WISCONSIN
Mr. Howard Veregin
University of
Wisconsin-Madison
Room 384, Science Hall
550 North Park Street
Madison, WI 53706
P: (608) 262-6852
F: (608) 262-5205
E: veregin@wisc.edu

WYOMING
Ms. Karen Rogers
GIS Enterprise Architect
Department of Enterprise
Technology Service
2001 Capitol Avenue, Room 237
Cheyenne, WY 82002
P: (307) 777-8688
E: Karen.Rogers@wyo.gov

Geological Survey

Conducts research on the state's terrain, mineral resources, and possible geological hazards such as earthquakes, faults, etc.

ALABAMA
Mr. Berry H. Tew Jr.
State Geologist & Oil and Gas Supervisor
Geological Survey of Alabama
State Oil & Gas Board
P.O. Box 869999
Tuscaloosa, AL 35486
P: (205) 349-2852
F: (205) 247-3676
E: ntew@gsa.state.al.us

ALASKA
Mr. Steve
    State Geologist & Director
Acting Director
Division of Geological & Geophysical Surveys
Department of Natural Resources
3354 College Road
Fairbanks, AK 99709
P: (907) 451-5000
F: (907) 451-5050
E: steve.masterman
    @alaska.gov

ARIZONA
Dr. M. Lee Allison
Director & State Geologist
Geological Survey
416 West Congress Street, Suite 100
Tucson, AZ 85701
P: (520) 770-3500
F: (520) 770-3505
E: Lee.Allison@azgs.az.gov

ARKANSAS
Ms. Bekki White
State Geologist & Director
Geological Survey
Vardelle Parham Geology Center
3815 West Roosevelt Road
Little Rock, AR 72204
P: (501) 296-1877
F: (501) 663-7360
E: bekki.white@arkansas.gov

CALIFORNIA
Dr. John Parrish
State Geologist
Geological Survey
Department of Conservation
801 K Street, MS 12-30
Sacramento, CA 95814
P: (916) 445-1825
F: (916) 445-5718
E: John.Parrish
    @conservation.ca.gov

COLORADO
Ms. Karen Berry
State Geologist & Director
Geological Survey
1313 Sherman Street, Room 715
Denver, CO 80203
P: (303) 866-2611
F: (303) 866-2461
E: kaberry@mines.edu

CONNECTICUT
Ms. Margaret A. Thomas
State Geologist
Geological & Natural History Survey
Department of Environmental Protection
79 Elm Street
Hartford, CT 06106
P: (860) 424-3583
F: (860) 424-4058
E: margaret.thomas@ct.gov

DELAWARE
Dr. David R. Wunsch
Director & State Geologist
Geological Survey
257 Academy Street
Newark, DE 19716
P: (302) 831-2833
F: (302) 831-3579
E: dwunsch@udel.edu

FLORIDA
Mr. Jonathan Arthur
State Geologist
Geological Survey
Department of Environmental Protection
903 West Tennessee Street
Tallahassee, FL 32304
P: (850) 617-0320
F: (850) 488-8086
E: jonathan.arthur
    @dep.state.fl.us

GEORGIA
Mr. Jim Kennedy
State Geologist
Environmental Protection Division
2 Martin Luther King Jr. Drive
Suite 1152 East Floyd Tower
Atlanta, GA 30334
P: (404) 657-5947
F: (404) 651-5778
E: jim.kennedy
    @dnr.state.ga.us

HAWAII
Mr. William M. Tam
Deputy Director
Commission on Water Resource Management
Department of Land & Water Resources
1151 Punchbowl Street, Room 227
Honolulu, HI 96809
P: (808) 587-0214
F: (808) 587-0219
E: dlnr.cwrm@hawaii.gov

IDAHO
Mr. Michael Ratchford
Director & State Geologist
Geological Survey
University of Idaho
875 Perimeter Drive, MS 3014
Moscow, ID 83844
P: (208) 885-7991
F: (208) 885-5826
E: edratchford@uidaho.edu

ILLINOIS
Mr. Robert Finley
Principal Geologist & Director
State Geological Survey
University of Illinois
615 East Peabody Drive
Champaign, IL 61820
P: (217) 333-0044
F: (217) 244-7004
E: finley@illinois.edu

INDIANA
Dr. John C. Steinmetz
Director & State Geologist
Geological Survey
Indiana University
611 North Walnut Grove
Bloomington, IN 47405
P: (812) 855-5067
F: (812) 855-2862
E: jsteinm@indiana.edu

IOWA
Mr. Robert L. Libra
State Geologist
Geological Survey
Department of Natural Resources
109 Trowbridge Hall
Iowa City, IA 52242
P: (319) 335-1575
F: (319) 335-2754
E: robert.libra
    @dnr.iowa.gov

KANSAS
Mr. Rex Buchanan
Interim Director
Geological Survey
University of Kansas
1930 Constant Avenue
Lawrence, KS 66047
P: (785) 864-3965
F: (785) 864-5317
E: rex@kgs.ku.edu

KENTUCKY
Mr. Jerry Weisenfluh
Interim State Geologist & Director
Geological Survey
228 Mining & Mineral Resources Building
University of Kentucky
Lexington, KY 40506
P: (859) 257-5500
F: (859) 257-1147
E: jerryw@uky.edu

LOUISIANA
Mr. Chacko J. John
Director & State Geologist
Geological Survey
Louisiana State University
3079 Energy, Coastal & Environment Bldg.
Baton Rouge, LA 70803
P: (225) 578-8681
F: (225) 578-3662
E: cjohn@lsu.edu

MAINE
Mr. Robert G. Marvinney
Bureau Director
Geological Survey
Department of Conservation
22 State House Station
Augusta, ME 04333
P: (207) 287-2801
F: (207) 287-2353
E: robert.g.marvinney
    @maine.gov

MARYLAND
Mr. Richard A. Ortt Jr.
Director
Geological Survey
Department of Natural
Resources
2300 St. Paul Street
Baltimore, MD 21218
P: (410) 554-5500
F: (410) 554-5502
E: richard.ortt
   @maryland.gov

MASSACHUSETTS
Mr. Stephen B. Mabee
State Geologist
Office of the State Geologist
611 North Pleasant Street
University of Massachusetts
Amherst, MA 01003
P: (413) 545-4814
F: (413) 545-1200
E: sbmabee@geo.umass.edu

MICHIGAN
Mr. John Yellich
Director
Geological Survey
Western Michigan University
Geosciences Department, 1184
Rood Hall
Kalamazoo, MI 49008
P: (269) 387-8649
E: john.yellich@wmich.edu

MINNESOTA
Mr. Harvey Thorleifson
Professor & Director
Geological Survey
University of Minnesota
2609 West Territorial Road
St. Paul, MN 55114
P: (612) 626-2969
F: (612) 627-4778
E: thorleif@umn.edu

MISSISSIPPI
Mr. Michael Bograd
State Geologist
Office of Geology
Department of Environmental
Quality
P.O. Box 2279
Jackson, MS 39225
P: (601) 961-5500
F: (601) 961-5521
E: Michael_Bograd
   @deq.state.ms.us

MISSOURI
Mr. Joe Gillman
State Geologist & Director
Division of Geology & Land
Survey
Department of Natural
Resources
P.O. Box 250
Rolla, MO 65402
P: (800) 361-4827
F: (573) 368-2111
E: joe.gillman@dnr.mo.gov

MONTANA
Mr. John J. Metesh
Director & State Geologist
Bureau of Mines & Geology
Montana Tech
1300 West Park Street
Butte, MT 59701
P: (406) 496-4159
F: (406) 496-4451
E: jmetesh@mtech.edu

NEBRASKA
Mr. R.M. Joeckel
State Geologist &Associate
Director for Conservation and
Survey
Conservation & Survey
Division
University of Nebraska
Hardin Hall, 3310 Holdrege
Street
Lincoln, NE 68583
P: (402) 472-3471
F: (402) 472-3610
E: rjoeckel3@unl.edu

NEVADA
Mr. James E. Faulds
Director & State Geologist
Bureau of Mines & Geology
University of Nevada Reno, MS
178
Reno, NV 89557
P: (775) 682-8751
F: (775) 784-1709
E: jfaulds@unr.edu

NEW HAMPSHIRE
Mr. Rick Chormann
State Geologist & Director
Geological Survey
Department of Environmental
Services
29 Hazen Drive, P.O. Box 95
Concord, NH 03302
P: (603) 271-3503
F: (603) 271-3305
E: frederick.chormann
   @des.nh.gov

NEW JERSEY
Dr. Karl Muessig
State Geologist
Geological & Water Survey
Department of Environmental
Protection
P.O. Box 420, Mail Code 29-01
Trenton, NJ 08625
P: (609) 292-1185
F: (609) 633-1004
E: karl.muessig
   @dep.state.nj.us

NEW MEXICO
Mr. L. Greer Price
Director & State Geologist
Bureau of Geology & Mineral
Resources
New Mexico Tech
801 Leroy Place
Socorro, NM 87801
P: (575) 835-5420
F: (575) 835-6333
E: greer@nmbg.nmt.edu

NORTH CAROLINA
Dr. Kenneth B. Taylor
State Geologist & Manager
Geological Survey
Division of Land Resources
1612 Mail Service Center
Raleigh, NC 27699
P: (919) 733-2423
F: (919) 733-0900
E: kenneth.b.taylor
   @ncdenr.gov

NORTH DAKOTA
Mr. Edward C. Murphy
State Geologist
Geological Survey
Department of Mineral
Resources
600 East Boulevard Avenue
Bismarck, ND 58505
P: (701) 328-8000
F: (701) 328-8010
E: emurphy@nd.gov

OHIO
Dr. Thomas J. Serenko
State Geologist & Division
Chief
Division of Geological Survey
Department of Natural
Resources
2045 Morse Road, Building C
Columbus, OH 43229
P: (614) 265-6576
F: (614) 447-1918
E: thomas.serenko
   @dnr.state.oh.us

OKLAHOMA
Mr. Richard D. Andrews
Interim Director
Geological Survey
University of Oklahoma
100 East Boyd, Suite N-131
Norman, OK 73019
P: (405) 325-3031
F: (405) 325-7069
E: rdandrews@ou.edu

OREGON
Mr. Ian P. Madin
Interim State Geologist
Department of Geology &
Mineral Industries
800 Northeast Oregon Street,
Suite 965
Portland, OR 97232
P: (971) 673-1555
F: (971) 673-1562

PENNSYLVANIA
Mr. George E.W. Love
Director & State Geologist
Department of Conservation &
Natural Resources
Geologic Survey
3240 Schoolhouse Road
Middletown, PA 17057
P: (717) 702-2017
F: (717) 702-2065

PUERTO RICO
Ms. Ruth H. Velez
State Geologist
Bureau of Geology
Natural & Environmental
Resources
P.O. Box 9066600
Puerta De Tierra, PR 00906
P: (787) 722-2526
F: (787) 723-4255
E: rhvelez@dnra.gobierno.pr

RHODE ISLAND
Dr. Jon C. Boothroyd
State Geologist
Geological Survey
9 East Alumni Ave., 314
Woodward Hall
University of Rhode Island
Kingston, RI 02881
P: (401) 874-2191
F: (401) 874-2190
E: jon_boothroyd@uri.edu

Geological Survey

SOUTH CAROLINA
Mr. Charles William
    Clendenin Jr.
State Geologist
Geological Survey
Department of Natural
Resources
5 Geology Road
Columbia, SC 29210
P: (803) 896-7714
F: (803) 896-7695
E: clendeninb@dnr.sc.gov

SOUTH DAKOTA
Mr. Derric L. Iles
State Geologist
Geological Survey
Environment & Natural
Resources
414 East Clark Street
Vermillion, SD 57069
P: (605) 677-5227
F: (605) 677-5895
E: derric.iles@usd.edu

TENNESSEE
Mr. Ronald P. Zurawski
State Geologist
Division of Geology
401 Church Street
L & C Tower, 13th Floor
Nashville, TN 37243
P: (615) 532-1500
F: (615) 532-1517
E: Ronald.Zurawski@tn.gov

TEXAS
Dr. Scott W. Tinker
Director
Bureau of Economic Geology
University of Texas At Austin
University Station, Box X
Austin, TX 78713
P: (512) 471-1534
F: (512) 471-0140
E: scott.tinker
    @beg.utexas.edu

UTAH
Mr. Rick Allis
Director
Geological Survey
Department of Natural
Resources
P.O. Box 146100
Salt Lake City, UT 84114
P: (801) 537-3300
F: (801) 537-3400
E: rickallis@utah.gov

VERMONT
Ms. Marjorie Gale
State Geologist
Geological Survey
Department of Environmental
Conservation
103 South Main Street, Logue
Cottage
Waterbury, VT 05671
P: (802) 241-3608
F: (802) 241-4585
E: marjorie.gale
    @state.vt.us

VIRGINIA
Mr. James P. Skorupa
Director
Division of Geology & Mineral
Resources
Department of Mines, Minerals
& Energy
900 Natural Resources Drive,
Suite 500
Charlottesville, VA 22903
P: (434) 951-6341
F: (434) 951-6365

WASHINGTON
Mr. Dave Norman
State Geologist & Division
Manager
Division of Geology & Earth
Resources
Department of Natural
Resources
P.O. Box 47007
Olympia, WA 98504
P: (360) 902-1450
F: (360) 902-1785
E: dave.norman@dnr.wa.gov

WEST VIRGINIA
Mr. Michael Ed Hohn
Director & State Geologist
Geological & Economic Survey
Department of Commerce
1 Mont Chateau Road
Morgantown, WV 26508
P: (304) 594-2331
F: (304) 594-2575
E: info@geosrv.wvnet.edu

WISCONSIN
Mr. James M. Robertson
Director & State Geologist
Geological & Natural History
Survey
3817 Mineral Point Road
Madison, WI 53705
P: (608) 262-1705
F: (608) 262-8086
E: james.robertson@uwex.edu

WYOMING
Mr. Tom Drean
Director & State Geologist
State Geological Survey
P.O. Box 1347
Laramie, WY 82073
P: (307) 766-2286
F: (307) 766-2605
E: tom.drean@wyo.gov

Governor

Information provided by:

National Governors Association
Dan Crippen
Executive Director
Hall of the States
444 North Capitol Street
Suite 267
Washington, DC 20001
P: (202) 624-5300
F: (202) 624-5313
www.nga.org

The Council of State Governments
David Adkins
Executive Director/CEO
2760 Research Park Drive
Lexington, KY 40511
P: (859) 244-8000
F: (859) 244-8001
www.csg.org

ALABAMA
Hon. Robert J. Bentley (R)
Governor
Office of the Governor
State Capitol
600 Dexter Avenue
Montgomery, AL 36130
P: (334) 242-7100
F: (334) 353-0004

ALASKA
Hon. Bill Walker (I)
Governor
Office of the Governor
State Capitol
P.O. Box 110001
Juneau, AK 99811
P: (907) 465-3500
F: (907) 465-3532

AMERICAN SAMOA
Hon. Lolo Matalasi
Moliga (I)
Governor
Office of the Governor
Executive Office Building,
Third Floor
Utulei
Pago Pago, AS 96799
P: (684) 633-4116
F: (684) 633-2269

ARIZONA
Hon. Doug Ducey (R)
Governor
Office of the Governor
State Capitol
1700 West Washington Street
Phoenix, AZ 85007
P: (602) 542-4331
F: (602) 542-7601

ARKANSAS
Hon. Asa Hutchinson (R)
Governor
Office of the Governor
State Capitol
Room 250
Little Rock, AR 72201
P: (501) 682-2345
F: (501) 682-1382

CALIFORNIA
Hon. Edmund G.
Brown Jr. (D)
Governor
Office of the Governor
State Capitol
Sacramento, CA 95814
P: (916) 445-2841
F: (916) 558-3160

COLORADO
Hon. John Hickenlooper (D)
Governor
Office of the Governor
136 State Capitol
Denver, CO 80203
P: (303) 866-2471
F: (303) 866-2003

CONNECTICUT
Hon. Dan Malloy (D)
Governor
Office of the Governor
210 Capitol Avenue
Hartford, CT 06106
P: (800) 406-1527
F: (860) 524-7395

DELAWARE
Hon. Jack Markell (D)
Governor
Office of the Governor
Legislative Hall
Dover, DE 19901
P: (302) 744-4101
F: (302) 739-2775

DISTRICT OF COLUMBIA
Hon. Muriel Bowser (D)
Mayor
Office of the Mayor
1350 Pennsylvania Avenue,
Northwest
Suite 316
Washington, DC 20004
P: (202) 727-6300
F: (202) 727-0505
E: eom@dc.gov

FLORIDA
Hon. Rick Scott (R)
Governor
Office of the Governor
PL 05, The Capitol
400 South Monroe Street
Tallahassee, FL 32399
P: (850) 488-7146
F: (850) 487-0801

GEORGIA
Hon. Nathan Deal (R)
Governor
Office of the Governor
203 State Capitol
Atlanta, GA 30334
P: (404) 656-1776
F: (404) 657-7332

GUAM
Hon. Eddie Baza Calvo (R)
Governor
Office of the Governor
Executive Chamber
P.O. Box 2950
Agana, GU 96932
P: (671) 472-8931
F: (671) 477-4826

HAWAII
Hon. David Y. Ige (D)
Governor
Office of the Governor
Executive Chambers
State Capitol
Honolulu, HI 96813
P: (808) 586-0034
F: (808) 586-0006

IDAHO
Hon. C.L. "Butch" Otter (R)
Governor
Office of the Governor
700 West Jefferson, Second
Floor
Boise, ID 83702
P: (208) 334-2100
F: (208) 334-2175

ILLINOIS
Hon. Bruce Rauner (R)
Governor
Office of the Governor
State Capitol
207 Statehouse
Springfield, IL 62706
P: (217) 782-0244
F: (217) 524-4049

INDIANA
Hon. Mike Pence (R)
Governor
Office of the Governor
State House, Room 206
Indianapolis, IN 46204
P: (317) 232-4567
F: (317) 232-3443

IOWA
Hon. Terry Branstad (R)
Governor
Office of the Governor
State Capitol
Des Moines, IA 50319
P: (515) 281-5211
F: (515) 281-6611

KANSAS
Hon. Sam Brownback (R)
Governor
Office of the Governor
Capitol
300 Southwest 10th Avenue,
Suite 212S
Topeka, KS 66612
P: (785) 296-3232
F: (785) 296-7973

KENTUCKY
Hon. Steve L. Beshear (D)
Governor
Office of the Governor
700 Capital Avenue, Suite 100
Frankfort, KY 40601
P: (502) 564-2611
F: (502) 564-0437

LOUISIANA
Hon. Bobby Jindal (R)
Governor
Office of the Governor
P.O. Box 94004
Baton Rouge, LA 70804
P: (225) 342-7015
F: (225) 342-7099

MAINE
Hon. Paul LePage (R)
Governor
Office of the Governor
#1 State House Station
Augusta, ME 04333
P: (207) 287-3531
F: (207) 287-1034

Governor

MARYLAND
Hon. Larry Hogan (R)
Governor
Office of the Governor
State House
100 State Circle
Annapolis, MD 21401
P: (410) 974-3901
F: (410) 974-3275

MASSACHUSETTS
Hon. Charles Baker (R)
Governor
Office of the Governor
Room 360
Boston, MA 02133
P: (617) 725-4005
F: (617) 727-9725

MICHIGAN
Hon. Rick Snyder (R)
Governor
Office of the Governor
P.O. Box 30013
Lansing, MI 48909
P: (517) 373-3400
F: (517) 335-6863

MINNESOTA
Hon. Mark Dayton (D)
Governor
Office of the Governor
130 State Capitol
75 Rev. Martin Luther King Jr.
Boulevard
St. Paul, MN 55155
P: (651) 201-3400
F: (651) 797-1850

MISSISSIPPI
Hon. Phil Bryant (R)
Governor
Office of the Governor
P.O. Box 139
Jackson, MS 39205
P: (601) 359-3150
F: (601) 359-3741
E: governor
    @governor.state.ms.us

MISSOURI
Hon. Jay Nixon (D)
Governor
Office of the Governor
Capitol Building, Room 216
P.O. Box 720
Jefferson City, MO 65102
P: (573) 751-3222
F: (573) 526-3291

MONTANA
Hon. Steve Bullock (D)
Governor
Office of the Governor
State Capitol
Helena, MT 59620
P: (406) 444-3111
F: (404) 444-5529

NEBRASKA
Hon. Pete Ricketts (R)
Governor
Office of the Governor
P.O. Box 94848
Lincoln, NE 68509
P: (402) 471-2244
F: (402) 741-6031

NEVADA
Hon. Brian Sandoval (R)
Governor
Office of the Governor
Capitol Building
Carson City, NV 89701
P: (775) 684-5670
F: (775) 684-5683

NEW HAMPSHIRE
Hon. Maggie Hassan (D)
Governor
Office of the Governor
107 North Main Street, Room
208
Concord, NH 03301
P: (603) 271-2121
F: (603) 271-7640

NEW JERSEY
Hon. Chris Christie (R)
Governor
Office of the Governor
The State House
P.O. Box 001
Trenton, NJ 08625
P: (609) 292-6000
F: (609) 292-3454

NEW MEXICO
Hon. Susana Martinez (R)
Governor
Office of the Governor
State Capitol, Fourth Floor
Santa Fe, NM 87501
P: (505) 476-2200
F: (505) 476-2226

NEW YORK
Hon. Andrew M. Cuomo (D)
Governor
Office of the Governor
State Capitol
Albany, NY 12224
P: (518) 474-7516

NORTH CAROLINA
Hon. Pat McCrory (R)
Governor
Office of the Governor
20301 Mail Service Center
Raleigh, NC 27699
P: (919) 733-4240
F: (919) 733-2120

NORTH DAKOTA
Hon. Jack Dalrymple (R)
Governor
Office of the Governor
Department 101
600 East Boulevard Avenue
Bismarck, ND 58505
P: (701) 328-2200
F: (701) 328-2205

**NORTHERN MARIANA
ISLANDS**
Hon. Eloy S. Inos (R)
Governor
Office of the Governor
Caller Box 10007
Saipan, MP 96950
P: (670) 664-2280
F: (670) 664-2211

OHIO
Hon. John Kasich (R)
Governor
Office of the Governor
77 South High Street, 30th Floor
Columbus, OH 43215
P: (614) 466-3555
F: (614) 466-9354

OKLAHOMA
Hon. Mary Fallin (R)
Governor
Office of the Governor
Capitol Building
2300 Lincoln Boulevard, Room
212
Oklahoma City, OK 73105
P: (405) 521-2342
F: (405) 521-3353

OREGON
Hon. Kate Brown (D)
Governor
Office of the Governor
State Capitol, Room 160
900 Court Street North
Salem, OR 97301
P: (503) 378-3111
F: (503) 378-8970

PENNSYLVANIA
Hon. Thomas W. Wolf (D)
Governor
Office of the Governor
Room 225, Main Capitol
Building
Harrisburg, PA 17120
P: (717) 787-2500
F: (717) 772-8284

PUERTO RICO
Hon. Alejandro
    García-Padilla (PDP)
Governor
Office of the Governor
La Fortaleza
P.O. Box 9020082
San Juan, PR 00902
P: (787) 721-7000
F: (787) 721-5072

RHODE ISLAND
Hon. Gina M. Raimondo (D)
Governor
Office of the Governor
State House
Providence, RI 02903
P: (401) 222-2080
F: (401) 222-8096
E: governor@governor.ri.gov

SOUTH CAROLINA
Hon. Nikki Haley (R)
Governor
Office of the Governor
1205 Pendleton Street
Columbia, SC 29201
P: (803) 734-2100
F: (803) 734-5167

SOUTH DAKOTA
Hon. Dennis Daugaard (R)
Governor
Office of the Governor
500 East Capitol Avenue
Pierre, SD 57501
P: (605) 773-3212
F: (605) 773-4711

TENNESSEE
Hon. Bill Haslam (R)
Governor
Office of the Governor
State Capitol
Nashville, TN 37243
P: (615) 741-2001
F: (615) 532-9711
E: bill.haslam@tn.gov

TEXAS
Hon. Greg Abbott (R)
Governor
Office of the Governor
P.O. Box 12428
Austin, TX 78711
P: (512) 463-2000
F: (512) 463-5571

U.S. VIRGIN ISLANDS
Hon. Kenneth Mapp (I)
Governor
Office of the Governor
Government House
21-22 Kongens Gade
St. Thomas, VI 00802
P: (340) 774-0001
F: (340) 693-4374

UTAH
Hon. Gary R. Herbert (R)
Governor
Office of the Governor
State Capitol, Suite 200
Salt Lake City, UT 84114
P: (801) 538-1000
F: (801) 538-1557

VERMONT
Hon. Peter E. Shumlin (D)
Governor
Office of the Governor
109 State Street
Pavilion Office Building
Montpelier, VT 05609
P: (802) 828-3333
F: (802) 828-3339

VIRGINIA
Hon. Terry McAuliffe (D)
Governor
Office of the Governor
State Capitol, Third Floor
Richmond, VA 23219
P: (804) 786-2211
F: (804) 371-6351

WASHINGTON
Hon. Jay Inslee (D)
Governor
Office of the Governor
P.O. Box 40002
Olympia, WA 98504
P: (360) 902-4111
F: (360) 753-4110

WEST VIRGINIA
Hon. Earl Ray Tomblin (D)
Governor
Office of the Governor
1900 Kanawha Street
Charleston, WV 25305
P: (304) 558-2000

WISCONSIN
Hon. Scott K. Walker (R)
Governor
Office of the Governor
115 East State Capitol
Madison, WI 53707
P: (608) 266-1212
F: (608) 267-8983

WYOMING
Hon. Matthew Mead (R)
Governor
Office of the Governor
State Capitol Building, Room 124
Cheyenne, WY 82002
P: (307) 777-7434
F: (307) 632-3909

Governor's Chief of Staff

Manages the office of the governor and assists in all duties performed by the governor.

Information provided by:

National Governors Association
Dan Crippen
Executive Director
Hall of the States
444 North Capitol Street
Suite 267
Washington, DC 20001
P: (202) 624-5300
F: (202) 624-5313
www.nga.org

ALABAMA
Mr. Seth Hammett
Chief of Staff
Office of the Governor
State Capitol
600 Dexter Avenue
Montgomery, AL 36130
P: (334) 242-7100
E: seth.hammett
    @governor.alabama.gov

ALASKA
Mr. Jim Whitaker
Chief of Staff
Office of the Governor
State Capitol
P.O. Box 110001
Juneau, AK 99811
P: (907) 465-3500
E: Jim.Whitaker@alaska.gov

AMERICAN SAMOA
Mr. John Saelua
Chief of Staff
Office of the Governor
Executive Office Building,
Third Floor
Pago Pago, AS 96799
P: (684) 633-4116
F: (684) 633-2269

ARIZONA
Mr. Kirk Adams
Chief of Staff
Office of the Governor
State Capitol
1700 West Washington
Phoenix, AZ 85007
P: (602) 542-1444
E: kadams@az.gov

ARKANSAS
Mr. Michael Lamoureux
Chief of Staff
Office of the Governor
State Capitol, Suite 250
Little Rock, AR 72201
P: (501) 682-2345
E: michael.lamoureux
    @arkansas.gov

CALIFORNIA
Ms. Nancy McFadden
Chief of Staff
Office of the Governor
State Capitol
Sacramento, CA 95814
P: (916) 445-2841

COLORADO
Mr. Kevin Patterson
Chief of Staff
Office of the Governor
136 State Capitol
Denver, CO 80203
P: (303) 866-2471
E: kevin.patterson
    @state.co.us

CONNECTICUT
Mr. Mark E. Ojakian
Chief of Staff
Office of the Governor
210 Capitol Avenue
Hartford, CT 06106
P: (800) 406-1527
F: (860) 524-7395
E: mark.ojakian@ct.gov

DELAWARE
Mr. Mike Barlow
Chief of Staff
Office of the Governor
Legislative Hall
Dover, DE 19902
P: (302) 744-4101
F: (302) 577-3118
E: michael.barlow
    @state.de.us

FLORIDA
Ms. Melissa Sellers
Chief of Staff
Office of the Governor
The Capitol
400 South Monroe Street
Tallahassee, FL 32399
P: (850) 488-7146
E: melissa.sellers
    @eog.myflorida.com

GEORGIA
Mr. Chris Riley
Chief of Staff
Office of the Governor
203 State Capitol
Atlanta, GA 30334
P: (404) 656-1776
F: (404) 657-7332

GUAM
Mr. Frank Arriola
Chief of Staff
Office of the Governor
Executive Chamber
P.O. Box 2950
Agana, GU 96932
P: (671) 472-8931
F: (671) 477-4826
E: franklin.arriola
    @guam.gov

HAWAII
Mr. Michael J. McCartney
Chief of Staff
Office of the Governor
Executive Chambers
State Capitol
Honolulu, HI 96813
P: (808) 586-0034
E: mike.mccartney
    @hawaii.gov

IDAHO
Mr. David Hensley
Chief of Staff
Office of the Governor
700 West Jefferson Street
2nd Floor, West Wing
Boise, ID 83702
P: (208) 854-3005
F: (208) 334-2175
E: dhensley@gov.idaho.gov

ILLINOIS
Mr. Mike Zolnierowicz
Chief of Staff
Office of the Governor
207 Sate House
Springfield, IL 62706
P: (217) 782-0244

INDIANA
Mr. Jim D. Atterholt
Chief of Staff
Office of the Governor
State Capitol, Room 206
Indianapolis, IN 46204
P: (317) 232-4567
E: jatterholt@gov.in.gov

IOWA
Mr. Matt Hinch
Chief of Staff
Office of the Governor
State Capitol
Des Moines, IA 50319
P: (515) 281-5211
F: (515) 281-6611

KANSAS
Mr. Jon Hummell
Chief of Staff
Office of the Governor
State Capitol, Suite 212S
300 Southwest 10th Avenue
Topeka, KS 66612
P: (785) 296-3232
E: jon.hummell@ks.gov

KENTUCKY
Mr. Larry Bond
Chief of Staff
Office of the Governor
700 Capitol Avenue, Suite 100
Frankfort, KY 40601
P: (502) 564-2611
F: (502) 564-0437
E: larry.bond@ky.gov

LOUISIANA
Mr. Kyle Plotkin
Chief of Staff
Office of the Governor
P.O. Box 94004
Baton Rouge, LA 70804
P: (225) 342-7015
E: kyle.plotkin@la.gov

MAINE
Mr. John McGough
Chief of Staff
Office of the Governor
1 State House Station
Augusta, ME 04333
P: (207) 287-3531
F: (207) 287-1034
E: John.McGough@maine.gov

MARYLAND
Mr. Craig Williams
Chief of Staff
Office of the Governor
State House
100 State Circle
Annapolis, MD 21401
P: (410) 974-3901
E: craig.williams
    @maryland.gov

Governor's Chief of Staff

MASSACHUSETTS
Mr. Steven Kadish
Chief of Staff
Office of the Governor
State House, Room 360
Boston, MA 02133
P: (617) 725-4005
E: steven.kadish
@state.ma.us

MICHIGAN
Mr. Dennis Muchmore
Chief of Staff
Office of the Governor
P.O. Box 30013
Lansing, MI 48909
P: (517) 373-3400
F: (517) 335-6863
E: muchmored@michigan.gov

MINNESOTA
Ms. Jaime Tincher
Chief of Staff
Office of the Governor
130 State Capitol
75 Rev. Martin Luther King Jr.
Boulevard
St. Paul, MN 55155
P: (651) 201-3400

MISSISSIPPI
Mr. Lucien Smith
Chief of Staff
Office of the Governor
P.O. Box 139
Jackson, MS 39205
P: (601) 359-3150
E: Lucien.Smith
@governor.ms.gov

MISSOURI
Mr. Chris Pieper
Chief of Staff
Office of the Governor
Capitol Building, Room 216
P.O. Box 720
Jefferson City, MO 65102
P: (573) 751-3222
E: chris.pieper@mo.gov

MONTANA
Ms. Tracy Stone-Manning
Chief of Staff
Office of the Governor
State Capitol
Helena, MT 59620
P: (406) 444-3111
F: (406) 444-4386
E: TStone-Manning@mt.gov

NEBRASKA
Mr. Matt Miltenberger
Chief of Staff
Office of the Governor
P.O. Box 94848
Lincoln, NE 68509
P: (402) 471-2244
E: matt.miltenberger
@nebraska.gov

NEVADA
Mr. Michael J. Willden
Chief of Staff
Office of the Governor
State Capitol Building
101 North Carson Street
Carson City, NV 89701
P: (775) 684-5670
E: mwillden@gov.nv.gov

NEW HAMPSHIRE
Ms. Pamela Walsh
Chief of Staff
Office of the Governor
State House
107 North Main Street, Room 208
Concord, NH 03301
P: (603) 271-2121
F: (603) 271-7640
E: pamela.walsh@nh.gov

NEW JERSEY
Ms. Regina Egea
Chief of Staff
Office of the Governor
The State House
P.O. Box 001
Trenton, NJ 08625
P: (609) 292-6000
E: Regina.Egea
@gov.state.nj.us

NEW MEXICO
Mr. Keith J. Gardner
Chief of Staff
Office of the Governor
State Capitol, Fourth Floor
Santa Fe, NM 87501
P: (505) 476-2200
F: (505) 476-2226
E: keith.gardner
@state.nm.us

NEW YORK
Mr. Howard Glaser
Chief of Staff
Office of the Governor
State Capitol
Albany, NY 12224
P: (518) 474-7516
E: Howard.Glaser
@chamber.state.ny.us

NORTH CAROLINA
Mr. Thomas Stith
Chief of Staff
Office of the Governor
20301 Mail Service Center
Raleigh, NC 27699
P: (919) 733-4240
F: (919) 733-2120
E: thomas.stith@nc.gov

NORTH DAKOTA
Mr. Ron Rauschenberger
Chief of Staff
Office of the Governor
State Capitol, Department 101
600 East Boulevard Avenue
Bismarck, ND 58505
P: (701) 328-2200
F: (701) 328-2205
E: rrausche@nd.gov

NORTHERN MARIANA ISLANDS
Ms. Esther Fleming
Chief of Staff
Office of the Governor
Caller Box 10007, Capitol Hill
Saipan, MP 96950
P: (670) 664-2212
F: (670) 664-2211

OHIO
Ms. Beth Hansen
Chief of Staff
Office of the Governor
77 South High Street, 30th Floor
Columbus, OH 43215
P: (614) 466-3555
F: (614) 466-9354
E: beth.hansen
@governor.ohio.gov

OKLAHOMA
Ms. Denise Northrup
Chief of Staff
Office of the Governor
State Capitol Building
2300 Lincoln Boulevard, Suite 212
Oklahoma City, OK 73105
P: (405) 521-2342
F: (405) 521-3353
E: Denise.Northrup
@gov.ok.gov

OREGON
Mr. Brian Shipley
Chief of Staff
Office of the Governor
State Capitol, Room 160
900 Court Street, Northeast
Salem, OR 97301
P: (503) 378-3111

PENNSYLVANIA
Ms. Katie McGinty
Chief of Staff
Office of the Governor
Main Capitol Building, Room 225
Harrisburg, PA 17120
P: (717) 787-2500

PUERTO RICO
Mr. Victor Suarez Melendez
Chief of Staff
Office of the Governor
La Fortaleza
P.O. Box 9020082
San Juan, PR 00902
P: (787) 721-7000

RHODE ISLAND
Mr. Stephen Neuman
Chief of Staff
Office of the Governor
State House
Providence, RI 02903
P: (401) 222-2080

SOUTH CAROLINA
Mr. James Burns
Chief of Staff
Office of the Governor
1205 Pendleton Street
Columbia, SC 29201
P: (803) 734-2100
E: jburns@gov.sc.gov

SOUTH DAKOTA
Mr. Tony Venhuizen
Chief of Staff
Office of the Governor
500 East Capitol Avenue
Pierre, SD 57501
P: (605) 773-3212
E: tony.venhuizen
@state.sd.us

TENNESSEE
Mr. Mark Cate
Chief of Staff
Office of the Governor
State Capitol
Nashville, TN 37243
P: (615) 741-2001
F: (615) 532-9711
E: mark.cate@tn.gov

TEXAS
Mr. Daniel Hodge
Chief of Staff
Office of the Governor
P.O. Box 12428
Austin, TX 78711
P: (512) 463-2000

Governor's Chief of Staff

U.S. VIRGIN ISLANDS
Mr. Randolph Knight
Chief of Staff
Office of the Governor
Government House, 21-22
Kongens Gade
Charlotte Amalie
St. Thomas, VI 00802
P: (340) 774-0001

UTAH
Mr. Justin Harding
Chief of Staff
Office of the Governor
State Capitol, Suite 200
Salt Lake City, UT 84114
P: (801) 538-1000

VERMONT
Ms. Elizabeth Miller
Chief of Staff
Office of the Governor
109 State Street
Pavilion Office Building
Montpelier, VT 05609
P: (802) 828-3333
F: (802) 828-3339

VIRGINIA
Mr. Paul J. Reagan
Chief of Staff
Office of the Governor
State Capitol, 3rd Floor
Richmond, VA 23219
P: (804) 786-2211
F: (804) 371-6351

WASHINGTON
Joby Shimomura
Chief of Staff
Office of the Governor
P.O. Box 40002
Olympia, WA 98504
P: (360) 902-4111

WEST VIRGINIA
Mr. Charles O. Lorensen
Chief of Staff
Office of the Governor
1900 Kanawha Street
Charleston, WV 25305
P: (304) 558-2000
E: Charles.O.Lorensen
 @wv.gov

WISCONSIN
Mr. Eric Schutt
Chief of Staff
Office of the Governor
115 East State Capitol
Madison, WI 53707
P: (608) 266-1212
F: (608) 267-8983
E: eric.schutt
 @wisconsin.gov

WYOMING
Ms. Kari Gray
Chief of Staff
Office of the Governor
State Capitol Building, Room
124
Cheyenne, WY 82002
P: (307) 777-7434
F: (307) 632-3909

Governor's Legislative Director

Oversees the governor's legislative priorities, aids in legislative administration, and assists the governor in all other legislative matters.

ALABAMA
Mr. Ross Gunnells
Director of Legislative Affairs
Office of the Governor
State Capitol
600 Dexter Avenue
Montgomery, AL 36130
P: (334) 242-7989

ALASKA
Mr. Darwin Peterson
Legislative Director
Office of the Governor
State Capitol
P.O. Box 110001
Juneau, AK 99811
P: (907) 465-3500
F: (907) 465-3532

ARIZONA
Ms. Gretchen Martinez
Director, Legislative Affairs
Office of the Governor
1700 West Washington
Phoenix, AZ 85007
P: (602) 542-4043

CALIFORNIA
Ms. Camille Wagner
Legislative Affairs Secretary
Office of the Governor
State Capitol
Sacramento, CA 95814
P: (916) 445-2841
F: (916) 445-4633

COLORADO
Mr. Kurtis Morrison
Legislative Director
Office of the Governor
136 State Capitol
Denver, CO 80203
P: (303) 866-2471
F: (303) 866-2003
E: kurt.morrison
    @state.co.us

DELAWARE
Ms. Drew Fennell
Deputy Chief of Staff
Office of the Governor
Tatnall Building
William Penn Street
Dover, DE 19901
P: (302) 739-4111
F: (302) 739-2775
E: drewry.fennell
    @state.de.us

GEORGIA
Mr. David Werner
Deputy Chief of Staff for
Legislative & External Affairs
Office of the Governor
142 State Capitol
Atlanta, GA 30334
P: (404) 656-1776
F: (404) 656-5947

GUAM
Mr. Frank Arriola
Chief of Staff
Office of the Governor
Executive Chamber
P.O. Box 2950
Agana, GU 96932
P: (671) 472-8931
F: (671) 477-4826
E: franklin.arriola
    @guam.gov

HAWAII
Mr. C. Mike Kido
Office of the Governor
415 South Beretania Street,
Room 417
Honolulu, HI 96813
P: (808) 586-0225
E: mike.kido@hawaii.gov

IDAHO
Mr. David Hensley
Chief of Staff
Office of the Governor
700 West Jefferson Street
2nd Floor, West Wing
Boise, ID 83702
P: (208) 854-3005
F: (208) 334-2175
E: dhensley@gov.idaho.gov

ILLINOIS
Mr. Richard Goldberg
Deputy Chief of Staff for
Legislative Affairs
Office of the Governor
State Capitol
207 Statehouse
Springfield, IL 62706
P: (217) 782-6830
F: (217) 524-4049

INDIANA
Mr. Sean Keefer
Legislative Director
Office of the Governor
State House
Indianapolis, IN 46204
P: (317) 232-4567
F: (317) 232-3443

KANSAS
Mr. Brandon Smith
Director of Policy
Office of the Governor
State Capitol, 2nd Floor
Topeka, KS 66612
P: (785) 296-3232
F: (785) 296-7973

KENTUCKY
Mr. Roger Thomas
Director of Legislative Affairs
Office of the Governor
700 Capitol Avenue, Suite 100
Frankfort, KY 40601
P: (502) 564-2611
F: (502) 564-2517
E: roger.thomas@ky.gov

LOUISIANA
Ms. Melissa Mann
Director of Legislative Affairs
Office of the Governor
P.O. Box 94004
Baton Rouge, LA 70804
P: (225) 342-7188
E: melissa.mann@la.gov

MAINE
Mr. John McGough
Chief of Staff
Office of the Governor
1 State House Station
Augusta, ME 04333
P: (207) 287-3531
F: (207) 287-1034
E: John.McGough@maine.gov

MARYLAND
Mr. Craig Williams
Chief of Staff
Office of the Governor
State House
100 State Circle
Annapolis, MD 21401
P: (410) 974-3901
E: craig.williams
    @maryland.gov

MASSACHUSETTS
Mr. Ryan Coleman
Legislative Affairs Director
Office of the Governor
State House, Room 360
Boston, MA 02133
P: (617) 725-4005

MICHIGAN
Mr. Dick Posthumus
Senior Advisor, Legislative
Affairs
Office of the Governor
P.O. Box 30013
Lansing, MI 48909
P: (517) 241-3950

MINNESOTA
Mr. Linden Zakula
Deputy Chief of Staff
Office of the Governor
116 Veterans Service Building
20 West 12 Street
St. Paul, MN 55155
P: (651) 201-3421
E: linden.zakula
    @state.mn.us

MISSOURI
Mr. Jason Zamkus
Director of Legislative Affairs
Office of the Governor
Capitol Building, Room 216
Jefferson City, MO 65101
P: (573) 751-3222
F: (573) 526-3291

MONTANA
Mr. Jim Molloy
Senior Policy Advisor
Office of the Governor
P.O. Box 200801
Helena, MT 59620
P: (406) 444-5503
E: jmolloy@mt.gov

NEW HAMPSHIRE
Mr. Chris Kennedy
Legislative Director
Office of the Governor
25 Capitol Street, Room 212
Concord, NH 03301
P: (603) 271-2121

NEW YORK
Mr. Michael Laskaway
Senior Policy Advisor
Office of the Governor
State Capitol
Albany, NY 12224
P: (518) 408-2576
F: (518) 474-8390

NORTH DAKOTA
Ms. Kayla Effertz
Senior Policy Advisor
Office of the Governor
State Capitol
600 East Boulevard Avenue
Bismarck, ND 58505
P: (701) 328-2229
F: (701) 328-2205
E: kmeffertz@nd.gov

Governor's Legislative Director

OHIO
Mr. Eric Poklar
Director of Legislative Affairs
Office of the Governor
77 South High Street, 30th Floor
Columbus, OH 43215
P: (614) 644-0856
E: eric.poklar
    @governor.ohio.gov

OKLAHOMA
Mr. Craig Perry
Legislative Director
Office of the Governor
State Capitol Building
2300 Lincoln Boulevard, Suite
212
Oklahoma, OK 73105
P: (405) 521-2342
F: (405) 521-3353

OREGON
Mr. Dmitri Palmateer
Legislative Director
Office of the Governor
900 Court Street, Northeast
Salem, OR 97301
P: (503) 373-1027

PENNSYLVANIA
Ms. Mary Isenhour
Secretary of Legislative Affairs
Office of the Governor
Room 225 Main Capitol
Building
Harrisburg, PA 17120
P: (717) 787-2500

RHODE ISLAND
Mr. R. David Cruise
Director of Legislative Affairs
Office of the Governor
State House
Providence, RI 02903
P: (401) 222-2080
F: (401) 273-5729

SOUTH CAROLINA
Ms. Katherine Veldran
Director of Legislative Affairs
Office of the Governor
P.O. Box 12267
Columbia, SC 29211
P: (803) 734-2100
F: (803) 734-5167

SOUTH DAKOTA
Mr. Jim Soyer
Legislative Director
Office of the Governor
State Capitol
500 East Capitol Avenue
Pierre, SD 57501
P: (605) 773-3212
F: (605) 773-5844
E: jim.soyer@state.sd.us

TENNESSEE
Ms. Leslie Hafner
Director of Legislation
Office of the Governor
State Capitol
Nashville, TN 37243
P: (615) 741-2001
F: (615) 532-9711

TEXAS
Mr. Randy Erben
Director of Legislative Affairs
Office of the Governor
P.O. Box 12428
Austin, TX 78711
P: (512) 463-1830

VIRGINIA
Mr. Felix Sarfo-Kantanka
Legislative Director
Office of the Governor
State Capitol, 3rd Floor
Richmond, VA 23219
P: (804) 786-2211
F: (804) 371-6351

WASHINGTON
Mr. Miguel Perez-Gibson
Executive Director of
Legislative Affairs
Office of the Governor
P.O. Box 40002
Olympia, WA 98504
P: (360) 902-4105
E: miguel.perezgibson
    @gov.wa.gov

WEST VIRGINIA
Mr. Joey Garcia
Legislative Director
Office of the Governor
State Capitol Complex
1900 Kanawha Boulevard, East
Charleston, WV 25305
P: (304) 558-2000
E: joseph.d.garcia@wv.gov

Governor's Media Contacts

Issues press releases on behalf of the governor, acts as a liaison with the media and public, and serves as the governor's spokesperson.

Information provided by:

National Governors Association
Dan Crippen
Executive Director
Hall of the States
444 North Capitol Street
Suite 267
Washington, DC 20001
P: (202) 624-5300
F: (202) 624-5313
www.nga.org

ALABAMA
Ms. Jennifer Ardis
Communications Director
Office of the Governor
State Capitol
600 Dexter Avenue
Montgomery, AL 36130
P: (334) 242-7150

ALASKA
Ms. Grace Jang
Press Secretary
Office of the Governor
State Capitol
P.O. Box 110001
Juneau, AK 99811
P: (907) 269-3031

AMERICAN SAMOA
Mr. Iu Joseph Pereira
Executive Assistant To the Governor/Press Officer
Office of the Governor
Pago Pago, AS 96799
P: (684) 633-4116

ARIZONA
Mr. Daniel Scarpinato
Deputy Chief of Staff for Communications
Office of the Governor
1700 West Washington
Phoenix, AZ 85007
P: (602) 542-2661

ARKANSAS
JR Davis
Communications Director
Office of the Governor
State Capitol, Room 250
Little Rock, AR 72201
P: (501) 683-6412

CALIFORNIA
Mr. Evan Westrup
Press Secretary
Office of the Governor
State Capitol, First Floor
Sacramento, CA 95814
P: (916) 445-4571

COLORADO
Ms. Kathy Green
Director of Communications
Office of the Governor
State Capitol, Room 127
Denver, CO 80203
P: (303) 866-4361

CONNECTICUT
Mr. Mark Bergman
Communications Director
Office of the Governor
State Capitol
210 Capitol Avenue
Hartford, CT 06106
P: (860) 524-7334

DELAWARE
Ms. Kelly Bachman
Press Secretary
Office of the Governor
Tatnall Building
William Penn Street
Dover, DE 19901
P: (302) 577-8495

FLORIDA
Ms. Jackie Schutz
Communications Director
Office of the Governor
State Capitol, Room 206
Tallahassee, FL 32399
P: (850) 488-5394

GEORGIA
Mr. Brian Robinson
Deputy Chief of Staff for Communications
Office of the Governor
State Capitol, Room 100
Atlanta, GA 30334
P: (404) 651-7783

GUAM
Oyo Ngirairikl
Communications Director
Office of the Governor
Executive Chamber
P.O. Box 2950
Hagatna, GU 96932
P: (671) 475-9379

HAWAII
Ms. Cindy McMillan
Director of Communications
Office of the Governor
State Capitol
415 South Beretania Street
Honolulu, HI 96813
P: (808) 586-0034

IDAHO
Mr. Mark Warbis
Communications Director
Office of the Governor
State Capitol
700 West Jefferson, 2nd Floor
Boise, ID 83720
P: (208) 334-2100

ILLINOIS
Mr. Lance Trover
Communications Director
Office of the Governor
James R. Thompson Center
100 West Randolph, Suite 16-100
Chicago, IL 60601
P: (312) 814-4220

INDIANA
Ms. Christy Denault
Communications Director
Office of the Governor
206 State House
Indianapolis, IN 46204
P: (317) 232-1622

IOWA
Mr. Jimmy Centers
Communications Director
Office of the Governor
State Capitol
Des Moines, IA 50319
P: (515) 725-3507

KANSAS
Ms. Eileen Hawley
Communications Director
Office of the Governor
State Capitol, Second Floor
Topeka, KS 66612
P: (785) 368-7138

KENTUCKY
Ms. Kerri Richardson
Communications Director
Office of the Governor
State Capitol
700 Capitol Avenue, Suite 100
Frankfort, KY 40601
P: (502) 564-2611

LOUISIANA
Mr. Mike Reed
Communications Director
Office of the Governor
P.O. Box 94004
Baton Rouge, LA 70804
P: (225) 342-8006
E: mike.reed@la.gov

MAINE
Mr. Peter Steele
Communications Director
Office of the Governor
State House, Station 1
Augusta, ME 04333
P: (207) 287-5086

MARYLAND
Mr. Matt Clark
Communications Director
Office of the Governor
State House
Annapolis, MD 21401
P: (410) 974-2316

MASSACHUSETTS
Mr. Tim Buckley
Communications Director
Office of the Governor
State House, Room 265
Boston, MA 02133
P: (617) 483-3395

MICHIGAN
Mr. Jarrod Agen
Director of Communications
Office of the Governor
P.O. Box 30013
Lansing, MI 48909
P: (517) 335-6397

MINNESOTA
Mr. Bob Hume
Deputy Chief of Staff for Communications
Office of the Governor
State Capitol, Room 130
St. Paul, MN 55155
P: (651) 201-3400

MISSISSIPPI
Ms. Nicole Webb
Communications Director/Press Secretary
Office of the Governor
P.O. Box 139
Jackson, MS 39205
P: (601) 576-2802

MISSOURI
Channing Ansley
Director of Communications
Office of the Governor
State Capitol
P.O. Box 720
Jefferson City, MO 65101
P: (573) 751-0290

Governor's Media Contacts

MONTANA
Mr. Dave Parker
Director of Communications
Office of the Governor
State Capitol
Helena, MT 59620
P: (406) 444-9844

NEBRASKA
Mr. Taylor Gage
Communications Director
Office of the Governor
P.O. Box 94848
Lincoln, NE 68509
P: (402) 471-7047

NEVADA
Ms. Mari St. Martin
Communications Director
Office of the Governor
State Capitol, Governor's Office
101 North Carson Street
Carson City, NV 89701
P: (775) 250-8210

NEW HAMPSHIRE
Mr. William Hinkle
Director of
Communications/Deputy Press
Office of the Governor
State House
Concord, NH 03301
P: (603) 271-2121

NEW JERSEY
Ms. Maria Comella
Director of Communications
Office of the Governor
Governor's Office, 125 West
State Street
P.O. Box 001
Trenton, NJ 08625
P: (609) 777-2600

NEW MEXICO
Mr. Enrique Knell
Communications Director
Office of the Governor
State Capitol, Fourth Floor
Santa Fe, NM 87501
P: (505) 476-2259

NEW YORK
Ms. Melissa DeRosa
Director of Communications
Office of the Governor
State Capitol, Room 200
Albany, NY 12224
P: (518) 474-8418

NORTH CAROLINA
Mr. Josh Ellis
Communications Director
Office of the Governor
20301 Mail Service Center
Raleigh, NC 27699
P: (908) 814-2100

NORTH DAKOTA
Mr. Jeff Zent
Communications Director
Office of the Governor
600 East Boulevard Avenue
Department 101
Bismarck, ND 58505
P: (701) 328-2200
F: (701) 328-2205

NORTHERN MARIANA ISLANDS
Mr. Ivan Blanco
Special Assistant for
Communications
Office of the Governor
Capitol Hill
Saipan, MP 96950
P: (670) 664-2224

OHIO
Mr. Scott Milburn
Communications Director
Office of the Governor
South High Street, 30th Floor
Columbus, OH 43215
P: (614) 466-3555

OKLAHOMA
Mr. Alex Weintz
Communications Director
Office of the Governor
State Capitol
Oklahoma City, OK 73105
P: (405) 522-8819

OREGON
Ms. Amy Wojcicki
Communications Director
Office of the Governor
State Capitol, Room 254
900 Court Street, Northeast
Salem, OR 97310
P: (971) 283-8817

PENNSYLVANIA
Mr. Mark Nicastre
Director of Communications
Office of the Governor
Main Capitol Building, Room
308
Harrisburg, PA 17120
P: (717) 783-1116

PUERTO RICO
Mr. Jose Javier Diaz
Communications Director
Office of the Governor
La Fortaleza
San Juan, PR 00902
P: (202) 778-0710

RHODE ISLAND
Ms. Joy Fox
Director of
Communications/Press Secretary
Office of the Governor
State House
Providence, RI 02903
P: (401) 222-8134

SOUTH CAROLINA
Mr. Doug Mayer
Communications Director
Office of the Governor
1205 Pendleton Street
Columbia, SC 29201
P: (803) 734-2100

SOUTH DAKOTA
Mr. Tony Venhuizen
Chief of Staff
Office of the Governor
500 East Capitol Avenue
Pierre, SD 57501
P: (605) 773-3212
E: tony.venhuizen
@state.sd.us

TENNESSEE
Ms. Alexia Poe
Director of Communications
Office of the Governor
State Capitol, Room G-9
Nashville, TN 37243
P: (615) 741-3763

TEXAS
Mr. Matt Hirsch
Director of Communications
Office of the Governor
P.O. Box 12428
Austin, TX 78711
P: (512) 936-3349

U.S. VIRGIN ISLANDS
Ms. Kimberly Jones
Press Secretary
Office of the Governor
Government House, 21-22
Kongens Gade
Charlotte Amalie
St. Thomas, VI 00802
P: (340) 693-4361

UTAH
Marty Carpenter
Communications Director
Office of the Governor
210 State Capitol, Suite 200
Salt Lake City, UT 84114
P: (801) 538-1000

VERMONT
Mr. Scott Coriell
Director of Communications
Office of the Governor
109 State Street
Montpelier, VT 05609
P: (802) 828-6463

VIRGINIA
Mr. Brian Coy
Communications Director
Office of the Governor
Patrick Henry Building, 3rd
Floor
1111 East Broad Street
Richmond, VA 23219
P: (804) 225-4260

WASHINGTON
Mr. David Postman
Executive Communications
Director
Office of the Governor
416 4th Avenue, Southwest
Olympia, WA 98504
P: (360) 902-4136

WEST VIRGINIA
Mr. Chris Stadelman
Director of Communications
Office of the Governor
State Capitol
Charleston, WV 25305
P: (304) 558-4977

WISCONSIN
Ms. Jocelyn Webster
Communications Director
Office of the Governor
State Capitol
115 East Capitol
Madison, WI 53702
P: (608) 267-7303

WYOMING
Ms. Michelle Panos
Communications Director
Office of the Governor
State Capitol
Cheyenne, WY 82002
P: (307) 777-7437

Hazardous Waste Management

Develops and maintains a comprehensive hazardous waste management program in the state.

ALABAMA
Mr. Stephen A. Cobb
Chief
Governmental Hazardous Waste
Environmental Management,
Land Division
P.O. Box 301463
Montgomery, AL 36130
P: (334) 271-7739
F: (334) 271-7950

ALASKA
Mr. Bob Blankenburg
Program Manager
Solid Waste Program
Department of Environmental
Health
555 Cordova Street
Anchorage, AK 99501
P: (907) 269-7802
F: (907) 269-7600
E: bob.blankenburg
    @alaska.gov

Ms. Kristin Ryan
Director
Division of Spill Prevention &
Response
Department of Environmental
Conservation
P.O. Box 111800
Anchorage, AK 99811
P: (907) 269-3094
F: (907) 269-7654
E: kristin.ryan@alaska.gov

ARIZONA
Ms. Laura L. Malone
Waste Programs Division
Director
Department of Environmental
Quality
1110 West Washington Street
Phoenix, AZ 85007
P: (602) 771-4567
F: (602) 771-2302
E: malone.laura@azdeq.gov

ARKANSAS
Ms. Tammie J. Hynum
Chief
Hazardous Waste Division
5301 Northshore Drive
North Little Rock, AR 72118
P: (501) 682-0831
F: (501) 682-0880
E: hynum@adeq.state.ar.us

CALIFORNIA
Ms. Caroll Mortensen
Director
Department of Resources,
Recycling & Recovery
1001 I Street
P.O. Box 4025
Sacramento, CA 95812
P: (916) 322-4025
F: (916) 319-7227
E: Caroll.Mortensen
    @calrecycle.ca.gov

COLORADO
Mr. Gary Baughman
Director
Hazardous Materials & Waste
Management Division
Public Health & Environment
4300 Cherry Creek Drive, South
Denver, CO 80246
P: (303) 692-3338
F: (303) 759-5355
E: gary.baughman
    @state.co.us

CONNECTICUT
Mr. Robert J. Klee
Commissioner
Department of Energy &
Environmental Protection
79 Elm Street
Hartford, CT 06106
P: (860) 424-3001
F: (860) 424-4051
E: deep.commissioner@ct.gov

DELAWARE
Ms. Nancy C. Marker
Administrator
Solid & Hazardous Waste
Management Section
89 Kings Highway
Dover, DE 19901
P: (302) 739-9403
F: (302) 739-5060
E: nancy.marker@state.de.us

DISTRICT OF COLUMBIA
Dr. Joxel Garcia
Director
Department of Health
899 North Capitol Street,
Northeast
Washington, DC 20002
P: (202) 442-5955
F: (202) 442-4795
E: doh@dc.gov

FLORIDA
Mr. Jorge Caspary
Director
Division of Waste Management
Department of Environmental
Protection
2600 Blair Stone Road
Tallahassee, FL 32399
P: (850) 245-8693
E: jorge.caspary
    @dep.state.fl.us

GEORGIA
Mr. Jeff Cown
Branch Chief
Land Protection Branch
4244 International Parkway,
Suite 104
Atlanta, GA 30354
P: (404) 362-2692
F: (404) 362-2693

HAWAII
Mr. Steven Y.K. Chang
Branch Chief
Solid & Hazardous Waste
Branch
Department of Health
919 Ala Moana Boulevard, #212
Honolulu, HI 96814
P: (808) 586-4226
F: (808) 586-7509
E: schang
    @eha.health.state.hi.us

IDAHO
Mr. Orville Green
Administrator
Waste Management &
Remediation Division
DEQ State Office
1410 North Hilton
Boise, ID 83706
P: (208) 373-0148
F: (208) 373-0154
E: orville.green
    @deq.idaho.gov

ILLINOIS
Dr. Kevin O'Brien
Director
Sustainable Technology Center
One Hazelwood Drive
Champaign, IL 61820
P: (217) 333-8940
F: (217) 333-8944
E: mkulkarni
    @istc.illinois.edu

INDIANA
Mr. Bruce Palin
Assistant Commissioner, Office
of Land Quality
Department of Environmental
Management
100 North Senate Avenue
Room IGCN 1154
Indianapolis, IN 46204
P: (317) 233-6591
F: (317) 233-6647
E: bpalin@idem.in.gov

KANSAS
Mr. William L. Bider
Director
Bureau of Waste Management
1000 Southwest Jackson Street
Suite 320
Topeka, KS 66612
P: (785) 296-1600
F: (785) 296-8909
E: wbider@kdheks.gov

KENTUCKY
Ms. April Webb
Branch Manager
Hazardous Waste Branch
Division of Waste Management
200 Fair Oaks Lane, 2nd Floor
Frankfort, KY 40601
P: (502) 564-6716
F: (502) 564-4049
E: April.Webb@ky.gov

LOUISIANA
Ms. Lourdes Iturralde
Administrator
Public Participation & Permits
Support Services
Department of Environmental
Quality
P.O. Box 4313
Baton Rouge, LA 70821
P: (225) 219-3180
F: (225) 219-3309

Hazardous Waste Management

MARYLAND
Ms. Hilary Miller
Acting Director
Land Management
Administration
Department of the Environment
1800 Washington Boulevard
Baltimore, MD 21230
P: (410) 537-3304
F: (410) 537-3321
E: hilary.miller
@maryland.gov

MASSACHUSETTS
Mr. Martin Suuberg
Commissioner
Department of Environmental
Protection
One Winter Street
Boston, MA 02108
P: (617) 292-5856
F: (617) 574-6880

MICHIGAN
Ms. DeLores Montgomery
Chief
Hazardous Waste Section
525 West Allegan Street
P.O. Box 30473
Lansing, MI 48909
P: (517) 284-6565
F: (517) 373-4797
E: MONTGOMERYD1
@michigan.gov

MINNESOTA
Mr. John Linc Stine
Commissioner
Pollution Control Agency
520 Lafayette Road North, Sixth
Floor
St. Paul, MN 55155
P: (651) 757-2016
F: (651) 296-6334
E: john.stine@state.mn.us

MISSISSIPPI
Mr. Mark Williams
Chief
Solid Waste Policy, Planning &
Grants Branch
515 Amite Street
P.O. Box 2261
Jackson, MS 39225
P: (601) 961-5304
F: (601) 961-5785
E: mark_williams
@deq.state.ms.us

MISSOURI
Mr. David Lamb
Director
Hazardous Waste
P.O. Box 176
Jefferson City, MO 65102
P: (573) 751-3176
F: (573) 751-7869
E: hazwaste@dnr.mo.gov

MONTANA
Mr. Ed Tinsley
Administrator
Department of Disaster &
Emergency Services
P.O. Box 4789
Fort Harrison, MT 59636
P: (406) 324-4777
F: (406) 324-4790
E: edtinsley@mt.gov

NEBRASKA
Mr. Jim Macy
Director
Department of Environmental
Quality
1200 N Street, Suite 400
Lincoln, NE 68508
P: (402) 471-3585
F: (402) 471-2909
E: Jim.Macy@nebraska.gov

NEVADA
Mr. Eric Noack
Bureau Chief
Bureau of Waste Management
Division of Environmental
Protection
901 South Stewart Street, Suite
4001
Carson City, NV 89701
P: (775) 687-9366
F: (775) 687-5856
E: enoack@ndep.nv.gov

NEW HAMPSHIRE
Mr. John Duclos
Bureau Administrator
Hazardous Waste Management
Bureau
29 Hazen Drive
P.O. Box 95
Concord, NH 03301
P: (603) 271-1998
F: (603) 271-0869
E: john.duclos@des.nh.gov

NEW JERSEY
Mr. John Giordano
Assistant Commissioner,
Compliance & Enforcement
Department of Environmental
Protection
P.O. Box 420
Trenton, NJ 08625
P: (609) 984-3285

NEW MEXICO
Mr. John E. Kielng
Chief
Hazardous Waste Bureau
2905 Rodeo Park Drive, East
Building 1
Santa Fe, NM 87505
P: (505) 476-6000
F: (505) 476-6030
E: john.kielng@state.nm.us

NEW YORK
Mr. Joe Martens
Commissioner
Department of Environmental
Conservation
625 Broadway, 14th Floor
Albany, NY 12233
P: (518) 402-8540
F: (518) 402-8541
E: joemartens
@gw.dec.state.ny.us

NORTH CAROLINA
Ms. Julie Woosley
Section Chief for Hazardous
Waste
Department of Environment &
Natural Resources
Division of Waste Management
1646 Mail Service Center
Raleigh, NC 27699
P: (919) 707-8203
F: (919) 715-0708
E: julie.woosley@ncdenr.gov

NORTH DAKOTA
Mr. Scott Radig
Director
Division of Waste Management
Department of Health
918 East Divide Avenue, 3rd
Floor
Bismark, ND 58501
P: (701) 328-5166
F: (701) 328-5200
E: sradig@nd.gov

**NORTHERN MARIANA
ISLANDS**
Mr. Joaquin P. Omar
Deputy Special Assistant for
EMO/OHS
Emergency Management Office
Office of the Governor
Caller Box 10007
Saipan, MP 96950
P: (670) 322-8001
F: (670) 322-7743
E: jpomar@cnmiemo.gov.mp

OHIO
Ms. Pam Allen
Chief
Division of Materials & Waste
Management
50 West Town Street, Suite 700
P.O. Box 1049
Columbus, OH 43216
P: (614) 644-2980
F: (614) 728-5315
E: pam.allen
@epa.state.oh.us

OKLAHOMA
Ms. Kelly Dixon
Division Director
Land Protection Division
Department of Environmental
Quality
P.O. Box 1677
Oklahoma City, OK 73101
P: (405) 702-5100
F: (405) 702-5101
E: kelly.dixon@deq.ok.gov

OREGON
Ms. Wendy Wiles
Land Quality Division
Administrator
Department of Environmental
Quality
811 Southwest 6th Avenue
Portland, OR 97204
P: (503) 229-6834
F: (503) 229-6977
E: wiles.wendy
@deq.state.or.us

PUERTO RICO
Mr. Augustine F. Carbo Lugo
Director
Solid Waste Management
Authority
P.O. Box 40285
San Juan, PR 00918
P: (787) 765-7575
F: (787) 753-2220

Mr. Jose Maeso Gonzalez
Executive Director
Energy Affairs Administration
P.O. Box 41314
San Juan, PR 00940
P: (787) 999-2200 Ext. 2888
F: (787) 999-2246
E: jose.maeso@aae.pr.gov

RHODE ISLAND
Ms. Janet Coit
Director
Department of Environmental
Management
235 Promenade Street, 4th Floor
Providence, RI 02908
P: (401) 222-2771
F: (401) 222-6802
E: janet.coit@dem.ri.gov

SOUTH CAROLINA
Ms. Daphne G. Neel
Bureau Chief
Bureau of Land & Waste
Management
Dept. of Health &
Environmental Control
2600 Bull Street
Columbia, SC 29201
P: (803) 896-4007
F: (803) 896-4001
E: neeldg@dhec.sc.gov

SOUTH DAKOTA
Ms. Carrie Jacobson
Environmental Scientist
Manager
Department of Environment &
Natural Resources
Waste Management Program
523 East Capitol Avenue
Pierre, SD 57501
P: (605) 773-3153
F: (605) 773-6035

TENNESSEE
Mr. Patrick J. Flood
Director
Division of Solid & Hazardous
Waste Management
William R. Snodgrass Tennessee
Tower
312 Rosa L Parks Ave, 14th
Floor
Nashville, TN 37243
P: (615) 532-0780
F: (615) 532-0886

TEXAS
Mr. Earl Lott
Director
Waste Permits Division
12100 Park 35 Circle
P.O. Box 13087
Austin, TX 78711
P: (512) 239-2047
F: (512) 239-0659

U.S. VIRGIN ISLANDS
Mr. David Simon
Director
Division of Environmental
Protection
Cyril E. King Airport
Terminal Building, 2nd Floor
St. Thomas, VI 00802
P: (340) 774-3320
E: david.simon@dpnr.gov.vi

UTAH
Mr. Scott Anderson
Director
Division of Solid & Hazardous
Waste
195 North 1950 West, 2nd Floor
P.O. Box 144880
Salt Lake City, UT 84114
P: (801) 536-0203
F: (801) 536-0222
E: standerson@utah.gov

VERMONT
Mr. Chuck Schwer
Director
Waste Management &
Prevention Division
1 National Life Drive - Davis 1
Montpelier, VT 05620
P: (802) 760-8041
F: (802) 828-1011
E: chuck.schwer@state.vt.us

VIRGINIA
Mr. David K. Paylor
Director
Department of Environmental
Quality
629 East Main Street
Richmond, VA 23219
P: (804) 698-4390
F: (804) 698-4019
E: david.paylor
    @deq.virginia.gov

WASHINGTON
K. Seiler
Program Manager
Hazardous Waste & Toxics
Reduction
300 Desmond Drive
P.O. Box 47600
Olympia, WA 98504
P: (360) 407-6702
F: (360) 407-6715
E: ksei461@ecy.wa.gov

WEST VIRGINIA
Ms. Patty Hickman
Director
Division of Land Restoration
601 57th Street
Charleston, WV 25304
P: (304) 926-0455
F: (304) 926-0457
E: Patricia.A.Hickman
    @wv.gov

WISCONSIN
Mr. Dave Siebert
Enforcement and Science Acting
Division Administrator
Office of Business Support &
Sustainability
P.O. Box 7921
Madison, WI 53707
P: (608) 264-1115
F: (608) 267-2768
E: david.siebert
    @wisconsin.gov

WYOMING
Mr. Luke Esch
Administrator
Solid & Hazardous Waste
Division
Department of Environmental
Quality
122 West 25th Street, Herschler
Building
Cheyenne, WY 82002
P: (307) 777-7192
F: (307) 777-5973
E: luke.esch1@wyo.gov

Health Services

Manages the development, administration and delivery of all health programs.

ALABAMA
Dr. Donald E. Williamson
State Health Officer
Department of Public Health
RSA Tower, 201 Monroe Street
P.O. Box 303017
Montgomery, AL 36130
P: (334) 206-5300
F: (334) 206-5609

ALASKA
Dr. Jay C. Butler
Chief Medical Officer &
Director
Division of Public Health
350 Main Street, Room 404
P.O. Box 110601
Juneau, AK 99811
P: (907) 465-3030
F: (907) 465-3068
E: jay.butler@alaska.gov

AMERICAN SAMOA
Motusa Tuileama Nua
Director
American Samoa Government
LBJ Tropical Medical Center
Pago Pago, AS 96799

ARIZONA
Dr. Cara M. Christ
Director
Department of Health Services
150 North 18th Avenue
Phoenix, AZ 85007
P: (602) 542-1025
F: (602) 542-1062

ARKANSAS
Dr. Nathaniel H. Smith
Director & State Health Officer
Department of Health
4815 West Markham Street
Little Rock, AR 72205
P: (501) 661-2000

CALIFORNIA
Dr. Karen Smith
Director
Department of Public Health
P.O. Box 997377
MS 0500
Sacramento, CA 95899
P: (916) 558-1784

COLORADO
Dr. Larry Wolk
Executive Director & Chief
Medical Officer
Department of Public Health &
Environment
4300 Cherry Creek Drive, South
Denver, CO 80246
P: (303) 692-2000
F: (303) 691-7702

CONNECTICUT
Dr. Jewel Mullen
Commissioner
Department of Public Health
410 Capitol Avenue
P.O. Box 340308
Hartford, CT 06134
P: (860) 509-8000
E: jewel.mullen@ct.gov

DELAWARE
Dr. Karyl T. Rattay
Director
Division of Public Health
Jesse Cooper Building
417 Federal Street
Dover, DE 19901
P: (302) 744-4700
F: (302) 739-6659

DISTRICT OF COLUMBIA
Dr. LaQuandra S. Nesbitt
Director
Department of Health
899 North Capitol Street,
Northeast
Washington, DC 20002
P: (202) 442-5955
F: (202) 442-4795
E: doh@dc.gov

FLORIDA
Dr. John H. Armstrong
State Surgeon General
Department of Health
4052 Bald Cypress Way, Bin #
A00
Tallahassee, FL 32399
P: (850) 245-4321
F: (850) 922-9453
E: Health@doh.state.fl.us

GEORGIA
Dr. Brenda C. Fitzgerald
Commissioner
Division of Public Health,
Department of Community
Health
Two Peachtree Street, Northwest
15th Floor
Atlanta, GA 30303
P: (404) 657-2700

GUAM
Mr. James W. Gillan
Director
Department of Public Health &
Social Services
123 Chalan Kareta
Mangilao, GU 96913
P: (671) 735-7305
F: (671) 734-2066

HAWAII
Dr. Virginia Pressler
Director of Health
State Department of Health
1250 Punchbowl Street
Honolulu, HI 96813
P: (808) 586-4410
F: (808) 586-4444

IDAHO
Ms. Elke Shaw-Tulloch
Public Health Administrator
Division of Public Health
Department of Health and
Welfare
450 West State Street, 4th Floor
Boise, ID 83702
P: (208) 334-6996

ILLINOIS
Dr. Nirav D. Shah
Acting Director of Public Health
Department of Public Health
535 West Jefferson Street, 5th
Floor
Springfield, IL 62761
P: (217) 782-4977
F: (217) 782-3987

INDIANA
Dr. Jerome Adams
State Health Commissioner
Department of Health
2 North Meridian
Indianapolis, IN 46204
P: (317) 233-1325

IOWA
Mr. Gerd W. Clabaugh
Interim Director
Department of Public Health
Lucas State Office Building
321 East 12th Street
Des Moines, IA 50319
P: (515) 281-7689
F: (515) 281-4958
E: gerd.clabaugh
    @idph.iowa.gov

KANSAS
Dr. Susan Mosier
Interim Secretary
Department of Health &
Environment
Curtis State Office Building
1000 Southwest Jackson
Topeka, KS 66612
P: (785) 296-1500
F: (785) 368-6368

KENTUCKY
Dr. Stephanie
    Mayfield Gibson
Commissioner
Department for Public Health
275 East Main Street
Frankfort, KY 40621

LOUISIANA
Mr. John Thomas Lane
Assistant Secretary for Public
Health
Office of Public Health
Department of Health and
Hospitals
P.O. Box 629
Baton Rouge, LA 70821
P: (225) 342-6188
E: jtlane@la.gov

MAINE
Mr. Kenneth J. Albert
Director
State Center for Disease Control
& Prevention
286 Water Street
11 State House Station
Augusta, ME 04333
P: (207) 287-8016
E: Kenneth.Albert@maine.gov

MARYLAND
Mr. Van T. Mitchell
Secretary
Department of Health & Mental
Hygiene
201 West Preston Street
Baltimore, MD 21201
P: (410) 767-6500
F: (410) 767-6489
E: van.mitchell
    @maryland.gov

MASSACHUSETTS
Dr. Monica Bharel
Commissioner
Department of Public Health
250 Washington Street
Boston, MA 02108
P: (617) 624-6000

MICHIGAN
Ms. Susan Moran
Senior Deputy Director, Public
Health Administrator & State
Health Officer
Department of Community
Health
Capitol View Building
201 Townsend Street
Lansing, MI 48913
P: (517) 373-3740
F: (517) 241-3082

MINNESOTA
Dr. Edward Ehlinger
Commissioner of Health
Department of Health
625 North Robert Street
Box 64975
St. Paul, MN 55164
P: (651) 201-5810
F: (651) 201-4986
E: Ed.Ehlinger@state.mn.us

MISSISSIPPI
Dr. Mary Currier
State Health Officer
State Department of Health
570 East Woodrow Wilson
P.O. Box 1700
Jackson, MS 39215
P: (601) 576-7634
E: mary.currier
   @msdh.state.ms.us

MISSOURI
Ms. Gail Vasterling
Director
Department of Health & Senior
Services
912 Wildwood Drive
P.O. Box 570
Jefferson City, MO 65102
P: (573) 751-6001
F: (573) 751-6010
E: info@health.mo.gov

MONTANA
Mr. Richard H. Opper
Director
Department of Public Health &
Human Services
111 North Sanders, Room 301
P.O. Box 4210
Helena, MT 59604
P: (406) 444-5622
F: (406) 444-1970
E: ropper@mt.gov

NEVADA
Dr. Tracey D. Green
State Health Officer
State Health Division
4150 Technology Way
Carson City, NV 89706
P: (775) 684-4200
F: (775) 684-4211
E: health@health.nv.gov

NEW HAMPSHIRE
Ms. Marcella Jordan
   Bobinsky
Acting Director
Division of Public Health
Services
129 Pleasant Street
Concord, NH 03301
P: (603) 271-4501
F: (603) 271-4827

NEW JERSEY
Ms. Mary E. O'Dowd
Commissioner
Department of Health & Senior
Services
P.O. Box 360
Trenton, NJ 08625
P: (609) 292-7837
F: (609) 292-0053

NEW MEXICO
Ms. Retta Ward
Secretary Designate
Department of Health
1190 South St. Francis Drive
P.O. Box 26110
Santa Fe, NM 87502
P: (505) 827-2613
F: (505) 827-2530

NEW YORK
Dr. Howard Zucker
Commissioner
Department of Health
Corning Tower
Empire State Plaza
Albany, NY 12237
P: (518) 474-2011
F: (518) 474-1449

NORTH CAROLINA
Mr. Danny Staley
Acting Director
Division of Public Health
1931 Mail Service Center
Raleigh, NC 27699
P: (919) 707-5000
F: (919) 870-4829

NORTH DAKOTA
Dr. Terry Dwelle
State Health Officer
Department of Health
600 East Boulevard Avenue
Bismarck, ND 58505
P: (701) 328-2372
F: (701) 328-4727
E: tdwelle@nd.gov

NORTHERN MARIANA ISLANDS
Ms. Esther L. Muna
Interim Secretary & CEO
Northern Mariana Islands
P.O. Box 500409 CK
Saipan, MP 96950

OHIO
Mr. Richard Hodges
Director of Health
Department of Health
246 North High Street
Columbus, OH 43215
P: (614) 466-3543
F: (614) 466-5866
E: director@odh.ohio.gov

OKLAHOMA
Dr. Terry L. Cline
Commissioner of Health
Department of Health
1000 Northeast 10th Street
Oklahoma City, OK 73117
P: (405) 271-5600

OREGON
Mr. Lillian M. Shirley
Public Health Director
Public Health Division
State Health Authority
800 Northeast Oregon Street
Portland, OR 97232
P: (971) 673-1222
F: (971) 673-1299

PENNSYLVANIA
Dr. Karen Murphy
Acting Secretary of Health
Department of Health
625 Forster Street, 8th Floor
West
Harrisburg, PA 17120
P: (717) 787-6436

PUERTO RICO
Dr. Ana Ruis
Secretary
Department of Health
P.O. Box 70184
San Juan, PR 00936
P: (787) 765-2929

RHODE ISLAND
Dr. Nicole Alexander-Scott
Director
Department of Health
3 Capitol Hill
Providence, RI 02908
P: (401) 222-5960
F: (401) 222-6548
E: health@ri.gov

SOUTH CAROLINA
Ms. Jamie Shuster
Director of Public Health &
State Health Officer
Department of Health &
Environmental Control
2600 Bull Street
Columbia, SC 29201
P: (803) 898-3432
E: info@dhec.sc.gov

SOUTH DAKOTA
Ms. Kim Malsam-Rysdon
Secretary
Department of Health
600 East Capitol Avenue
Pierre, SD 57501
P: (605) 773-3361
E: kim.malsam-rysdon
   @state.sd.us

TENNESSEE
Dr. John J. Dreyzehner
Commissioner
Department of Health
Andrew Johnson Tower
710 James Robertson Parkway
Nashville, TN 37243
P: (615) 741-3111
F: (615) 741-6230

TEXAS
Mr. Kirk Cole
Associate Commissioner
Department of State Health
Services
1100 West 49th Street
P.O.Box 149347
Austin, TX 78714
P: (512) 776-7375

U.S. VIRGIN ISLANDS
Dr. Phyllis Wallace
Commissioner
Department of Health
Charles Harwood Complex
3500 Richmond
St. Croix, VI 00820

Health Services

UTAH
Dr. W. David Patton
Executive Director
Department of Health
P.O. Box 141010
Salt Lake City, UT 84114
P: (801) 538-6003
F: (801) 538-6306
E: david.patton@utah.gov

VERMONT
Dr. Harry L. Chen
Commissioner of Health
Department of Health
108 Cherry Street
Burlington, VT 05402
P: (802) 863-7200
F: (802) 865-7754
E: hchen@vdh.state.vt.us

VIRGINIA
Dr. Marissa J. Levine
Commissioner of Health
Department of Health
109 Governor Street
P.O. Box 2448
Richmond, VA 23218
P: (804) 864-7026
F: (804) 864-7022
E: Marissa.Levine
   @vdh.virginia.gov

WASHINGTON
Dr. John M. Wiesman
Secretary of Health
Department of Health
P.O. Box 47890
Olympia, WA 98504
P: (360) 236-4030
E: Secretary@doh.wa.gov

WEST VIRGINIA
Dr. Rahul Gupta
Commissioner & State Health
Officer
Bureau for Public Health
350 Capitol Street, Room 702
Charleston, WV 25301
P: (304) 558-2971
F: (304) 558-1035

WISCONSIN
Ms. Karen D. McKeown
Administrator/State Health
Official
Division of Public Health
Department of Health Services
P.O. Box 2659
Madison, WI 53701
P: (608) 266-1251
F: (608) 267-2832

WYOMING
Dr. Wendy E. Braund
State Health Officer
Public Health Division
Department of Health
6101 Yellowstone Road
Cheyenne, WY 82002
P: (307) 777-6340
F: (307) 777-8264

Higher Education

Serves as coordinating and planning agency for state-supported post-secondary education.

Information provided by:

State Higher Education Executive Officers
George Pernsteiner
President
3035 Center Green Drive, Suite 100
Boulder, CO 80301
P: (303) 541-1600
F: (303) 541-1639
www.sheeo.org

ALABAMA
Mr. Gregory G. Fitch
Executive Director
Commission on Higher Education
100 North Union Street
P.O. Box 302000
Montgomery, AL 36130
P: (334) 242-2123
F: (334) 242-0268
E: gregory.fitch
 @ache.alabama.gov

ALASKA
Ms. Diane Barrans
Executive Director
Commission on Postsecondary Education
3030 Vintage Boulevard
Juneau, AK 99801
P: (907) 465-6740
F: (907) 465-3293
E: diane.barrans@alaska.gov

Mr. Patrick K. Gamble
President
University of Alaska System
202 Butrovich
P.O. Box 755000
Fairbanks, AK 99775
P: (907) 450-8009
F: (907) 450-8012
E: ua.president@alaska.edu

ARIZONA
Ms. Eileen Klein
President
Board of Regents
2020 North Central Avenue, Suite 230
Phoenix, AZ 85004
P: (602) 229-2505
F: (602) 229-2555
E: eileen.klein
 @azregents.edu

ARKANSAS
Mr. Brett Powell
Director
Department of Higher Education
423 Main Street, Suite 400
Little Rock, AR 72201
P: (501) 371-2031
F: (501) 371-2003
E: Brett.Powell@adhe.edu

CALIFORNIA
Mr. Timothy P. White
Chancellor
State University System
Office of the Chancellor
401 Golden Shore
Long Beach, CA 90802
P: (562) 951-4000

COLORADO
Hon. Joe Garcia (D)
Lieutenant Governor
Department of Higher Education
130 State Capitol
Denver, CO 80203
P: (303) 866-2087
F: (303) 866-5469
E: josephgarcia
 @state.co.us

CONNECTICUT
Ms. Jane A. Ciarleglio
Executive Director
Office of Higher Education
61 Woodland Street
Hartford, CT 06105
P: (860) 947-1801
F: (860) 947-1311
E: jciarleglio@ctdhe.org

Mr. Gregory W. Gray
President
Board of Regents for Higher Education
39 Woodland Street
Hartford, CT 06105
P: (860) 493-0011
F: (860) 493-0009
E: grayg@ct.edu

DELAWARE
Ms. Shana Payne
Director
Higher Education Office
The Townsend Building
401 Federal Street, Suite 2
Dover, DE 19901
P: (302) 735-4120
F: (302) 739-5894
E: Shana.Payne
 @doe.k12.de.us

DISTRICT OF COLUMBIA
Ms. Antoinette S. Mitchell
Assistant Superintendent, Postsecondary and Career Education
Office of the State Superintendent of Education
810 1st Street Northeast, 9th Floor
Washington, DC 20002
P: (202) 727-6436
E: osse@dc.gov

FLORIDA
Mr. Marshall Criser III
Chancellor
State University System of Board of Governors
325 West Gaines Street, Suite 1614
Tallahassee, FL 32399
P: (850) 245-0466
F: (850) 245-9685
E: Marshall.Criser
 @flbog.edu

GEORGIA
Mr. Henry M. Huckaby
Chancellor
Board of Regents of the University System
270 Washington Street, Southwest
Suite 7025
Atlanta, GA 30334
P: (404) 656-2202
F: (404) 657-6979
E: chancellor@usg.edu

HAWAII
Mr. David Lassner
President
University of Hawaii System
2444 Dole Street, Bachman Hall 202
Honolulu, HI 96822
P: (808) 956-8207
F: (808) 956-5286
E: david@hawaii.edu

IDAHO
Mr. Michael Rush
Executive Director
State Board of Education
650 West State Street, Room 307
Boise, ID 83702
P: (208) 332-1565
F: (208) 334-2632
E: mike.rush@osbe.idaho.gov

ILLINOIS
Mr. James Applegate
Executive Director
Board of Higher Education
1 North Old State Capitol Plaza
Suite 333
Springfield, IL 62701
P: (217) 782-2551
F: (217) 782-8548
E: applegate@ibhe.org

INDIANA
Ms. Teresa S. Lubbers
Commissioner
Commission for Higher Education
101 West Ohio Street, Suite 300
Indianapolis, IN 46204
P: (317) 232-1020
E: tlubbers@che.in.gov

IOWA
Mr. Robert Donley
Executive Director
Board of Regents
11260 Aurora Avenue
Urbandale, IA 50322
P: (515) 281-6426
F: (515) 281-6420
E: bdonley@iastate.edu

KANSAS
Mr. Andy Tompkins
President & CEO
Board of Regents
1000 Southwest Jackson Street, Suite 520
Topeka, KS 66612
P: (785) 296-3421
F: (785) 296-0983
E: atompkins@ksbor.org

KENTUCKY
Mr. Robert L. King
President
Council on Postsecondary Education
1024 Capital Center Drive, Suite 320
Frankfort, KY 40601
P: (502) 573-1652
F: (502) 573-1535
E: robert.king@ky.gov

Higher Education

LOUISIANA
Mr. Joseph Rallo
Commissioner of Higher
Education
Board of Regents
P.O. Box 3677
Baton Rouge, LA 70821
P: (225) 342-4253
F: (225) 342-9318
E: joseph.rallo@la.gov

MAINE
Mr. James H. Page
Chancellor
University of Maine System
16 Central Street
Bangor, ME 04401
P: (207) 973-3205
F: (207) 973-3296
E: jpage@maine.edu

MARYLAND
Ms. Jennie C. Hunter-Cevera
Acting Secretary of Higher
Education
Higher Education Commission
6 North Liberty Street
Baltimore, MD 21201
P: (410) 767-3301
F: (410) 332-0270
E: jennie.hunter-cevera
    @maryland.gov

MASSACHUSETTS
Mr. Richard M. Freeland
Commissioner
Department of Higher Education
One Ashburton Place, Room
1401
Boston, MA 02108
P: (617) 994-6901
F: (617) 727-6397
E: rfreeland@bhe.mass.edu

MINNESOTA
Mr. Lawrence J. Pogemiller
Commissioner
Office of Higher Education
1450 Energy Park Drive, Suite
350
St. Paul, MN 55108
P: (651) 259-3900
F: (651) 642-0597
E: larry.pogemiller
    @state.mn.us

Mr. Steven J. Rosenstone
Chancellor
State Colleges & Universities
Wells Fargo Place
30 7th Street East, Suite 350
St. Paul, MN 55101
P: (651) 201-1696
F: (651) 297-7465
E: steven.rosenstone
    @so.mnscu.edu

MISSISSIPPI
Mr. Glenn Boyce
Commissioner of Higher
Education
State Institutions of Higher
Learning
3825 Ridgewood Road
Jackson, MS 39211
P: (601) 432-6623
E: gboyce@ihl.state.ms.us

MISSOURI
Mr. David R. Russell
Commissioner of Higher
Education
Department of Higher Education
205 Jefferson Street
Jefferson City, MO 65102
P: (573) 751-1876
F: (573) 751-6635
E: David.Russell@dhe.mo.gov

MONTANA
Mr. Clayton Christian
Commissioner of Higher
Education
State University System
2500 Broadway Street
P.O. Box 203201
Helena, MT 59620
P: (406) 444-0374
F: (406) 444-1469
E: cchristian@montana.edu

NEBRASKA
Mr. Michael Baumgartner
Executive Director
Coordinating Commission for
Postsecondary Education
140 North 8th Street, Suite 300
P.O. Box 95005
Lincoln, NE 68509
P: (402) 471-0029
F: (402) 471-2886
E: mike.baumgartner
    @nebraska.gov

NEVADA
Mr. Daniel J. Klaich
Chancellor
State System of Higher
Education
2601 Enterprise Road
Reno, NV 89512
P: (775) 784-3222
F: (775) 784-1127
E: dklaich@nevada.edu

NEW HAMPSHIRE
Mr. Todd Leach
Chancellor
University System
Dunlap Center
25 Concord Road
Durham, NH 03824
P: (603) 862-0963
F: (603) 862-0908
E: todd.leach@usnh.edu

Mr. Edward R. MacKay
Director
Department of Education,
Division of Higher Education,
Higher Education Commission
101 Pleasant Street
Concord,, NH 03301
P: (603) 271-0256
F: (603) 271-1953
E: edward.mackay@doe.nh.gov

NEW JERSEY
Ms. Rochelle Hendricks
Secretary of Higher Education
Office of the Secretary of
Higher Education
P.O. Box 542
Trenton, NJ 08625
P: (609) 292-8052
F: (609) 292-7225
E: rochelle.hendricks
    @njhe.state.nj.us

NEW MEXICO
Ms. Barbara Damron
Cabinet Secretary
Higher Education Department
2044 Galisteo Street, Suite 4
Santa Fe, NM 87505
P: (505) 476-8404
E: Exec.Admin@state.nm.us

NEW YORK
Mr. John D'Agati
Deputy Commissioner
State Education Department
Office of Higher Education
Room 977, Education Building
Annex
Albany, NY 12234
P: (518) 486-3633
F: (518) 486-2254
E: john.dagati@nysed.gov

NORTH CAROLINA
Mr. Thomas W. Ross
President
University of North Carolina
910 Raleigh Road
P.O. Box 2688
Chapel Hill, NC 27514
P: (919) 962-4622
F: (919) 843-9695
E: tomross
    @northcarolina.edu

NORTH DAKOTA
Mr. Larry C. Skogen
Interim Chancellor
State University System
Department 215, 10th Floor
State Capitol
600 East Boulevard Avenue
Bismarck, ND 58505
P: (701) 328-2974
F: (701) 328-2961
E: rebecca.a.duben@ndus.edu

OHIO
Mr. John Carey
Chancellor
State Board of Regents
25 South Front Street
Columbus, OH 43215
P: (614) 466-6000
F: (614) 466-5866
E: chancellor
    @regents.state.oh.us

OKLAHOMA
Mr. Glen D. Johnson Jr.
Chancellor
State Regents for Higher
Education
655 Research Parkway, Suite
200
Oklahoma City, OK 73104
P: (405) 225-9120
F: (405) 225-9235
E: gjohnson@osrhe.edu

OREGON
Mr. Ben Cannon
Executive Director
Higher Education Coordinating
Commission
775 Court Street, Northeast
Salem, OR 97301
P: (503) 947-2379
E: ben.cannon@state.or.us

PENNSYLVANIA
Ms. Theresa Barnaby
Acting Deputy Secretary
Department of Education,
Office of Postsecondary &
Higher Education
333 Market Street
Harrisburg, PA 17126
P: (717) 772-4737
E: tbarnaby@pa.gov

Mr. Frank T. Brogan
Chancellor
State System of Higher
Education
Dixon University Center
2986 North Second Street
Harrisburg, PA 17110
P: (717) 720-4205
F: (717) 720-4011
E: fbrogan@passhe.edu

PUERTO RICO
Mr. David Baez Davila
Acting Executive Director
Council on Education
P.O. Box 19900
San Juan, PR 00910
P: (787) 641-7100
F: (787) 641-2573
E: dbaez@ce.pr.gov

RHODE ISLAND
Mr. Jim Purcell
Commissioner
Office of the Postsecondary
Commissioner
Shepard Building
80 Washington Street
Providence, RI 02903
P: (401) 456-6000
F: (401) 456-6028
E: jim.purcell@ribghe.org

SOUTH CAROLINA
Ms. Julie J. Carullo
Interim Executive Director
Commission on Higher
Education
1122 Lady Street, Suite 300
Columbia, SC 29201
P: (803) 737-2275
F: (803) 737-2297
E: jcarullo@che.sc.gov

SOUTH DAKOTA
Dr. Jack R. Warner
Executive Director & CEO
State Board of Regents
306 East Capitol Avenue, Suite
200
Pierre, SD 57501
P: (605) 773-3455
F: (605) 773-5320
E: jack.warner@sdbor.edu

TENNESSEE
Mr. Russ Deaton
Interim Executive Director
State Higher Education
Commission
404 James Robertson Parkway,
Suite 1900
Nashville, TN 37243
P: (615) 532-3860
F: (615) 741-6230
E: russ.deaton@tn.gov

TEXAS
Dr. Raymund A. Paredes
Commissioner of Higher
Education
State Higher Education
Coordinating Board
1200 East Anderson Lane
P.O. Box 12788
Austin, TX 78752
P: (512) 427-6101
F: (512) 427-6127
E: raymund.paredes
    @thecb.state.tx.us

UTAH
Mr. David L. Buhler
Commissioner of Higher
Education
State System of Higher
Education
Board of Regents Building, Two
Gateway
60 South 400 West
Salt Lake City, UT 84101
P: (801) 321-7162
F: (801) 321-7156
E: dbuhlerl@utahsbr.edu

VERMONT
Mr. Jeb Spaulding
Chancellor
State Colleges
Office of the Chancellor
P.O. Box 7
Montpelier, VT 05601
P: (802) 224-3000
F: (802) 224-3035
E: jeb.spaulding@vsc.edu

Mr. Thomas Sullivan
President
University of Vermont
344-353 Waterman Building
85 South Prospect Street
Burlington, VT 05405
P: (802) 656-7878
F: (802) 656-9220
E: Thomas.Sullivan@uvm.edu

VIRGINIA
Mr. Peter Blake
Director
State Council of Higher
Education
101 North 14th Street
James Monroe Building, 10th
Floor
Richmond, VA 23219
P: (804) 225-2611
F: (804) 225-2908
E: peterblake@schev.edu

WASHINGTON
Mr. Gene Sharratt
Executive Director
State Student Achievement
Council
917 Lakeridge Way, Southwest
Olympia, WA 98502
P: (360) 753-7810
F: (360) 753-7808
E: genes@wsac.wa.gov

WEST VIRGINIA
Mr. Paul L. Hill
Chancellor
State Higher Education Policy
Commission
1018 Kanawha Boulevard East,
Suite 700
Charleston, WV 25301
P: (304) 558-0699
F: (304) 558-1011
E: paul.hill@hepc.wvnet.edu

WISCONSIN
Mr. Ray Cross
President
University of Wisconsin System
1720 Van Hise Hall
1220 Linden Drive
Madison, WI 53706
P: (608) 262-2321
F: (608) 262-3985
E: rcross@uwsa.edu

WYOMING
Mr. Richard McGinity
President
University of Wyoming
Old Main Room 206,
Department 3434
1000 East University Avenue
Laramie, WY 82071
P: (307) 766-4121
F: (307) 766-4126
E: uwpres@uwyo.edu

Dr. James O. Rose
Executive Director
State Community College
Commission
2300 Capitol Avenue, 5th Floor,
Suite B
Cheyenne, WY 82002
P: (307) 777-7763
F: (307) 777-6567
E: jrose@commission.wcc.edu

Historic Preservation

Surveys, restores and preserves structures and/or sites of historical or architectural significance in the state.

ALABAMA
Mr. Frank White
Executive Director & State Historic Preservation Officer
Historical Commission
468 South Perry Street
Montgomery, AL 36130
P: (334) 230-2690
F: (334) 240-3477
E: frank.white
@preserveala.org

ALASKA
Ms. Judith Bittner
State Historic Preservation Officer
Office of History & Archeology
Department of Natural Resources
550 West 7th Avenue, Suite 1310
Anchorage, AK 99501
P: (907) 269-8721
F: (907) 269-8908
E: judy.bittner@alaska.gov

AMERICAN SAMOA
Mr. David J. Herdrich
Historic Preservation Officer
Historic Preservation Office
Executive Offices of the Governor
American Samoa Government
Pago Pago, AS 96799
P: (684) 699-2316
F: (684) 699-2276
E: david_j_herdrich
@samoatelco.com

ARIZONA
Mr. James W. Garrison
State Historic Preservation Officer
State Parks
1300 West Washington
Phoenix, AZ 85007
P: (602) 542-4009
F: (602) 542-4188
E: jgarrison
@azstateparks.gov

ARKANSAS
Ms. Stacy Hurst
Director
Department of Arkansas Heritage
323 Center Street
1500 Tower Building
Little Rock, AR 72201
P: (501) 324-8150
F: (501) 324-9154
E: stacy.hurst
@arkansasheritage.org

CALIFORNIA
Dr. Carol Roland-Nawi
State Historic Preservation Officer
Office of Historic Preservation
Department of Parks & Recreation
1725 23rd Street, Suite 100
Sacramento, CA 95816
P: (916) 445-7000
F: (916) 445-7053
E: carol.roland-nawi
@parks.ca.gov

COLORADO
Mr. Edward C. Nichols
President & CEO, State Historic Preservation Officer
History Colorado
1200 Broadway
Denver, CO 80203
P: (303) 866-3355
F: (303) 866-4464
E: Ed.Nichols@state.co.us

CONNECTICUT
Mr. Daniel Forrest
Director of Arts & Historic Preservation & State Historic Preservation Officer
Department of Economic & Community Development
One Constitution Plaza, 2nd Floor
Hartford, CT 06103
P: (860) 256-2761
F: (860) 256-2811
E: Daniel.Forrest@ct.gov

DELAWARE
Mr. Timothy A. Slavin
Director
Division of Historical & Cultural Affairs
21 The Green
Dover, DE 19901
P: (302) 736-7400
F: (302) 739-5660
E: timothy.slavin
@state.de.us

DISTRICT OF COLUMBIA
Mr. David Maloney
State Historic Preservation Officer
Historic Preservation Office
1100 4th Street, Southwest, Suite E650
Washington, DC 20024
P: (202) 442-7600
F: (202) 442-7638
E: historic.preservation
@dc.gov

FLORIDA
Mr. Robert Bendus
State Historic Preservation Officer & Director
Division of Historical Resources
R.A. Gray Building
500 South Bronough Street
Tallahassee, FL 32399
P: (850) 245-6300
F: (850) 245-6436
E: robert.bendus
@dos.myflorida.com

GEORGIA
Mr. Mark Williams
Commissioner
Department of Natural Resources
2 Martin Luther King Jr. Drive Southeast
Suite 1252, East Tower
Atlanta, GA 30334
P: (404) 656-3500
F: (404) 656-0770

GUAM
Ms. Lynda Bordallo Aguon
State Historic Preservation Officer
Historic Preservation Office
Department of Parks & Recreation
490 Chalan Palasyo
Agana Heights, GU 96910
P: (671) 475-6294
F: (671) 477-2822
E: lynda.aguon@dpr.guam.gov

HAWAII
Mr. William J. Aila Jr.
Chairperson
Department of Land & Natural Resources
1151 Punchbowl Street, Room 130
Honolulu, HI 96813
P: (808) 587-0400
F: (808) 587-0390
E: dlnr@hawaii.gov

IDAHO
Ms. Janet Gallimore
Executive Director & State Historic Preservation Officer
State Historical Society
2205 Old Penitentiary Road
Boise, ID 83712
P: (208) 334-2682
E: Janet.Gallimore
@ishs.idaho.gov

ILLINOIS
Ms. Amy Martin
Historic Preservation Director
Historic Preservation Agency
313 South Sixth
Springfield, IL 62701
P: (217) 785-7930
F: (217) 524-7525
E: Amy.Martin@illinois.gov

INDIANA
Mr. Mitch Zoll Jr.
Division Director
Historic Preservation & Archaeology
Department of Natural Resources
402 West Washington Street, W274
Indianapolis, IN 46204
P: (317) 232-3492
F: (317) 232-0693
E: mzoll@dnr.in.gov

IOWA
Mr. Steve King
Deputy State Historic Preservation Officer
Historic Preservation Office
Capitol Complex
East 6th and Locust Street
Des Moines, IA 50319
P: (515) 281-4013
E: Steve.King@iowa.gov

KANSAS
Ms. Jennie Chinn
State Historic Preservation Officer & Executive Director
State Historical Society
6425 Southwest 6th Avenue
Topeka, KS 66615
P: (785) 272-8681 Ext. 205
F: (785) 272-8682
E: jchinn@kshs.org

KENTUCKY
Mr. Craig Potts
Executive Director & State Historic Preservation Officer
State Heritage Council
300 Washington Street
Frankfort, KY 40601
P: (502) 564-7005
F: (502) 564-5820
E: craig.potts@ky.gov

Historic Preservation

LOUISIANA
Ms. Pam Breaux
Assistant Secretary
Office of Cultural Development
P.O. Box 44247
Baton Rouge, LA 70804
P: (225) 342-8160
F: (225) 219-9772
E: pbreaux@crt.la.gov

MAINE
Mr. Earle G.
    Shettleworth Jr.
State Historian
Historic Preservation
Commission
55 Capitol Street
Augusta, ME 04333
P: (207) 287-2132
F: (207) 287-2335
E: earle.shettleworth
    @maine.gov

MARYLAND
Mr. J. Rodney Little
Director & State Historic
Preservation Officer
State Historical Trust
Department of Planning
100 Community Place
Crownsville, MD 21032
P: (410) 514-7601
F: (410) 514-7678
E: rodney.little
    @maryland.gov

MASSACHUSETTS
Ms. Brona Simon
State Historic Preservation
Officer & Executive Director
Historical Commission
220 Morrissey Boulevard
Boston, MA 02125
P: (617) 727-8470
F: (617) 727-5128
E: Brona.Simon@state.ma.us

MICHIGAN
Mr. Brian D. Conway
State Historic Preservation
Officer
State Housing Development
Authority
735 East Michigan Avenue
P.O. Box 30044
Lansing, MI 48909
P: (517) 373-1630
F: (517) 335-0348
E: conwayb1@michigan.gov

MINNESOTA
Mr. D. Stephen Elliot
Director
State Historical Society
345 West Kellogg Boulevard
St. Paul, MN 55102
P: (651) 259-3100
F: (651) 296-1004
E: director@mnhs.org

MISSISSIPPI
Ms. Katherine Blount
Executive Director
Department of Archives &
History
200 North Street
P.O. Box 571
Jackson, MS 39205
P: (601) 576-6850
F: (601) 576-6964
E: blount@mdah.state.ms.us

MISSOURI
Ms. Sara Parker Pauley
Director
Department of Natural
Resources
P.O. Box 176
Jefferson City, MO 65102
P: (573) 751-3443
F: (573) 751-7627
E: sara.pauley@ded.mo.gov

MONTANA
Dr. Mark F. Baumler
State Historic Preservation
Officer
State Historic Preservation
Office
1410 8th Avenue
P.O. Box 201202
Helena, MT 59620
P: (406) 444-7717
F: (406) 444-2696
E: mbaumler@mt.gov

NEBRASKA
Mr. Michael Smith
Director & State Historic
Preservation Officer
State Historical Society
1500 R Street
P.O. Box 82554
Lincoln, NE 68501
P: (402) 471-4745
F: (402) 471-3100
E: michael.smith
    @nebraska.gov

NEVADA
Ms. Rebecca Palmer
State Historic Preservation
Officer
Historic Preservation Office
901 South Stewart Street, Suite
5004
Carson City, NV 89701
P: (775) 684-3448
F: (775) 684-3442
E: rpalmer@shpo.nv.gov

NEW MEXICO
Dr. Jeff Pappas
Director & State Historic
Preservation Officer
Historic Preservation Division
Department of Cultural Affairs
407 Galisteo Street, Suite 236
Santa Fe, NM 87501
P: (505) 827-6320
F: (505) 827-6338
E: jeff.pappas@state.nm.us

NEW YORK
Ms. Rose Harvey
State Historic Preservation
Officer & Commissioner
Office of Parks, Recreation &
Historic Preservation
Empire State Plaza
Albany, NY 12238
P: (518) 474-0443
F: (518) 474-4492

NORTH CAROLINA
Dr. Kevin Cherry
Director of Archives & Records
Office of Archives & History
109 East Jones Street
4614 Mail Service Center
Raleigh, NC 27699
F: (919) 715-7274
E: kevin.cherry@ncdcr.gov

NORTH DAKOTA
Ms. Claudia Berg
State Historical Preservation
Officer
State Historical Society
612 East Boulevard Avenue
Bismarck, ND 58505
P: (701) 328-2666
F: (701) 328-3710
E: cberg@nd.gov

**NORTHERN MARIANA
ISLANDS**
Ms. Laura T. Ogumoro
Secretary
Department of Community &
Cultural Affairs
1341 Ascension Court
Caller Box 10007
Saipan, MP 96950
P: (670) 664-2120
F: (670) 664-2139
E: laura.ogumoro@gov.mp

OHIO
Ms. Amanda Schraner Terrell
Director
Historic Preservation Office
Historical Society
800 East 17th Avenue
Columbus, OH 43211
P: (614) 298-2002
F: (614) 298-2037
E: aterrell@ohiohistory.org

OKLAHOMA
Dr. Bob L. Blackburn
Executive Director
Historical Society
History Center
800 Nazih Zuhdi Drive
Oklahoma City, OK 73105
P: (405) 521-6249
F: (405) 522-0816
E: bblackburn@okhistory.org

OREGON
Ms. Lisa Van Laanen
Director
Parks & Recreation Department
725 Summer Street, Northeast,
Suite C
Salem, OR 97301
P: (503) 986-0719
F: (503) 986-0794
E: lisa.vanlaanen
    @state.or.us

PENNSYLVANIA
Ms. Serena Bellew
Bureau Director & State Historic
Preservation Officer
Bureau for Historic Preservation
Commonwealth Keystone
Building
400 North Street, 2nd Floor
Harrisburg, PA 17120
P: (717) 705-4035
F: (717) 772-0920
E: sbellew@pa.gov

Historic Preservation

PUERTO RICO
Ms. Diana Lopez Sotomayor
State Historic Preservation
Officer
State Historic Preservation
Office
P.O. Box 9023935
San Juan, PR 00902
P: (787) 721-3737
F: (787) 721-3773
E: dlopez
    @prshpo.gobierno.pr

RHODE ISLAND
Mr. Edward F. Sanderson
Executive Director & State
Historic Preservation Officer
Historical Preservation &
Heritage Commission
Old State House
150 Benefit Street
Providence, RI 02903
P: (401) 222-4130
F: (401) 222-2968
E: Edward.Sanderson
    @preservation.ri.gov

SOUTH CAROLINA
Mr. Eric Emerson
Director
Department of Archives &
History
8301 Parklane Road
Columbia, SC 29223
P: (803) 896-6187
F: (803) 896-6167
E: eemerson
    @scdah.state.sc.us

SOUTH DAKOTA
Mr. Jay D. Vogt
Director
State Historical Society
900 Governors Drive
Pierre, SD 57501
P: (605) 773-3458
F: (605) 773-6041
E: jay.vogt@state.sd.us

TENNESSEE
Mr. Patrick McIntyre Jr.
Executive Director & State
Historic Preservation Officer
State Historical Commission
2941 Lebanon Road
Nashville, TN 37243
P: (615) 532-1550
F: (615) 532-1549
E: patrick.mcintyre@tn.gov

TEXAS
Mr. Mark S. Wolfe
Executive Director
State Historical Commission
1511 Colorado Street
P.O. Box 12276
Austin, TX 78711
P: (512) 936-4323
F: (512) 475-4872
E: mark.wolfe
    @thc.state.tx.us

U.S. VIRGIN ISLANDS
Mr. Jean-Pierre Oriol
Acting State Historic
Preservation Officer
Department of Planning &
Natural Resources
Cyril E. King Airport
Terminal Building, 2nd Floor
St. Thomas, VI 00802
P: (340) 776-8605
F: (340) 776-7236
E: jp.oriol@dpnr.vi.gov

UTAH
Mr. Brad Westwood
Director
Division of State History
300 South Rio Grande Street
Salt Lake City, UT 84101
P: (801) 245-7248
F: (801) 533-3503
E: bradwestwood@utah.gov

VERMONT
Ms. Noelle MacKay
Commissioner
Department of Housing &
Community Development
1 National Life Drive, 6th Floor
Montpelier, VT 05620
P: (802) 828-5216
F: (802) 828-3258
E: noelle.mackay
    @state.vt.us

VIRGINIA
Ms. Julie Langan
State Historic Preservation
Officer
Department of Historic
Resources
2801 Kensington Avenue
Richmond, VA 23221
P: (804) 367-2323
F: (804) 367-2391
E: julie.langan
    @dhr.virginia.gov

WASHINGTON
Dr. Allyson Brooks
State Historic Preservation
Officer
Department of Archaeology &
Historic Preservation
1063 South Capitol Way, Suite
106
P.O. Box 48343
Olympia, WA 98504
P: (360) 586-3066
F: (360) 586-3067
E: allyson.brooks
    @dahp.wa.gov

WEST VIRGINIA
Mr. Randall Reid-Smith
State Historic Preservation
Officer
Division of Culture & History
Historic Preservation Office
1900 Kanawha Boulevard East
Charleston, WV 25305
P: (304) 558-0220
F: (304) 558-2779

WISCONSIN
Mr. Jim Draeger
State Historic Preservation
Officer
State Historical Society
816 State Street
Madison, WI 53706
P: (608) 264-6511
F: (608) 264-6504
E: jim.draeger
    @wisconsinhistory.org

WYOMING
Ms. Mary Hopkins
State Historic Preservation
Officer
State Historic Preservation
Office
2301 Central Avenue, 3rd Floor
Cheyenne, WY 82002
P: (307) 777-7697
F: (307) 777-6421
E: hopkins@uwyo.edu

Housing Finance

Administers the state's housing assistance programs, provides low and moderate income housing by financing low interest loans.

ALABAMA
Mr. Robert Strickland
Executive Director
Housing Finance Authority
7460 Halcyon Pointe Drive,
Suite 200
P.O. Box 242967
Montgomery, AL 36124
P: (334) 244-9200
F: (334) 244-9214
E: rstrickland@ahfa.com

ALASKA
Mr. Bryan Butcher
Executive Director/CEO
Housing Finance Corporation
4300 Boniface Parkway
P.O. Box 101020
Anchorage, AK 99510
P: (907) 330-8452
F: (907) 338-9218
E: bbutcher@ahfc.us

AMERICAN SAMOA
Hon. Lolo Matalasi
    Moliga (I)
Governor
Development Bank of American
Samoa
Executive Office Building,
Third Floor
Utulei
Pago Pago, AS 96799
P: (684) 633-4116
F: (684) 633-2269

ARIZONA
Mr. Michael Trailor
Director
Department of Housing
1110 West Washington #310
Phoenix, AZ 85001
P: (602) 771-1007
F: (602) 771-1002
E: michael.trailor
    @azhousing.gov

ARKANSAS
Mr. Aaron Burkes
President
Development Finance Authority
900 West Capitol, Suite 310
P.O. Box 8023
Little Rock, AR 72203
P: (501) 682-3339
F: (501) 682-5939
E: aaron.burkes
    @adfa.arkansas.gov

CALIFORNIA
Ms. Tia Boatman Patterson
Executive Director
Housing Finance Agency
500 Capitol Mall, Suite 1400
P.O. Box 4034
Sacramento, CA 95812
P: (916) 326-8000
F: (916) 324-8640

COLORADO
Mr. Cris A. White
Executive Director/CEO
Housing & Finance Authority
1981 Blake Street
Denver, CO 80202
P: (303) 297-7302
E: cwhite@chfainfo.com

CONNECTICUT
Ms. Evonne M. Klein
Chair
Housing Finance Authority
999 West Street
Rocky Hill, CT 06067
P: (860) 721-9501

DELAWARE
Mr. Anas Ben Addi
Director
State Housing Authority
18 The Green
Dover, DE 19901
P: (302) 739-4263
F: (302) 739-6122

DISTRICT OF COLUMBIA
Ms. Maria K. Day-Marshall
Interim Director
Department of Housing &
Community Development
1800 Martin Luther King Jr.
Avenue
Southeast
Washington, DC 20020
P: (202) 442-7200
F: (202) 645-6727
E: dhcd@dc.gov

FLORIDA
Mr. Stephen P. Auger
Housing Executive Director
Housing Finance Corporation
227 North Bronough Street
Suite 5000
Tallahassee, FL 32301
P: (850) 488-4197
F: (850) 488-9809
E: stephen.auger
    @floridahousing.org

GEORGIA
Ms. Carmen Chubb
Deputy Commissioner
Housing Finance Division
60 Executive Park South,
Northeast
Atlanta, GA 30329
P: (404) 679-0607
F: (404) 679-4837
E: carmen.chubb@dca.ga.gov

GUAM
Mr. Michael T. Duenas
Executive Director
Housing & Urban Renewal
Authority
117 Bien Venida Avenue
Sinajana, GU 96910
P: (671) 477-9851
F: (671) 300-7565
E: mjduenas@ghura.org

HAWAII
Mr. Craig K. Hirai
Executive Director
Housing Finance &
Development Corporation
677 Queen Street
Honolulu, HI 96813
P: (808) 587-0597
F: (808) 587-3416

IDAHO
Mr. Gerald M. Hunter
Executive Director
Housing & Finance Association
565 West Myrtle
P.O. Box 7899
Boise, ID 83707
P: (208) 331-4889
F: (208) 331-4804
E: geraldh@ihfa.org

ILLINOIS
Ms. Mary Kenney
Executive Director
Housing Development Authority
401 North Michigan Avenue,
Suite 700
Chicago, IL 60611
P: (312) 836-5200
F: (312) 832-2170
E: mkenney@IHDA.org

INDIANA
Mr. Jacob Sipe
Executive Director
Housing & Community
Development Authority
30 South Meridian Street, Suite
1000
Indianapolis, IN 46204
P: (317) 232-7777
F: (317) 232-7778
E: jsipe@ihcda.in.gov

IOWA
Mr. Dave Jamison
Executive Director
Finance Authority
2015 Grand Avenue
Des Moines, IA 50312
P: (515) 725-4977
F: (515) 725-4901
E: dave.jamison@iowa.gov

KANSAS
Mr. Dennis L. Mesa
Executive Director
Housing Resources Corporation
611 South Kansas Avenue, Suite
300
Topeka, KS 66603
P: (785) 217-2001
F: (785) 232-8084
E: dmesa@kshousingcorp.org

KENTUCKY
Ms. J. Kathryn Peters
Executive Director
Housing Corporation
1231 Louisville Road
Frankfort, KY 40601
P: (502) 564-7630 Ext. 299
F: (502) 564-5708
E: kpeters@kyhousing.org

LOUISIANA
Ms. Michelle Thomas
Chief Administrative Officer
Housing Corporation
2415 Quail Drive
Baton Rouge, LA 70808
P: (225) 763-8700
F: (225) 763-8710

MAINE
Mr. John Gallagher
Director
State Housing Authority
353 Water Street
Augusta, ME 04330
P: (207) 626-4600
F: (207) 626-4678
E: jgallagher
    @mainehousing.org

Housing Finance

MARYLAND
Mr. Kenneth C. Holt
Acting Secretary
Department of Housing &
Community Development
100 Community Place
Crownsville, MD 21032
P: (410) 514-7001
F: (410) 987-4070
E: kenneth.holt
   @maryland.gov

MASSACHUSETTS
Mr. Thomas R. Gleason
Executive Director
MassHousing
One Beacon Street
Boston, MA 02108
P: (617) 854-1000
F: (617) 854-1029

MICHIGAN
Mr. Kevin Elsenheimer
Executive Director
State Housing Development
Authority
735 East Michigan Avenue
P.O. Box 30044
Lansing, MI 48909
P: (517) 373-8370
F: (517) 335-4797

MINNESOTA
Ms. Mary Tingerthal
Commissioner
Housing Finance Agency
400 Sibley Street, Suite 300
St. Paul, MN 55101
P: (651) 296-5738
F: (651) 296-8139
E: Mary.Tingerthal
   @state.mn.us

MISSISSIPPI
Mr. Scott Spivey
Executive Director
Home Corporation
735 Riverside Drive
Jackson, MS 39202
P: (601) 718-4642
F: (601) 718-4643
E: scott.spivey@mshc.com

MISSOURI
Mr. Kip Stetzler
Executive Director
Housing Development
Commission
3435 Broadway Street
Kansas City, MO 64111
P: (816) 759-6600
F: (816) 759-6608

MONTANA
Ms. Meg O'Leary
Director
Department of Commerce
301 South Park Avenue
P.O. Box 200501
Helena, MT 59620
P: (406) 841-2700
F: (406) 841-2701

NEBRASKA
Ms. Brenda Hicks-Sorensen
Director
Department of Economic
Development
550 South 16th Street
Lincoln, NE 68508
P: (402) 471-3125
E: brenda.hicks-sorensen
   @nebraska.gov

NEVADA
Mr. C.J. Manthe
Administrator
Housing Division
1535 Old Hot Springs Road, #50
Carson City, NV 89706
P: (775) 687-2040
F: (775) 687-4040
E: cjmanthe@housing.nv.gov

NEW HAMPSHIRE
Mr. Dean J. Christon
Executive Director
Housing Finance Authority
P.O. Box 5087
Bedford, NH 03108
P: (603) 472-8623
F: (603) 472-2663
E: dean.christon@nhhfa.org

NEW JERSEY
Mr. Anthony L. Marchetta
Executive Director
Housing & Mortgage Finance
Agency
637 South Clinton Avenue
P.O. Box 18550
Trenton, NJ 08650
P: (609) 278-7400
F: (609) 278-1754

NEW MEXICO
Mr. Jay Czar
Executive Director
Mortgage Finance Authority
334 Fourth Street Southwest
Albuquerque, NM 87102
P: (505) 843-6880
F: (505) 243-3289
E: jczar@housingnm.org

NEW YORK
Mr. Darryl C. Towns
Commissioner/CEO
State Homes & Community
Renewal
641 Lexington Avenue, 4th
Floor
New York, NY 10022
P: (212) 688-4000
F: (518) 872-0789

NORTH CAROLINA
Mr. Bob Kucab
Executive Director
Housing Finance Agency
3508 Bush Street
P.O. Box 28066
Raleigh, NC 27611
P: (919) 877-5700
F: (919) 877-5701
E: arkucab@nchfa.com

NORTH DAKOTA
Ms. Jolene Kline
Executive Director
Housing Finance Agency
2624 Vermont Avenue
P.O. Box 1535
Bismarck, ND 58502
P: (701) 328-8072
F: (701) 328-8090
E: jkline@ndhfa.org

**NORTHERN MARIANA
ISLANDS**
Mr. Jesse S. Palacios
Corporate Director
Housing Corporation
P.O. Box 500514
Saipan, MP 96950
P: (670) 234-6866
F: (670) 234-7144
E: jspalacios@nmhc.gov.mp

OHIO
Mr. Douglas A. Garver
Executive Director
Housing Finance Agency
57 East Main Street
Columbus, OH 43215
P: (614) 466-8050
E: dgarver@ohiohome.org

OKLAHOMA
Mr. Dennis Shockley
Executive Director
Housing Finance Agency
100 Northwest 63rd Street, Suite
200
P.O. Box 26720
Oklahoma City, OK 73126
P: (405) 848-1144
F: (405) 840-1109

OREGON
Ms. Margaret S. Van Vliet
Director
Housing & Community Services
725 Summer Street, Northeast,
Suite B
Salem, OR 97301
P: (503) 986-2005
F: (503) 986-2020

PENNSYLVANIA
Mr. Brian A. Hudson Sr.
Executive Director & CEO
Housing Finance Agency
211 North Front Street
P.O. Box 8029
Harrisburg, PA 17105
P: (717) 780-3911
F: (717) 780-1865
E: bhudson@phfa.org

PUERTO RICO
Mr. Jose A. Sierra-Morales
Executive Director
Housing Finance Authority
P.O. Box 71361
San Juan, PR 00936
P: (787) 765-7577
F: (787) 620-3521

RHODE ISLAND
Ms. Barbara Fields
Executive Director
Rhode Island Housing
44 Washington Street
Providence, RI 02903
P: (401) 457-1234
F: (401) 222-2803
E: bfields
   @rhodeislandhousing.org

SOUTH CAROLINA
Ms. Valarie Williams
Executive Director
State Housing Finance &
Development Authority
300-C Outlet Point Boulevard
Columbia, SC 29210
P: (803) 896-9006
F: (803) 551-4876
E: Valarie.Williams
   @schousing.com

SOUTH DAKOTA
Mr. Mark Lauseng
Executive Director
Housing Development Authority
3060 East Elizabeth Street
P.O. Box 1237
Pierre, SD 57501
P: (605) 773-3181
F: (605) 773-5154
E: mark@sdhda.org

TENNESSEE
Mr. Ralph Perrey
Executive Director
Housing Development Agency
404 James Robertson Parkway,
Suite 1200
Nashville, TN 37243
P: (615) 815-2015
F: (615) 564-2700
E: rperrey@thda.org

TEXAS
Mr. Tim Irvine
Executive Director
Department of Housing &
Community Affairs
221 East 11th Street
P.O. Box 13941
Austin, TX 78711
P: (512) 475-3800
F: (512) 469-9606
E: tim.irvine
    @tdhca.state.tx.us

U.S. VIRGIN ISLANDS
Ms. Adrienne L. Williams
Executive Director
Housing Finance Authority
3202 Demarara Plaza, Suite 200
St. Thomas, VI 00802
P: (340) 777-4432
F: (340) 775-7913
E: inquiries@vihfa.gov

UTAH
Mr. Grant S. Whitaker
President & CEO
Housing Corporation
2479 South Lake Park
Boulevard
West Valley City, UT 84120
P: (801) 902-8290
F: (801) 902-8325
E: gwhitaker@uthc.org

VERMONT
Ms. Sarah E. Carpenter
Executive Director
Housing Finance Agency
164 St. Paul Street
P.O. Box 408
Burlington, VT 05402
P: (802) 652-3421
F: (802) 864-5746
E: scarpenter@vhfa.org

VIRGINIA
Ms. Susan F. Dewey
Executive Director
Housing Development Authority
600 South Belvidere Street
Richmond, VA 23230
P: (804) 343-5701
F: (804) 783-6704
E: susan.dewey@vhda.com

Mr. William C. Shelton
Director
Department of Housing &
Community Development
The Jackson Center
501 North 2nd Street
Richmond, VA 23219
P: (804) 371-7002
F: (804) 371-6524
E: bill.shelton
    @dhcd.virginia.gov

WASHINGTON
Mr. Kim Herman
Executive Director
Housing Finance Commission
1000 2nd Avenue, Suite 2700
Seattle, WA 98104
P: (206) 464-7139
F: (206) 587-5113
E: askus@wshfc.org

WEST VIRGINIA
Ms. Erica L. Boggess
Acting Executive Director
Housing Development Fund
5710 MacCorkle Avenue,
Southeast
Charleston, WV 25304
P: (304) 391-8600

WISCONSIN
Mr. Wyman B. Winston
Executive Director
Housing & Economic
Development Authority
201 West Washington Avenue,
Suite 700
P.O. Box 1728
Madison, WI 53703
P: (608) 266-2893
F: (608) 267-1099
E: wyman.winston@wheda.com

WYOMING
Mr. Dave Haney
Executive Director
Community Development
Authority
P.O. Box 634
Casper, WY 82601
P: (307) 265-0603
F: (307) 266-5414
E: haney@wyomingcda.com

Human Services

Manages the development, administration, and delivery of all human and social service programs.

ALABAMA
Ms. Nancy T. Buckner
Commissioner
Department of Human Resources
Gordon Persons Building, Suite 2104
50 North Ripley Street
Montgomery, AL 36130
P: (334) 242-1310
F: (334) 353-1115
E: Nancy.Buckner
   @dhr.alabama.gov

ALASKA
Ms. Valerie Davidson
Commissioner
Department of Health & Social Services
350 Main Street, Room 404
P.O. Box 110601
Juneau, AK 99811
P: (907) 465-3030
F: (907) 465-3068
E: valerie.davidson
   @alaska.gov

AMERICAN SAMOA
Dr. Taeaoafua Meki Solomona
Director
Department of Human & Social Services
P.O. Box 997534
Pago Pago, AS 96799
P: (684) 633-1664
F: (684) 633-7449
E: mtsolomona@dhss.as

ARKANSAS
Mr. John Selig
Director
Department of Human Services
Donaghey Plaza, 7th and Main Streets
Little Rock, AR 72203
P: (501) 682-8648
F: (501) 682-6836
E: John.Selig
   @dhs.arkansas.gov

CALIFORNIA
Ms. Diana S. Dooley
Secretary
Health & Human Services Agency
1600 Ninth Street, Room 460
Sacramento, CA 95814
P: (916) 654-3454
F: (916) 654-3343

COLORADO
Mr. Reginald L. Bicha
Executive Director
Department of Human Services
1575 Sherman Street
Denver, CO 80203
P: (303) 866-3475
F: (303) 866-2606
E: reggie.bicha@state.co.us

CONNECTICUT
Mr. Roderick L. Bremby
Commissioner
Department of Social Services
55 Farmington Avenue
Hartford, CT 06105
P: (860) 424-5024
E: commis.dss@ct.gov

DELAWARE
Ms. Rita M. Landgraf
Secretary
Department of Health & Social Services
Main Building
1901 North DuPont Highway
New Castle, DE 19720
P: (302) 255-9040
F: (302) 255-4429

DISTRICT OF COLUMBIA
Mr. David A. Berns
Director
Department of Human Services
64 New York Avenue, Northeast
6th Floor
Washington, DC 20002
P: (202) 671-4200
F: (202) 671-4326
E: dhs@dc.gov

FLORIDA
Mr. Mike Carroll
Secretary
Department of Children & Families
1317 Winewood Boulevard
Building 1, Room 202
Tallahassee, FL 32399
P: (850) 487-1111
F: (850) 922-2993
E: mike_carroll
   @dcf.state.fl.us

GEORGIA
Mr. Keith Horton
Commissioner
Department of Human Services
2 Peachtree Street, Northwest
Suite 29-250
Atlanta, GA 30303
P: (404) 656-5680
F: (404) 651-8669

HAWAII
Ms. Patricia McManaman
Director
Department of Human Services
1390 Miller Street, Room 209
P.O. Box 339
Honolulu, HI 96809
P: (808) 586-4997
F: (808) 586-4890
E: dhs@dhs.hawaii.gov

IDAHO
Mr. Richard Armstrong
Director
Department of Health & Welfare
P.O. Box 83720
Boise, ID 83720
P: (208) 334-5500
F: (208) 334-6558
E: armstrongr@dhw.idaho.gov

ILLINOIS
Ms. Michelle R.B. Saddler
Secretary
Department of Human Services
100 South Grand Avenue
Harris Building, Third Floor
Springfield, IL 62762
P: (217) 557-1601
F: (217) 557-1647

INDIANA
Mr. Lance Rhodes
Director of Family Resources
Family & Social Services Administration
402 West Washington Street, Room W392
P.O. Box 7083
Indianapolis, IN 46207
P: (317) 234-2373
F: (317) 232-4490
E: Lance.Rhodes@fssa.IN.gov

IOWA
Mr. Charles M. Palmer
Director
Department of Human Services
Hoover State Office Building
1305 East Walnut Street
Des Moines, IA 50319
P: (515) 281-5452
F: (515) 281-4980
E: cpalmer1@dhs.state.ia.us

KANSAS
Ms. Phyllis Gilmore
Secretary
Department for Children & Families
915 Southwest Harrison Street
Topeka, KS 66612
P: (785) 296-3274
F: (785) 296-2173

KENTUCKY
Ms. Audrey Tayse Haynes
Secretary
Cabinet for Health & Family Services
275 East Main Street, 5W-A
Frankfort, KY 40621
P: (502) 564-7042
F: (502) 564-7091

LOUISIANA
Ms. Suzy Sonnier
Secretary
Department of Children & Family Services
P.O. Box 3776
Baton Rouge, LA 70821
P: (225) 342-0286
F: (225) 342-8636
E: Suzy.Sonnier@dcfs.la.gov

MAINE
Ms. Mary Mayhew
Commissioner
Department of Health & Human Services
221 State Street
Augusta, ME 04333
P: (207) 287-3707
F: (207) 287-3005
E: mary.mayhew@maine.gov

MARYLAND
Mr. Sam Malhotra
Secretary
Department of Human Resources
311 West Saratoga Street
Baltimore, MD 21201
P: (410) 767-7109
F: (410) 333-0099
E: sam.malhotra
   @maryland.gov

MASSACHUSETTS
Mr. John Polanowicz
Secretary
Executive Office of Health & Human Services
One Ashburton Place, 11th Floor
Boston, MA 02108
P: (617) 573-1600
F: (617) 727-5134

Human Services

MICHIGAN
Ms. Maura D. Corrigan
Director
Department of Human Services
235 South Grand Avenue
P.O. Box 30037
Lansing, MI 48909
P: (313) 456-4887
F: (517) 335-6101
E: dhsweb@michigan.gov

MISSISSIPPI
Mr. Rickey Berry
Executive Director
Department of Human Services
750 North State Street
Jackson, MS 39202
P: (601) 359-4457

Dr. Mary Currier
State Health Officer
State Department of Health
570 East Woodrow Wilson
P.O. Box 1700
Jackson, MS 39215
P: (601) 576-7634
E: mary.currier
 @msdh.state.ms.us

MISSOURI
Ms. Gail Vasterling
Director
Department of Health & Senior
Services
912 Wildwood Drive
P.O. Box 570
Jefferson City, MO 65102
P: (573) 751-6001
F: (573) 751-6010
E: info@health.mo.gov

MONTANA
Mr. Richard H. Opper
Director
Department of Public Health &
Human Services
111 North Sanders, Room 301
P.O. Box 4210
Helena, MT 59604
P: (406) 444-5622
F: (406) 444-1970
E: ropper@mt.gov

NEW HAMPSHIRE
Mr. Nicholas A. Toumpas
Commissioner
Department of Health & Human
Services
129 Pleasant Street
Concord, NH 03301
P: (603) 271-9200
F: (603) 271-4912
E: ntoumpas
 @dhhs.state.nh.us

NEW JERSEY
Ms. Jennifer Velez
Commissioner
Department of Human Services
222 South Warren Street
P.O. Box 700
Trenton, NJ 08625
P: (609) 292-3717

NEW MEXICO
Ms. Sidonie Squier
Secretary
Human Services Department
P.O. Box 2348
Santa Fe, NM 87504
P: (505) 827-7750
F: (505) 827-6286
E: Jonni.pool@state.nm.us

NEW YORK
Ms. Kristin M. Proud
Commissioner
Office of Temporary &
Disability Assistance
40 North Pearl Street
Albany, NY 12243
P: (518) 473-1090

NORTH CAROLINA
Dr. Aldona Wos
Secretary
Department of Health & Human
Services
Adams Building, 101 Blair
Drive
2001 Mail Service Center
Raleigh, NC 27699
P: (919) 855-4800
F: (919) 715-4645
E: aldona.wos@dhhs.nc.gov

NORTH DAKOTA
Ms. Maggie D. Anderson
Executive Director
Department of Human Services
State Capitol, Judicial Wing
600 East Boulevard Avenue,
Dept. 325
Bismarck, ND 58505
P: (701) 328-2538
F: (701) 328-1545
E: manderson@nd.gov

Ms. Carol K. Olson
Executive Director
Department of Human Services
State Capitol, Judicial Wing
600 East Boulevard Avenue,
Dept. 325
Bismarck, ND 58505
P: (701) 328-2538
F: (701) 328-1545
E: colson@nd.gov

**NORTHERN MARIANA
ISLANDS**
Mr. Joseph P. Villagomez
Secretary of Public Health
Department of Public Health
P.O. Box 500409
Saipan, MP 96950
P: (670) 234-8950
F: (670) 234-8930
E: jkvsaipan@aol.com

OHIO
Ms. Cynthia J. Dungey
Director
Department of Job & Family
Services
30 East Broad Street, 32nd Floor
Columbus, OH 43215
P: (614) 466-9195
F: (614) 466-2815

OREGON
Ms. Erinn L. Kelley-Siel
Director
Department of Human Services
500 Summer Street, Northeast,
E-15
Salem, OR 97301
P: (503) 945-7001
F: (503) 378-2897
E: erinn.kelley-siel
 @state.or.us

PENNSYLVANIA
Mr. Theodore Dallas
Secretary
Department of Human
Resources
P.O. Box 2675
Harrisburg, PA 17105
P: (717) 787-2600

PUERTO RICO
Ms. Idalia Columbus Rondon
Secretary
Department of the Family
P.O. Box 11398
Hato Rey, PR 00917
P: (787) 294-4900
F: (787) 294-0732

RHODE ISLAND
Ms. Melba Depena Affigne
Director
Department of Human Services
600 New London Avenue
Cranston, RI
F: (401) 462-3677
E: Director@dhs.ri.gov

SOUTH CAROLINA
Ms. V. Susan Alford
Director
Department of Social Services
1535 Confederate Avenue
Extension
P.O. Box 1520
Columbia, SC 29202
P: (803) 898-7360
F: (803) 898-7277

SOUTH DAKOTA
Ms. Gloria Pearson
Secretary
Department of Human Services
3800 E. Hwy 34, Hillsview
Properties Pl.
C/o 500 East Capitol Avenue
Pierre, SD 57501
P: (605) 773-5990
F: (605) 773-5483

TENNESSEE
Dr. Raquel Hatter
Commissioner
Department of Human Services
400 Deaderick Street, 15th Floor
Nashville, TN 37243
P: (615) 313-4700
F: (615) 741-4165
E: raquel.hatter@tn.gov

TEXAS
Dr. Kyle L. Janek
Executive Commissioner
Health & Human Services
Commission
4900 North Lamar Boulevard
P.O. Box 13247
Austin, TX 78711
P: (512) 424-6502
F: (512) 491-1967

Mr. Jon Weizenbaum
Commissioner
Department of Aging &
Disability Services
701 West 51st Street
P.O. Box 149030
Austin, TX 78714
P: (512) 438-3030
F: (512) 438-3011

U.S. VIRGIN ISLANDS
Mr. Christopher E. Finch
Commissioner
Department of Human Services
Knud Hansen Complex,
Building A
1303 Hospital Ground
St. Thomas, VI 00802
P: (340) 774-0930
F: (340) 773-2980

Human Services

UTAH
Ms. Ann S. Williamson
Executive Director
Department of Human Services
195 North 1950 West
Salt Lake City, UT 84116
P: (801) 538-4017
F: (801) 538-4016
E: annwilliamson@utah.gov

VERMONT
Mr. Douglas A. Racine
Secretary
Agency of Human Services
208 Hurricane Lane, Suite 103
Williston, VT 05495
P: (802) 871-3252
F: (802) 871-3008
E: Doug.Racine@state.vt.us

VIRGINIA
Mr. Bill Hazel
Secretary
Office of the Secretary of
Health & Human Services
1111 East Broad Street
Patrick Henry Building
Richmond, VA 23219
P: (804) 786-7765
F: (804) 786-3389
E: bill.hazel
    @governor.virginia.gov

Ms. Margaret Schultze
Commissioner
Department of Social Services
801 East Main Street
Richmond, VA 23219
P: (804) 726-7000
E: margaret.schultze
    @dss.virginia.gov

WASHINGTON
Mr. Kevin W. Quigley
Secretary
Department of Social & Health
Services
P.O. Box 45130
Olympia, WA 98504
P: (360) 902-7800

WEST VIRGINIA
Ms. Karen L. Bowling
Cabinet Secretary
Department of Health & Human
Resources
One Davis Square, Suite 100
East
Charleston, WV 25301
P: (304) 558-0684
F: (304) 558-1130
E: DHHRSecretary@wv.gov

WYOMING
Dr. Steve Corsi
Director
Department of Family Services
Hathaway Building, 3rd Floor
2300 Capitol Avenue
Cheyenne, WY 82002
P: (307) 777-7561
F: (307) 777-7747
E: steve.corsi@wyo.gov

Information Systems

Provides statewide computer services or coordinates the operation of various data processing systems within state government.

ALABAMA
Mr. Jack Doane
Director
Information Services Division
Folsom Administrative Building
64 North Union Street
Montgomery, AL 36130
P: (334) 242-3658
F: (334) 242-7002
E: jack.doane
@isd.alabama.gov

ALASKA
Mr. Jim Bates
Director & Chief Information
Officer
Division of Enterprise
Technology Services
Department of Administration
P.O. Box 110206
Juneau, AK 99811
P: (907) 269-4744
F: (907) 465-3450
E: jim.bates@alaska.gov

AMERICAN SAMOA
Hon. Falema'o M. Pili
Treasurer
Office of the Treasurer
American Samoa Government
Pago Pago, AS 96799
P: (684) 633-4155
F: (684) 633-4100

ARIZONA
Mr. Donald Hennington
Chief Operations Officer
State Data Center
Department of Administration
100 North 15th Avenue, Suite
400
Phoenix, AZ 85007
P: (602) 542-1422
F: (602) 542-0120

CALIFORNIA
Ms. Barbara Garrett
Deputy Director
Statewide Telecommunications
& Network Division
P.O. Box 1810
Rancho Cordova, CA 95741
P: (916) 464-3400
E: barbara.garrett
@state.ca.gov

COLORADO
Ms. Suma Nallapati
Secretary of Technology &
Chief Information Officer
Governor's Office of
Information Technology
601 East 18th Avenue, Suite 250
Denver, CO 80203
P: (303) 764-7700
E: oit@state.co.us

CONNECTICUT
Mr. Mark D. Raymond
Chief Information Officer
Bureau of Enterprise Systems &
Technology
Department of Administrative
Services
55 Farmington Avenue
Hartford, CT 06105
P: (860) 622-2419
F: (860) 291-8665
E: mark.raymond@ct.gov

DISTRICT OF COLUMBIA
Mr. Rob Mancini
Chief Technology Officer
Office of the Chief Technology
Officer
200 I Street, Southeast
Washington, DC 20003
P: (202) 727-2277
F: (202) 727-6857
E: octo@dc.gov

FLORIDA
Mr. David W. Taylor
Executive Director & Chief
Information Officer
Agency for Enterprise
Information Technology
4030 Esplanade Way, Suite 135
Tallahassee, FL 32399
P: (850) 922-7502
F: (850) 487-9937
E: David.Taylor
@aeit.myflorida.com

GEORGIA
Mr. Calvin Rhodes
Executive Director & Chief
Information Officer
Technology Authority
47 Trinity Avenue, Southwest
Atlanta, GA 30334
P: (404) 463-2340
F: (404) 463-2380
E: calvn.rhodes@gta.ga.gov

GUAM
Ms. Benita A. Manglona
Director
Department of Administration
P.O. Box 884
Hagatna, GU 96932
P: (671) 475-1101
F: (671) 477-6788

HAWAII
Ms. Sharon Wong
Acting Administrator
Information & Communications
Services Division
Accounting & General Services
1151 Punchbowl Street
Honolulu, HI 96813
P: (808) 586-1920
F: (808) 586-1922
E: ICSD.Administration
@hawaii.gov

IDAHO
Ms. Teresa Luna
Director & Chief Information
Officer
Department of Administration
650 West State Street, Room
100
Len B. Jordan Building, P.O.
Box 83720
Boise, ID 83720
P: (208) 332-1826
F: (208) 334-2307
E: jennifer.pike
@adm.idaho.gov

ILLINOIS
Ms. Lana Kains
Division Manager
Office of Communication &
Information
120 West Jefferson
Communication Center, 3rd
Floor
Springfield, IL 62702
P: (217) 524-6895

INDIANA
Mr. Paul Baltzell
Chief Information Officer
Office of Technology
Government Center North
1000 North Senate Avenue,
Room N551
Indianapolis, IN 46204
P: (317) 234-4392
F: (317) 324-0917
E: pbaltzell@iot.in.gov

KANSAS
Mr. Loren Westerdale
Director
Division of Information Systems
Information Technology
Services
900 Southwest Jackson, Room
751S
Topeka, KS 66612
P: (785) 296-6236
E: loren.westerdale@ks.gov

KENTUCKY
Ms. Lori Hudson Flanery
Secretary
Finance & Administration
Cabinet
383 Capitol Annex
Frankfort, KY 40601
P: (502) 564-4240
F: (502) 564-5856
E: Lori.Flanery@ky.gov

LOUISIANA
Mr. Richard Howze
State Chief Information Officer
Office of Information
Technology
Division of Administration
P.O. Box 94095
Baton Rouge, LA 70804
P: (225) 342-7105
F: (225) 219-9465
E: cio@la.gov

MAINE
Mr. Greg McNeal
Chief Information Officer
Office of Information
Technology
26 Edison Drive
145 State House Station
Augusta, ME 04333
P: (207) 624-8800

MARYLAND
Mr. Elliot H. Schlanger
State Director of Cyber Security
Department of Information
Technology
45 Calvert Street
Annapolis, MD 21401
P: (410) 767-9805
F: (410) 974-5615
E: Elliot.Schlanger
@maryland.gov

MASSACHUSETTS
Mr. Charlie Desourdy
Acting Chief Information
Officer
Information Technology
Division
One Ashburton Place, Room 804
Boston, MA 02108
P: (617) 626-4434
F: (617) 626-4411

Information Systems

MICHIGAN
Mr. David Behen
Chief Information Officer &
Department Director
Department of Technology,
Management & Budget
320 South Walnut Street, 2nd
Floor
P.O. Box 30026
Lansing, MI 48909
P: (517) 373-3209
E: behend@michigan.gov

MINNESOTA
Mr. Matt Massman
Commissioner
Department of Administration
116 Veterans Service Building
20 West 12 Street
St. Paul, MN 55155
P: (651) 201-3421
E: Matt.Massman@state.mn.us

MISSISSIPPI
Dr. Craig P. Orgeron
Chief Information Officer &
Executive Director
Department of Information
Technology Services
3771 Eastwood Drive
Jackson, MS 39211
P: (601) 432-8000
F: (601) 713-6380
E: craig.orgeron@its.ms.gov

MISSOURI
Mr. Tim Robyn
Chief Information Officer
Information Technology
Services Division
301 West High Street, Room
280
P.O. Box 809
Jefferson City, MO 65101
P: (573) 751-1504
F: (573) 751-3299
E: Tim.Robyn@oa.mo.gov

MONTANA
Mr. Ron Baldwin
Chief Information Officer
Information Technology
Services Division
125 North Roberts Street
P.O. Box 200113
Helena, MT 59620
P: (406) 444-2777
F: (406) 444-2701

NEBRASKA
Mr. Ed Toner
Chief Information Officer
Office of the Chief Information
Officer
501 South 14th Street
Lincoln, NE 68508
P: (402) 471-3717

NEW HAMPSHIRE
Mr. Peter Hastings
Commissioner & Chief
Information Officer
Department of Information
Technology
27 Hazen Drive
Concord, NH 03301
P: (603) 223-5703
F: (603) 271-6531

NEW JERSEY
Mr. E. Steven Emanuel
Chief Information Officer
Office of Information
Technology
200/300 Riverview Plaza
P.O. Box 212
Trenton, NJ 08625
P: (609) 777-5865
F: (609) 633-9100
E: steven.emanuel
   @oit.state.nj.us

NEW MEXICO
Mr. Darryl Ackley
Secretary & Chief Information
Officer
Department of Information
Technology
715 Alta Vista Street
P.O. Box 22550
Santa Fe, NM 87502
P: (505) 827-0000
F: (505) 827-2948

NORTH CAROLINA
Mr. Chris Estes
Chief Information Officer
Office of Information
Technology Services
P.O. Box 17209
Raleigh, NC 27619
P: (919) 754-6576
E: chris.estes@nc.gov

NORTH DAKOTA
Mr. Mike J. Ressler
Chief Information Officer
Information Technology
Department
4201 Normandy Street
Bismarck, ND 58503
P: (701) 328-1000
F: (701) 328-1075
E: mressler@nd.gov

**NORTHERN MARIANA
ISLANDS**
Mr. Joe I. Quitugua
Director
Commonwealth of Northern
Mariana Islands
P.O. Box 5234 CHRB
Saipan, MP 96950
P: (670) 664-1400
F: (670) 664-1415
E: finanedp02
   @gtepacifica.net

OHIO
Mr. Stuart R. Davis
Chief Information Officer &
Assistant Director
Office of Information
Technology
Department of Administrative
Services
30 East Broad Street, 39th Floor
Columbus, OH 43215
P: (614) 644-6446
F: (614) 728-5297
E: Stu.Davis@das.ohio.gov

OREGON
Mr. Alex Pettit
Chief Information Officer
Office of State Finance
Executive Building
155 Cottage Street Northeast, 4th
Floor
Salem, OR 97301
P: (503) 378-3175
F: (503) 378-3795
E: alex.pettit
   @das.state.or.us

PENNSYLVANIA
Mr. John MacMillan
Deputy Secretary for
Information Technology & Chief
Information Officer
Office for Information
Technology
Governor's Office of
Administration
209 Finance Building
Harrisburg, PA 17120
P: (717) 787-5440
F: (717) 787-4523
E: cio@pa.gov

RHODE ISLAND
Mr. Thom Guertin
Chief Digital Officer
Division of Information
Technology
Division of Information
Technology
One Capitol Hill
Providence, RI 02908
P: (401) 574-9220

SOUTH CAROLINA
Mr. Kyle Herron
Chief Operating Officer
Division of Technology
P.O. Box 12444
Columbia, SC 29211
P: (803) 896-0222
E: kherron@cio.sc.gov

SOUTH DAKOTA
Mr. Dom Bianco
Commissioner & Chief
Information Officer
Bureau of Information &
Telecommunications
700 Governors Drive
Pierre, SD 57501
P: (605) 773-4165
F: (605) 773-6040
E: dom.bianco@state.sd.us

TENNESSEE
Mr. Mark Bengel
Chief Information Officer
Office for Information
Resources
Department of Finance &
Administration
312 Rosa L. Parks Avenue
Nashville, TN 37343
P: (615) 741-7951
F: (615) 532-0471

TEXAS
Mr. Todd Kimbriel
Interim Executive Director &
CIO
Department of Information
Resources
300 West 15th Street, Suite 1300
P.O. Box 13564
Austin, TX 78711
P: (512) 475-0579
F: (512) 475-4759

U.S. VIRGIN ISLANDS
Mr. Reuben Molloy
Chief Information Officer
Bureau of Information
Technology
#9059 Est. Castle Coakley
Christiansted, VI 00820
P: (340) 713-0354
F: (340) 719-1623

UTAH
Mr. Mark VanOrden
Chief Information Officer
Department of Technology
Services
1 State Office Buidling, Floor 6
Salt Lake City, UT 84114
P: (801) 538-3298
F: (801) 538-3622
E: mvanorden@utah.gov

VERMONT
Mr. Richard Boes
Commissioner & Chief
Information Officer
Department of Information &
Innovation
Agency of Administration
133 State Street
Montpelier, VT 05633
P: (802) 828-4141
F: (802) 828-3398
E: richard.boes@state.vt.us

VIRGINIA
Ms. Karen R. Jackson
Secretary of Technology
Office of the Secretary of
Technology
1111 East Broad Street
Patrick Henry Building
Richmond, VA 23219
P: (804) 786-9579
F: (804) 786-9584
E: karen.jackson
    @virginia.goveror.gov

WASHINGTON
Mr. Rob St. John
Director
Department of Consolidated
Technology Services
P.O. Box 41501
Olympia, WA 98504
P: (360) 407-9150
F: (360) 586-5885
E: rob.st.john@cts.wa.gov

WEST VIRGINIA
Mr. John Dunlap
Director of Infrastructure
Office of Technology
1900 Kanawha Boulevard, East
Capitol Complex, Building 5,
10th Floor
Charleston, WV 25305
P: (304) 957-6864
F: (304) 558-0136
E: John.D.Dunlap@wv.gov

WISCONSIN
Mr. David Cagigal
Chief Information Officer
Division of Enterprise
Technology
Department of Administration
P.O. Box 7844
Madison, WI 53707
P: (608) 261-8406
F: (608) 267-0626
E: David.Cagigal
    @wisconsin.gov

WYOMING
Mr. Rick Imbrogno
Administrator
Information Technology
Division
Emerson Building, Room 237
2001 Capitol Avenue
Cheyenne, WY 82002
P: (307) 777-5840
F: (307) 777-6725

Insurance

Licenses and regulates insurance agents and insurance and title companies in the state.

ALABAMA
Mr. Jim L. Ridling
Commissioner
Department of Insurance
201 Monroe Street, Suite 502
P.O. Box 303351
Montgomery, AL 36130
P: (334) 269-3550
F: (334) 241-4192

ALASKA
Ms. Lori K. Wing-Heier
Director
Department of Commerce,
Community & Economic
Development
Division of Insurance
550 West 7th Avenue, Suite 1560
Anchorage, AK 99501
P: (907) 269-7900
F: (907) 269-7910

AMERICAN SAMOA
Tau Tanuvasa
Insurance Commissioner
Office of the Governor
American Samoa Government
A.P. Lutali Executive Office
Building
Pago Pago, AS 96799
P: (684) 633-4116
F: (684) 633-2269

ARIZONA
Ms. Germaine L. Marks
Director
Department of Insurance
2910 North 44th Street, Suite
210
Phoenix, AZ 85018
P: (602) 364-3100
F: (602) 364-3470

ARKANSAS
Mr. Allen Kerr
Commissioner
State Insurance Department
1200 West Third Street
Little Rock, AR 72201
P: (501) 371-2600
F: (501) 371-2618

CALIFORNIA
Mr. Dave Jones
Commissioner
State Department of Insurance
300 Capitol Mall, Suite 1700
Sacramento, CA 95814
P: (916) 492-3500
F: (916) 445-5280

COLORADO
Ms. Marguerite Salazar
Commissioner
Division of Insurance
Department of Regulatory
Agencies
1560 Broadway, Suite 850
Denver, CO 80202
P: (303) 894-7499
F: (303) 894-7455

CONNECTICUT
Ms. Katharine L. Wade
Commissioner
State Insurance Department
153 Market Street, 7th Floor
P.O. Box 816
Hartford, CT 06142
P: (860) 297-3800
F: (860) 566-7410

DELAWARE
Hon. Karen Weldin
   Stewart (D)
Commissioner
State Department of Insurance
841 Silver Lake Boulevard
Dover, DE 19904
P: (302) 674-7300
F: (302) 739-5280
E: karen.stewart
   @state.de.us

DISTRICT OF COLUMBIA
Mr. Chester A. McPherson
Acting Commissioner
Department of Insurance,
Securities & Banking
Government of the District of
Columbia
810 First Street Northeast, Suite
701
Washington, DC 20002
P: (202) 727-8000
F: (202) 535-1196
E: disb@dc.gov

FLORIDA
Mr. Kevin M. McCarty
Commissioner
Office of Insurance Regulation
The Larson Building
200 East Gaines Street, Room
101A
Tallahassee, FL 32399
P: (850) 413-5914
F: (850) 488-3334
E: kevin.mccarty@fldfs.com

GEORGIA
Hon. Ralph T. Hudgens (R)
Commissioner
Office of Insurance & Safety
Fire Commissioner
2 Martin Luther King Jr. Drive
West Tower, Suite 704
Atlanta, GA 30334
P: (404) 656-2070
F: (404) 657-8542

GUAM
Mr. Artemio B. Ilagan
Banking & Insurance
Commissioner
Regulatory Division
Department of Revenue &
Taxation
P.O. Box 23607
GMF Barrigada, GU 96921
P: (671) 635-1817
F: (671) 633-2643
E: art.ilagan@revtax.gov.gu

HAWAII
Mr. Gordon I. Ito
Commissioner, Insurance
Division
Department of Commerce &
Consumer Affairs
335 Merchant Street, Room 213
P.O. Box 3614
Honolulu, HI 96811
P: (808) 586-2790
F: (808) 586-2806
E: insurance
   @dcca.hawaii.gov

IDAHO
Mr. Tom Donovan
Acting Director
Department of Insurance
700 West State Street, 3rd Floor
P.O. Box 83720
Boise, ID 83720
P: (208) 334-4250
F: (208) 334-4398

ILLINOIS
Mr. James Stephens
Acting Director
Department of Insurance
320 West Washington Street
Springfield, IL 62767
P: (217) 782-4515
F: (217) 782-5020

INDIANA
Mr. Stephen W. Robertson
Commissioner
State Department of Insurance
311 West Washington Street,
Suite 103
Indianapolis, IN 46204
P: (317) 232-2385
F: (317) 232-5251

IOWA
Mr. NIck Gerhart
Commissioner
State Insurance Division
Two Ruan Center
601 Locust, 4th Floor
Des Moines, IA 50309
P: (515) 281-5705
F: (515) 281-3059

KANSAS
Hon. Ken Selzer (R)
Commissioner of Insurance
State Insurance Department
420 Southwest 9th Street
Topeka, KS 66612
P: (785) 296-3071
F: (785) 296-7805
E: commissioner
   @ksinsurance.org

KENTUCKY
Ms. Sharon P. Clark
Commissioner
State Department of Insurance
215 West Main Street
P.O. Box 517
Frankfort, KY 40602
P: (502) 564-3630
F: (502) 564-1453
E: Debbie.Stamper@ky.gov

LOUISIANA
Hon. James J. Donelon (R)
Commissioner
State Department of Insurance
1702 North 3rd Street
P.O. Box 94214
Baton Rouge, LA 70804
P: (225) 342-5900
F: (225) 342-8622

MAINE
Mr. Eric A. Cioppa
Superintendent
State Bureau of Insurance
Professional & Financial
Regulation
34 State House Station
Augusta, ME 04333
P: (207) 624-8475
F: (207) 624-8599

MARYLAND
Mr. Alfred Redmer Jr.
Commissioner
State Insurance Administration
200 St. Paul Place, Suite 2700
Baltimore, MD 21202
P: (410) 468-2090
F: (410) 468-2020

Insurance

MASSACHUSETTS
Mr. Daniel R. Judson
Commissioner
State Division of Insurance
Consumer Affairs & Business
Regulation
1000 Washington Street, 8th
Floor
Boston, MA 02118
P: (617) 521-7794
F: (617) 753-6830

MICHIGAN
Ms. Ann Flood
Director
Department of Insurance &
Financial Services
611 West Ottawa, 3rd Floor
P.O. Box 30220
Lansing, MI 48909
P: (517) 373-0220
F: (517) 335-4978
E: difs-info@michigan.gov

MINNESOTA
Mr. Mike Rothman
Commissioner
Department of Commerce
85 East 7th Place, Suite 500
St. Paul, MN 55101
P: (651) 539-1638
F: (651) 296-4328
E: commerce.commissioner
@state.mn.us

MISSISSIPPI
Hon. Mike Chaney (R)
Commissioner
State Insurance Department
1001 Woolfolk State Office
Building
501 North West Street, P.O. Box
79
Jackson, MS 39205
P: (601) 359-3569
F: (601) 359-2474
E: mike.chaney
@mid.state.ms.us

MISSOURI
Mr. John Huff
Director
State Department of Insurance,
Financial Institutions &
Professional Registration
301 West High Street, Room
530
P.O. Box 690
Jefferson City, MO 65102
P: (573) 751-4126
F: (573) 751-1165

MONTANA
Hon. Monica J. Lindeen (D)
Commissioner of Securities &
Insurance, State Auditor
Office of the Commissioner of
Securities & Insurance, State
Auditor
840 Helena Avenue
Helena, MT 59601
P: (406) 444-2040
F: (406) 444-3497
E: stateauditor@mt.gov

NEBRASKA
Mr. Bruce R. Ramge
Director
State Department of Insurance
941 O Street, Suite 400
P.O. Box 82089
Lincoln, NE 68501
P: (402) 471-2201
F: (402) 471-4610

NEVADA
Mr. Scott J. Kipper
Commissioner
Division of Insurance
Department of Business &
Industry
1818 East College Parkway,
Suite 103
Carson City, NV 89706
P: (775) 687-0700
F: (775) 687-0787

NEW HAMPSHIRE
Mr. Roger A. Sevigny
Commissioner
State Insurance Department
21 South Fruit Street, Suite 14
Concord, NH 03301
P: (603) 271-2261
F: (603) 271-1406
E: roger.sevigny@ins.nh.gov

NEW JERSEY
Mr. Kenneth E. Kobylowski
Commissioner
Department of Banking &
Insurance
State of New Jersey
20 West State Street, P.O. Box
325
Trenton, NJ 08625
P: (609) 292-7272
F: (609) 984-5273
E: commissioner
@dobi.state.nj.us

NEW MEXICO
Mr. John G. Franchini
Superintendent
Office of Superintendent of
Insurance
P.E.R.A. Building
1120 Paseo De Peralta, P.O. Box
1689
Santa Fe, NM 87504
P: (505) 827-4601
F: (505) 827-4734

NEW YORK
Mr. Benjamin M. Lawsky
Superintendent
State Department of Financial
Services
One State Street
New York, NY 10004
P: (212) 709-3500
F: (212) 709-3520

NORTH CAROLINA
Hon. Wayne Goodwin (D)
Commissioner
State Department of Insurance
430 North Salisbury Street
Dobbs Building, 1201 Mail
Service Center
Raleigh, NC 27699
P: (919) 807-6000
F: (919) 733-6495
E: Commissioner@ncdoi.gov

NORTH DAKOTA
Hon. Adam Hamm (R)
Commissioner
State Insurance Department
State Capitol, 5th Floor
600 East Boulevard Avenue
Bismarck, ND 58505
P: (701) 328-2440
F: (701) 328-4880
E: insurance@nd.gov

**NORTHERN MARIANA
ISLANDS**
Mr. Mark O. Rabauliman
Secretary of Commerce
Department of Commerce
Caller Box 10007 CK
Saipan, MP 96950
P: (670) 664-3000
F: (670) 664-3067

OHIO
Hon. Mary Taylor (R)
Lieutenant Governor
State Department of Insurance
77 High Street, 30th Floor
Columbus, OH 43215
P: (614) 644-0935
F: (614) 466-9354

OKLAHOMA
Hon. John D. Doak
Commissioner
State Insurance Department
Five Corporate Plaza
3625 Northwest 56th Street,
Suite 100
Oklahoma City, OK 73112
P: (405) 521-2828
F: (405) 521-6635

OREGON
Ms. Laura N. Cali
Insurance Commissioner/Chief
Actuary
Department of Consumer &
Business Services
Insurance Division, P.O. Box
14480
350 Winter Street, Northeast
Salem, OR 97309
P: (503) 947-7980
F: (503) 378-4351

PENNSYLVANIA
Ms. Teresa D. Miller
Acting Commissioner
State Insurance Department
1326 Strawberry Square
Harrisburg, PA 17120
P: (717) 783-0442
F: (717) 772-1969

PUERTO RICO
Ms. Angela Weyne
Commissioner
Office of the Commissioner of
Insurance
B5 Calle Tabonuco Street
Suite 216 PMB 356
Guaynabo, PR 00968
P: (787) 304-8686
F: (787) 273-6365

RHODE ISLAND
Mr. Joseph Torti III
Superintendent
Division of Insurance
Department of Business
Regulation
1511 Pontiac Avenue, Building
69-2
Cranston, RI 02920
P: (401) 462-9520
F: (401) 462-9602
E: InsuranceInquiry
@dbr.state.ri.us

Insurance

SOUTH CAROLINA
Mr. Raymond G. Farmer
Director
Department of Insurance
1201 Main Street, Suite 1000
P.O. Box 100105
Columbia, SC 29202
P: (803) 737-6160
F: (803) 737-6205

SOUTH DAKOTA
Mr. Larry Deiter
Division of Insurance
State Department of Labor &
Regulation
124 South Euclid Avenue, 2nd
Floor
Pierre, SD 57501
P: (605) 773-3563
F: (605) 773-5369

TENNESSEE
Ms. Julie Mix McPeak
Commissioner
State Department of Commerce
& Insurance
Davy Crockett Tower, Twelfth
Floor
500 James Robertson Parkway
Nashville, TN 37243
P: (615) 741-6007
F: (615) 532-6934
E: ask.tdci@tn.gov

TEXAS
Ms. David Mattax
Commissioner
Department of Insurance
333 Guadalupe Street
P.O. Box 149104
Austin, TX 78714
P: (512) 676-6000
F: (512) 490-1045

U.S. VIRGIN ISLANDS
Hon. Osbert Potter (I)
Lieutenant Governor
Division of Banking &
Insurance
1331 Kings Street, Suite101
St. Croix, VI 00802
P: (340) 773-6449
F: (340) 773-0330

UTAH
Mr. Todd E. Kiser
Commissioner
State Insurance Department
3110 State Office Building
Salt Lake City, UT 84114
P: (801) 538-3800
F: (801) 538-3829
E: toddkiser@le.utah.gov

VERMONT
Ms. Susan L. Donegan
Commissioner
Department of Financial
Regulation
89 Main Street
Montpelier, VT 05620
P: (802) 828-3301
F: (802) 828-3306
E: susan.donegan
    @state.vt.us

VIRGINIA
Ms. Jacqueline K.
    Cunningham
Commissioner
Bureau of Insurance
State Corporation Commission
1300 East Main Street, P.O. Box
1157
Richmond, VA 23218
P: (804) 371-9741
F: (804) 371-9873

WASHINGTON
Hon. Mike Kreidler (D)
Commissioner
Office of the Insurance
Commissioner
P.O. Box 40256
Olympia, WA 98504
P: (360) 725-7000
F: (360) 586-3535
E: askMike@oic.wa.gov

WEST VIRGINIA
Mr. Michael D. Riley
Commissioner
Offices of the Insurance
Commissioner
1124 Smith Street, Room 403
P.O. Box 50540
Charleston, WV 25305
P: (304) 558-3354
F: (304) 558-0412
E: michael.riley
    @wvinsurance.gov

WISCONSIN
Mr. Ted Nickel
Commissioner
Office of the Commissioner of
Insurance
125 South Webster Street
GEF III, Second Floor, P.O. Box
7873
Madison, WI 53707
P: (608) 266-3585
F: (608) 266-9935

WYOMING
Mr. Tom Glause
State Insurance Department
106 East 6th Avenue
Cheyenne, WY 82002
P: (307) 777-7401
F: (307) 777-2446

International Trade

Promotes state exports, attracts overseas investments in the state and directs trade and investment missions.

ALABAMA
Ms. Hilda Lockhart
Director, International Trade
Division
Department of Commerce
401 Adams Avenue, Suite 630
Montgomery, AL 36130
P: (334) 242-0442
F: (334) 242-0415
E: hilda.lockhart
   @commerce.alabama.gov

ALASKA
Ms. Cynthia Sims
Director
Office of International Trade
550 West 7th Street, Suite 1700
Anchorage, AK 99501
P: (907) 269-7450
F: (907) 269-7461
E: cynthia.sims@alaska.gov

ARIZONA
Mr. Fernando C. Jimenez
Vice President, International
Trade
State Commerce Authority
333 North Central, Suite 1900
Phoenix, AZ 85004
P: (602) 845-1257
E: Fernando@azcommerce.com

ARKANSAS
Mr. W. Dan Hendrix
President & CEO
Arkansas World Trade Center
3300 Market Street, Suite 400
Rogers, AR 72758
P: (479) 418-4800

CALIFORNIA
Karnig Kazarian
Assistant Secretary of Economic
Development
Business, Transportation &
Housing Agency
Office of Economic
Development
980 9th Street, Suite 2450
Sacramento, CA 95814
P: (916) 323-5408
F: (916) 323-5440
E: karnig.kazarian
   @bth.ca.gov

COLORADO
Ms. Sandi Moilanen
International Division Director
Office of Economic
Development & International
Trade
1625 Broadway, Suite 2700
Denver, CO 80202
P: (303) 892-3857
F: (303) 892-3848
E: sandi.moilanen
   @state.co.us

CONNECTICUT
Ms. Beatriz Gutierrez
Director
Office of International &
Domestic Business
Development
Economic & Community
Development
505 Hudson Street
Hartford, CT 06106
P: (860) 270-8013
F: (860) 707-1809
E: beatriz.gutierrez@ct.gov

DELAWARE
Ms. Andrea Tinianow
Director of Corporate &
International Development
International Trade &
Development
820 North French Street
Wilmington, DE 19801
P: (302) 577-8285
F: (302) 577-1176
E: andrea.tinianow
   @state.de.us

DISTRICT OF COLUMBIA
Mr. Gizachew Andargeh
Manager
Export DC
Small & Local Business
Development
441 4th Street Northwest, Suite
850N
Washington, DC 20001
P: (202) 727-3900
E: gizachew.andargeh@dc.gov

FLORIDA
Mr. Manny Mencia
Senior Vice President,
International Trade &
Development
Enterprise Florida
201 Alhambra Circle, Suite 610
Coral Gables, FL 33134
P: (305) 808-3660
F: (305) 808-3660
E: mmencia@eflorida.com

GEORGIA
Ms. Mary Waters
Deputy Commissioner
International Trade
Department of Economic
Development
75 Fifth Street Northwest, Suite
1200
Atlanta, GA 30308
P: (404) 962-4120
F: (404) 962-4121
E: mwaters@georgia.org

HAWAII
Mr. Theodore E. Liu
Director
Economic Development &
Tourism
Department of Business
250 South Hotel Street, 5th Floor
Honolulu, HI 96813
P: (808) 586-2355
F: (808) 586-2377
E: director
   @dbedt.hawaii.gov

IDAHO
Ms. Jennifer Verdon
International Trade Specialist
Idaho Commerce
700 West State Street
Boise, ID 83702
P: (208) 287-3165
F: (208) 794-9191
E: jennifer.verdon
   @commerce.idaho.gov

ILLINOIS
Ms. Jennifer Stout
International Trade Specialist
Office of Trade & Investment
100 West Randolph, Suite 3-400
Chicago, IL 60601
P: (217) 785-6453
F: (312) 814-6581
E: Jennifer.L.Stout
   @illinoise.gov

INDIANA
Mr. Kent Anderson
Vice President of Business
Development
Economic Development
Corporation
One North Capitol Avenue,
Suite 700
Indianapolis, IN 46204
P: (812) 390-4816
F: (317) 232-4146
E: keanderson@iedc.in.gov

IOWA
Ms. Kathy Hill
International Trade Office Team
Leader & Marketing Manager
International Trade Office
Economic Development
Authority
200 East Grand Avenue
Des Moines, IA 50309
P: (515) 725-3141
F: (515) 725-3010
E: kathy.hill@iowa.gov

KANSAS
Mr. Randi Tveitaraas Jack
International Development
Manager
Department of Commerce,
Trade Development Division
1000 Southwest Jackson Street
Curtis State Office Building,
Suite 100
Topeka, KS 66612
P: (785) 296-7868
E: rjack@kansascommerce.com

KENTUCKY
Mr. Mark Peachey
State Trade Director &
International Trade Director
Cabinet for Economic
Development
300 West Broadway
Old Capitol Annex
Frankfort, KY 40601
P: (502) 564-7140
F: (502) 564-3256
E: mark.peachey@ky.gov

LOUISIANA
Ms. Katherine Falls
Executive Director, International
Commerce
State Economic Development
1051 North Third Street
Baton Rouge, LA 70802
P: (225) 342-4323
F: (225) 342-5349
E: Kathe.Falls@la.gov

MAINE
Ms. Janine Bisaillon-Cary
President
International Trade Center
511 Congress Street
Portland, ME 04101
P: (207) 541-7400
F: (207) 541-7420
E: jbcary@mitc.com

International Trade

MARYLAND
Ms. Signe Pringle
Program Director
Department of Business &
Economic Development
World Trade Center
401 East Pratt Street, 7th Floor
Baltimore, MD 21202
P: (410) 767-3542
F: (410) 333-4302
E: signe.pringle
    @maryland.gov

MASSACHUSETTS
Ms. Brittany McDonough
Manager of Business
Development
Office of International Trade &
Investment
State Transportation Building
10 Park Plaza, Suite 4510
Boston, MA 02116
P: (617) 448-9144
F: (617) 227-3488
E: Brittany.Mcdonough
    @state.ma.us

MICHIGAN
Ms. Deanna Richeson
Director, International Trade
Operations
Economic Development
Corporation
International Trade Office
300 North Washington Square
Lansing, MI 48913
P: (517) 241-2471
E: richesond@michigan.org

MINNESOTA
Ms. Kathleen Motzenbecker
Executive Director
Trade Office
1st National Bank Building,
Suite E200
332 Minnesota Street
St. Paul, MN 55101
P: (651) 259-7489
F: (651) 296-3555
E: kathleen.motzenbecker
    @state.mn.us

MISSISSIPPI
Ms. Rosario Boxx
Bureau Manager, International
Trade Office
State Development Authority
P.O. Box 849
Jackson, MS 39205
P: (601) 359-3045
F: (601) 359-3605
E: rboxx@mississippi.org

MISSOURI
Ms. Ann Pardalos
Director
International Trade &
Investment Office
Harry S. Truman Building
301 West High Street, Suite 750
Jefferson City, MO 65101
P: (573) 751-6605
F: (573) 526-1567
E: ann.pardalos@ded.mo.gov

MONTANA
Ms. Lonie Denise Stimac
Director
Office of Trade & International
Relations
Department of Commerce
P.O. Box 200505
Helena, MT 59620
P: (406) 841-2752
F: (406) 841-2728
E: Lstimac@mt.gov

NEBRASKA
Ms. Susan Rouch
Director
Office of International Trade &
Investment
Department of Economic
Development
301 Centennial Mall, South
Lincoln, NE 68509
P: (402) 471-4668
F: (402) 471-3778
E: susan.rouch@nebraska.gov

NEVADA
Mr. Kristopher J. Sanchez
Director of International Trade
International Trade Division
Office of Economic
Development
555 East Washington Avenue,
Suite 5400
Las Vegas, NV 89101
P: (702) 486-2700
F: (775) 486-2701
E: ksanchez
    @diversifynevada.com

NEW HAMPSHIRE
Ms. Tina Kasim
International Program Manager
International Trade Resource
Center
Division of Economic
Development
172 Pembroke Road
Concord, NH 03301
P: (603) 271-8444
F: (603) 271-6784
E: tina.kasim@dred.nh.gov

NEW JERSEY
Mr. Eddy S. Mayen
Director
Office of International Business
Development & Protocol
P.O. Box 820
Trenton, NJ 08625
P: (609) 633-1182
F: (609) 292-5509
E: eddy.mayen
    @sos.state.nj.us

NEW MEXICO
Mr. Edward Herrera
Director
Office of International Trade
Economic Development
Department
1100 South St. Francis Drive,
Room 1244
Santa Fe, NM 87505
P: (505) 827-0278
F: (505) 827-0328
E: Edward.Herrera
    @state.nm.us

NEW YORK
Ms. Claire McLeveighn
Vice President, Trade &
Investment
Global New York Division
Empire State Development
633 Third Avenue, 36th Floor
New York, NY 10017
P: (212) 803-3769
E: Claire.McLeveighn
    @esd.ny.gov

NORTH CAROLINA
Mr. John Loyack
Vice President, Global Business
Services
International Trade Division
Economic Development
Partnership
15000 Weston Parkway
Cary, NC 27513
P: (919) 447-7739
E: john.loyack@edpnc.com

NORTH DAKOTA
Mr. Donavon Johnson
Director, Global Resource
Management Group
State Trade Office
811 2nd Avenue, North
Suite 284
Fargo, ND 58108
P: (701) 330-1419
F: (701) 231-1151
E: donavon@ndto.com

OKLAHOMA
Ms. Jennifer Springer
Manager of International Trade
& Foreign Investment
Global Business Services
Department of Commerce
900 North Stiles Avenue
Oklahoma City, OK 73104
P: (405) 815-5158
E: Jennifer_Springer
    @okcommerce.gov

OREGON
Ms. Karen Goddin
Managing Director, Business
Innovation & Trade Division
Business Development
Department
One World Trade Center
121 Southwest Salmon, Suite
205
Portland, OR 97204
P: (503) 229-6054
F: (503) 222-5050
E: karen.goddin@oregon.gov

PENNSYLVANIA
Mr. Peter O'Neill
Executive Director, Center for
Export Development
Office of International Business
Development
Commonwealth Keystone
Building
400 North Street, 4th Floor
Harrisburg, PA 17120
P: (717) 214-5453
F: (717) 772-5106
E: peoneill@pa.gov

RHODE ISLAND
Ms. Katherine Therieau
Director, International Trade
Programs
State Commerce Corporation
315 Iron Horse Way, Suite 101
Providence, RI 02908
P: (401) 278-9100 Ext. 139
F: (401) 273-8270
E: ktherieau@commerceri.com

SOUTH CAROLINA
Mr. Clarke Thompson
International Trade Director
Department of Commerce
1201 Main Street, Suite 1600
Columbia, SC 29201
P: (803) 737-0438
F: (803) 737-0538
E: cthompson@sccommerce.com

SOUTH DAKOTA
Mr. Steve Watson
Business & Community
Development Director
Governor's Office of Economic
Development
711 East Wells Avenue
Pierre, SD 57501
P: (605) 367-4518
E: Steve.Watson@state.sd.us

TENNESSEE
Leslee Alexander
Trade Director
Department of Economic &
Community Development
312 Rosa L. Parks Avenue, 26th
Floor
Nashville, TN 37243
P: (615) 483-7293
F: (615) 741-5829
E: leslee.alexander@tn.gov

TEXAS
Mr. Michael Treyger
Manager, International Business
Economic Development &
Tourism
Office of the Governor
P.O. Box 12428
Austin, TX 78711
P: (512) 936-0530
F: (512) 936-0445
E: michael.treyger
    @gov.texas.gov

UTAH
Mr. Aaron Neuenschwander
International Trade &
Diplomacy Coordinator
International Trade &
Diplomacy Office
Office of Economic
Development
60 East South Temple, 3rd Floor
Salt Lake City, UT 84111
P: (801) 538-8737
F: (801) 538-8888
E: aneuenschwander@utah.gov

VERMONT
Mr. Brent Raymond
Executive Director, International
Trade & Foreign Investment
Global Trade Partnership
1 National Life Drive, 6th Floor
Montpelier, VT 05620
P: (802) 522-2540
F: (802) 828-3258
E: Brent.Raymond
    @state.vt.us

VIRGINIA
Mr. Paul Grossman
Director, International Trade
Economic Development
Partnership
P.O. Box 798
Richmond, VA 23218
P: (804) 545-5752
F: (804) 545-5751
E: pgrossman
    @yesvirginia.org

WASHINGTON
Mr. Mark Calhoon
Senior Managing Director
Department of Commerce
2001 6th Avenue, Suite 2600
Seattle, WA 98121
P: (206) 256-6137
F: (206) 256-6158
E: mark.calhoon
    @commerce.wa.gov

WEST VIRGINIA
Mr. Steve Spence
Director, International Division
State Development Office
1900 Kanawha Boulevard, East
Charleston, WV 25305
P: (304) 558-2234
F: (304) 558-1957
E: Stephen.E.Spence@wv.gov

WISCONSIN
Ms. Katy Sinnott
Vice President, Division of
International Business
Development
Economic Development
Corporation
201 West Washington Avenue
Madison, WI 53703
P: (608) 210-6838
F: (608) 266-5551
E: Katy.sinnott@wedc.org

WYOMING
Ms. Cindy Garretson-Weibel
Agribusiness Director
State Business Council
214 West15th Street
Cheyenne, WY 82002
P: (307) 777-6589
F: (307) 777-2838
E: cindy.weibel
    @wybusiness.org

Juvenile Rehabilitation

Administers rehabilitative facilities and programs for delinquent youth committed by the courts.

ALABAMA
Mr. J. Walter Wood Jr.
Executive Director
Department of Youth Services
P.O. Box 66
Mount Meigs, AL 36057
P: (334) 215-3800
F: (334) 215-1453
E: walter.wood
@dys.alabama.gov

ALASKA
Mr. Rob Wood
Acting Director
Division of Juvenile Justice
P.O. Box 110635
Juneau, AK 99811
P: (907) 465-2212
F: (907) 465-2333
E: Hss.djj@alaska.gov

AMERICAN SAMOA
Mr. William E. Haleck
Commissioner
Department of Public Safety
American Samoa Government
P.O. Box 1086
Pato Pato, AS 96799
P: (684) 633-1111
F: (684) 633-7296
E: commissioner@dps.as.gov

ARIZONA
Ms. Dona Marie Markley
Assistant Director
Department of Juvenile
Corrections
1624 West Adams
Phoenix, AZ 85007
P: (602) 364-4051
F: (602) 542-5156
E: dmarkley@azdjc.gov

ARKANSAS
Mr. Marcus C. Devine
Director
Division of Youth Services
P.O. Box 1437, Slot S501
Little Rock, AR 72209
P: (501) 682-8755
F: (501) 682-1351
E: Marcus.Devine
@dhs.arkansas.gov

CALIFORNIA
Mr. Michael Minor
Director
Division of Juvenile Justice
P.O. Box 588501
Elk Grove, CA 95758
P: (916) 683-7460
F: (916) 683-7770

COLORADO
Mr. Charles Parkins
Director
Division of Youth Corrections
4255 South Knox Court
Denver, CO 80236
P: (303) 866-4544
E: Charles.Parkins
@state.co.us

CONNECTICUT
Mr. Scott Semple
Commissioner
Department of Correction
24 Wolcott Hill Road
Wethersfield, CT 06109
P: (860) 692-7480

DELAWARE
Ms. Nancy S. Dietz
Director
Division of Youth Rehabilitative
Services
1825 Faulkland Road
Wilmington, DE 19805
P: (302) 633-2500
F: (302) 633-2636
E: info.dscyf@state.de.us

DISTRICT OF COLUMBIA
Mr. Neil A. Stanley
Director
Department of Youth
Rehabilitation Services
450 H Street, Northwest
Washington, DC 20001
P: (202) 576-8175
F: (202) 576-8457
E: dyrs@dc.gov

FLORIDA
Ms. Wansley Waters
Secretary
Department of Juvenile Justice
2737 Centerview Drive
Knight Building
Tallahassee, FL 32399
P: (850) 488-1850
F: (850) 922-2992
E: Secretary.DJJ
@djj.state.fl.us

GEORGIA
Mr. Avery D. Niles
Commissioner
Department of Juvenile Justice
3408 Covington Highway
Decatur, GA 30032
P: (404) 508-6500
F: (404) 508-7289

IDAHO
Ms. Sharon Harrigfeld
Director
Department of Juvenile
Corrections
954 West Jefferson Street
P.O. Box 83720
Boise, ID 83720
P: (208) 334-5100
F: (208) 334-5120
E: sharon.harrigfeld
@idjc.idaho.gov

INDIANA
Ms. Christine Blessinger
Deputy Director
Division of Youth Services
Department of Correction
302 West Washington Street,
Room E-334
Indianapolis, IN 46204
P: (317) 234-2969
E: CBlessinger@idoc.in.gov

IOWA
Ms. Wendy Rickman
Administrator
Division of Adult, Children &
Family Services
Department of Human Services
1305 East Walnut
Des Moines, IA 50319
P: (515) 281-5521
F: (515) 242-6036
E: wrickma@dhs.state.ia.us

KANSAS
Ms. Terri Williams
Deputy Secretary
Juvenile Services Division
714 Southwest Jackson Avenue,
Suite 300
Topeka, KS 66603
P: (785) 296-0042
F: (785) 296-1412

KENTUCKY
Mr. Bob Hayter
Acting Commissioner
Department of Juvenile Justice
1025 Capital Center Drive
Frankfort, KY 40601
P: (502) 573-2738
F: (502) 573-4308

LOUISIANA
Dr. Mary L. Livers
Deputy Secretary
Office of Juvenile Justice
7919 Independence Boulevard
P.O. Box 66458
Baton Rouge, LA 70896
P: (225) 287-7900
F: (225) 287-7969
E: Debbie.Linder@la.gov

MAINE
Dr. Joseph Fitzpatrick
Commissioner
Juvenile Services Division
State House Station 111
Augusta, ME 04333
P: (207) 287-2711
F: (207) 287-4370
E: joseph.fitzpatrick
@maine.gov

MARYLAND
Mr. Sam Abed
Secretary
Department of Juvenile Services
One Center Plaza
120 West Fayette Street
Baltimore, MD 21201
P: (410) 230-3101
F: (410) 333-4199
E: Sam.Abed@maryland.gov

MASSACHUSETTS
Mr. Peter Forbes
Commissioner
Department of Youth Services
600 Washington Street, 4th
Floor
Boston, MA 02111
P: (617) 727-7575
F: (617) 727-0696

MICHIGAN
Ms. Maura D. Corrigan
Director
Department of Human Services
235 South Grand Avenue
P.O. Box 30037
Lansing, MI 48909
P: (313) 456-4887
F: (517) 335-6101
E: dhsweb@michigan.gov

Mr. Herman McCall
Director of Juvenile Programs
Department of Human Services
P.O. Box 30037
Lansing, MI 48909
P: (517) 335-3489
F: (517) 241-5632
E: mccallh@michigan.gov

Juvenile Rehabilitation

MINNESOTA
Mr. Tom Roy
Commissioner
Department of Corrections
1450 Energy Park Drive, Suite 200
St. Paul, MN 55108
P: (651) 361-7200
F: (651) 642-0414
E: tom.roy@state.mn.us

MISSISSIPPI
Ms. Joyce Word
Director
Office of Justice Programs
Department of Public Safety
1025 Northpark Drive
Ridgeland, MS 39157
P: (601) 987-3700
F: (601) 987-3764
E: jword@dps.ms.gov

MISSOURI
Mr. Tim Decker
Director
Division of Youth Services
3418 Knipp, Suite A-1
P.O. Box 447
Jefferson City, MO 65102
P: (573) 751-3324
F: (573) 526-4494
E: tim.decker@dss.mo.gov

MONTANA
Mr. Mike Batista
Director
Department of Corrections
5 South Last Chance Gulch
P.O. Box 201301
Helena, MT 59620
P: (406) 444-3930
F: (406) 444-4920

NEBRASKA
Mr. Tony Green
Acting Director
Division of Children & Family Services
P.O. Box 95026
Lincoln, NE 60509
P: (402) 471-9272
E: Tony.Green@nebraska.gov

NEVADA
Ms. Amber Howell
Administrator
Division of Child & Family Services
Department of Health & Human Services
4126 Technology Way, Suite 100
Carson City, NV 89706
P: (775) 684-4000
F: (775) 684-4010
E: ahowell@dcfs.nv.gov

NEW HAMPSHIRE
Mr. Jay A. Apicelli
Administrator of Finance
Division for Juvenile Justice Services
Department of Health & Human Services
1056 North River Road
Manchester, NH 03104
P: (603) 625-5471
F: (603) 625-1110
E: jay.a.appicelli
   @dhhs.state.nh.us

NEW JERSEY
Mr. Kevin M. Brown
Executive Director
Juvenile Justice Commission
1001 Spruce Street, Suite 202
P.O. Box 107
Trenton, NJ 08625
P: (609) 292-1400
F: (609) 943-4611

NEW MEXICO
Ms. Monique Jacobson
Cabinet Secretary
Children, Youth & Families Department
P.O. Drawer 5160
Santa Fe, NM 87502
P: (505) 827-7602
F: (505) 827-4053
E: monique.jacobson
   @state.nm.us

NEW YORK
Ms. Sheila Poole
Acting Commissioner
Office of Children & Family Services
Capitol View Office Park
52 Washington Street
Rensselaer, NY 12144
P: (518) 473-7793
F: (518) 486-7550

NORTH CAROLINA
J.R. Gorham
Commissioner
Division of Juvenile Justice
4212 Mail Service Center
Raleigh, NC 27699
P: (919) 733-3388
E: james.gorham@ncdps.gov

NORTH DAKOTA
Ms. Lisa Bjergaard
Director
Department of Corrections & Rehabilitation
Division of Juvenile Services
3100 Railroad Avenue, P.O. Box 1898
Bismarck, ND 58502
P: (701) 328-6362
F: (701) 328-6651
E: lbjergaa@nd.gov

NORTHERN MARIANA ISLANDS
Ms. Debra Inos
Director
Division of Youth Services
Caller Box 10007, Capital Hill
Saipan, MP 96950
P: (670) 664-2550
F: (670) 664-2560

OHIO
Mr. Harvey J. Reed
Director
Department of Youth Services
30 West Spring Street
Columbus, OH 43215
P: (614) 466-4314
F: (614) 752-9078

OREGON
Fariborz Pakseresht
Director
Youth Authority
530 Center Street, Northeast, Suite 200
Salem, OR 97301
P: (503) 373-7212
F: (503) 373-7622
E: fariborz.pakseresht
   @state.or.us

PUERTO RICO
Mr. Jesus Gonzalez Cruz
Administrator
Juvenile Institutions Administration
P.O. Box 19175
San Juan, PR 00910
P: (787) 767-9600
F: (787) 765-3394

RHODE ISLAND
Mr. Joseph Cardin
Deputy Superintendent
Juvenile Corrections Services
101 Friendship Street
Providence, RI 02903
P: (401) 462-7391

SOUTH CAROLINA
Ms. Margaret Barber
Director
Department of Juvenile Justice
4900 Broad River Road
P.O. Box 21069
Columbia, SC 29221
P: (803) 896-9749
F: (803) 896-9767

SOUTH DAKOTA
Mr. Doug Herrmann
Director, Juvenile Services
Juvenile Corrections
Department of Corrections
1600 Sedivy Lane
Rapid City, SD 57703
P: (605) 394-6645
F: (605) 394-6649
E: doug.herrmann
   @state.sd.us

TENNESSEE
Mr. James M. Henry
Commissioner
Department of Children's Services
Andrew Jackson Office Building
500 Deadrick Street, 15th Floor
Nashville, TN 37243
P: (615) 253-6885
F: (615) 253-4089
E: jim.henry@tn.gov

TEXAS
Mr. Mike Griffiths
Executive Director
Juvenile Justice Department
Building H, 11209 Metric Boulevard
P.O. Box 12757
Austin, TX 78758
P: (512) 490-7004
F: (512) 490-7717
E: tyc@tyc.state.tx.us

U.S. VIRGIN ISLANDS
Mr. Christopher E. Finch
Commissioner
Department of Human Services
Knud Hansen Complex, Building A
1303 Hospital Ground
St. Thomas, VI 00802
P: (340) 774-0930
F: (340) 773-2980

Juvenile Rehabilitation

UTAH
Ms. Susan Burke
Director
Division of Juvenile Justice
Services
Department of Human Services
195 North 1950 West
Salt Lake City, UT 84116
P: (801) 538-4330
E: sburke@utah.gov

VERMONT
Ms. Cindy K. Walcott
Deputy Commissioner
Family Services Division
Department for Children &
Families
103 South Main Street, Osgood 3
Waterbury, VT 05671
P: (802) 769-6502
F: (802) 241-2407
E: Cindy.Walcott
    @state.vt.us

VIRGINIA
Mr. Andrew Block
Executive Director
Department of Juvenile Justice
700 East Franklin Street
Richmond, VA 23219
P: (804) 371-0704
F: (804) 371-0773
E: andrew.block
    @djj.virginia.gov

WASHINGTON
Mr. John Clayton
Assistant Secretary
Juvenile Rehabilitation
Administration
14th & Jefferson Street
P.O. Box 45045
Olympia, WA 98504
P: (360) 902-7957
F: (360) 902-7848

WEST VIRGINIA
Ms. Stephanie Bond
Acting Director
Division of Juvenile Services
1200 Quarrier Street
Charleston, WV 25301
P: (304) 558-9800
F: (304) 558-6032
E: stephanie.j.bond@wv.gov

WISCONSIN
Mr. Paul Westerhaus
Administrator
Division of Juvenile Corrections
P.O. Box 7925
Madison, WI 53707
P: (608) 240-5900
F: (608) 240-3371
E: Paul.Westerhaus
    @Wisconsin.gov

WYOMING
Marty Nelson
Administrator, Social Services
Division
Department of Family Services
Hathaway Building, 3rd Floor
2300 Capitol Avenue
Cheyenne, WY 82002
P: (307) 777-6203
F: (307) 234-5306

Labor

Overall responsibility for administering and enforcing the state's labor laws.

ALABAMA
Mr. Fitzgerald Washington
Commissioner
Department of Labor
649 Monroe Street
Montgomery, AL 36131
P: (334) 242-8990

ALASKA
Ms. Heidi Drygas
Commissioner
Department of Labor &
Workforce Development
P.O. Box 111149
Juneau, AK 99811
P: (907) 465-2700
F: (907) 465-2784
E: heidi.drygas@alaska.gov

ARIZONA
Ms. Karen Axsom
Director, Labor Department
Industrial Commission
800 West Washington Street
Phoenix, AZ 85007
P: (602) 542-4515
F: (602) 542-7889
E: LaborAdmin@azica.gov

ARKANSAS
Mr. Leon Jones Jr.
Director
Department of Labor
10421 West Markham Street
Little Rock, AR 72205
P: (501) 682-4541

CALIFORNIA
Mr. David M. Lanier
Secretary
Labor & Workforce
Development Agency
800 Capitol Mall, MIC-55
Sacramento, CA 95814
P: (916) 653-9900

COLORADO
Ms. Ellen Golombek
Executive Director
Department of Labor &
Employment
633 17th Street, Suite 201
Denver, CO 80202
P: (303) 318-8020
F: (303) 318-8047
E: Ellen.Golombek
    @state.co.us

CONNECTICUT
Ms. Sharon Palmer
Commissioner
Department of Labor
200 Folly Brook Boulevard
Westerfield, CT 06109
P: (860) 263-6505
F: (850) 263-6529
E: sharon.palmer@ct.gov

DELAWARE
Mr. John McMahon
Secretary of Labor
Department of Labor
4425 North Market Street
Wilmington, DE 19802
P: (302) 761-8000
F: (302) 761-6621
E: john.mcmahon@state.de.us

DISTRICT OF COLUMBIA
Ms. Deborah A. Carroll
Director
Department of Employment
Services
4058 Minnesota Avenue,
Northeast
Washington, DC 20019
P: (202) 724-7000
F: (202) 673-6993
E: does@dc.gov

FLORIDA
Mr. Jesse Panuccio
Director
Department of Economic
Opportunity
107 East Madison Street
Caldwell Building
Tallahassee, FL 32399
P: (850) 245-7105

GEORGIA
Hon. Mark Butler (R)
Commissioner
Department of Labor
148 International Boulevard
Northeast
Atlanta, GA 30303
P: (404) 232-7300
F: (404) 656-2683
E: commissioner@gdol.ga.gov

GUAM
Mr. Manuel Q. Cruz
Director
Department of Labor
Government of Guam
P.O. Box 9970
Tamuning, GU 96931
P: (671) 647-6510
F: (671) 674-6517

HAWAII
Ms. Linda Chu Takayama
Director
Department of Labor &
Industrial Relations
830 Punchbowl Street
Honolulu, HI 96813
P: (808) 586-8844
F: (808) 586-9099
E: dlir.director@hawaii.gov

IDAHO
Mr. Kenneth D. Edmunds
Director
Department of Labor
317 West Main Street
Boise, ID 83735
P: (208) 334-6110
F: (208) 334-6430
E: kenneth.edmunds
    @labor.idaho.gov

ILLINOIS
Mr. Hugo Chaviano
Director
Department of Labor
160 North LaSalle Street, Suite
C-1300
Chicago, IL 60601
P: (312) 793-1808
F: (312) 793-5257
E: hugo.chaviano
    @illinois.gov

INDIANA
Mr. Rick J. Ruble
Commissioner
Department of Labor
402 West Washington Street,
Room W195
Indianapolis, IN 46204
P: (317) 232-2655
F: (317) 233-3790
E: rruble@dol.in.gov

IOWA
Mr. Michael A. Mauro
Commissioner
Division of Labor Services
1000 East Grand Avenue
Des Moines, IA 50319
P: (515) 281-3447
F: (515) 281-4698
E: michael.mauro
    @iwd.iowa.gov

KANSAS
Ms. Lana Gordon
Secretary of Labor
Department of Labor
401 Southwest Topeka
Boulevard
Topeka, KS 66603
P: (785) 296-5058
F: (785) 368-5289
E: lana.gordon@dol.ks.gov

KENTUCKY
Mr. Larry Roberts
Secretary
Labor Cabinet
1047 US Highway 127 South,
Suite 4
Frankfort, KY 40601
P: (502) 564-3070
F: (502) 564-5387

LOUISIANA
Mr. Curt Eysink
Executive Director
Workforce Commission
1001 North 23rd Street
P.O. Box 94094
Baton Rouge, LA 70804
P: (225) 342-3111
F: (225) 342-3778
E: owd@lwc.la.gov

MAINE
Ms. Jeanne Paquette
Commissioner
Department of Labor
54 State House Station
Augusta, ME 04333
P: (207) 623-7900
F: (207) 623-7934
E: jeanne.paquette
    @maine.gov

MARYLAND
Ms. Kelly M. Schulz
Secretary
Department of Labor, Licensing
& Regulation
500 North Calvert Street #401
Baltimore, MD 21201
P: (410) 230-6020
F: (410) 333-0853

MASSACHUSETTS
Mr. Ronald L. Walker II
Secretary
Executive Office of Labor &
Workforce Development
One Ashburton Place, Suite
2112
Boston, MA 02108
P: (617) 626-7122
F: (617) 727-1090

MICHIGAN
Mr. Mike Zimmer
Director
Department of Licensing &
Regulatory Affairs
P.O. Box 30004
Lansing, MI 48909
P: (517) 373-1820
F: (517) 373-2129
E: zimmerm@michigan.gov

Labor

MINNESOTA
Mr. Ken Peterson
Commissioner
Department of Labor & Industry
443 Lafayette Road North
St. Paul, MN 55155
P: (651) 284-5010
F: (651) 284-5720
E: ken.peterson@state.mn.us

MISSISSIPPI
Mr. Mark Henry
Executive Director
Department of Employment
Security
1235 Echelon Parkway
P.O. Box 1699
Jackson, MS 39215
P: (601) 321-6000
F: (601) 321-6104
E: mhenry@mdes.ms.gov

MISSOURI
Mr. Ryan McKenna
Director
Department of Labor &
Industrial Relations
421 East Dunklin Street
P.O. Box 504
Jefferson City, MO 65102
P: (573) 751-4091
F: (573) 751-4135
E: ryan.mckenna
    @labor.mo.gov

MONTANA
Ms. Pam Bucy
Commissioner
Department of Labor & Industry
P.O. Box 1728
Helena, MT 59624
P: (406) 444-2840
F: (406) 444-1419
E: pbucy@mt.gov

NEBRASKA
Ms. Brenda Hicks-Sorensen
Director
Department of Economic
Development
550 South 16th Street
Lincoln, NE 68508
P: (402) 471-3125
E: brenda.hicks-sorensen
    @nebraska.gov

NEVADA
Ms. Shannon M. Chambers
Commissioner
Office of the Labor
Commissioner
675 Fairview Drive, Suite 226
Carson City, NV 89701
P: (775) 687-4850
F: (775) 687-6409
E: mail1
    @laborcommissioner.com

NEW HAMPSHIRE
Mr. James W. Craig
Commissioner of Labor
Department of Labor
95 Pleasant Street
Concord, NH 03301
P: (603) 271-3171
F: (603) 271-6852
E: jcraig@labor.state.nh.us

NEW JERSEY
Mr. Harold Wirths
Commissioner
Department of Labor &
Workforce Development
P.O. Box 110
Trenton, NJ 08625
P: (609) 292-2323
F: (609) 633-9271
E: hal.wirths
    @dol.state.nj.us

NEW MEXICO
Ms. Celina Bussey
Secretary
Department of Workforce
Solutions
401 Broadway, Northeast
P.O. Box 1928
Albuquerque, NM 87103
P: (505) 841-8405
F: (505) 841-8491
E: celina.bussey
    @state.nm.us

NEW YORK
Mr. Mario J. Musolino
Acting Commissioner
Department of Labor
W. Averell Harriman State
Office Campus
Building 12
Albany, NY 12240
P: (518) 457-9000
F: (518) 485-6297
E: mario.musolino
    @labor.state.ny.us

NORTH CAROLINA
Hon. Cherie K. Berry (R)
Commissioner
Department of Labor
1101 Mail Service Center
Raleigh, NC 27699
P: (919) 807-2796
F: (919) 733-7640
E: cherie.berry
    @labor.nc.gov

NORTH DAKOTA
Ms. Bonnie Storbakken
Commissioner of Labor
Department of Labor
600 East Boulevard Avenue
Department 406
Bismarck, ND 58505
P: (701) 328-2660
F: (701) 328-2031
E: bstorbakken@nd.gov

OHIO
Mr. David Williamson
Superintendent
Division of Industrial
Compliance & Labor
Department of Commerce
P.O. Box 4009
Reynoldsburg, OH 43068
P: (614) 644-2223
E: ic@com.state.oh.us

OKLAHOMA
Hon. Mark Costello (R)
Commissioner of Labor
Department of Labor
3017 North Stiles, Suite 100
Oklahoma City, OK 73105
P: (405) 521-6100
F: (405) 521-6018
E: mark.costello
    @labor.ok.gov

OREGON
Hon. Brad Avakian (D)
Commissioner
Bureau of Labor & Industries
800 Northeast Oregon Street
Suite 1045
Portland, OR 97232
P: (971) 673-0781
F: (971) 673-0762
E: brad.avakian@state.or.us

PENNSYLVANIA
Ms. Kathy M. Manderino
Secretary
Department of Labor & Industry
651 Boas Street, Room 1700
Harrisburg, PA 17121
P: (717) 787-5279
F: (717) 787-8826

PUERTO RICO
Mr. Vance Thomas
Secretary
Department of Labor & Human
Resources
P.O. Box 195540
Hato Rey, PR 00918
P: (787) 754-2119
F: (787) 753-9550

RHODE ISLAND
Mr. Scott Jensen
Director
Department of Labor & Training
Center General Complex
1511 Pontiac Avenue
Cranston, RI 02920
P: (401) 462-8000
F: (401) 462-8872
E: director-dlt@dlt.ri.gov

SOUTH CAROLINA
Ms. Richele Taylor
Director
Department of Labor, Licensing
& Regulation
P.O. Box 11329
Columbia, SC 29211
P: (803) 896-4390
F: (803) 896-4393

SOUTH DAKOTA
Ms. Marcia Hultman
Secretary
Department of Labor &
Regulation
700 Governors Drive
Pierre, SD 57501
P: (605) 773-3101
F: (605) 773-6184
E: marcia.hultman
    @state.sd.us

TENNESSEE
Mr. Burns Phillips
Commissioner
Department of Labor &
Workforce Development
220 French Landing Drive
Nashville, TN 37243
P: (615) 741-6642
F: (615) 741-5078
E: burns.phillips@tn.gov

TEXAS
Mr. Ronald G. Congleton
Commissioner Representing
Labor
Workforce Commission
101 East 15th Street, Room 674
Austin, TX 78778
P: (512) 463-2829
F: (512) 475-2152
E: ronald.congleton
    @twc.state.tx.us

Mr. Larry E. Temple
Executive Director
Workforce Commission
101 East 15th Street
Austin, TX 78778
P: (512) 463-0735
F: (512) 475-2321
E: larry.temple
　@twc.state.tx.us

U.S. VIRGIN ISLANDS
Ms. Catherine Ann Hendry
Commissioner of Labor
Department of Labor
4401 Sion Farm
Christiansted, VI 00820
P: (340) 773-1994
F: (340) 773-0094
E: chendry@vidol.gov

UTAH
Ms. Sherrie M. Hayashi
Commissioner & Department
Director
Labor Commission
160 East 300 South, 3rd Floor
P.O. Box 146600
Salt Lake City, UT 84114
P: (801) 530-6848
F: (801) 530-6390
E: shayashi@utah.gov

VERMONT
Ms. Annie Noonan
Commissioner
Department of Labor
5 Green Mountain Drive
P.O. Box 488
Montpelier, VT 05601
P: (802) 828-4301
F: (802) 828-4022
E: annie.noonan@state.vt.us

VIRGINIA
Mr. Maurice A. Jones
Secretary of Commerce & Trade
Office of the Secretary
P.O. Box 1475
Richmond, VA 23218
P: (804) 786-7831
F: (804) 371-0250
E: maurice.jones
　@governor.virginia.gov

WASHINGTON
Mr. Joel Sacks
Director
Department of Labor &
Industries
P.O. Box 44000
Olympia, WA 98504
P: (360) 902-5799
F: (360) 902-5792
E: joel.sacks@lni.wa.gov

WEST VIRGINIA
Mr. John R. Junkins
Acting Commissioner
Division of Labor
Department of Commerce
749 B, Building 6, Capitol
Complex
Charleston, WV 25305
P: (304) 558-7890
F: (304) 558-2415
E: john.r.junkins@wv.gov

WISCONSIN
Mr. Reggie Newson
Secretary
Department of Workforce
Development
201 East Washington Avenue
GEF-1, Room A400, P.O. Box
7946
Madison, WI 53707
P: (608) 266-3131
F: (608) 266-1784
E: reggie.newson
　@dwd.wisconsin.gov

WYOMING
Ms. Joan K. Evans
Director
Department of Workforce
Services
122 West 25th Street
Herschler Building, 2nd Floor
East
Cheyenne, WY 82002
P: (307) 777-8728
F: (307) 777-5857
E: joan.evans@wyo.gov

Law Enforcement

Conducts state-level criminal investigations.

ALABAMA
Mr. Spencer Collier
Director
Law Enforcement Agency
301 South Ripley Street
P.O. Box 1511
Montgomery, AL 36102
P: (334) 242-4394
F: (334) 242-0512

ALASKA
Mr. Gary Folger
Commissioner
Department of Public Safety
5700 East Tudor Road
Anchorage, AK 99507
P: (907) 269-5086
F: (907) 269-4543
E: gary.folger@alaska.gov

AMERICAN SAMOA
Mr. William E. Haleck
Commissioner
Department of Public Safety
American Samoa Government
P.O. Box 1086
Pato Pato, AS 96799
P: (684) 633-1111
F: (684) 633-7296
E: commissioner@dps.as.gov

ARIZONA
Mr. Frank Milstead
Director
Department of Public Safety
P.O. Box 6638
Phoenix, AZ 85005
P: (602) 223-2000
F: (602) 223-2917

CALIFORNIA
Hon. Kamala Harris (D)
Attorney General
Office of the Attorney General
1300 I Street, Sutie 1740
Sacramento, CA 95814
P: (916) 445-9555

COLORADO
Mr. Ron Sloan
Director
Bureau of Investigation
690 Kipling Street, Suite 3000
Lakewood, CO 80215
P: (303) 239-4201
F: (303) 235-0568
E: ron.sloan@state.co.us

CONNECTICUT
Mr. Kevin T. Kane
Chief State's Attorney
Division of Criminal Justice
300 Corporate Place
Rocky Hill, CT 06067
P: (860) 258-5800
F: (860) 258-5858
E: conndcj@ct.gov

DELAWARE
Colonel Nathaniel McQueen
Commissioner
State Police
1441 North DuPont Highway
P.O. Box 430
Dover, DE 19903
P: (302) 739-5291

DISTRICT OF COLUMBIA
Ms. Cathy L. Lanier
Chief of Police
Metropolitan Police Department
300 Indiana Avenue, Northwest
Room 5059
Washington, DC 20001
P: (202) 727-9099
F: (202) 727-4106
E: mpd@dc.gov

FLORIDA
Mr. Rick Swearingen
Commissioner
Department of Law
Enforcement
2331 Phillips Road
P.O. Box 1489
Tallahassee, FL 32302
P: (850) 410-7001
E: RickSwearingen
    @fdle.state.fl.us

GEORGIA
Mr. Vernon M. Keenan
Director
Bureau of Investigation
3121 Panthersville Road
Decatur, GA 30034
P: (404) 244-2600
F: (404) 270-8352
E: vernon.keenan@gbi.ga.gov

GUAM
Mr. Fred E. Bordallo Jr.
Chief of Police
Police Department
#13-16A Mariner Avenue
P.O. Box 23909
Tiyan, GU 96913
P: (671) 475-8508
F: (671) 472-4036
E: chief@gpd.guam.gov

HAWAII
Mr. Shawn H. Tsuha
Deputy Director of Law
Enforcement
Department of Public Safety
919 Ala Moana Boulevard, 4th
Floor
Honolulu, HI 96814
P: (808) 587-1288
F: (808) 587-1282
E: psd.
    office.of.the.director
    @hawaii.gov

ILLINOIS
Mr. Hiram Grau
State Director
State Police
801 South 7th Street, Suite 1100
 – S
Springfield, IL 62703
P: (217) 782-7263
E: hiram.grau@illinois.gov

INDIANA
Mr. Douglas G. Carter
Superintendent
State Police
Indiana Government Center
North
100 North Senate Avenue
Indianapolis, IN 46204
P: (317) 232-8248
E: ISP@isp.in.gov

IOWA
Mr. Larry L. Noble
Commissioner
Department of Public Safety
215 East 7th Street
Des Moines, IA 50319
P: (515) 725-6182
E: noble@dps.state.ia.us

KANSAS
Mr. Kirk D. Thompson
Director
Bureau of Investigation
1620 Southwest Tyler Street
Topeka, KS 66612
P: (785) 296-8200

KENTUCKY
Mr. Rodney Brewer
Commissioner
State Police
919 Versailles Road
Frankfort, KY 40601
P: (502) 782-1800
F: (502) 573-1479

LOUISIANA
Lt. Col. Murphy Paul
Deputy Superintendent
Bureau of Investigations
State Police
7919 Independence Boulevard
Baton Rouge, LA 70806
P: (800) 434-8007

MAINE
Hon. Janet T. Mills (D)
Attorney General
Office of the Attorney General
State House Station 6
Augusta, ME 04333
P: (207) 626-8800

MARYLAND
Colonel William Pallozzi
Superintendent
Department of State Police
1201 Reisterstown Road
Pikesville, MD 21208
P: (410) 653-4219
E: msp.superintendent
    @maryland.gov

MASSACHUSETTS
Colonel Richard D. McKeon
Superintendent
State Police
470 Worcester Road
Framingham, MA 01702
P: (508) 820-2300
F: (617) 727-6874

MICHIGAN
Colonel Kriste Kibbey Etue
Director
State Police
333 South Grand Avenue
P.O. Box 30634
Lansing, MI 48909
P: (517) 332-2521
F: (517) 241-0409
E: EtueK@michigan.gov

MINNESOTA
Ms. Ramona Dohman
Commissioner
Department of Public Safety
445 Minnesota Street, Suite
1000
St. Paul, MN 55101
P: (651) 201-7160
F: (651) 297-5728
E: Mona.Dohman@state.mn.us

MISSISSIPPI
Mr. Albert Santa Cruz
Commissioner
Department of Public Safety
P.O. Box 958
Jackson, MS 39205
P: (601) 987-1212
F: (601) 987-1488
E: commissioner
    @mdps.state.ms.us

MISSOURI
Mr. George Lombardi
Director
Department of Corrections
2729 Plaza Drive
P.O. Box 236
Jefferson City, MO 65102
P: (573) 751-2389
F: (573) 751-4099

MONTANA
Hon. Tim Fox (R)
Attorney General
Department of Justice
Justice Building
215 North Sanders
Helena, MT 59620
P: (406) 444-2026
F: (406) 444-3549
E: contactdoj@mt.gov

NEBRASKA
Colonel Bradley Rice
Superintendent of Law
Enforcement & Public Safety
State Patrol
P.O. Box 94907
Lincoln, NE 68509
P: (402) 471-4545
F: (402) 479-4002
E: bradley.rice
    @nebraska.gov

NEVADA
Mr. Patrick J. Conmay
Chief
Investigations Division
Department of Public Safety
555 Wright Way
Carson City, NV 89711
P: (775) 684-7412
F: (775) 687-4405
E: NDIHQC@dps.state.nv.us

NEW HAMPSHIRE
Colonel Robert L. Quinn
Director
Division of State Police
Department of Safety
33 Hazen Drive
Concord, NH 03305
P: (603) 223-8813
F: (603) 271-1153
E: SPHeadquarters
    @dos.nh.gov

NEW JERSEY
Col. Rick Fuentes
Superintendent
State Police
P.O. Box 7068
West Trenton, NJ 08628
P: (609) 882-2000
F: (609) 530-4383

NEW MEXICO
Mr. Pete N. Kassetas
Chief of Police
Department of Public Safety
4491 Cerrillos Road
P.O. Box 1628
Santa Fe, NM 87504
P: (505) 827-9002
F: (505) 827-3394
E: NMSP.Chief@state.nm.us

NEW YORK
Mr. Joseph D'Amico
Superintendent
State Police
1220 Washington Avenue,
Building 22
Albany, NY 12226
P: 518) 457-6721

NORTH CAROLINA
Mr. Greg McLeod
Director
State Bureau of Investigation
P.O. Box 29500
Raleigh, NC 27626
P: (919) 662-4500
F: (919) 662-4523
E: gsmcleod@ncdoj.gov

NORTH DAKOTA
Mr. Dallas Carlson
Director
Bureau of Criminal
Investigation
Office of the Attorney General
P.O. Box 1054
Bismark, ND 58502
P: (701) 328-5500
F: (701) 328-5510
E: dcarlson@nd.gov

Colonel James Prochniak
Superintendent
Highway Patrol
600 East Boulevard Avenue
Department 504
Bismarck, ND 58505
P: (701) 328-2455
F: (701) 328-1717
E: jprochni@nd.gov

OHIO
Colonel John Born
Director
Department of Public Safety
1970 West Broad Street
P.O. Box 182081
Columbus, OH 43218
P: (614) 466-3383
F: (614) 466-0433

OKLAHOMA
Mr. Michael C. Thompson
Commissioner
Department of Public Safety
P.O. Box 11415
Oklahoma City, OK 73136
P: (405) 425-2424
E: mike.thompson
    @dps.state.ok.us

PUERTO RICO
Mr. Hector Pesquera
Superintendent
Puerto Rico Police
P.O. Box 70166
San Juan, PR 00936
P: (787) 793-1234
F: (787) 781-0080

RHODE ISLAND
Colonel Steven G. O'Donnell
Commissioner & Superintendent
Department of Public Safety
311 Danielson Pike
North Scituate, RI 02857
P: (401) 444-1000
F: (401) 444-1105
E: sodonnell
    @risp.state.ri.us

SOUTH CAROLINA
Mr. Mark A. Keel
Chief
State Law Enforcement Division
4400 Broad River Road
P.O. Box 21398
Columbia, SC 29221
P: (803) 896-9223
F: (803) 896-7041

SOUTH DAKOTA
Mr. Bryan Gortmaker
Director
Division of Criminal
Investigation
Office of the Attorney General
1302 East Highway 14, Suite 5
Pierre, SD 57501
P: (605) 773-3331
F: (605) 773-4629
E: atghelp@state.sd.us

TENNESSEE
Mr. Mark Gwyn
Director
Bureau of Investigation
901 R.S. Gass Boulevard
Nashville, TN 37216
P: (615) 744-4000

TEXAS
Mr. Kim Vickers
Executive Director
Commission on Law
Enforcement
6330 East Highway 290, Suite
200
Austin, TX 78723
P: (512) 936-7700 Ext. 7713
F: (512) 936-7766
E: kim.vickers
    @tcole.texas.gov

U.S. VIRGIN ISLANDS
Mr. Rodney F. Querrard
Commissioner
Police Department
Alexander Farrelly Criminal
Justice Ctr.
Charlotte Amalie
St. Thomas, VI 00802
P: (340) 715-5605
F: (340) 715-5517

UTAH
Col. Daniel Fuhr
Superintendent
Department of Public Safety
Utah Highway Patrol
4501 South 2700 West, P.O. Box
141100
Salt Lake City, UT 84114
P: (801) 965-4518
F: (801) 965-4716
E: dfuhr@utah.gov

Law Enforcement

VIRGINIA
Col. W. Steven Flaherty
Superintendent
Department of State Police
7700 Midlothian Turnpike
P.O. Box 27472
Richmond, VA 23235
P: (804) 674-2087
F: (804) 674-2132
E: steve.flaherty
    @vsp.virginia.gov

WASHINGTON
Mr. John R. Batiste
Chief
State Patrol
General Administration Building
P.O. Box 42600
Olympia, WA 98504
P: (360) 596-4000
E: john.batiste@wsp.wa.gov

WEST VIRGINIA
Colonel Jay Smithers
Superintendent
State Police
725 Jefferson Road
South Charleston, WV 25309
P: (304) 746-2115
F: (304) 746-2230
E: Jay.Smithers@wvsp.gov

WISCONSIN
Mr. David S. Matthews
Administrator
Division of Criminal
Investigation
Department of Justice
P.O. Box 7857
Madison, WI 53707
P: (608) 266-1671

WYOMING
Mr. Steve Woodson
Director
Division of Criminal
Investigation
208 South College Drive
Cheyenne, WY 82002
P: (307) 777-7181
F: (307) 777-7252

Law Library

Legal resource for the state's highest court.

ALABAMA
Mr. Timothy A. Lewis
Director & State Law Librarian
State Law Library
300 Dexter Avenue
Montgomery, AL 36104
P: (334) 229-0560
F: (334) 242-0543
E: tlewis
    @appellate.state.al.us

ALASKA
Ms. Susan Falk
State Law Librarian
State Court Law Library
303 K Street
Anchorage, AK 99501
P: (907) 264-0585
E: sfalk@courts.state.ak.us

AMERICAN SAMOA
Hon. Talauega Eleasalo V.
    Ale
Attorney General
Office of the Attorney General
American Samoa Government
Exeutive Office Building,
Utulei
Pago Pago, AS 96799
P: (684) 633-4163

ARIZONA
Ms. Joan Clark
State Librarian
State Library, Archives &
Public Records
State Capitol, Room 200
1700 West Washington
Phoenix, AZ 85007
P: (602) 926-4035
F: (602) 256-7983
E: jclark@azlibrary.gov

ARKANSAS
Ms. Ava Hicks
Director
Supreme Court Library
Justice Building, Suite 1500
625 Marshall
Little Rock, AR 72201
P: (501) 682-2041
F: (501) 682-6877
E: ava.hicks@arkansas.gov

COLORADO
Mr. Dan Cordova
Librarian
Supreme Court Library
Ralph L. Carr Judicial Center
2 East 14th Avenue
Denver, CO 80203
P: (720) 625-5100
F: (720) 625-5110
E: library
    @judicial.state.co.us

CONNECTICUT
Ms. Ann Doherty
Deputy Director
Law Libraries
Judicial Branch
95 Washington Street
Hartford, CT 06106
P: (860) 706-5145
F: (860) 548-2868
E: ann.doherty@jud.ct.gov

DELAWARE
Ms. Patricia Burris
Law Librarian
State Law Library
38 The Green, Suite 100
414 Federal Street
Dover, DE 19901
P: (302) 674-7470
F: (302) 674-7471
E: patricia.burris
    @state.de.us

DISTRICT OF COLUMBIA
Ms. Letty Limbach
Librarian
Court of Appeals
500 Indiana Avenue, Northwest
Washington, DC 20001
P: (202) 879-2767

FLORIDA
Ms. Billie J. Blaine
Librarian
Supreme Court Library
500 South Duvall Street
Tallahassee, FL 32399
P: (850) 488-8919
F: (850) 922-5219
E: library@flcourts.org

GUAM
Ms. Geraldine Amparo Cepeda
Executive Director/Librarian
Law Library
141 San Ramon Street
Hagatna, GU 96910
P: (671) 477-7623
F: (671) 472-1246
E: gll@guamlawlibrary.org

HAWAII
Ms. Jenny Fujinaka
Law Librarian
Supreme Court Law Library
Ali'iolani Hale, Room 115
417 South King Street
Honolulu, HI 96813
P: (808) 539-4964
F: (808) 539-4974
E: LawLibrary
    @courts.hawaii.gov

ILLINOIS
Mr. Geoffrey Pelzek
Librarian
Courts of Illinois
Supreme Court Building
421 East Capitol Avenue
Springfield, IL 62701
P: (217) 782-2424
F: (217) 782-5287

INDIANA
Ms. Terri Ross
Law Librarian
Supreme Court Law Library
200 West Washington Street
State House, Room 316
Indianapolis, IN 46204
P: (317) 232-2557
F: (317) 233-8693
E: tross@courts.state.in.us

IOWA
Mr. Cory Quist
Law Librarian
State Law Library
State Library
1007 East Grand Avenue
Des Moines, IA 50319
P: (515) 281-4307
F: (515) 281-5405
E: cory.quist
    @lib.state.ia.us

KENTUCKY
Ms. Jennifer Frazier
State Law Librarian
State Law Library
State Capitol, Suite 200
700 Capitol Avenue
Frankfort, KY 40601
P: (502) 564-4848
F: (502) 564-5041

LOUISIANA
Ms. Georgia Chadwick
Director
Law Library
Supreme Court
400 Royal Street, 2nd Floor
New Orleans, LA 70130
P: (504) 310-2402
F: (504) 310-2419
E: library@lasc.org

MAINE
Mr. John R. Barden
Director
State Law & Legislative
Reference Library
43 State House Station
Augusta, ME 04333
P: (207) 287-1600
F: (207) 287-6467
E: lawlib.office
    @legislature.maine.gov

MARYLAND
Mr. Steve P. Anderson
Director
State Law Library
Murphy Courts of Appeal
Building
361 Rowe Boulevard
Annapolis, MD 21401
P: (410) 260-1432
F: (410) 260-1572

MICHIGAN
Ms. Kim Koscielniak
Law Librarian
State Law Library
702 West Kalamazoo Street
P.O. Box 30007
Lansing, MI 48909
P: (517) 373-4697
F: (517) 373-3915
E: koscielniakk
    @michigan.gov

MISSISSIPPI
Ms. Clara Joorfetz
State Librarian
State Law Library
P.O. Box 1040
Jackson, MS 39215
P: (601) 359-3672
F: (601) 359-2912
E: cjoorfetz@courts.ms.gov

MISSOURI
Ms. Gail Miller
Director of Library & Public
Services
Supreme Court Library
207 West High Street, Second
Floor
Jefferson City, MO 65101
P: (573) 751-2636
F: (573) 751-2573

MONTANA
Ms. Lisa Jackson
State Law Librarian
State Law Library
215 North Sanders Street
P.O. Box 203004
Helena, MT 59620
P: (406) 444-3660
F: (406) 444-3603

Law Library

NEBRASKA
Mr. Corey Steel
State Court Administrator
Supreme Court
P.O. Box 98910
Lincoln, NE 68509
P: (402) 471-3730
F: (402) 471-2197
E: corey.steel@nebraska.gov

NEVADA
Ms. Kathleen L. Harrington
Law Librarian
Supreme Court Law Library
201 South Carson Street
Carson City, NV 89701
P: (775) 684-1640
F: (775) 684-1662
E: harrington
    @nvcourts.nv.gov

NEW HAMPSHIRE
Ms. Mary S. Searles
Director
State Law Library
Supreme Court Building
One Charles Doe Drive
Concord, NH 03301
P: (603) 271-3777
F: (603) 513-5450
E: msearles
    @courts.state.nh.us

NEW MEXICO
Mr. Robert Mead
State Law Librarian
Supreme Court Law Library
237 Don Gaspar
Santa Fe, NM 87501
P: (505) 827-4850
F: (505) 827-4852

NORTH CAROLINA
Mr. Thomas P. Davis
Librarian
Supreme Court Library
500 Justice Building
2 East Morgan Street
Raleigh, NC 27601
P: (919) 831-5709
E: tpd@sc.state.nc.us

NORTH DAKOTA
Mr. Ted Smith
Law Librarian
Supreme Court Law Library
500 East Capitol Avenue
Pierre, ND 57501
P: (701) 328-4594
F: (701) 328-3609
E: TSmith@ndcourts.gov

**NORTHERN MARIANA
ISLANDS**
Ms. Margarita M. Palacios
Court Administrator
Supreme Court
P.O. Box 502165
Saipan, MP 96950
P: (670) 236-9800
F: (670) 236-9702
E: supreme.court@saipan.com

OHIO
Mr. Kenneth Kozlowski
Director
Law Library
Supreme Court of Ohio
65 South Front Street, 11th Floor
Columbus, OH 43215
P: (614) 387-9680
F: (614) 387-9689
E: libref@sc.ohio.gov

OKLAHOMA
Mr. Douglas Amos
Law Librarian
Cartwright Memorial Library
2300 North Lincoln Boulevard,
Room B-8
Oklahoma City, OK 73105
P: (405) 522-3213
F: (405) 521-2753

OREGON
Ms. Cathryn E. Bowie
State Law Librarian
State Law Library
1163 State Street
Salem, OR 97301
P: (503) 986-5640
F: (503) 986-5623
E: cathryn.e.bowie
    @ojd.state.or.us

PENNSYLVANIA
Ms. Alice L. Lubrecht
Director
Bureau of State Library
Department of Education
Forum Building, 607 South
Drive
Harrisburg, PA 17120
P: (717) 783-5968
F: (717) 772-8268
E: alubrecht@pa.gov

RHODE ISLAND
Ms. Colleen Hanna
Acting State Law Librarian
State Law Library
Main Library
250 Benefit Street
Providence, RI
P: (402) 222-4275
F: (401) 222-3865
E: channa@courts.ri.gov

SOUTH CAROLINA
Ms. Janet Meyer
Librarian
Supreme Court Library
Supreme Court Building
1231 Gervais Street
Columbia, SC 29211
P: (803) 734-1080
F: (803) 734-0519

TEXAS
Mr. Dale W. Propp
Director
State Law Library
205 West 14th , Room G01
P.O. Box 12367
Austin, TX 78711
P: (512) 463-1722
F: (512) 463-1728

U.S. VIRGIN ISLANDS
Ms. Mary Barnes
Law Librarian
Law Library
Justice Center, 5400 Veteran's
Drive
3rd Floor, East Wing, Room
E311
St. Thomas, VI 00802
P: (340) 774-6680 Ext. 6419
F: (340) 776-9889
E: LawLibrary-Stt
    @visuperiorcourt.org

UTAH
Ms. Jessica Van Buren
Director
State Law Library
450 South State Street
P.O. Box 140220
Salt Lake City, UT 84114
P: (801) 238-7991
F: (801) 238-7993
E: jessicavb@utcourts.gov

VERMONT
Ms. Martha Reid
State Librarian
Department of Libraries
109 State Street
Montpelier, VT 05609
P: (802) 828-3265
F: (802) 828-2199
E: martha.reid@state.vt.us

VIRGINIA
Ms. Gail Warren
State Law Librarian
Supreme Court
100 North Ninth Street
Richmond, VA 23219
P: (804) 786-2075
F: (804) 786-4542

WASHINGTON
Ms. Kay E. Newman
State Law Librarian
State Law Library
415 12th Avenue, Southwest
P.O. Box 40751
Olympia, WA 98504
P: (360) 357-2136
F: (360) 357-2153
E: kay.newman@courts.wa.gov

WEST VIRGINIA
Ms. Kaye L. Maerz
State Law Librarian
State Law Library
Building One, Room E-404
1900 Kanawha Boulevard
Charleston, WV 25305
P: (304) 558-2607
F: (304) 558-3673
E: kaye.maerz@courtswv.gov

WISCONSIN
Ms. Julie Tessmer
State Law Librarian
State Law Library
120 Martin Luther King Jr.
Boulevard
P.O. Box 7881
Madison, WI 53707
P: (608) 261-2340
F: (608) 267-2319
E: julie.tessmer
    @wicourts.gov

WYOMING
Ms. Diane Forge Bauersfeld
State Law Librarian
State Law Library
Supreme Court Building
2301 Capitol Avenue
Cheyenne, WY 82002
P: (307) 777-7509
F: (307) 777-7240
E: dbauersfeld
    @courts.state.wy.us

Licensing (Occupational and Professional)

Licenses and regulates the function of various professions in the state. Since there are hundreds of autonomous boards in the states, it is the centralized agencies that are represented in this listing.

ALASKA
Mr. Don Habeger
Division Director
Division of Corporations, Business & Professional Licensing
P.O. Box 110806
Juneau, AK 99811
P: (907) 465-2550
F: (907) 465-2974
E: don.habeger@alaska.gov

CALIFORNIA
Ms. Denise Brown
Director
Department of Consumer Affairs
1625 North Market Boulevard
Suite N 112
Sacramento, CA 95834
P: (916) 574-8200
F: (916) 574-8613
E: denise.brown@dca.ca.gov

COLORADO
Mr. Greg Ferland
Interim Division Director
Division of Registrations
Department of Regulatory Agencies
1560 Broadway, Suite 1350
Denver, CO 80202
P: (303) 894-7800
F: (303) 894-7693
E: greg.ferland
   @dora.state.co.us

CONNECTICUT
Mr. Richard Hurlburt
Director
Occupational & Professional Licensing Division
165 Capitol Avenue
Hartford, CT 06106
P: (860) 713-6135
F: (860) 713-7230
E: richard.hurlburt@ct.gov

DISTRICT OF COLUMBIA
Mr. Clifford Cooks
Program Manager
Department of Consumer & Regulatory Affairs
1100 Fourth Street, Southwest
Washington, DC 20024
P: (202) 442-4400
F: (202) 698-4329
E: dcra@dc.gov

Dr. Rikin S. Mehta
Senior Deputy Director
Health Regulation & Licensing Administration
Department of Health
899 North Capitol Street, NE, 2nd Floor
Washington, DC 20002
P: (202) 724-4900
F: (202) 724-5145

FLORIDA
Ms. Lucy C. Gee
Division Director
Division of Medical Quality Assurance/Licensure Services
Department of Health
4052 Bald Cypress Way
Tallahassee, FL 32399
P: (850) 245-4224
F: (850) 245-4791
E: lucy_gee@doh.state.fl.us

Mr. Ken Lawson
Secretary
Department of Business & Professional Regulation
1940 North Monroe Street
Tallahassee, FL 32399
P: (850) 487-1395
F: (850) 488-1830
E: Call.Center
   @dbpr.state.fl.us

GEORGIA
Mr. Randall D. Vaughn
Division Director
Professional Licensing Boards Division
Office of Secretary of State
237 Coliseum Drive
Macon, GA 31217
P: (478) 207-2440
F: (478) 207-1363
E: rvaughn@sos.state.ga.us

HAWAII
Ms. Celia Suzuki
Licensing Administrator
Professional & Vocational Licensing Division
Dept. of Commerce & Consumer Affairs
P.O. Box 3469
Honolulu, HI 96801
P: (808) 586-2690
F: (808) 586-2689
E: pvl@dcca.hawaii.gov

IDAHO
Ms. Tana Cory
Bureau Chief
Bureau of Occupational Licenses
1109 Main Street, Suite 220
Boise, ID 83702
P: (208) 334-3233
F: (208) 334-3945
E: tcory@ibol.idaho.gov

ILLINOIS
Mr. Manuel Flores
Acting Secretary
Department of Financial & Professional Regulation
320 West Washington Street
Springfield, IL 62786
P: (217) 785-0820
F: (217) 558-6001

INDIANA
Mr. Nicholas Rhoad
Executive Director
Professional Licensing Agency
402 West Washington Street, Room W072
Indianapolis, IN 46204
P: (317) 232-2960
F: (317) 233-4236
E: NRhoad@pla.IN.gov

IOWA
Ms. Barbara Huey
Bureau Chief
Bureau of Professional Licensure
Lucas State Office Building
321 East 12th Street, 5th Floor
Des Moines, IA 50266
P: (515) 281-0254
F: (515) 281-3121
E: barbara.huey
   @idph.iowa.gov

KENTUCKY
Mr. Gordon Slone
Executive Director
Office of Occupations & Professions
P.O. Box 1360
Frankfort, KY 40601
P: (502) 564-3296 Ext. 224
F: (502) 564-4818
E: Gordon.Slone@ky.gov

MAINE
Ms. Anne L. Head
Commissioner
Department of Professional & Financial Regulation
35 State House Station
Augusta, ME 04333
P: (207) 624-8511
F: (207) 624-8690
E: anne.l.head@maine.gov

MARYLAND
Dr. Joshua M. Sharfstein
Secretary
Department of Health & Mental Hygiene
201 West Preston Street
Baltimore, MD 21201
P: (410) 767-6500
F: (410) 767-6489
E: joshua.sharfstein
   @maryland.gov

MASSACHUSETTS
Ms. Jean Pontikas
Director
Division of Health Professions Licensure
Office of Health and Human Services
239 Causeway Street, 5th Floor
Boston, MA 02114
P: (617) 973-0948
F: (617) 973-0983
E: jean.pontikas
   @state.ma.us

Mr. George K. Weber
Director
Division of Professional Licensure
Consumer Affairs & Business Regulation
1000 Washington Street, Suite 710
Boston, MA 02118
P: (617) 727-3074
F: (617) 727-1944
E: george.k.weber
   @state.ma.us

Licensing (Occupational and Professional)

MICHIGAN
Mr. Steve Arwood
CEO
Department of Licensing &
Regulatory Affairs
300 North Washington Square
Lansing, MI 48913
P: (517) 241-1400
F: (517) 241-3683
E: arwoods1@michigan.org

MISSOURI
Ms. Jane A. Rackers
Division Director
Division of Professional
Regulation
3605 Missouri Boulevard
P.O. Box 1335
Jefferson City, MO 65102
P: (573) 751-1081
F: (573) 751-4176
E: jane.rackers@pr.mo.gov

MONTANA
Mr. Adam De Yong
Acting Division Administrator
Business Standards Division
Dept. of Labor & Industry
301 South Park, Room 430
Helena, MT 59620
P: (406) 841-2333

NEBRASKA
Ms. Helen L. Meeks
Administrator
Health & Human Services
Regulation & Licensure
301 Centennial Mall South
P.O. Box 94986
Lincoln, NE 68509
P: (402) 471-4923
F: (402) 471-3577
E: helen.meeks@hhss.ne.gov

NEW JERSEY
Mr. Steve C. Lee
Acting Director
Division of Consumer Affairs
124 Halsey Street
Newark, NJ 07102
P: (973) 504-6200
F: (973) 273-8035
E: askconsumeraffairs
    @lps.state.nj.us

NEW MEXICO
Mr. Robert Mike Unthank
Superintendent
Regulation & Licensing
Department
2550 Cerrillos Road, 3rd Floor
Sante Fe, NM 87505
P: (505) 476-4508
F: (505) 476-4511

NEW YORK
Mr. Douglas E. Lentivech
Deputy Commissioner
Office of the Professions
State Education Department
89 Washington Avenue
Albany, NY 12234
P: (518) 474-3862
F: (518) 474-1449
E: dlentivech
    @mail.nysed.gov

OREGON
Ms. Holly Mercer
Director
Health Licensing Agency
700 Summer Street, Northeast
Suite 320
Salem, OR 97301
P: (503) 373-2084
F: (503) 370-9004
E: holly.mercer@state.or.us

PENNSYLVANIA
Mr. Travis N. Gery
Commissioner
Bureau of Professional &
Occupational Affairs
Department of State
P.O. Box 2649
Harrisburg, PA 17105
P: (717) 787-8503
F: (717) 783-0510
E: RA-BPOA@pa.gov

SOUTH CAROLINA
Ms. Richele Taylor
Director
Department of Labor, Licensing
& Regulation
P.O. Box 11329
Columbia, SC 29211
P: (803) 896-4390
F: (803) 896-4393

TENNESSEE
Mr. Bill Giannini
Assistant Commissioner
Division of Regulatory Boards
Department of Commerce &
Insurance
500 James Robertson Parkway,
2nd Floor
Nashville, TN 37243
P: (615) 741-3449
F: (615) 741-6470

Ms. Elizabeth Miller
Director
Division of Health Related
Boards
Department of Health
227 French Landing, Suite 300
Nashville, TN 37243
P: (615) 741-2040
F: (615) 532-5369
E: elizabeth.miller
    @state.tn.us

TEXAS
Mr. William H. Kuntz
Executive Director
Department of Licensing &
Regulation
P.O. Box 12157
Austin, TX 78711
P: (512) 463-3170
F: (512) 475-2874
E: executive.director
    @license.state.tx.us

Ms. Kathryn Perkins
Assistant Commissioner
Division of Regulatory Services
Department of State Health
Services
P.O.Box 149347
Austin, TX 78714
P: (512) 834-6660
F: (512) 834-6635
E: debbie.peterson
    @dshs.state.tx.us

UTAH
Mr. Mark B. Steinagel
Director
Division of Occupational &
Professional Licensing
160 East 300, South
P.O. Box 146741
Salt Lake City, UT 84114
P: (801) 530-6292
F: (801) 530-6511
E: msteinagel@utah.gov

VERMONT
Mr. Christopher D. Winters
Director
Office of Professional
Regulation
Secretary of State's Office
89 Main Street, 3rd Floor
Montpelier, VT 05620
P: (802) 828-2367
F: (802) 828-2396
E: chris.winters
    @sec.state.vt.us

VIRGINIA
Mr. Gordon Dixon
Director
Department of Professional &
Occupational Regulation
9960 Mayland Drive, Suite 400
Richmond, VA 23233
P: (804) 367-8519
F: (804) 367-9537
E: director
    @dpor.virginia.gov

Ms. Dianne Reynolds-Cane
Director
Department of Health
Professions
9960 Mayland Drive, Suite 300
Richmond, VA 23233
P: (804) 662-9919
F: (804) 662-9114
E: dianne.cane
    @dhp.virginia.gov

WASHINGTON
Ms. Pat Kohler
Agency Director
Department of Licensing
P.O. Box 9020
Olympia, WA 98507
P: (360) 902-3600
F: (360) 902-4042
E: doldirector@dol.wa.gov

Mr. Martin Mueller
Assistant Secretary
State Health Systems Quality
Assurance
P.O. Box 47830
Olympia, WA 98504
P: (360) 236-4601
F: (360) 236-4626

WISCONSIN
Mr. Dave Ross
Secretary
Department of Safety &
Professional Services
1400 East Washington Avenue
P.O. Box 8935
Madison, WI 53708
P: (608) 266-1352
F: (608) 261-2381
E: DRLOfficeOfTheSecretary
    @wisconsin.gov

Lieutenant Governor

The statewide elected official who is next in line of succession to the governorship. (In Maine, New Hampshire, New Jersey, Tennessee and West Virginia, the presidents (or speakers) of the Senate are the next in line of succession to the governorship. In Tennessee, the speaker of the Senate bears the statutory title of lieutenant governor. In Arizona, Oregon, and Wyoming, the secretary of state is next in line of succession to the governorship.)

Information provided by:

National Lieutenant Governors Association
Julia Nienaber Hurst
Executive Director
71 Cavalier Boulevard
Suite 226
Florence, KY 41042
P: (859) 283-1400
F: (859) 244-8001
jhurst@csg.org
www.nlga.us

ALABAMA
Hon. Kay Ivey (R)
Lieutenant Governor
Office of the Lieutenant Governor
11 South Union Street, Suite 725
Montgomery, AL 36130
P: (334) 242-7900
F: (334) 242-4661
E: kay.ivey
    @ltgov.alabama.gov

ALASKA
Hon. Byron Mallot (I)
Lieutenant Governor
Office of the Lieutenant Governor
550 West 7th Street, Suite 1700
Anchorage, AK 99501
P: (907) 269-7460
F: (907) 269-0263

AMERICAN SAMOA
Hon. Lemanu Peleti
    Mauga (I)
Lieutenant Governor
Office of the Lieutenant Governor
Territory of American Samoa
Pago Pago, AS 96799
P: (684) 633-4116
F: (684) 633-2269

ARIZONA
Hon. Michele Reagan (R)
Secretary of State
Office of the Secretary of State
Capitol Executive Tower, 7th Floor
1700 West Washington
Phoenix, AZ 85007
P: (602) 542-4285
F: (602) 542-1575
E: sosadmin@azsos.gov

ARKANSAS
Hon. Tim Griffin (R)
Lieutenant Governor
Office of the Lieutenant Governor
270 State Capitol
Little Rock, AR 72201
P: (501) 682-2144
F: (501) 682-2894

CALIFORNIA
Hon. Gavin Newsom (D)
Lieutenant Governor
Office of the Lieutenant Governor
State Capitol, Room 1114
Sacramento, CA 95814
P: (916) 445-8994
F: (916) 323-4998

COLORADO
Hon. Joe Garcia (D)
Lieutenant Governor
Office of the Lieutenant Governor
130 State Capitol
Denver, CO 80203
P: (303) 866-2087
F: (303) 866-5469
E: josephagarcia
    @state.co.us

CONNECTICUT
Hon. Nancy Wyman (D)
Lieutenant Governor
Office of the Lieutenant Governor
State Capitol, Room 304
210 Capitol Avenue
Hartford, CT 06106
P: (860) 524-7384
F: (860) 524-7304

DELAWARE
Vacant
Office of the Lt. Governor
401 Federal Street
Dover, DE 19901
P: (302) 739-4111
F: (302) 739-3811

FLORIDA
Hon. Carlos
    Lopez-Cantera (R)
Lieutenant Governor
Office of the Lieutenant Governor
The State Capitol
Tallahassee, FL 32399
P: (850) 488-4711
F: (850) 921-6114

GEORGIA
Hon. Casey Cagle (R)
Lieutenant Governor
Office of the Lieutenant Governor
240 State Capitol
Atlanta, GA 30334
P: (404) 656-5030
F: (404) 656-6739

GUAM
Hon. Ray Tenorio (R)
Lieutenant Governor
Office of the Lieutenant Governor
R.J. Bordallo Governor's Complex
P.O. Box 2950
Hagatna, GU 96932
P: (671) 475-9380
F: (671) 477-2007
E: webmaster
    @guamletgovernor.net

HAWAII
Hon. Shan S. Tsutsui (D)
Lieutenant Governor
Office of the Lieutenant Governor
Executive Chambers
State Capitol
Honolulu, HI 96813
P: (808) 586-0255
F: (808) 586-0231
E: shan.tsutsui@hawaii.gov

IDAHO
Hon. Brad Little (R)
Lieutenant Governor
Office of the Lieutenant Governor
State Capitol
Boise, ID 83720
P: (208) 334-2200
F: (208) 334-3259

ILLINOIS
Hon. Evelyn Sanguinetti (R)
Lieutenant Governor
Office of the Lieutenant Governor
214 State House
Springfield, IL 62706
P: (217) 558-3085
F: (217) 558-3086

INDIANA
Hon. Sue Ellspermann (R)
Lieutenant Governor
Office of the Lieutenant Governor
State Capitol, Room 333
Indianapolis, IN 46204
P: (317) 232-4545
F: (317) 232-4788

IOWA
Hon. Kim Reynolds (R)
Lieutenant Governor
Office of the Lieutenant Governor
State Capitol, Room 9
Des Moines, IA 50319
P: (515) 281-5211
F: (515) 725-3527

KANSAS
Hon. Jeff Colyer M.D. (R)
Lieutenant Governor
Office of the Lieutenant Governor
State Capitol, 2nd Floor
300 Southwest 10th Avenue
Topeka, KS 66612
P: (785) 296-2214
F: (785) 296-5669

KENTUCKY
Hon. Crit Luallen (D)
Lieutenant Governor
Office of the Lieutenant Governor
700 Capitol Avenue, Suite 142
Frankfort, KY 40601
P: (502) 564-2611
F: (502) 564-2849
E: Crit.Luallen
    @auditor.ky.gov

LOUISIANA
Hon. Jay Dardenne (R)
Lieutenant Governor
Office of the Lieutenant Governor
1051 North 3rd Street
Capitol Annex Building, P.O. Box 44243
Baton Rouge, LA 70804
P: (225) 342-7009
F: (225) 342-1949
E: ltgov@crt.la.gov

Lieutenant Governor

MAINE
Sen. Michael D.
    Thibodeau (R)
Senate President
Office of the Senate President
3 State House Station
Augusta, ME 04333
P: (207) 287-1500
F: (207) 287-1527
E: senatorthibodeau@aol.com

MARYLAND
Hon. Boyd Rutherford (R)
Lieutenant Governor
Office of the Lieutenant
Governor
100 State Circle
Annapolis, MD 21401
P: (410) 974-2804
E: ltgov@gov.state.md.us

MASSACHUSETTS
Hon. Karyn E. Polito (R)
Lieutenant Governor
Office of the Lieutenant
Governor
McCormack Building
One Ashburton Place
Boston, MA 02108
P: (617) 727-7030
F: (617) 742-4528

MICHIGAN
Hon. Brian Calley (R)
Lieutenant Governor
Office of the Lieutenant
Governor
P.O. Box 30013
Lansing, MI 48909
P: (517) 373-6800
F: (517) 241-5026

MINNESOTA
Hon. Tina Smith (D)
Lieutenant Governor
Office of the Lieutenant
Governor
130 State Capitol
75 Rev. Martin Luther King Jr.
Boulevard
St. Paul, MN 55155
P: (651) 201-3400
F: (651) 797-1850

MISSISSIPPI
Hon. Tate Reeves (R)
Lieutenant Governor
Office of the Lieutenant
Governor
New Capitol, Room 315
P.O. Box 1018
Jackson, MS 39215
P: (601) 359-3200
F: (601) 359-2001
E: ltgov@senate.ms.gov

MISSOURI
Hon. Peter Kinder (R)
Lieutenant Governor
Office of the Lieutenant
Governor
State Capitol, Room 224
Jefferson City, MO 65101
P: (573) 751-4727
F: (573) 751-9422
E: ltgovinfo@mail.mo.gov

MONTANA
Hon. Angela McLean (D)
Lieutenant Governor
Office of the Lieutenant
Governor
Capitol Station, Room 207
P.O. Box 200801
Helena, MT 59620
P: (406) 444-5665
F: (406) 444-4648

NEBRASKA
Hon. Mike Foley (R)
Lieutenant Governor
Office of the Lieutenant
Governor
State Capitol, Room 2315
P.O. Box 94863
Lincoln, NE 68509
P: (402) 471-2256
F: (402) 471-6031
E: mike.foley@nebraska.gov

NEVADA
Hon. Mark Hutchison (R)
Lieutenant Governor
Office of the Lieutenant
Governor
101 North Carson Street, Suite 2
Carson City, NV 89701
P: (775) 684-7111
F: (775) 684-7110

NEW JERSEY
Hon. Kim Guadagno (R)
Lieutenant Governor
Office of the Secretary of State
P.O. Box 001
Trenton, NJ 08625
P: (609) 292-6000
F: (609) 292-3454
E: lt.governor
    @gov.state.nj.us

NEW MEXICO
Hon. John A. Sanchez (R)
Lieutenant Governor
Office of the Lieutenant
Governor
State Capitol, Suite 417
Santa Fe, NM 87501
P: (505) 476-2250
F: (505) 476-2257

NEW YORK
Hon. Kathy Hochul (D)
Lieutenant Governor
Office of the Lieutenant
Governor
State Capitol
Albany, NY 12224
P: (518) 474-8390
F: (518) 474-7513

NORTH CAROLINA
Hon. Dan Forest (R)
Lieutenant Governor
Office of the Lieutenant
Governor
310 North Blount Street
Raleigh, NC 27601
P: (919) 733-7350
F: (919) 733-6595
E: lt.gov@nc.gov

NORTH DAKOTA
Hon. Drew Wrigley (R)
Lieutenant Governor
Office of the Lieutenant
Governor
State Capitol
Bismarck, ND 58505
P: (701) 328-2200
F: (701) 328-2205

**NORTHERN MARIANA
ISLANDS**
Sen. Ralph Torres (R)
Lieutenant Governor
Office of the Lieutenant
Governor
Caller Box 10007
Capitol Hill
Saipan, MP 96950
P: (670) 664-2300
F: (670) 664-2311

OHIO
Hon. Mary Taylor (R)
Lieutenant Governor
Office of the Lieutenant
Governor
77 High Street, 30th Floor
Columbus, OH 43215
P: (614) 644-0935
F: (614) 466-9354

OKLAHOMA
Hon. Todd Lamb (R)
Lieutenant Governor
Office of the Lieutenant
Governor
State Capitol, Room 211
Oklahoma City, OK 73105
P: (405) 521-2161
F: (405) 522-8694

OREGON
Hon. Ted Wheeler
State Treasurer
Office of the State Treasurer
900 Court Street, Room 159
Salem, OR 97301
P: (503) 378-4329
F: (503) 373-7051
E: Oregon.Treasurer
    @state.or.us

PENNSYLVANIA
Hon. Michael J. Stack (D)
Lieutenant Governor
Office of the Lieutenant
Governor
200 Main Capitol Building
Harrisburg, PA 17120
P: (717) 787-3300
F: (717) 783-0150

PUERTO RICO
Hon. David Bernier (PDP)
Secretary of State
Office of the Secretary of State
Department of State
Box 9023271
San Juan, PR 00902
P: (787) 722-2121
F: (787) 722-2684

RHODE ISLAND
Hon. Daniel McKee (D)
Lieutenant Governor
Office of the Lieutenant
Governor
116 State House
Providence, RI 02903
P: (401) 222-2371
F: (401) 222-2012

SOUTH CAROLINA
Hon. Henry D. McMaster (R)
Lieutenant Governor
Office of the Lieutenant
Governor
P.O. Box 142
Columbia, SC 29202
P: (803) 734-2080
F: (803) 734-2082
E: HenryMcMaster
    @scsenate.gov

SOUTH DAKOTA
Hon. Matthew Michels (R)
Lieutenant Governor
Office of the Lieutenant
Governor
500 East Capitol Street
Pierre, SD 57501
P: (605) 773-3661
F: (605) 773-4711

TENNESSEE
Hon. Ron Ramsey (R)
    (elected by the Senate)
Lieutenant Governor/Senate
President
Office of the Lieutenant
Governor
Legislative Plaza
Nashville, TN 37243
P: (615) 741-4524
F: (615) 253-0197
E: lt.gov.ron.ramsey
    @capitol.tn.gov

TEXAS
Hon. Dan Patrick (R)
Lieutenant Governor
Office of the Lieutenant
Governor
Capitol Station
P.O. Box 12068
Austin, TX 78711
P: (512) 463-0001
F: (512) 463-0677

U.S. VIRGIN ISLANDS
Hon. Osbert Potter (I)
Lieutenant Governor
Office of the Lieutenant
Governor
1331 Kings Street, Suite101
St. Croix, VI 00802
P: (340) 773-6449
F: (340) 773-0330

UTAH
Hon. Spencer J. Cox (R)
Lieutenant Governor
Office of the Lieutenant
Governor
P.O. Box 142325
Salt Lake City, UT 84114
P: (801) 538-1041
F: (801) 538-1133

VERMONT
Hon. Phil Scott (R)
Lieutenant Governor
Office of the Lieutenant
Governor
115 State Street
Montpelier, VT 05633
P: (802) 828-2226
F: (802) 828-3198
E: pscott14@aol.com

VIRGINIA
Hon. Ralph S. Northam (D)
Lieutenant Governor
Office of the Lieutenant
Governor
102 Governor Street
Richmond, VA 23219
P: (804) 786-2078
F: (804) 786-7514
E: ltgov@ltgov.virginia.gov

WASHINGTON
Hon. Brad Owen (D)
Lieutenant Governor
Office of the Lieutenant
Governor
416 14th Avenue, Southwest
P.O. Box 40400
Olympia, WA 98504
P: (360) 786-7700
F: (360) 786-7749
E: ltgov@leg.wa.gov

WEST VIRGINIA
Sen. Bill Cole (R)
Senate President/Lieutenant
Governor
Office of the Lieutenant
Governor
Room 227M, Building 1
Capitol Complex
Charleston, WV 25305
P: (304) 357-7801
F: (304) 357-7839
E: bill.cole@wvsenate.gov

WISCONSIN
Hon. Rebecca Kleefisch (R)
Lieutenant Governor
Office of the Lieutenant
Government
Room 19, East State Capitol
P.O. Box 2043
Madison, WI 53702
P: (608) 266-3516
F: (608) 267-3571

WYOMING
Hon. Ed Murray (R)
Secretary of State
Office of the Secretary of State
State Capitol Building, Room
106
200 West 24th Street
Cheyenne, WY 82002
P: (307) 777-7378
F: (307) 777-6217
E: secofstate@wyo.gov

Lobby Law Administration

Administers registration and reporting requirements for lobbyists.

ALABAMA
Hon. John Merrill (R)
Secretary of State
Office of the Secretary of State
P.O. Box 5616
Montgomery, AL 36103
P: (334) 242-7200
F: (334) 242-4993
E: john.merrill
@sos.alabama.gov

ALASKA
Mr. Paul Dauphinais
Executive Director
Public Offices Commission
Department of Administration
2221 East Northern Lights,
Room 128
Anchorage, AK 99508
P: (907) 276-4176
F: (907) 276-7018
E: Paul.Dauphinais
@alaska.gov

ARKANSAS
Hon. Mark Martin (R)
Secretary of State
Office of the Secretary of State
256 State Capitol Building
Little Rock, AR 72201
P: (501) 682-1010
F: (501) 682-3510
E: info@sos.arkansas.gov

CALIFORNIA
Ms. Jana Lean
Chief of Elections
Elections Division
1500 11th Street, 5th Floor
Sacramento, CA 95814
P: (916) 657-2166
F: (916) 653-3214
E: jana.lean@sos.ca.gov

COLORADO
Hon. Wayne Williams (R)
Secretary of State
Office of the Secretary of State
1700 Broadway, Suite 200
Denver, CO 80290
P: (303) 894-2200
F: (303) 869-4860
E: secretary
@sos.state.co.us

CONNECTICUT
Ms. Carol Carson
Executive Director
Office of State Ethics
18-20 Trinity Street, Suite 205
Hartford, CT 06106
P: (860) 263-2384
F: (860) 263-2402
E: carol.carson@ct.gov

DELAWARE
Ms. Deborah Moreau
Commission's Legal Counsel
Public Integrity Commission
Margaret O'Neill Building
410 Federal Street, Suite 3
Dover, DE 19901
P: (302) 739-2399
F: (302) 739-2398

DISTRICT OF COLUMBIA
Ms. Cecily E.
    Collier-Montgomery
Director
Office of Campaign Finance
Frank D. Reeves Municipal
Building
2000 14th Street, Northwest,
Suite 433
Washington, DC 20009
P: (202) 671-0547
F: (202) 671-0658
E: ocf@dc.gov

FLORIDA
Ms. Christie Burrus
Legislative Affairs Director
Office of Legislative Affairs
R. A. Gray Building, Suite 115
500 South Bronough Street
Tallahassee, FL 32399
P: (850) 245-6512
F: (850) 245-6125
E: Christie.Burrus
    @DOS.MyFlorida.com

Ms. Virlindia Doss
Executive Director
Commission on Ethics
P.O. Drawer 15709
Tallahassee, FL 32317
P: (904) 488-7864
F: (904) 488-3077
E: doss.virlindia
    @leg.state.fl.us

HAWAII
Mr. Leslie H. Kondo
Executive Director
State Ethics Commission
1001 Bishop Street, Suite 970
P.O. Box 616
Honolulu, HI 96809
P: (808) 587-0460
F: (808) 587-0470
E: ethics@hawaiiethics.org

IDAHO
Hon. Lawerence Denney (R)
Secretary of State
Office of the Secretary of State
P.O. Box 83720
Boise, ID 83720
P: (208) 334-2300
F: (208) 334-2282
E: ldenney@sos.idaho.gov

ILLINOIS
Mr. David Weisbaum
Director
Department of Index
111 East Monroe Street
Springfield, IL 62756
P: (217) 782-7017
F: (217) 524-0930

INDIANA
Mr. Charles W. Harris
Acting Director
Lobby Registration Commission
10 West Market Street, Suite
1760
Indianapolis, IN 46204
P: (317) 232-9860
F: (317) 233-0077
E: charris@lrc.in.gov

IOWA
Mr. Michael E. Marshall
Secretary of the Senate
General Assembly
State Capitol
1007 East Grand Avenue
Des Moines, IA 50319
P: (515) 281-5307
E: Mike.Marshall
    @legis.iowa.gov

KANSAS
Mr. Brad Bryant
Deputy Assistant for Elections
Office of the Secretary of State -
Elections & Legislative Matters
120 Southwest 10th Avenue
Memorial Hall, 1st Floor
Topeka, KS 66612
P: (785) 296-4561
F: (785) 291-3051
E: Brad.Bryant@sos.ks.gov

KENTUCKY
Hon. Alison Lundergan
    Grimes (D)
Secretary of State
Office of the Secretary of State
700 Capital Avenue, Suite 152
Frankfort, KY 40601
P: (502) 564-3490
F: (502) 564-5687
E: sos.secretary@ky.gov

LOUISIANA
Ms. Kathleen Allen
Ethics Administrator
Ethics Administration Program
617 North Third Street, Suite
10-36
P.O. Box 4368
Baton Rouge, LA 70821
P: (225) 219-5600
F: (225) 381-7271
E: kathleen.allen@la.gov

MAINE
Mr. Jonathan Wayne
Executive Director
Commission on Governmental
Ethics & Election Practices
135 State House Station
Augusta, ME 04333
P: (207) 287-4179
F: (207) 287-6775
E: Jonathan.Wayne@maine.gov

MARYLAND
Ms. Jennifer K. Allgair
General Counsel
State Ethics Commission
45 Calvert Street, 3rd Floor
Annapolis, MD 21401
P: (410) 260-7770
F: (410) 260-7746
E: Jennifer.Allgair
    @Maryland.gov

Mr. Michael W. Lord
Executive Director
State Ethics Commission
45 Calvert Street, 3rd Floor
Annapolis, MD 21401
P: (410) 260-7770
F: (410) 260-7747
E: Michael.Lord
    @Maryland.gov

MASSACHUSETTS
Hon. William Francis
    Galvin (D)
Secretary of the Commonwealth
Office of the Secretary of the
Commonwealth
State House, Room 337
Boston, MA 02133
P: (617) 727-9180
F: (617) 742-4722
E: cis@sec.state.ma.us

Lobby Law Administration

MICHIGAN
Mr. Christopher M. Thomas
Director
Bureau of Elections
Richard H. Austin Building,
First Floor
430 West Allegan Street
Lansing, MI 48918
P: (517) 335-2789
F: (517) 373-0941
E: ChristopherT
@michigan.gov

MINNESOTA
Mr. Gary Goldsmith
Executive Director
Campaign Finance & Public
Disclosure Board
Centennial Office Building,
Suite 190
658 Cedar Street
St. Paul, MN 55155
P: (651) 539-1190
F: (651) 539-1196
E: gary.goldsmith
@state.mn.us

Hon. Steve Simon (DFL)
Secretary of State
Office of the Secretary of State
180 State Office Building
100 Martin Luther King Jr.
Boulevard
St. Paul, MN 55155
P: (651) 201-1328
F: (651) 269-9073
E: secretary.state
@state.mn.us

MISSISSIPPI
Ms. Kim Turner
Senior Attorney
Elections Division
Secretary of State's Office
401 Mississippi Street
Jackson, MS 39201
P: (601) 359-5137
F: (601) 359-1499
E: Kim.Turner@sos.ms.gov

MISSOURI
Mr. James Klahr
Executive Director
Ethics Commission
3411A Knipp Drive
P.O. Box 1370
Jefferson City, MO 65102
P: (573) 751-2020
F: (573) 526-4506
E: helpdesk@mec.mo.gov

MONTANA
Mr. Jonathan R. Motl
Commissioner
Commissioner of Political
Practices
P.O. Box 202401
Helena, MT 59620
P: (406) 444-2942
F: (406) 444-1643
E: jmotl@mt.gov

NEBRASKA
Mr. Patrick J. O'Donnell
Clerk of the Legislature
State Legislature
State Capitol, Room 2018
P.O. Box 94604
Lincoln, NE 68509
P: (402) 471-2271
F: (402) 471-2126
E: podonnell@leg.ne.gov

NEVADA
Mr. Lorne J. Malkiewich
Director
Legislative Counsel Bureau
Legislative Building
401 South Carson Street
Carson City, NV 89701
P: (775) 684-6800
F: (775) 684-6600
E: malkiewich
@lcb.state.nv.us

NEW HAMPSHIRE
Hon. William M. Gardner (D)
Secretary of State
Office of the Secretary of State
State House, Room 204
Concord, NH 03301
P: (603) 271-3242
F: (603) 271-6316
E: kladd@sos.state.nh.us

NEW JERSEY
Mr. Jeffrey M. Brindle
Executive Director
Election Law Enforcement
Commission
P.O. Box 185
Trenton, NJ 08625
P: (609) 292-8700
F: (609) 777-1448
E: jeff.brindle
@elec.state.nj.us

NEW MEXICO
Hon. Dianna J. Duran (R)
Secretary of State
Office of the Secretary of State
325 Don Gaspar, Suite 300
Capitol Annex
Santa Fe, NM 87501
P: (505) 827-3600
F: (505) 827-8081
E: diannaj.duran
@state.nm.us

NEW YORK
Ms. Letizia Tagliafierro
Director
Joint Commission on Public
Ethics
540 Broadway
Albany, NY 12207
P: (518) 408-3976
F: (518) 408-3975
E: jcope@jcope.ny.gov

NORTH CAROLINA
Hon. Elaine F. Marshall (D)
Secretary of State
Office of the Secretary of State
P.O. Box 29622
Raleigh, NC 27626
P: (919) 807-2005
F: (919) 807-2010
E: emarshal@sosnc.com

NORTH DAKOTA
Hon. Alvin A. Jaeger (R)
Secretary of State
Office of the Secretary of State
600 East Boulevard
Department 108
Bismarck, ND 58505
P: (701) 328-2900
F: (701) 328-1690
E: ajaeger@nd.gov

OHIO
Mr. Tony W. Bledsoe
Legislative Inspector
General/Executive Director
Office of the Legislative
Inspector General
50 West Broad Street, Suite
1308
Columbus, OH 43215
P: (614) 728-5100
F: (614) 728-5074
E: info
@jlec-olig.state.oh.us

OREGON
Mr. Ronald A. Bersin
Executive Director
Government Ethics Commission
3218 Pringle Road, Southeast,
Suite 220
Salem, OR 97302
P: (503) 378-5105
F: (503) 373-1456
E: ron.a.bersin@state.or.us

SOUTH CAROLINA
Hon. Mark Hammond (R)
Secretary of State
Office of the Secretary of State
1205 Pendleton Street, Suite 525
Columbia, SC 29201
P: (803) 734-2170
F: (803) 734-1661
E: rdaggerhart@sos.sc.gov

Mr. Herbert R. Hayden Jr.
Executive Director
State Ethics Commission
5000 Thurmond Mall, Suite 250
Columbia, SC 29201
P: (803) 253-4192
F: (803) 253-7539
E: herb@ethics.state.sc.us

TENNESSEE
Mr. Drew Rawlins
Executive Director
Bureau of Ethics & Campaign
Finance
404 James Robertson Parkway,
Suite 104
Nashville, TN 37243
P: (615) 741-7959
F: (615) 532-8905
E: drew.ralins@tn.gov

TEXAS
Mr. Keith Ingram
Director of Elections
Elections Division
Office of the Secretary of State.
P.O.Box 12697
Austin, TX 78711
P: (512) 463-9871
F: (512) 475-2811
E: kingram@sos.state.tx.us

VERMONT
Hon. Jim Condos (D)
Secretary of State
Office of the Secretary of State
128 State Street
Montpelier, VT 05633
P: (802) 828-2148
F: (802) 828-2496
E: jim.condos
@sec.state.vt.us

Lobby Law Administration

WASHINGTON
Mr. Fred Kiga
Interim Executive Director
Public Disclosure Commission
711 Capitol Way, #206
P.O. Box 40908
Olympia, WA 98504
P: (360) 664-2735
F: (360) 753-1112
E: Fred.Kiga@pdc.wa.gov

WEST VIRGINIA
Ms. Rebecca L. Stepto
Executive Director
Ethics Commission
210 Brooks Street, Suite 300
Charleston, WV 25301
P: (304) 558-0664
F: (304) 558-2169
E: rebecca.l.stepto@wv.gov

WISCONSIN
Mr. Jonathan Becker
Division Administrator
Ethics Division
P.O. Box 7984
Madison, WI 53707
P: (608) 267-0647
E: jonathan.becker@wi.gov

WYOMING
Hon. Ed Murray (R)
Secretary of State
Office of the Secretary of State
State Capitol Building, Room 106
200 West 24th Street
Cheyenne, WY 82002
P: (307) 777-7378
F: (307) 777-6217
E: secofstate@wyo.gov

Lottery

Administers the state lottery system.

ARIZONA
Mr. Tony V. Bouie
Executive Director
State Lottery
4740 East University Drive
Phoenix, AZ 85034
P: (480) 921-4400

ARKANSAS
Mr. William Bishop Woosley
Director
State Scholarship Lottery
124 West Capitol, Suite 1400
Little Rock, AR 72201
P: (501) 683-2000

CALIFORNIA
Ms. Paula D. LaBrie
Acting Director
State Lottery
700 North 10th Street
Sacramento, CA 95811
P: (800) 568-8379

COLORADO
Ms. Laura Solano
Director
State Lottery
225 North Main Street
Pueblo, CO 81003
P: (719) 546-5327
E: colorado.lottery
    @state.co.us

CONNECTICUT
Ms. Anne M. Noble
President & CEO
State Lottery Corporation
777 Brook Street
Rocky Hill, CT 06067
P: (860) 713-2800
F: (860) 713-2805
E: ctlottery@ctlottery.org

DELAWARE
Mr. Vernon Kirk
Director
State Lottery
McKee Business Park
1575 McKee Road, Suite 102
Dover, DE 19904
P: (302) 739-5291
F: (302) 739-6706
E: brian.peters@state.de.us

DISTRICT OF COLUMBIA
Ms. Tracey Cohen
Acting Executive Director
Lottery & Charitable Games
Control Board
2101 Martin Luther King Jr.
Avenue
Southeast
Washington, DC 20020
P: (202) 645-7900

FLORIDA
Ms. Cynthia F. O'Connell
Secretary
State Lottery
250 Marriott Drive
Tallahassee, FL 32399
P: (850) 487-7777
F: (850) 487-7709

GEORGIA
Ms. Debbie D. Alford
President & CEO
State Lottery Corporation
Suite 3000, 250 Williams Street
Atlanta, GA 30303
P: (404) 215-5000
F: (404) 215-8871
E: glottery@galottery.org

IDAHO
Mr. Jeffrey R. Anderson
Director
State Lottery
1349 East Beechcraft Court
Boise, ID 83716
P: (208) 947-9402
F: (208) 947-9401
E: info@idaholottery.com

ILLINOIS
B.R. Lane
Director
State Lottery
122 South Michigan Avenue
19th Floor
Chicago, IL 20020
P: (312) 793-1681

INDIANA
Ms. Sarah Taylor
Executive Director
Hoosier Lottery
Buick Building
1302 North Meridian Street
Indianapolis, IN 46202
P: (317) 264-4800
E: info@hoosierlottery.com

IOWA
Mr. Terry Rich
President & CEO
State Lottery
13001 University Avenue
Clive, IA 50325
P: (515) 725-7900
F: (515) 725-7905
E: wmaster@ialottery.com

KANSAS
Terry Presta
Executive Director
State Lottery
128 North Kansas Avenue
Topeka, KS 66603
P: (785) 296-5700
E: lotteryinfo
    @kslottery.net

KENTUCKY
Mr. Arch Gleason
President & CEO
State Lottery
1011 West Main Street
Louisville, KY 40202
P: (502) 560-1500
F: (502) 560-1532
E: custsrvs@kylottery.com

LOUISIANA
Ms. Rose Hudson
President/CEO
State Lottery Corporation
555 Laurel Street
Baton Rouge, LA 70801
P: (225) 297-2000
F: (225) 297-2005
E: info
    @louisianalottery.com

MAINE
Mr. Gregg Mineo
Director
State Lottery
10 Water Street
Hallowell, ME 04347
P: (207) 287-3721

MARYLAND
Mr. Gordon Medenica
Director
Lottery & Gaming Control
Agency
Montgomery Park Business
Center
1800 Washington Boulevard,
Suite 330
Baltimore, MD 21230
P: (410) 230-8800
E: ask.lotteryandgaming
    @maryland.gov

MASSACHUSETTS
Ms. Beth Bresnahan
Executive Director
State Lottery
60 Columbian Street
Braintree, MA 02184
P: (781) 849-5555
F: (781) 849-5546

MICHIGAN
Mr. Scott Bowen
Lottery Commissioner
Bureau of State Lottery
101 East Hillsdale
Lansing, MI 48909
P: (517) 335-5600
F: (517) 335-5651
E: milottery@michigan.gov

MINNESOTA
Mr. Ed Van Petten
Executive Director
State Lottery
2645 Long Lake Road
Roseville, MN 55113
P: (651) 635-8100
E: lottery@mnlottery.com

MISSOURI
Ms. May Scheve Reardon
Executive Director
State Lottery
1823 Southridge Drive
Jefferson City, MO 65109
P: (573) 751-4050

MONTANA
Ms. Angela Wong
Director
State Lottery
2525 North Montana Avenue
Helena, MT 59601
P: (406) 444-5825
F: (406) 444-5830

NEBRASKA
Ms. Jill Marshall
Acting Director
State Lottery
1800 "O" Street, Suite 101
Lincoln, NE 68509
P: (402) 471-6100

NEW HAMPSHIRE
Mr. Charles McIntyre
Executive Director
State Lottery Commission
14 Integra Drive
Concord, NH 03301
P: (603) 271-3391

Lottery

NEW JERSEY
Ms. Carole Hedinger
Executive Director
State Lottery
One Lawrence Park Complex
Brunswick Avenue Circle
Lawrenceville, NJ 08648
P: (609) 599-5800
E: publicinfo
    @lottery.state.nj.us

NEW MEXICO
Mr. David M. Barden
CEO
State Lottery
4511 Osuna Road, Northeast
P.O. Box 93130
Albuquerque, NM 87109
P: (505) 342-7600
E: custservice
    @nmlottery.com

NEW YORK
Mr. Gardner Gurney
Director
State Gaming Commission
One Broadway Center
P.O. Box 7500
Schenectady, NY 12301
P: (518) 388-3300
E: questions@lottery.ny.gov

NORTH CAROLINA
Ms. Alice Garland
Executive Director
Education Lottery
2100 Yonkers Road
Raleigh, NC 27604
P: (919) 715-6886
F: (919) 715-8833
E: playerinfo@lotterync.net

NORTH DAKOTA
Mr. Randall Miller
Director
State Lottery
1050 East Interstate Avenue,
Suite 200
Bismarck, ND 58503
P: (701) 328-1574

OHIO
Mr. Dennis Berg
Director
The Ohio Lottery
615 West Superior Avenue
Cleveland, OH 44113
P: (216) 774-5900
E: olcwebmail
    @olc.state.oh.us

OKLAHOMA
Mr. Rollo Daniel Redburn
Executive Director
State Lottery
3817 North Santa Fe
Oklahoma City, OK 73118
P: (405) 522-7700
F: (405) 521-0528

OREGON
Mr. Jack Roberts
Director
State Lottery
P.O. Box 12649
Salem, OR 97309
P: (503) 540-1000
E: webcenter@state.or.us

PENNSYLVANIA
Mr. Drew Svitko
Executive Director
State Lottery
1200 Fulling Mill Road
Middletown, PA 17057
P: (717) 702-8000
F: (717) 702-8024
E: info@palottery.com

PUERTO RICO
Ms. Maria Leon
Auxiliary Director
Electronic Lottery
Fundacion Angel Ramos
Building
383 Roosevelt Avenue, Suite 107
San Juan, PR 00918
P: (787) 250-8150 Ext. 223
E: info
    @loteriaelectronicapr.com

RHODE ISLAND
Mr. Gerald Aubin
Director
State Lottery
1425 Pontiac Avenue
Cranston, RI 02920
P: (401) 463-6500
F: (401) 463-5669
E: mferriola@rilot.ri.gov

SOUTH CAROLINA
Ms. Paula Harper-Bethea
Executive Director
State Education Lottery
Commission
1333 Main Street, Suite 400
Columbia, SC 29201
P: (803) 737-2002
F: (803) 737-2005
E: questions@sclot.com

SOUTH DAKOTA
Mr. Norman Lingle
Executive Director
State Lottery
Dolly-Reed Plaza
711 East Wells Avenue
Pierre, SD 57501
P: (605) 773-5770
F: (605) 773-5786
E: lottery@state.sd.us

TENNESSEE
Ms. Rebecca Paul Hargrove
President & CEO
Education Lottery Corporation
26 Century Boulevard, Suite 200
Nashville, TN 37214
P: (615) 324-6500
F: (615) 324-6512

TEXAS
Mr. Gary Grief
Executive Director
Lottery Commission
611 East Sixth Street
P.O.Box 16630
Austin, TX 78761
P: (512) 344-5160
F: (512) 478-3682
E: gary.grief
    @lottery.state.tx.us

U.S. VIRGIN ISLANDS
Mr. Juan Figueroa
Executive Director
State Lottery
8A Ross Estate
Barbel Plaza
St. Thomas, VI 00802
P: (340) 774-2502, Ext. 25

VERMONT
Mr. Gregory Smith
Executive Director
State Lottery
1311 U.S. Route 302, Suite 100
Barre, VT 05641
P: (802) 479-5686
F: (802) 479-4294
E: info@vtlottery.com

VIRGINIA
Ms. Paula I. Otto
Executive Director
State Lottery
900 East Main Street
Richmond, VA 23219
P: (804) 692-7000
F: (804) 692-7102
E: info@valottery.com

WASHINGTON
Mr. Bill Hanson
Director
State Lottery
P.O. Box 43000
Olympia, WA 98504
P: (360) 664-4800
F: (360) 586-1039
E: director's_office
    @walottery.com

WEST VIRGINIA
Mr. John Musgrave
Director
State Lottery
P.O. Box 2067
Charleston, WV 25327
P: (304) 558-0500
F: (304) 558-3321
E: jmusgrave
    @tax.state.wv.us

WISCONSIN
Mr. Michael Edmonds
Director
State Lottery
2135 Rimrock Road, #231
Madison, WI 53708
P: (608) 261-8800
F: (608) 264-6644

WYOMING
Mr. Jon Clontz
CEO
State Lottery Corporation
1620 Central Avenue, Suite 100
Cheyenne, WY 82001
P: (307) 432-9300

Medicaid

Administers the medical assistance program that finances medical care for income assistance recipients and other eligible medically needy persons.

ALABAMA
Ms. Stephanie Azar
Acting Commissioner
Medicaid Agency
501 Dexter Avenue
P.O. Box 5624
Montgomery, AL 36103
P: (334) 242-5600
E: stephanie.azar
  @medicaid.alabama.gov

ALASKA
Ms. Margaret Brodie
Director
Health Care Services
Department of Health & Social
Services
4501 Business Park Boulevard,
Building L
Anchorage, AK 99504
P: (907) 334-2520

AMERICAN SAMOA
Ms. Sandra King Young
Medicaid Director
Medicaid State Agency
American Samoa Government
Pago Pago, AS 96799
P: (684) 633-4818

ARIZONA
Mr. Tom J. Betlach
Director
Health Care Cost Containment
System
801 East Jefferson Street, MD
4100
Phoenix, AZ 85034
P: (602) 417-4711
F: (602) 252-6536

ARKANSAS
Ms. Dawn Stehle
Director
Division of Medicaid Services
Department of Human Services
112 West 8th Street, Slot S401
Little Rock, AR 72201
P: (501) 682-8740
F: (501) 682-1197

CALIFORNIA
Ms. Mari Cantwell
Chief Deputy Director
Department of Health Care
Services
1501 Capitol Avenue, 6th Floor
MS 0000
Sacramento, CA 95814
P: (916) 440-7418
F: (916) 440-7404

COLORADO
Ms. Gretchen Hammer
Medicaid Director
Department of Health Care
Policy & Financing
Medicaid & Child Health Plan
(CHP+)
1570 Grant Street
Denver, CO 80203
P: (303) 866-5929
F: (303) 866-4411

CONNECTICUT
Ms. Kate McEvoy
State Medicaid Director
Department of Social Services
25 Sigourney Street
Hartford, CT 06106
P: (860) 424-5067
E: mark.schaefer@ct.gov

DELAWARE
Mr. Stephen Groff
Medicaid Director
Department of Health & Social
Services
1901 North DuPont Highway
P.O. Box 906, Lewis Building
New Castle, DE 19720
P: (302) 255-9626

DISTRICT OF COLUMBIA
Ms. Claudia Schlosberg
Medicaid Director
Department of Health Care
Finance
One Judiciary Square
441 4th Street, Northwest
Washington, DC 20001
P: (202) 442-9075

FLORIDA
Mr. Justin Senior
Deputy Secretary for Medicaid
Agency for Healthcare
Administration
2727 Mahan Drive, Mail Stop 8
Tallahassee, FL 32308
P: (850) 412-4007
F: (850) 488-2520

GEORGIA
Ms. Linda Wiant
Chief of the Medicaid Assistance
Plans
Department of Community
Health
2 Peachtree Street, Northwest,
Suite 364
Atlanta, GA 30303
P: (404) 651-8681

GUAM
Ms. Tess Arcangel
Administrator
Department of Public Health &
Social Services
123 Chalan Kareta
Mangilcio, GU 96913
P: (671) 735-7282

HAWAII
Ms. Leslie Tawata
Acting Med-QUEST Division
Administrator
Department of Human Services
601 Kamokila Boulevard, Room
518
P.O. Box 700190
Kapolei, HI 96709
P: (808) 692-8050
F: (808) 692-8155

IDAHO
Ms. Lisa Hettinger
Administrator
Department of Health &
Welfare
450 West State Street
PTC Building, 10th Floor
Boise, ID 83705
P: (208) 334-1804

INDIANA
Mr. Joe Moser
Director of Medicaid
Family & Social Services
Administration
Family & Social Services
Administration
402 West Washington Street
Indianapolis, IN 46204
P: (317) 234-8725
E: Joe.Moser@fssa.IN.gov

IOWA
Ms. Julie Lovelady
Interim Medicaid Director
Department of Human Services
100 Army Post Road
Des Moines, IA 50315
P: (515) 256-4640
F: (515) 725-1360

KANSAS
Dr. Susan Mosier
Interim Secretary
Department of Health &
Environment
Curtis State Office Building
1000 Southwest Jackson
Topeka, KS 66612
P: (785) 296-1500
F: (785) 368-6368

KENTUCKY
Ms. Lisa Lee
Commissioner
Department for Medicaid
Services
Cabinet for Health & Family
Services
275 East Main Street, 6 West A
Frankfort, KY 40601
P: (502) 564-4321
F: (502) 564-0509

LOUISIANA
Ms. Ruth Kennedy
Medicaid Director
Department of Health &
Hospitals
628 North 4th Street
Baton Rouge, LA 70802
P: (225) 342-9240
F: (225) 342-3893

MAINE
Ms. Stefanie Nadeau
Director
Office of MaineCare Services
Department of Health & Human
Services
221 State Street
Augusta, ME 04333
P: (207) 287-2674
F: (207) 287-2675
E: Stefanie.Nadeau
  @maine.gov

MARYLAND
Ms. Shannon McMahon
Deputy Secretary, Health Care
Financing
Department of Health & Mental
Hygiene
201 West Preston Street, Room
525
Baltimore, MD 21201
P: (410) 767-4139

Medicaid

MASSACHUSETTS
Mr. Daniel Tsai
Assistant Secretary for
MassHealth
Office of Medicaid
Department of Health & Human
Services
1 Ashburn Place, 11th Floor,
Room 1109
Boston, MA 02108
P: (617) 573-1770
F: (617) 573-1894

MICHIGAN
Mr. Stephen Filton
Medicaid Director
Department of Community
Health
400 South Pine Street
Lansing, MI 48913
P: (517) 241-7882
F: (517) 335-5007

MINNESOTA
Ms. Marie Zimmerman
Medicaid Director
Department of Human Services
540 Cedar Street
P.O. Box 64983
St. Paul, MN 55167
P: (651) 431-2182
F: (651) 431-7421

MISSISSIPPI
Dr. David J. Dzielak
Executive Director, Division of
Medicaid
Department of Human Services
550 High Street, Suite 1000
Walters Sillers Building
Jackson, MS 39201
P: (601) 359-9562

MISSOURI
Mr. Joe Parks
Director
HealthNet Division
Department of Social Services
615 Howerton Court, P.O. Box
6500
Jefferson City, MO 65102
P: (573) 751-6922

MONTANA
Ms. Mary Dalton
State Medicaid Director
Department of Public Health &
Human Services
111 North Sanders
P.O. Box 4210
Helena, MT 59604
P: (406) 444-4084
F: (406) 444-1970
E: mary.dalton@mt.gov

NEBRASKA
Mr. Calder Lynch
Director, Division of Medicaid
& Long-Term Care
Department of Health & Human
Services
301 Centennial Mall South, 3rd
Floor
P.O. Box 95026
Lincoln, NE 68509
P: (402) 471-2135

NEVADA
Ms. Laurie Squartsoff
Administrator
Division of Health Care
Financing & Policy
Department of Health & Human
Services
1100 East William Street, Suite
101
Carson City, NV 89710
P: (775) 684-3677

NEW HAMPSHIRE
Ms. Kathleen A. Dunn
Director
Office of Medicaid Business &
Policy
Department of Health & Human
Services
129 Pleasant Street
Concord, NH 03301
P: (603) 271-9421
F: (603) 271-4727
E: kdunn@dhhs.state.nh.us

NEW JERSEY
Ms. Valerie Harr
Director
Division of Medical Assistance
& Health Services
Department of Human Services
7 Quakerbridge Plaza, P.O. Box
712
Trenton, NJ 08625
P: (609) 588-2600
F: (609) 588-3583

NEW MEXICO
Ms. Nancy Smith-Leslie
Director
Medical Assistance Division
Department of Human Services
P.O. Box 2348
Santa Fe, NM 87504
P: (505) 827-6253

NEW YORK
Mr. Jason Helgerson
State Medicaid Director, Deputy
Commissioner
Department of Health
Empire State Plaza
Corning Tower, Room 1466
Albany, NY 12237
P: (518) 474-3018

NORTH CAROLINA
Dr. Robin Cummings
Medicaid Director
Department of Health & Human
Services
1985 Umstead Drive
2501 Mail Service Center
Raleigh, NC 27699
P: (919) 855-4100

**NORTHERN MARIANA
ISLANDS**
Ms. Helen Sablan
Medicaid Administrator
Medicaid Program
P.O. Box 409CK
Saipan, MP 96950
P: (670) 664-4884
F: (670) 664-4885
E: dlnrgov@vzpacifica.net

OHIO
Mr. John McCarthy
Medicaid Director
Department of Medicaid
50 West Town Street, 4th Floor
Columbus, OH 43215
P: (614) 466-4443

OKLAHOMA
Dr. Garth Splinter
Medicaid Director
Health Care Authority
4345 North Lincoln Boulevard
Oklahoma City, OK 73105
P: (405) 522-7365
F: (405) 530-3218

OREGON
Ms. Judy Mohr Peterson
Medicaid Director
State Health Authority
500 Summer Street, Northeast,
E49
Salem, OR 97301
P: (503) 945-5768
F: (503) 373-7689
E: dhs.info@state.or.us

PENNSYLVANIA
Ms. Leesa M. Allen
Executive Medicaid Director
Department of Public Welfare
Office of the Secretary
331 Health & Welfare Building
Harrisburg, PA 17120
P: (717) 787-2600

PUERTO RICO
Mr. Ricardo A.
   Colon-Padilla
Executive Director
Medicaid Program
Department of Health
P.O. Box 70184
San Juan, PR 00936
P: (787) 765-2929

RHODE ISLAND
Ms. Deidre Gifford
Medicaid Director
Executive Office, Health &
Human Services
600 New London Avenue
Cranston, RI 02920
P: (401) 462-2121

SOUTH CAROLINA
Mr. Christian Soura
Director
Department of Health & Human
Services
1801 Main Street
P.O. Box 8206
Columbia, SC 29201
P: (803) 898-2504

TENNESSEE
Mr. Darin J. Gordon
Director of TennCare & Deputy
Commissioner
Department of Finance &
Administration
310 Great Circle Road
Nashville, TN 37243
P: (615) 507-6443
F: (615) 253-5607

TEXAS
Ms. Kay Ghahremani
Associate Commissioner for
Medicaid/CHIP
Health & Human Services
Commission
11209 Metric Boulevard,
Building H
Mail Code H100, P.O. Box
85200
Austin, TX 78758
P: (512) 491-1339

U.S. VIRGIN ISLANDS
Ms. Renee Joseph-Rhymer
Medicaid Director
Medical Assistance Program
Department of Human Services
1303 Hospital Ground, Building A
St. Thomas, VI 00802
P: (340) 774-0930

UTAH
Mr. Michael Hales
Deputy Director
Department of Health
P.O. Box 143101
Salt Lake City, UT 84114
P: (801) 538-6689
F: (801) 538-6099
E: mthales@utah.gov

VERMONT
Mr. Steven Costantino
Commissioner
Department of Vermont Health Access
312 Hurricane Lane, Suite 201
Williston, VT 05495
P: (802) 879-5901

VIRGINIA
Ms. Cynthia B. Jones
Director
Department of Medical Assistance Services
600 East Broad Street, Suite 1300
Richmond, VA 23219
P: (804) 786-8099
E: cindi.jones
    @dmas.virginia.gov

WASHINGTON
Ms. MaryAnne Lindeblad
Director
Health Care Authority
626 8th Avenue
P.O. Box 45502
Olympia, WA 98504
P: (360) 725-1040

WEST VIRGINIA
Ms. Cynthia Beane
Acting Commissioner
Department of Health & Human Resources
350 Capitol Street, Room 251
Charleston, WV 25301
P: (304) 558-1700

WISCONSIN
Mr. Kevin Moore
Medicaid Director
Department of Health Services
1 West Wilson Street, Room 350
P.O. Box 309
Madison, WI 53701
P: (608) 266-1271

WYOMING
Ms. Teri Green
State Medicaid Agent
Department of Health
6101 Yellowstone Road, Suite 210
Cheyenne, WY 82009
P: (307) 777-7531
F: (307) 777-6964

Mentall Health

Administers the mental services of the state and/or plans and coordinates programs for persons with mental illness.

ALABAMA
Mr. Jim Reddoch
Commissioner
Department of Mental Health
100 North Union Street
Montgomery, AL 36130
P: (334) 242-3640
F: (334) 242-0684
E: James.reddoch
  @mh.alabama.gov

ALASKA
Mr. Albert Wall
Director
Behavioral Health & Social
Services
P.O. Box 110620
Juneau, AK 99811
P: (907) 465-4841
F: (907) 465-2668
E: albert.wall@alaska.gov

AMERICAN SAMOA
Dr. Taeaoafua Meki Solomona
Director
Department of Human & Social
Services
P.O. Box 997534
Pago Pago, AS 96799
P: (684) 633-1664
F: (684) 633-7449
E: mtsolomona@dhss.as

ARIZONA
Mr. Cory Nelson
Deputy Director
Division of Behavioral Health
Services
Department of Health Services
150 North 18th Avenue, Suite
500
Phoenix, AZ 85007
P: (602) 364-4566
F: (602) 542-1062
E: cory.nelson@azdhs.gov

ARKANSAS
Mr. Charlie Green
Director
Division of Behavioral Health
Services
305 South Palm Street
Little Rock, AR 72205
P: (501) 686-9981
F: (501) 686-9182
E: charlie.green
  @dhs.arkansas.gov

CALIFORNIA
Ms. Brenda Grealish
Chief
Mental Health Services Division
1501 Capitol Avenue, MS 4000
Sacramento, CA 95899
P: (916) 440-7947
F: (916) 319-8219
E: brenda.grealish
  @dhcs.ca.gov

COLORADO
Mr. Patrick K. Fox
Acting Director
Office of Behavioral Health
Department of Human Services
3824 West Princeton Circle
Denver, CO 80236
P: (303) 866-7655
F: (303) 866-7090
E: patrick.fox@state.co.us

CONNECTICUT
Dr. Miriam E.
  Delphin-Rittmon
Commissioner
Department of Mental Health &
Addiction Services
410 Capitol Avenue, 4th Floor
P.O. Box 341431
Hartford, CT 06134
P: (860) 418-6850
F: (860) 418-6691
E: Miriam.delphin-rittmon
  @ct.gov

DELAWARE
Dr. Gerard Gallucci
Acting Director, Division of
Substance Abuse and Mental
Health
Health & Social Services
Main Administration Building,
Room 187
1901 North Dupont Highway
New Castle, DE 19720
P: (302) 255-9398
F: (302) 255-4427
E: Gerard.Gallucci
  @state.de.us

DISTRICT OF COLUMBIA
Dr. Barbara Bazron
Interim Director
Department of Behavioral
Health
64 New York Avenue, Northeast
Washington, DC 20002
P: (202) 671-2992
E: barbara.bazron@dc.gov

FLORIDA
Ute Gazioch
Director
Substance Abuse & Mental
Health
Department of Children &
Families
1317 Winewood Boulevard,
Building 6
Tallahassee, FL 32399
P: (850) 717-4322
F: (850) 488-2828
E: ute.gazioch
  @myflfamilies.com

GEORGIA
Mr. Frank W. Berry III
Commissioner
Department of Behavioral
Health & Developmental
Disabilities
2 Peachtree Street, Northwest
Suite 24.290
Atlanta, GA 30303
P: (404) 463-7945
F: (770) 408-5480
E: fwberry@dbhdd.ga.gov

GUAM
Mr. Rey Vega
Director
Department of Mental Health &
Substance Abuse
790 Gov. Carlos Camancho
Road
Tamuing, GU 96913
P: (671) 647-1901
F: (671) 647-6948
E: rey.vega
  @mail.dmhsa.guam.gov

HAWAII
Ms. Lynn N. Fallin
Deputy Director
Behavioral Health
Administration
Department of Health
1250 Punchbowl Street,
Director's Office
Honolulu, HI 96813
P: (808) 586-4416
F: (808) 586-4368
E: lynn.fallin
  @doh.hawaii.gov

IDAHO
Mr. Ross Edmunds
Administrator
Division of Behavioral Health
450 West State Street
Boise, ID 83720
P: (208) 334-5726
F: (208) 334-5998
E: edmundsr@dhw.idaho.gov

ILLINOIS
Ms. Theodora Binion
Acting Director
Division of Mental Health
160 North LaSalle, 10th Floor
Chicago, IL 60601
P: (312) 814-3784 Ext. 1115
F: (312) 814-2964
E: theodra.binion
  @illinois.gov

INDIANA
Mr. Kevin Moore
Director
Division of Mental Health &
Addiction
Family & Social Services
Administration
402 West Washington Street,
Room W353
Indianapolis, IN 46204
P: (317) 232-7860
F: (317) 233-1986
E: kevin.moore@fssa.in.gov

IOWA
Mr. Rick Shults
Division Administrator
Division of Mental Health &
Disability Services
Department of Human Services
Hoover Building 5SE, 1305 East
Walnut
Des Moines, IA 50319
P: (515) 281-8580
F: (515) 242-6036
E: rshults@dhs.state.ia.us

KANSAS
Ms. Carla Drescher
Behavioral Health Assistant
Director
Community Services &
Programs Commission
Aging & Disability Services
503 South Kansas Avenue
Topeka, KS 66603
P: (785) 296-4079
F: (785) 296-0256
E: Carla.Drescher
  @kdads.ks.gov

KENTUCKY
Ms. Mary Begley
Commissioner
Department for Behavioral
Health, Development &
Intellectual Disabilities
100 Fair Oaks Lane
Frankfort, KY 40601
P: (502) 564-4527
F: (502) 564-5478
E: mary.begley@ky.gov

Mental Health and Mental Retardation

LOUISIANA
Dr. Rochelle Head-Dunham
Assistant Secretary/Medical Director
Office of Behavioral Health
Department of Health & Hospitals
P. O. Box 629
Baton Rouge, LA 70821
P: (225) 342-2540
F: (225) 342-5066
E: rochelle.dunham@la.gov

MAINE
Mr. Sheldon Wheeler
Acting Director
Office of Substance Abuse & Mental Health Services
Department of Health & Human Services
41 Anthony Avenue
Augusta, ME 04333
P: (207) 287-2595
F: (207) 287-4334
E: Sheldon.wheeler
@maine.gov

MARYLAND
Dr. Brian Hepburn
Executive Director
Mental Hygiene Administration,
Department of Health & Mental Hygiene
Spring Grove Hospital Center
Dix Building
Catonsville, MD 21228
P: (410) 402-8452
F: (410) 402-8441
E: brian.hepburn
@maryland.gov

MASSACHUSETTS
Ms. Joan Mikula
Interim Commissioner
Department of Mental Health
25 Staniford Street
Boston, MA 02114
P: (617) 626-8123
F: (617) 626-8131
E: joan.mikula
@dmh.state.ma.us

MICHIGAN
Ms. Lynda Zeller
Deputy Director
Behavioral Health & Developmental Disabilities Administration
Department of Community Health
320 South Walnut Street
Lansing, MI 48913
P: (517) 335-0196
F: (517) 335-4798
E: zellerl2@michigan.gov

MINNESOTA
Ms. Jennifer DeCubellis
Assistant Commissioner
Department of Human Services
Community Supports Administration
540 Cedar Street
St. Paul, MN 55164
P: (651) 431-2323
F: (651) 431-7455
E: Jennifer.decubellis
@state.mn.us

MISSISSIPPI
Ms. Diana Mikula
Executive Director
Department of Mental Health
1101 Robert E. Lee Building
239 North Lamar Street
Jackson, MS 39201
P: (601) 359-1288
F: (601) 359-6295
E: diana.mikula
@dmh.state.ms.us

MISSOURI
Mr. Mark G. Stringer
Director
Division of Behavioral Health
Department of Mental Health
1706 East Elm Street
Jefferson City, MO 65102
P: (573) 751-9499
F: (573) 751-7814
E: mark.stringer@dmh.mo.gov

MONTANA
Ms. Glenda Oldenburg
Administrator
DPHHS Addictive & Mental Disorders Division
P.O. Box 202905
Helena, MT 59620
P: (406) 444-3936
F: (406) 444-4435
E: goldenburg@mt.gov

NEBRASKA
Ms. Sheri Dawson
Acting Director
Division of Behavioral Health
Department of Health & Human Services
301 Centennial Mall South, 3rd Floor
Lincoln, NE 68509
P: (402) 471-8553
F: (402) 471-9449
E: sheri.dawson
@nebraska.gov

NEVADA
Mr. Richard Whitley
Administrator
Division of Mental Health & Developmental Services
4150 Technology Way, Suite 300
Carson City, NV 89706
P: (775) 684-4224
F: (775) 684-4211
E: rwhitley@health.nv.gov

NEW HAMPSHIRE
Mr. Geoffrey C. Souther
Director
Bureau of Behavioral Health
Department of Health & Human Services
105 Pleasant Street
Concord, NH 03301
P: (603) 271-5007
F: (603) 271-5048
E: gsouther
@dhhs.state.nh.us

NEW JERSEY
Ms. Lynn A. Kovich
Assistant Commissioner
Division of Mental Health & Addiction Services
Department of Human Services
222 South Warren Street, 3rd Floor
Trenton, NJ 08625
P: (609) 777-0702
F: (609) 341-2302
E: lynn.kovich
@dhs.state.nj.us

NEW MEXICO
Dr. Wayne W. Lindstrom
Director
Behavioral Health Services Division
Department of Health
P.O. Box 2348
Santa Fe, NM 87504
P: (505) 476-9252
F: (505) 476-9272
E: wayne.lindstrom
@state.nm.us

NEW YORK
Dr. Ann Marie T. Sullivan
Commissioner
State Office of Mental Health
44 Holland Avenue
Albany, NY 12229
P: (518) 474-4403
F: (518) 474-2149
E: ann.sullivan@omh.ny.gov

NORTH CAROLINA
Dr. Courtney M. Cantrell
Director
Division of Mental Health, Developmental Disabilities & Substance Abuse Services
Department of Health & Human Services
3001 Mail Service Center
Raleigh, NC 27699
P: (919) 733-7011
F: (919) 508-0951
E: courtney.m.cantrell
@dhhs.nc.gov

NORTH DAKOTA
Ms. Pam Sagness
Director
Division of Behavioral Health
Department of Human Services
1237 West Divide Avenue, Suite 1C
Bismarck, ND 58501
P: (701) 328-8824
F: (701) 328-8969
E: psagness@nd.gov

OHIO
Ms. Tracy J. Plouck
Director
Department of Mental Health & Addiction Services
30 East Broad Street, 36th Floor
Columbus, OH 43215
P: (614) 466-2337
F: (614) 752-9453
E: tracy.plouck
@mha.ohio.gov

OKLAHOMA
Ms. Terri White
Commissioner
Department of Mental Health & Substance Abuse Services
Executive Department
P.O. Box 53277
Oklahoma City, OK 73152
P: (405) 522-3877
F: (405) 522-0637
E: tlwhite@odmhsas.org

OREGON
Dr. Pam Martin
Director
Addictions & Mental Health Division
State Health Authority
500 Summer Street Northeast, E86
Salem, OR 97301
P: (503) 945-5879
F: (503) 378-8467
E: pamela.a.martin
@dhsoha.state.or.us

Mental Health and Mental Retardation

PENNSYLVANIA
Mr. Dennis Marion
Deputy Secretary
Office of Mental Health &
Substance Abuse Services
Department of Public Welfare
20 Azalea Drive
Harrisburg, PA 17105
P: (717) 787-6443
F: (717) 787-5394
E: dmarion@pa.gov

PUERTO RICO
Mr. Jose Flores
Acting Administrator
Mental Health Services
P.O. Box 607087
Bayamon, PR 00960
P: (787) 763-7575
F: (787) 765-5858
E: jflores
@assmca.gobierno.pr

RHODE ISLAND
Ms. Maria Montanaro
Director
Department of Behavioral
Healthcare
Barry Hall
14 Harrington Road
Cranston, RI 02920
P: (401) 462-2339
F: (401) 462-3204
E: maria.montanaro
@bhddh.ri.gov

SOUTH CAROLINA
Mr. John H. Magill
State Director
Department of Mental Health
Office of State Director
2414 Bull Street, Suite 321
Columbia, SC 29201
P: (803) 898-8319
F: (803) 898-1383
E: jhm03@scdmh.org

SOUTH DAKOTA
Ms. Tiffany Wolfgang
Division Director of Behavioral
Health
Department of Social Services
811 East 10th Street,
Department 9
Sioux Falls, SD 57103
P: (605) 367-5078
F: (605) 367-5239
E: Tiffany.Wolfgang
@state.sd.us

TENNESSEE
Mr. E. Douglas Varney
Commissioner
Department of Mental Health &
Substance Abuse Services
Andrew Jackson Building
Nashville, TN 37243
P: (615) 532-6503
F: (615) 532-6514
E: Doug.Varney@tn.gov

TEXAS
Ms. Lauren Lacefield Lewis
Assistant Commissioner of
Mental Health & Substance
Abuse
Department of State Health
Services
P.O. Box 149347
Austin, TX 78714
P: (512) 206-5145
F: (512) 206-5306
E: lauren.lacefieldlewis
@dshs.state.tx.us

U.S. VIRGIN ISLANDS
Ms. Doris
Farrington-Hepburn
Director of the Division of
Mental Health
Division of Mental Health,
Alcoholism & Drug
Dependency Services
Charles Harwood #3500
Christiansted
St. Croix, VI 00828
P: (340) 773-1311
F: (340) 712-6223
E: doris.hepburn@doh.vi.gov

UTAH
Mr. Doug Thomas
Director
Division of Substance Abuse &
Mental Health
Department of Human Services
195 North 1950 West
Salt Lake City, UT 84116
P: (801) 538-4298
F: (801) 538-9892
E: dothomas@utah.gov

VERMONT
Mr. Paul Depre
Commissioner
Department of Mental Health
26 Terrace Street
Montpelier, VT 05609
P: (802) 828-3808
F: (802) 828-1717
E: paul.depre@state.vt.us

VIRGINIA
Dr. Debra Ferguson
Commissioner
Department of Behavioral
Health & Developmental
Services
1220 Bank Street
P.O. Box 1797
Richmond, VA 23218
P: (804) 786-3921
F: (804) 371-6638
E: debra.ferguson
@dbhds.virginia.gov

WASHINGTON
Ms. Jane Beyer
Assistant Secretary
Behavioral Health & Service
Integration Administration
Department of Social & Health
Services
P.O. Box 45050
Lacey, WA 98504
P: (360) 725-2260
F: (360) 407-0304
E: jane.beyer@dshs.wa.gov

WEST VIRGINIA
Ms. Victoria L. Jones
Commissioner
Bureau for Behavioral Health &
Health Facilities
Department of Health & Human
Resources
350 Capitol Street, Room 350
Charleston, WV 25301
P: (304) 356-4538
F: (304) 558-2230
E: Victoria.L.Jones@wv.gov

WISCONSIN
Ms. Joyce Bohn Allen
Director, Bureau of Prevention
Treatment and Recovery
Division of Mental Health &
Substance Abuse Services,
Department of Health Services
1 West Wilson Street, Room
#850
Madison, WI 53707
P: (608) 266-1351
F: (608) 266-2579
E: joyce.allen
@wisconsin.gov

WYOMING
Ms. Chris Newman
Senior Administrator
Behavioral Health Division
Department of Health
6101 Yellowstone Road, Suite
220
Cheyenne, WY 82002
P: (307) 777-6494
F: (307) 777-5849
E: chris.newman@wyo.gov

Minority Affairs

Serves as an advocate for state minority communities and promotes minority business enterprises within the state.

AMERICAN SAMOA
Dr. Taeaoafua Meki Solomona
Director
Department of Human & Social Services
P.O. Box 997534
Pago Pago, AS 96799
P: (684) 633-1664
F: (684) 633-7449
E: mtsolomona@dhss.as

ARIZONA
Ms. Sandra Watson
President & CEO
Commerce Authority
333 North Central Avenue, Suite 1900
Phoenix, AZ 85004
P: (602) 845-1200
F: (602) 845-1201
E: commerce@azcommerce.com

CONNECTICUT
Ms. Melody A. Currey
Commissioner
Department of Administrative Services
165 Capitol Avenue
Hartford, CT 06106
P: (860) 713-5100
F: (860) 713-7481
E: Melody.Currey@ct.gov

IDAHO
Ms. Pamela Parks
Administrator
Human Rights Cpmmission
317 West Main Street, Second Floor
Boise, ID 83735
P: (208) 334-2873
F: (208) 334-2664
E: Pamela.Parks
   @ihrc.idaho.gov

INDIANA
Ms. Terrie F. Daniel
Deputy Commissioner
Minority & Women's Business Enterprises
Department of Administration
402 West Washington Street, Room W469
Indianapolis, IN 46204
P: (317) 232-3061
F: (317) 233-6921
E: TDaniel@idoa.IN.gov

IOWA
Ms. Beth Townsend
Agency Director
Civil Rights Commission
1000 East Grand Avenue
Des Moines, IA 50319
P: (515) 281-5364
E: beth.townsend
   @iwd.iowa.gov

KANSAS
Dr. Mildred Edwards
Executive Director
African-American Affairs Commission
900 Southwest Jackson, Suite 100
Topeka, KS 66612
P: (785) 296-4874
F: (785) 296-1795
E: kaaac@ks.gov

Ms. Adrienne Foster
Executive Director
Hispanic & Latino American Affairs Commission
900 Southwest Jackson, Room 100
Topeka, KS 66612
P: (785) 296-3465
F: (785) 296-8118
E: khlaac@ks.gov

KENTUCKY
Mr. Delquan Dorsey
Executive Director
Governor's Office of Minority Empowerment
700 Capital Avenue, Suite 138
Frankfort, KY 40601
P: (502) 564-2611
F: (502) 564-0437
E: ome@ky.gov

LOUISIANA
Mr. Patrick Bell
Assistant Commissioner
Division of Diversity & Opportunity
Department of Insurance
P.O. Box 94214
Baton Rouge, LA 70804
P: (225) 342-8393
F: (225) 342-4652
E: pbell@ldi.la.gov

MAINE
Ms. Joyce Oreskovich
Director
Bureau of Human Resources
Administrative & Financial Services
4 State House Station
Augusta, ME 04333
P: (207) 624-7761
F: (207) 287-4414
E: joyce.a.oreskovich
   @maine.gov

MARYLAND
Mr. Jimmy Rhee
Special Secretary
Governor's Office of Minority Affairs
Baltimore, MD 21202
P: (410) 767-8232
E: jimmy.rhee@maryland.gov

MASSACHUSETTS
Ms. Sandra E. Borders
Director
Office of Diversity & Equal Opportunity
One Ashburton Place, Room 213
Boston, MA 02108
P: (617) 727-7441
F: (617) 878-9830

MINNESOTA
Mr. Kevin Lindsey
Commissioner
Department of Human Rights
Freeman Building
625 Robert Street, North
St. Paul, MN 55155
P: (651) 296-5675
F: (651) 296-9042
E: Kevin.Lindsey
   @state.mn.us

MISSOURI
Mr. Walter Pearson
Interim Director
Office of Equal Opportunity
301 West High Street, Room 630
P.O. Box 809
Jefferson City, MO 65102
P: (573) 751-8130
F: (573) 522-8078

MONTANA
Ms. Meg O'Leary
Director
Department of Commerce
301 South Park Avenue
P.O. Box 200501
Helena, MT 59620
P: (406) 841-2700
F: (406) 841-2701

NORTH DAKOTA
Ms. Bonnie Storbakken
Commissioner of Labor
Department of Labor
600 East Boulevard Avenue
Department 406
Bismarck, ND 58505
P: (701) 328-2660
F: (701) 328-2031
E: bstorbakken@nd.gov

OHIO
Mr. G. Michael Payton
Executive Director
Civil Rights Commission
Rhodes State Office Tower
30 East Broad Street, 5th Floor
Columbus, OH 43215
P: (614) 466-2785
F: (614) 466-7742
E: paytonm@ocrc.state.oh.us

OKLAHOMA
Ms. Lucinda Meltabarger
Administrator
Human Capital Management Division
2101 North Lincoln Boulevard, Room G-80
Oklahoma City, OK 73105
P: (405) 521-3928
F: (405) 522-0694
E: lucinda.meltabarger
   @omes.ok.gov

OREGON
Ms. Robin Johnson
Equity Policy Coordinator
Diversity & Inclusion (Affirmative Action)
Governor's Office
225 Capitol Street, Northeast
Salem, OR 97301
P: (503) 378-8271
F: (503) 378-3225
E: robin.johnson@oregon.gov

SOUTH CAROLINA
Mr. Thomas J. Smith
Executive Director
Commission for Minority Affairs
2221 Devine Street, Suite 408
Columbia, SC 29205
P: (803) 333-9621
F: (803) 333-9627
E: tsmith@cfma.sc.gov

SOUTH DAKOTA
Mr. Leroy J.R. LaPlante
Secretary of Tribal Relations
Department of Tribal Governmental Relations
302 East Dakota
Pierre, SD 57501
P: (605) 773-3415
F: (605) 773-6592

Minority Affairs

TENNESSEE
Ms. Beverly L. Watts
Executive Director
Human Rights Commission
710 James Robertson Parkway,
Suite 100
Corner of Rosa Parks Boulevard
Nashville, TN 37243
P: (615) 741-5825
F: (615) 253-1886

VIRGINIA
Ms. Ida McPherson
Director
Department of Minority
Business Enterprise
1100 East Main Street, Suite 300
Richmond, VA 23219
P: (804) 371-6228
F: (804) 371-7359
E: ida.mcpherson
    @dmbe.virginia.gov

WEST VIRGINIA
Dr. Darrell Cummings
Chair
Human Rights Commission
1321 Plaza East, Room 108A
Charleston, WV 25301
P: (304) 558-2616
F: (304) 558-0085

WISCONSIN
Ms. Jeanette Johnson
Administrator
Division of Affirmative Action
101 East Wilson Street
P.O. Box 7855
Madison, WI 53707
P: (608) 266-3017
F: (608) 267-1020
E: oserdaa@wi.gov

Motor Vehicle Administration

Issues and maintains all records related to motor vehicle registration, operators' licenses and certificates of titles in the state.

ALABAMA
Mr. Spencer Collier
Director
Law Enforcement Agency
301 South Ripley Street
P.O. Box 1511
Montgomery, AL 36102
P: (334) 242-4394
F: (334) 242-0512

ALASKA
Colonel James Cockrell
Director
Division of State Troopers
Department of Public Safety
5700 East Tudor Road
Anchorage, AK 99507
P: (907) 269-5511
F: (907) 337-2059
E: james.cockrell
     @alaska.gov

Ms. Amy Erickson
Director
Division of Motor Vehicles
Department of Administration
1300 West Benson Boulevard
Anchorage, AK 99503
P: (907) 269-5551
F: (907) 269-3762
E: amy.erickson@alaska.gov

AMERICAN SAMOA
Mr. William E. Haleck
Commissioner
Department of Public Safety
American Samoa Government
P.O. Box 1086
Pato Pato, AS 96799
P: (684) 633-1111
F: (684) 633-7296
E: commissioner@dps.as.gov

ARIZONA
Mr. Frank Milstead
Director
Department of Public Safety
P.O. Box 6638
Phoenix, AZ 85005
P: (602) 223-2000
F: (602) 223-2917

Ms. Stacey K. Stanton
Assistant Director
Motor Vehicle Division
Department of Transportation
P.O. Box 2100, MD 555M
Phoenix, AZ 85001
P: (602) 255-0072
F: (602) 712-6539
E: sstanton@azdot.gov

ARKANSAS
Mr. Roger Duren
Administrator of Motor Vehicles
Office of Motor Vehicles
Ragland Building
7th & Battery Streets, Room 2042
Little Rock, AR 72201
P: (501) 682-4630
F: (501) 682-1116
E: roger.duren
     @dfa.arkansas.gov

Ms. Tonie Shields
Administrator of Driver Services
Office of Driver Services
Ragland Building
1900 West 7th Street, Room 2067
Little Rock, AR 72201
P: (501) 371-5581
F: (501) 682-7688
E: tonie.shields
     @dfa.arkansas.gov

Mr. John H. Theis
Assistant Commissioner, Policy and Legal
Department of Finance & Administration
Ledbetter Building
1816 West 7th Street, Suite 2440
Little Rock, AR 72201
P: (501) 682-7000
F: (501) 683-1161
E: john.theis
     @dfa.arkansas.gov

CALIFORNIA
Mr. Joseph A. Farrow
Commissioner
Highway Patrol
601 North 7th Street
P.O. Box 942898
Sacramento, CA 94298
P: (916) 843-3001
F: (916) 843-3266

Ms. Jean Shiomoto
Director
Department of Motor Vehicles
2415 1st Avenue, Mail Station F101
Sacramento, CA 95818
P: (916) 657-6940
F: (916) 657-7393
E: jshiomoto@dmv.ca.gov

DELAWARE
Colonel Nathaniel McQueen
Commissioner
State Police
1441 North DuPont Highway
P.O. Box 430
Dover, DE 19903
P: (302) 739-5291

Mr. Scott Vien
Director
Division of Motor Vehicles
303 Transportation Circle
P.O. Box 698
Dover, DE 19903

DISTRICT OF COLUMBIA
Ms. Lucinda M. Babers
Director
Department of Motor Vehicles
P.O. Box 90120
Washington, DC 20090
P: (202) 737-4404
E: dmv@dc.gov

FLORIDA
Ms. Terry L. Rhodes
Executive Director
Department of Highway Safety & Motor Vehicles
Neil Kirkman Building
2900 Apalachee Parkway
Tallahassee, FL 32399
P: (850) 617-3100
F: (850) 922-6274
E: terryrhodes@flhsmv.gov

GEORGIA
Ms. Vicki Lambert
Director
Motor Vehicle Division
4125 Welcome All Road
Atlanta, GA 30349
P: (855) 406-5221
E: motorvehicleinquiry
     @dor.ga.gov

Mr. Rob Mikell
Commissioner
Department of Driver Services
2206 East View Parkway
P.O. Box 80447
Conyers, GA 30013
P: (404) 657-9300
F: (678) 413-8661

GUAM
Mr. Steve Aguon
Supervisor, Vehicle Registration Branch
Department of Revenue & Taxation
Motor Vehicle Division
P.O. Box 23607
GMF, GU 96921
P: (671) 635-7652
F: (671) 633-2643
E: saguon@revtax.gov.gu

HAWAII
Mr. Ford Fuchigami
Director
Department of Transportation
Aliiaimoku Building, Room 509
869 Punchbowl Street
Honolulu, HI 96813
P: (808) 587-2150
F: (808) 587-2167

IDAHO
Mr. Alan Frew
Administrator
Motor Vehicles Division
3311 West State Street
P.O. Box 7129
Boise, ID 83707
P: (208) 334-4443
F: (208) 334-8739
E: alan.frew@itd.idaho.gov

ILLINOIS
Mr. Ernie Dannenberger
Director
Vehicle Services Department
Michael J. Howlett Building
501 South Second Street, Room 312
Springfield, IL 62756
P: (217) 785-3000
F: (217) 785-4727
E: edannenberger@ilsos.net

Mr. Hiram Grau
State Director
State Police
801 South 7th Street, Suite 1100 – S
Springfield, IL 62703
P: (217) 782-7263
E: hiram.grau@illinois.gov

Ms. Stephanie Lacey
Director, Metro Operation
Driver Services Department
17 North State Street
Suite 1100
Chicago, IL 60602
P: (312) 793-1010
F: (312) 814-2974
E: glazzerini@ilsos.net

Motor Vehicle Administration

Mr. Michael J. Mayer
Director, Downstate Operations
Driver Services Department
2701 South Dirksen Parkway
Springfield, IL 62723
P: (217) 782-6212
F: (217) 785-2472
E: mmayer@lisos.net

INDIANA
Mr. Kent Abernathy
Commissioner
Bureau of Motor Vehicles
100 North Senate Avenue
Government Center North,
Room 400
Indianapolis, IN 46204
P: (317) 232-5914
E: KAbernathy@bmv.IN.gov

Mr. Douglas G. Carter
Superintendent
State Police
Indiana Government Center
North
100 North Senate Avenue
Indianapolis, IN 46204
P: (317) 232-8248
E: ISP@isp.in.gov

IOWA
Col. Patrick J. Hoye
Colonel
State Patrol Division
Department of Public Safety
215 East 7th Street
Des Moines, IA 50319
P: (515) 725-6101
E: hoye@dps.state.ia.us

Mr. Mark Lowe
Director
Motor Vehicle Division
6310 Southeast Convenience
Boulevard
Des Moines, IA 50306
P: (515) 244-9124
F: (515) 237-3152
E: mark.lowe@dot.iowa.gov

Mr. Larry L. Noble
Commissioner
Department of Public Safety
215 East 7th Street
Des Moines, IA 50319
P: (515) 725-6182
E: noble@dps.state.ia.us

KANSAS
Mr. Mark Bruce
Superintendent
Highway Patrol
122 Southwest 7th Street
Topeka, KS 66603
P: (785) 296-6800
F: (785) 296-3049

Mr. Nick Jordan
Secretary
Department of Revenue
Docking State Office Building,
2nd Floor
915 Southwest Harrison Street
Topeka, KS 66612
P: (785) 296-3909
F: (785) 296-7928

KENTUCKY
Mr. Mike Hancock
Secretary
Transportation Cabinet
200 Mero Street
Frankfort, KY 40622
P: (502) 564-4890
F: (502) 564-4809

Mr. Rodney Kuhl
Commissioner
Department of Vehicle
Regulation
Transportation Cabinet
P.O. Box 2014
Frankfort, KY 40602
P: (502) 564-7000
F: (502) 564-6403
E: rodney.kuhl@ky.gov

LOUISIANA
Mr. Stephen F. Campbell
Commissioner
Office of Motor Vehicles
P.O. Box 64886
Baton Rouge, LA 70896
P: (225) 925-6146
F: (225) 925-1838

Col. Michael D. Edmonson
Deputy Secretary
State Police
Public Safety Services
7919 Independence Boulevard
Baton Rouge, LA 70806
P: (225) 925-6118
F: (225) 925-6006

MAINE
Colonel Robert A. Williams
Chief
State Police
42 State House Station
45 Commerce Drive
Augusta, ME 04333
P: (207) 624-7200
E: robert.a.williams
    @maine.gov

MARYLAND
Mr. Milt Chaffee
Administrator
Motor Vehicle Administration
6601 Ritchie Highway Northeast
Room 200
Glen Burnie, MD 21062
P: (410) 768-7295
E: mchaffee1
    @marylandmva.com

Colonel William Pallozzi
Superintendent
Department of State Police
1201 Reisterstown Road
Pikesville, MD 21208
P: (410) 653-4219
E: msp.superintendent
    @maryland.gov

MASSACHUSETTS
Mr. Matthew Carlin
Commissioner
Department of Public Safety
One Ashburton Place, Room
1301
Boston, MA 02108
P: (617) 727-3200
F: (617) 727-5732

MICHIGAN
Colonel Kriste Kibbey Etue
Director
State Police
333 South Grand Avenue
P.O. Box 30634
Lansing, MI 48909
P: (517) 332-2521
F: (517) 241-0409
E: EtueK@michigan.gov

Hon. Ruth Johnson (R)
Secretary of State
Office of the Secretary of State
430 West Allegan Street
Lansing, MI 48918
P: (517) 373-2510
F: (517) 373-0727
E: secretary@michigan.gov

MINNESOTA
Ms. Patricia McCormack
Director
Driver & Vehicle Services
Division
445 Minnesota Street
Suite 195
St. Paul, MN 55101
P: (651) 201-7580
F: (651) 296-3141
E: patricia.mccormack
    @state.mn.us

MISSISSIPPI
Mr. Ed Morgan
Commissioner
Department of Revenue
P.O. Box 1033
Jackson, MS 39215
P: (601) 923-7000
F: (601) 923-7423

Mr. Albert Santa Cruz
Commissioner
Department of Public Safety
P.O. Box 958
Jackson, MS 39205
P: (601) 987-1212
F: (601) 987-1488
E: commissioner
    @mdps.state.ms.us

MONTANA
Ms. Brenda Nordlund
Administrator
Motor Vehicle Division
Scott Hart Building, 2nd Floor
302 North Roberts, P.O. Box
201430
Helena, MT 59620
P: (406) 444-3933
F: (406) 444-2086
E: mvd@mt.gov

Mr. Duane Williams
Administrator
Motor Carrier Services Division
P.O. Box 4639
Helena, MT 59604
P: (406) 444-7312
F: (406) 444-0800
E: duwilliams@mt.gov

NEBRASKA
Ms. Rhonda Lahm
Director
Department of Motor Vehicles
301 Centennial Mall South
P.O. Box 94789
Lincoln, NE 68509
P: (402) 471-2281
F: (402) 471-9594
E: rhonda.lahm@nebraska.gov

NEVADA
Mr. Troy L. Abney
Chief
Highway Patrol
Department of Public Safety
555 Wright Way
Carson City, NV 89711
P: (775) 687-5300
E: tabney@dps.state.nv.us

Mr. Troy L. Dillard
Director
Department of Motor Vehicles
555 Wright Way
Carson City, NV 89711
P: (775) 684-4549
F: (775) 684-4692

Colonel Dennis S. Osborn
Chief
Highway Patrol
Department of Public Safety
555 Wright Way
Carson City, NV 89711
P: (775) 687-5300

Mr. James Wright
Director
Department of Public Safety
555 Wright Way
Carson City, NV 89711
P: (775) 684-4808
F: (775) 684-4809

NEW HAMPSHIRE
Mr. John J. Barthelmes
Commissioner
Department of Safety
James H. Hayes Safety Building
33 Hazen Drive
Concord, NH 03305
P: (603) 223-3889
F: (603) 271-3903
E: john.barthelmes
@dos.nh.gov

NEW JERSEY
Mr. Raymond P. Martinez
Chief Administrator
Motor Vehicle Commission
P.O. Box 403
Trenton, NJ 08666
P: (609) 292-6500
F: (609) 777-4171
E: raymond.martinez
@dot.state.nj.us

NEW MEXICO
Ms. Demesia Padilla
Secretary
Taxation & Revenue
Department
1100 South St. Francis Drive
Santa Fe, NM 87504
P: (505) 827-0700
F: (505) 827-0331

NEW YORK
Mr. Joseph D'Amico
Superintendent
State Police
1220 Washington Avenue,
Building 22
Albany, NY 12226
P: 518) 457-6721

Ms. Barbara J. Fiala
Commissioner
Department of Motor Vehicles
6 Empire State Plaza
Albany, NY 12228
P: (518) 474-0841
F: (518) 474-9578

NORTH CAROLINA
Kelly J. Thomas
Commissioner
Division of Motor Vehicles
Department of Transportation
1100 New Bern Avenue
Raleigh, NC 27601
P: (919) 715-7000
F: (919) 733-0126
E: kellyjthomas@ncdot.gov

NORTH DAKOTA
Mr. Grant Levi
Director
Department of Transportation
608 East Boulevard Avenue
Bismarck, ND 58505
P: (701) 328-2581
F: (701) 328-0310
E: glevi@nd.gov

Mr. Mark Nelson
Interim Deputy Director
Driver & Vehicle Services
Department of Transportation
608 East Boulevard Avenue
Bismarck, ND 58505
P: (701) 328-2500
F: (701) 328-0310
E: mnelson@nd.gov

NORTHERN MARIANA ISLANDS
Mr. James C.
Deleon Guerrero
Commissioner
Department of Public Safety
Jose M. Sablan Building
Caller Box 10007
Saipan, MP 96950
P: (670) 664-9022
F: (670) 664-9070

OHIO
Colonel John Born
Director
Department of Public Safety
1970 West Broad Street
P.O. Box 182081
Columbus, OH 43218
P: (614) 466-3383
F: (614) 466-0433

Colonel Paul A. Pride
Superintendent
State Highway Patrol
1970 West Broad Street
P.O. Box 182074
Columbus, OH 43223
P: (614) 466-2990

Mr. Mike Rankin
Registrar
Bureau of Motor Vehicles
1970 West Broad Street
P.O. Box 16520
Columbus, OH 43216
P: (614) 752-7500
F: (614) 261-9601

OKLAHOMA
Mr. Russ Nordstrom
Director
Motor Vehicle Division
2501 North Lincoln Boulevard
Oklahoma City, OK 73194
P: (405) 521-3221
F: (405) 521-6937
E: rnordstrom
@eris.oktax.state.ok.us

OREGON
Mr. Gregg Dal Ponte
Administrator
Motor Carrier Transportation
Division
Department Of Transportation
3930 Fairview Industrial Drive
Southeast
Salem, OR 97302
P: (503) 378-6351
F: (503) 373-1940
E: gregg.l.dalponte
@odot.state.or.us

Mr. Thomas McClellan
Administrator
Division of Driver & Motor
Vehicle
1905 Lana Avenue, Northeast
Salem, OR 97314
P: (503) 945-5100
F: (503) 945-0893
E: thomas.l.mcclellan
@state.or.us

PENNSYLVANIA
Colonel Marcus L. Brown
Acting Commissioner
State Police
1800 Elmerton Avenue
Harrisburg, PA 17110
P: (717) 783-5517
F: (717) 783-7690

Leslie S. Richards
Secretary
Department of Transportation
Keystone Building
400 North Street
Harrisburg, PA 17120
P: (717) 787-5574
F: (717) 787-5491

PUERTO RICO
Mr. Hector Pesquera
Superintendent
Puerto Rico Police
P.O. Box 70166
San Juan, PR 00936
P: (787) 793-1234
F: (787) 781-0080

RHODE ISLAND
Ms. Clare Sedlock
Acting Administrator
Division of Motor Vehicles
Department of Revenue
600 New London Avenue
Cranston, RI 02920
P: (401) 462-4368
F: (401) 462-5784

SOUTH CAROLINA
Ms. Marcia S. Adams
Executive Director
Budget & Control Board
1200 Senate Streer, Suite 600
Columbia, SC 29201
P: (803) 734-2320
F: (803) 734-2117
E: madams@oed.sc.gov

Motor Vehicle Administration

Mr. Mark A. Keel
Chief
State Law Enforcement Division
4400 Broad River Road
P.O. Box 21398
Columbia, SC 29221
P: (803) 896-9223
F: (803) 896-7041

Colonel Michael Oliver
Commander
Highway Patrol
10311 Wilson Boulevard
P.O. Box 1993
Blythewood, SC 29016
P: (803) 896-7920
F: (803) 896-7922

SOUTH DAKOTA
Ms. Debra Hillmer
Director
Motor Vehicles Division
Department of Revenue
445 East Capitol Avenue
Pierre, SD 57501
P: (605) 773-3541
F: (605) 773-2550
E: motorv@state.sd.us

TENNESSEE
Mr. Leon Stribling
Executive Director
Motor Vehicle Commission
500 James Robertson Parkway
Nashville, TN 37243
P: (615) 741-2711
F: (615) 741-0651
E: Leon.Stribling
   @state.tn.us

Colonel Tracy Trott
Director
Highway Patrol
1150 Foster Avenue
Nashville, TN 37243
P: (615) 251-5175
F: (615) 532-1051

TEXAS
Mr. Jeremiah Kuntz
Director
Vehicle Titles & Registration
Division
Department of Motor Vehicles
4000 Jackson Avenue
Austin, TX 78731
P: (512) 465-4023

Mr. Steve McCraw
Director
Department of Public Safety
5805 North Lamar Boulevard
P.O. Box 4087
Austin, TX 78773
P: (512) 424-2000
F: (512) 483-5708

U.S. VIRGIN ISLANDS
Mr. Rodney F. Querrard
Commissioner
Police Department
Alexander Farrelly Criminal
Justice Ctr.
Charlotte Amalie
St. Thomas, VI 00802
P: (340) 715-5605
F: (340) 715-5517

UTAH
Mr. Brad L. Simpson
Division Director
Division of Motor Vehicles
Tax Commission
P.O. Box 30412
Salt Lake City, UT 84130
P: (801) 297-7687
F: (801) 297-7697
E: bsimpson@utah.gov

VERMONT
Mr. Robert Ide
Commissioner
Department of Motor Vehicles
Agency of Transportation
120 State Street
Montpelier, VT 05603
P: (802) 828-2011
F: (802) 828-2170
E: robert.ide@state.vt.us

Colonel Thomas J.
   L'Esperance
Director
State Police
103 South Main Street
Waterbury, VT 05671
P: (802) 875-2112
E: Tom.LEsperance
   @state.vt.us

VIRGINIA
Mr. Richard D. Holcomb
Commissioner
Department of Motor Vehicles
P.O. Box 27412
Richmond, VA 23269
P: (804) 367-6606
F: (804) 367-2296
E: richard.holcomb
   @dmv.virginia.gov

WASHINGTON
Mr. John R. Batiste
Chief
State Patrol
General Administration Building
P.O. Box 42600
Olympia, WA 98504
P: (360) 596-4000
E: john.batiste@wsp.wa.gov

Ms. Pat Kohler
Agency Director
Department of Licensing
P.O. Box 9020
Olympia, WA 98507
P: (360) 902-3600
F: (360) 902-4042
E: doldirector@dol.wa.gov

WEST VIRGINIA
Pat Reed
Commissioner
Division of Motor Vehicles
Capitol Complex Building 3,
Room 337
1900 Kanawha Boulevard, East
Charleston, WV 25305
P: (304) 558-3900
F: (304) 926-3884
E: dot.dmvcommissioner
   @wv.gov

WISCONSIN
Mr. Patrick Fernan
Administrator
Division of Motor Vehicles
4802 Sheboygan Avenue
Madison, WI 53705
P: (608) 266-7079
F: (608) 267-6974

Mr. Stephen Fitzgerald
Superintendent
Division of State Patrol
4802 Sheboygan Avenue, Room
551
P.O. Box 7912
Madison, WI 53707
P: (608) 266-3212
F: (608) 267-4495
E: Stephen.Fitzgerald
   @dot.wi.gov

WYOMING
Colonel John Butler
Administrator
Highway Patrol
5300 Bishop Boulevard
Cheyenne, WY 82009
P: (307) 777-4301
F: (307) 777-3897

Mr. John F. Cox
Director
Department of Transportation
5300 Bishop Boulevard
Cheyenne, WY 82009
P: (307) 777-4484
F: (307) 777-4163

Natural Resources

Formulates and coordinates policies to protect, develop, utilize, restore and enhance the state's natural resources.

ALABAMA
Mr. N. Gunter Guy Jr.
Commissioner of Conservation
Department of Conservation &
Natural Resources
64 North Union Street
Montgomery, AL 36130
P: (334) 242-3486
E: dcnr.commissioner
@dcnr.alabama.gov

ALASKA
Mr. Mark Myers
Commissioner
Department of Natural
Resources
550 West 7th Avenue, Suite 800
Anchorage, AK 99501
P: (907) 269-8431
F: (907) 269-8918
E: mark.myers@alaska.gov

AMERICAN SAMOA
Dr. Ruth S. Matagi-Tofiga
Director
Department of Marine &
Wildlife Resources
American Samoa Government
Pago Pago, AS 96799
P: (684) 633-4456
F: (684) 633-5590

ARIZONA
Mr. Stephen Williams
Director
State Land Department, Natural
Resources
1616 West Adams Street
Phoenix, AZ 85007
P: (602) 542-2693

ARKANSAS
Mr. J. Randy Young
Executive Director
Natural Resources Commission
101 East Capitol Avenue, Suite
350
Little Rock, AR 72201
P: (501) 682-3961
F: (501) 682-3991
E: randy.young@arkansas.gov

CALIFORNIA
Mr. Mark W. Cowin
Director
Department of Water Resources
1416 Ninth Street
P.O. Box 942836
Sacramento, CA 94236
P: (916) 653-5791
F: (916) 653-4684
E: mcowin@water.ca.gov

COLORADO
Mr. Mike King
Executive Director
Department of Natural
Resources
Executive Director's Office
1313 Sherman Street, Room 718
Denver, CO 80203
P: (303) 866-3311
F: (303) 866-2115
E: Mike.King@state.co.us

CONNECTICUT
Mr. Robert J. Klee
Commissioner
Department of Energy &
Environmental Protection
79 Elm Street
Hartford, CT 06106
P: (860) 424-3001
F: (860) 424-4051
E: deep.commissioner@ct.gov

DISTRICT OF COLUMBIA
Mr. Keith A. Anderson
Director
Department of the Environment
1200 First Street, Northeast
Washington, DC 20002
P: (202) 535-2600
F: (202) 535-2881
E: ddoe@dc.gov

FLORIDA
Mr. Jon Steverson
Secretary
Department of Environmental
Protection
3900 Commonwealth Boulevard
Tallahassee, FL 32399
P: (850) 245-2011
F: (850) 245-2128
E: jon.steverson
@dep.state.fl.us

GEORGIA
Mr. Mark Williams
Commissioner
Department of Natural
Resources
2 Martin Luther King Jr. Drive
Southeast
Suite 1252, East Tower
Atlanta, GA 30334
P: (404) 656-3500
F: (404) 656-0770

GUAM
Ms. Mariquita F. Taitague
Director
Department of Agriculture
163 Dairy Road
Mangilao, GU 96913
P: (671) 734-3942
F: (671) 734-6569

HAWAII
Ms. Suzanne D. Case
Chairperson
Department of Land & Natural
Resources
Kalanimoku Building
1151 Punchbowl Street
Honolulu, HI 96813
P: (808) 587-0400
F: (808) 587-0390
E: dlnr@hawaii.gov

IDAHO
Mr. Curt Fransen
Director
Department of Environmental
Quality
1410 North Hilton
Boise, ID 83706
P: (208) 373-0240
F: (208) 373-0417
E: curt.fransen
@deq.idaho.gov

ILLINOIS
Mr. Wayne Rosenthal
Director
Department of Natural
Resources
One Natural Resources Way
Springfield, IL 62702
P: (217) 785-0075
F: (217) 785-9236
E: wayne.rosenthal
@illinois.gov

INDIANA
Mr. Mitch Zoll Jr.
Division Director
Historic Preservation &
Archaeology
Department of Natural
Resources
402 West Washington Street,
W274
Indianapolis, IN 46204
P: (317) 232-3492
F: (317) 232-0693
E: mzoll@dnr.in.gov

IOWA
Mr. Chuck Gipp
Director
Department of Natural
Resources
4th Floor, Wallace Building
502 East 9th Street
Des Moines, IA 50319
P: (515) 281-5817
F: (515) 281-8895
E: chuck.gipp@dnr.iowa.gov

KANSAS
Mr. Greg Foley
Executive Director
Division of Conservation
109 Southwest 9th Street, 2A
Topeka, KS 66612
P: (785) 296-7085
F: (785) 296-6172
E: greg.foley@kda.ks.gov

KENTUCKY
Mr. Steve Hohmann
Commissioner
Department for Natural
Resources
#2 Hudson Hollow
Frankfort, KY 40601
P: (502) 564-6940
F: (502) 564-5698
E: steve.hohmann@ky.gov

LOUISIANA
Mr. Stephen Chustz
Secretary
Department of Natural
Resources
617 North Third Street
P.O. Box 94396
Baton Rouge, LA 70804
P: (225) 342-2710
F: (225) 342-3790
E: Stephen.Chustz@LA.GOV

MAINE
Mr. Walter E. Whitcomb
Commissioner
Department of Agriculture,
Conservation & Forestry
28 State House Station
18 Elkins Lane
Augusta, ME 04333
P: (207) 287-3419
F: (207) 287-7548
E: dacf@maine.gov

MASSACHUSETTS
Ms. Carol Sanchez
Commissioner
Department of Conservation &
Recreation
251 Causeway Street, Suite 900
Boston, MA 02114
P: (617) 626-1250
F: (617) 626-1351

Natural Resources

MINNESOTA
Mr. Tom Landwehr
Commissioner
Department of Natural
Resources
500 Lafayette Road
St. Paul, MN 55155
P: (651) 259-5022
F: (651) 296-4799
E: Tom.Landwehr@state.mn.us

MISSISSIPPI
Mr. Gary Rikard
Executive Director
Department of Environmental
Quality
515 East Amite Street
Jackson, MS 39201
P: (601) 961-5001
F: (601) 961-5093
E: gary_rikard
      @deq.state.ms.us

MISSOURI
Ms. Sara Parker Pauley
Director
Department of Natural
Resources
P.O. Box 176
Jefferson City, MO 65102
P: (573) 751-3443
F: (573) 751-7627
E: sara.pauley@ded.mo.gov

Ms. Toni Prawl
State Historic Preservation
Office
Department of Natural
Resources
P.O. Box 176
Jefferson City, MO 65102
P: (573) 751-7858
F: (573) 751-7627

MONTANA
Mr. Jeff Hagener
Director
Department of Fish, Wildlife &
Parks
1420 East Sixth Avenue
P.O. Box 200701
Helena, MT 59620
P: (406) 444-3186
F: (406) 444-4952
E: fwpgen@mt.gov

Mr. John Tubbs
Director
Department of Natural
Resources & Conservation
1625 Eleventh Avenue
P.O. Box 201601
Helena, MT 59620
P: (406) 444-2074
F: (406) 444-2684

NEBRASKA
Mr. Jim Schneider
Director
Department of Natural
Resources
301 Centennial Mall South
Lincoln, NE 68509
P: (402) 471-2366
F: (402) 471-2900
E: jim.schneider
      @nebraska.gov

NEVADA
Mr. Leo Drozdoff
Director
Department of Conservation &
Natural Resources
901 South Stewart Street, Suite
5001
Carson City, NV 89701
P: (775) 687-9301
F: (775) 687-5856
E: ldrozdoff@dcnr.nv.gov

NEW JERSEY
Mr. John Sacco
Chief
Office of Natural Resource
Restoration
P.O. Box 404, Station Plaza 5
Trenton, NJ 08625
P: (609) 984-5475
F: (609) 984-0836
E: Onrr@dep.state.nj.us

NEW MEXICO
Mr. David Martin
Cabinet Secretary
Energy, Minerals & Natural
Resources Department
1220 South St. Francis Drive
Santa Fe, NM 87505
P: (505) 476-3200
F: (505) 476-3220
E: david.martin@state.nm.us

NEW YORK
Mr. Joe Martens
Commissioner
Department of Environmental
Conservation
625 Broadway, 14th Floor
Albany, NY 12233
P: (518) 402-8540
F: (518) 402-8541
E: joemartens
      @gw.dec.state.ny.us

NORTH DAKOTA
Mr. Greg Link
Division Chief
Conservation &
Communications Division
Game & Fish Department
100 North Bismarck Expressway
Bismarck, ND 58501
P: (701) 328-6331
F: (701) 328-6352
E: glink@nd.gov

OHIO
Mr. James J. Zehringer
Director
Department of Natural
Resources
2045 Morse Road, Building D
Columbus, OH 43229
P: (614) 265-6565
F: (614) 261-9601

OKLAHOMA
Mr. Michael Teague
Secretary of Energy &
Environment
Office of the Secretary of
Energy & Environment
3800 North Classen Boulevard
Oklahoma City, OK 73118
P: (405) 530-8995
F: (405) 530-8999

OREGON
Mr. Curt Melcher
Director
Department of Fish & Wildlife
4034 Fairview Industrial Drive,
Southeas
Salem, OR 97302
P: (503) 947-6044

PENNSYLVANIA
Ms. Cindy Adams Dunn
Secretary
Department of Conservation &
Natural Resources
209 Finance Building
Harrisburg, PA 17120
P: (717) 787-5440
F: (717) 787-4523

PUERTO RICO
Ms. Carmen Guerrero Perez
Secretary
Department of Natural &
Environmental Resources
P.O. Box 366147
San Juan, PR 00936
P: (787) 999-2200
F: (787) 999-2303

RHODE ISLAND
Mr. Larry Mouradjian
Associate Director
Department of Environmental
Management
Bureau of Natural Resources
235 Promenade Street
Providence, RI 02908
P: (401) 222-4700 Ext. 2414
F: (401) 222-3162
E: larry.mouradjian
      @dem.ri.gov

SOUTH CAROLINA
Mr. Alvin A. Taylor
Director
Department of Natural
Resources
1000 Assembly Street
P.O. Box 167
Columbia, SC 29202
P: (803) 734-4020
F: (803) 734-6310
E: taylora@dnr.sc.gov

SOUTH DAKOTA
Mr. Steven M. Pirner
Secretary
Department of Environment &
Natural Resources
Joe Foss Building
523 East Capital Avenue
Pierre, SD 57501
P: (605) 773-5559
F: (605) 773-6035
E: steve.pirner@state.sd.us

TENNESSEE
Mr. Brock Hill
Deputy Commissioner
Bureau of Parks & Conservation
401 Church Street
7th Floor, L&C Annex
Nashville, TN 37243
P: (615) 532-0001
F: (615) 741-8858

TEXAS
Dr. Bryan W. Shaw
Chair
Commission on Environmental
Quality
12100 Park 35 Circle
P.O. Box 13087
Austin, TX 78711
P: (512) 239-5510
F: (512) 239-5533
E: bryan.shaw
      @tceq.texas.gov

U.S. VIRGIN ISLANDS
Ms. Alicia Barnes
Department of Planning &
Natural Resources
Dronningens Gade 71&72A,
Kongens Quarter
Charlotte Amalie, VI 00802
P: (340) 774-3320
F: (340) 773-1082

UTAH
Mr. Michael R. Styler
Executive Director
Department of Natural
Resources
1594 West North Temple
P.O. Box 145610
Salt Lake City, UT 84114
P: (801) 538-7201
F: (801) 538-7315
E: mikestyler@utah.gov

VERMONT
Ms. Deborah L. Markowitz
Secretary
Agency of Natural Resources
103 South Main Street, Center
Building
Waterbury, VT 05671
P: (802) 241-3808
F: (802) 244-1102
E: deb.markowitz
   @state.vt.us

VIRGINIA
Ms. Molly Ward
Secretary
Office of the Secretary of
Natural Resources
1111 East Broad Street
Patrick Henry Building
Richmond, VA 23219
P: (804) 786-0044
F: (804) 371-8333
E: molly.ward
   @governor.virginia.gov

WASHINGTON
Hon. Peter J. Goldmark (D)
Commissioner of Public Lands
Department of Natural
Resources
1111 Washington Street,
Southeast
P.O. Box 47000
Olympia, WA 98504
P: (360) 902-1000
F: (360) 902-1775
E: cpl@dnr.wa.gov

WEST VIRGINIA
Mr. Robert A. Fala
Director
Division of Natural Resources
324 Fourth Avenue, Building 74
South Charleston, WV 25303
P: (304) 558-3315
F: (304) 558-2768

WISCONSIN
Ms. Cathy Stepp
Secretary
Department of Natural
Resources
101 South Webster Street
Madison, WI 53703
P: (608) 266-0865
F: (608) 266-6983
E: DNRSecretary
   @Wisconsin.gov

WYOMING
Mr. Bob Budd
Executive Director
Wildlife & Natural Resource
Trust
Hathaway Building, 1st Floor
2300 Capitol Avenue, Suite 117
Cheyenne, WY 82002
P: (307) 777-8024

Occupational Safety

Enforces safety standards for the protection of employees in places of employment.

ALABAMA
Mr. Fitzgerald Washington
Commissioner
Department of Labor
649 Monroe Street
Montgomery, AL 36131
P: (334) 242-8990

ALASKA
Mr. Grey Mitchell
Director
Division of Labor Standards &
Safety
P.O. Box 111149
Juneau, AK 99811
P: (907) 465-4855
F: (907) 465-6012
E: grey.mitchell@alaska.gov

AMERICAN SAMOA
Mr. Le'i S. Thompson
Director
Department of Human
Resources
Executive Office Building
AP Lutali, 2nd Floor
Pago Pago, AS 96799
P: (684) 644-4485
F: (684) 633-1139
E: sonnythompson
   @samoatelco.com

ARIZONA
Ms. Laura L. McGrory
Director
Industrial Commission
800 West Washington Street
Phoenix, AZ 85007
P: (602) 542-4411
F: (602) 542-7889
E: lmcgrory@ica.state.az.us

CALIFORNIA
Ms. Juliann Sum
Acting Chief
Division of Occupational Safety
& Health
Department of Industrial
Relations
1515 Clay Street, Suite 1901
Oakland, CA 94612
P: (510) 286-7000
F: (510) 286-7037
E: jsum@dir.ca.gov

CONNECTICUT
Ms. Sharon Palmer
Commissioner
Department of Labor
200 Folly Brook Boulevard
Westerfield, CT 06109
P: (860) 263-6505
F: (850) 263-6529
E: sharon.palmer@ct.gov

DELAWARE
Mr. James G. Cagle Jr.
Director
Division of Industrial Affairs
4425 North Market Street, 3rd
Floor
Wilmington, DE 19802
P: (302) 761-8200
F: (302) 761-6601

DISTRICT OF COLUMBIA
Mr. F. Thomas Luparello
Acting Director
Department of Employment
Services
4058 Minnesota Avenue,
Northeast
Washington, DC 20019
P: (202) 724-7000
F: (202) 673-6993
E: does@dc.gov

FLORIDA
Mr. Tanner Holloman
Director
Division of Workers'
Compensation
200 East Gaines Street
Tallahassee, FL 32399
P: (850) 413-1600
E: Tanner.Holloman
   @myfloridacfo.com

GEORGIA
Mr. Earl Everett
Director of Safety &
Engineering
Safety Engineering Division
1700 Century Circle, Suite 100
Atlanta, GA 30345
P: (404) 679-0687
F: (404) 982-3405
E: earl.everett
   @dol.state.ga.us

GUAM
Mr. Manuel Q. Cruz
Director
Department of Labor
Government of Guam
P.O. Box 9970
Tamuning, GU 96931
P: (671) 647-6510
F: (671) 674-6517

HAWAII
Ms. Elaine Young
Acting Director
Department of Labor &
Industrial Relations
Ke'elikolani Building
830 Punchbowl Street
Honolulu, HI 96813
P: (808) 586-8844
F: (808) 586-9099
E: dlir.director@hawaii.gov

ILLINOIS
Ms. Carolyn Parks
Executive Director
Workers' Compensation
Commission
100 West Randolph Street,
#8-200
Chicago, IL 60601
P: (312) 814-7268

INDIANA
Mr. Rick J. Ruble
Commissioner
Department of Labor
402 West Washington Street,
Room W195
Indianapolis, IN 46204
P: (317) 232-2655
F: (317) 233-3790
E: rruble@dol.in.gov

IOWA
Mr. Michael A. Mauro
Commissioner
Division of Labor Services
1000 East Grand Avenue
Des Moines, IA 50319
P: (515) 281-3447
F: (515) 281-4698
E: michael.mauro
   @iwd.iowa.gov

KANSAS
Ms. Lana Gordon
Secretary of Labor
Department of Labor
401 Southwest Topeka
Boulevard
Topeka, KS 66603
P: (785) 296-5058
F: (785) 368-5289
E: lana.gordon@dol.ks.gov

Mr. Terri Sanchez
Director
Industrial Safety & Health
Division
700 Southwest Jackson, Room
420
Topeka, KS 66603
P: (785) 296-4386
F: (785) 296-1775
E: Terri.Sanchez@dol.ks.gov

KENTUCKY
Mr. Mike Dixon
Executive Director
Occupational Safety & Health
Program
1047 US Highway 127 South
Suite 4
Frankfort, KY 40601
P: (502) 564-3070
F: (502) 696-1902

LOUISIANA
Mr. Patrick Robinson
Interim Director
Office of Workers'
Compensation Administration
Workforce Commission
P.O. Box 94040
Baton Rouge, LA 70804
P: (225) 342-7555
F: (225) 342-5665
E: owca@lwc.la.gov

MAINE
Mr. Steve Greeley
Director
Workplace Safety Division
Department of Labor
45 State House Station
Augusta, ME 04333
P: (207) 623-7900
F: (207) 623-7934
E: webmaster.bls@Maine.gov

MARYLAND
Mr. Eric Uttenreither
Assistant Commissioner
Department of Labor, Licensing
& Regulation
Occupational Safety and Health
10946 Golden West Drive, Suite
160
Hunt Valley, MD 21031
P: (410) 527-2065
F: (410) 527-4481
E: uttenreither.eric
   @dol.gov

MASSACHUSETTS
Mr. Daniel Bennett
Secretary
Executive Office of Public
Safety & Security
One Ashburton Place, Suite
2133
Boston, MA 02108
P: (617) 727-7775
F: (617) 727-4764

MICHIGAN
Ms. Martha B. Yoder
Director
Occupational Safety & Health
Administration
P.O. Box 30643
Lansing, MI 48909
P: (517) 322-1814
F: (517) 322-1775
E: YoderM@michigan.gov

MINNESOTA
Mr. Ken Peterson
Commissioner
Department of Labor & Industry
443 Lafayette Road North
St. Paul, MN 55155
P: (651) 284-5010
F: (651) 284-5720
E: ken.peterson@state.mn.us

MISSOURI
Mr. Ryan McKenna
Director
Department of Labor &
Industrial Relations
421 East Dunklin Street
P.O. Box 504
Jefferson City, MO 65102
P: (573) 751-4091
F: (573) 751-4135
E: ryan.mckenna
    @labor.mo.gov

MONTANA
Ms. Pam Bucy
Commissioner
Department of Labor & Industry
P.O. Box 1728
Helena, MT 59624
P: (406) 444-2840
F: (406) 444-1419
E: pbucy@mt.gov

NEBRASKA
Ms. Brenda Hicks-Sorensen
Director
Department of Economic
Development
550 South 16th Street
Lincoln, NE 68508
P: (402) 471-3125
E: brenda.hicks-sorensen
    @nebraska.gov

NEVADA
Mr. Donald L. Soderberg
Director
Division of Industrial Relations
500 East Third Street
Carson City, NV 89713
P: (775) 684-3849
F: (775) 684-3850
E: dsoderberg
    @business.nv.gov

NEW HAMPSHIRE
Mr. James W. Craig
Commissioner of Labor
Department of Labor
95 Pleasant Street
Concord, NH 03301
P: (603) 271-3171
F: (603) 271-6852
E: jcraig@labor.state.nh.us

NEW JERSEY
Dr. Christina Tan
Assistant Commissioner
Division of Epidemiology,
Environmental & Occupational
Health
P.O. Box 369
Trenton, NJ 08625
P: (609) 588-7463
E: epi@doh.state.nj.us

NEW MEXICO
Mr. Bob Genoway
Bureau Chief
Occupational Health & Safety
Bureau
525 De Los Marquez, Suite 3
Santa Fe, NM 87505
P: (505) 476-8700
F: (505) 476-8734
E: Robert.Genoway
    @state.nm.us

NEW YORK
Mr. Peter M. Rivera
Commissioner
Department of Labor
W. Averell Harriman State
Office Campus
Building 12
Albany, NY 12240
P: (518) 457-9000
F: (518) 485-6297

NORTH CAROLINA
Mr. Allen McNeely
Director
Department of Labor
Occupational Safety & Health
Division
1101 Mail Service Center
Raleigh, NC 27699
P: (919) 807-2900
E: allen.mcneely
    @labor.nc.gov

NORTH DAKOTA
Mr. Nick Jolliffe
Director
Loss Control Department
Workforce Safety & Insurance
500 East Front Avenue
Bismarck, ND 58504
P: (701) 328-3886
F: (701) 328-3820
E: njolliffe@nd.gov

**NORTHERN MARIANA
ISLANDS**
Mr. Gil M. San Nicolas
Secretary
Department of Labor
Capitol Hill
Saipan, MP 96950
P: (670) 664-3196
F: (670) 664-3197

OHIO
Mr. Andre T. Porter
Chair
Department of Commerce
180 East Broad Street
Columbus, OH 43215
P: (614) 466-3016
F: (614) 466-7366
E: andre.porter
    @puc.state.oh.us

OKLAHOMA
Ms. Diana Jones
Director of Safety Pays OSHA
Consultation
Department of Labor
3017 North Stiles, Suite 100
Oklahoma City, OK 73105
P: (405) 521-6139
F: (405) 521-6018
E: diana.jones@labor.ok.gov

OREGON
Mr. Michael Wood
Division Administrator
Occupational Safety & Health
Division
Labor & Industries Building
350 Winter Street, Northeast,
Room 430
Salem, OR 97301
P: (503) 947-7400
F: (503) 947-7461
E: michael.wood@oregon.gov

PENNSYLVANIA
Mr. Edward L. Leister
Director
Bureau of Occupational &
Industrial Safety
1613 Labor & Industry Building
Harrisburg, PA 17121
P: (717) 787-3806
F: (717) 787-8363

PUERTO RICO
Mr. Vance Thomas
Secretary
Department of Labor & Human
Resources
P.O. Box 195540
Hato Rey, PR 00918
P: (787) 754-2119
F: (787) 753-9550

RHODE ISLAND
Mr. Scott Jensen
Director
Department of Labor & Training
Center General Complex
1511 Pontiac Avenue
Cranston, RI 02920
P: (401) 462-8000
F: (401) 462-8872
E: director-dlt@dlt.ri.gov

SOUTH CAROLINA
Ms. Richele Taylor
Director
Department of Labor, Licensing
& Regulation
P.O. Box 11329
Columbia, SC 29211
P: (803) 896-4390
F: (803) 896-4393

SOUTH DAKOTA
Mr. James E. Marsh
Director
Division of Labor &
Management
Department of Labor &
Regulation
700 Governors Drive
Pierre, SD 57501
P: (605) 773-3101
F: (605) 773-6184
E: james.marsh@state.sd.us

TENNESSEE
Mr. Steve Hawkins
Administrator
Occupational Safety & Health
Administration
Labor and Workforce
Development
220 French Landing Drive
Nashville, TN 37243
P: (615) 741-2793
F: (615) 741-3325
E: Steve.Hawkins@tn.gov

Occupational Safety

TEXAS
Mr. Kirk Cole
Associate Commissioner
Department of State Health
Services
1100 West 49th Street
P.O.Box 149347
Austin, TX 78714
P: (512) 776-7375

U.S. VIRGIN ISLANDS
Mr. Albert Bryan Jr.
Commissioner of Labor
Department of Labor
4401 Sion Farm
Christiansted, VI 00820
P: (340) 773-1994
F: (340) 773-0094
E: abryan@vidol.gov

UTAH
Mr. Scott McKenzie
Director
Occupational Safety & Health
Division
Labor Commission
P.O. Box 146650
Salt Lake City, UT 84114
P: (801) 530-6898
F: (801) 530-7606
E: smckenzie@utah.gov

VERMONT
Mr. Dan Whipple
Manager
VOSHA
Department of Labor
P.O. Box 488
Montpelier, VT 05601
P: (802) 828-5084
F: (802) 828-4022
E: dan.whipple@state.vt.us

VIRGINIA
Mr. William Burge
Assistant Commissioner/Acting
Commissioner
Department of Labor & Industry
600 East Main Street, Room 207
Richmond, VA 23219
P: (804) 786-2377
F: (804) 371-6524

WASHINGTON
Ms. Anne Soiza
Assistant Director
Division of Occupational Safety
& Health
P.O. Box 44600
Olympia, WA 98504
P: (360) 902-5090
F: (360) 902-5619
E: soiz235@lni.wa.gov

WEST VIRGINIA
Mr. John R. Junkins
Acting Commissioner
Division of Labor
Department of Commerce
749 B, Building 6, Capitol
Complex
Charleston, WV 25305
P: (304) 558-7890
F: (304) 558-2415
E: john.r.junkins@wv.gov

WISCONSIN
Ms. Nancy Mistele
Division Administrator
Department of Safety &
Professional Services
Division of Industry Services
P.O. Box 2599
Madison, WI 53701
P: (608) 266-1816
F: (608) 266-9946
E: nancy.mistele@wi.gov

WYOMING
Mr. Steven R. Czoschke
Interim Executive Secretary
Workers' Compensation Medical
Commission
P.O. Box 20247
Cheyenne, WY 82003
P: (307) 777-5422
F: (307) 777-5201

Oil & Gas Regulation

Regulates the drilling, operation, maintenance and abandonment of oil and gas wells in the state.

ALABAMA
Mr. Berry H. Tew Jr.
State Geologist & Oil and Gas
Supervisor
Geological Survey of Alabama
State Oil & Gas Board
P.O. Box 869999
Tuscaloosa, AL 35486
P: (205) 349-2852
F: (205) 247-3676
E: ntew@gsa.state.al.us

ARIZONA
Dr. M. Lee Allison
Director & State Geologist
Geological Survey
416 West Congress Street, Suite 100
Tucson, AZ 85701
P: (520) 770-3500
F: (520) 770-3505
E: Lee.Allison@azgs.az.gov

ARKANSAS
Mr. Lawrence Bengal
Director
Oil & Gas Commission
301 Natural Resources Drive, Suite 102
Little Rock, AR 72205
P: (501) 683-5814
F: (501) 683-5818
E: Larry.Bengal
   @aogc.state.ar.us

CALIFORNIA
Pat Perez
Acting State Oil & Gas
Supervisor
Division of Oil, Gas &
Geothermal Resources
801 K Street, MS 18-00
Sacramento, CA 95814
P: (916) 445-9686
F: (916) 323-0424
E: pat.perez
   @conservation.ca.gov

COLORADO
Mr. Matt Lepore
Director
Oil & Gas Conservation
Commission
1120 Lincoln Street, Suite 801
Denver, CO 80203
P: (303) 894-2100
F: (303) 894-2109
E: Matt.Lepore@state.co.us

FLORIDA
Mr. Ed Garrett
Professional
Geologist/Administrator
Oil & Gas Program
Department of Environmental
Protection
2600 Blair Stone Road, MS 3588
Tallahassee, FL 32399
P: (850) 245-8848
F: (850) 488-1254
E: Ed.Garrett
   @dep.state.fl.us

GEORGIA
Mr. William G. Smith
Program Manager
Regulatory Support Program
4220 International Parkway,
Suite 101
Atlanta, GA 30354
P: (404) 656-3214
F: (404) 657-8379

GUAM
Mr. Carl V. Dominguez
Director
Department of Public Works
542 North Marine Corp Drive
Tamuning, GU 96913
P: (671) 646-3131
F: (671) 649-6178
E: carl.dominguez
   @dpw.guam.gov

IDAHO
Mr. Tom Schultz
Director
Department of Lands
300 North 6th Street, Suite 103
P.O. Box 83720
Boise, ID 83720
P: (208) 334-0242
F: (208) 334-5342
E: tschultz@idl.idaho.gov

ILLINOIS
Mr. Mike Mankowski
Director of Oil & Gas
Division of Oil & Gas
One Natural Resources Way
Springfield, IL 62702
P: (217) 782-7756
E: mike.mankowski
   @illinois.gov

INDIANA
Mr. Herschel McDivitt
Director
Oil & Gas Division
402 West Washington Street,
Room 293
Indianapolis, IN 46204
P: (317) 232-4058
F: (317) 232-1550
E: hmcdivitt@dnr.in.gov

KANSAS
Mr. Ryan Hoffman
Director
Oil & Gas Conservation
Division
Finney State Office Building
130 South Market, Room 2078
Wichita, KS 67202
P: (316) 337-6200
F: (316) 337-6211

KENTUCKY
Kim Collings
Director
Division of Oil & Gas
1025 Capital Center Drive
Frankfort, KY 40601
P: (502) 573-0147
F: (502) 573-1099
E: Kim.Collings@ky.gov

LOUISIANA
Mr. David Elfert
Director
Geological Oil & Gas Division
617 North Third Street
P.O. Box 94275
Baton Rouge, LA 70804
P: (225) 342-5501
F: (225) 342-8199
E: David.Elfert@la.gov

MARYLAND
Ms. Hilary Miller
Acting Director
Land Management
Administration
Department of the Environment
1800 Washington Boulevard
Baltimore, MD 21230
P: (410) 537-3304
F: (410) 537-3321
E: hilary.miller
   @maryland.gov

MASSACHUSETTS
Mr. Martin Suuberg
Commissioner
Department of Environmental
Protection
One Winter Street
Boston, MA 02108
P: (617) 292-5856
F: (617) 574-6880

MICHIGAN
Mr. Harold R. Fitch
Chief
Office of Oil, Gas & Minerals
P.O. Box 30256
Lansing, MI 48909
P: (517) 284-6823
F: (517) 241-1595
E: fitchh@michigan.gov

MINNESOTA
Mr. Burl Haar
Executive Secretary
Public Utilities Commission
121 Seventh Place East, Suite 350
St. Paul, MN 55101
P: (651) 201-2222
F: (651) 297-7073
E: burl.haar@state.mn.us

MISSISSIPPI
Ms. Lisa Ivshin
Executive Director
Oil & Gas Board
500 Greymont Avenue, Suite E
Jackson, MS 39202
P: (601) 576-4900
F: (601) 354-6873
E: livshin@ogb.state.ms.us

MONTANA
Mr. Jim Halvorson
Interim Administrator
Board of Oil & Gas
Conservation
Billings Technical Office
2535 St. Johns Avenue
Billings, MT 59102
P: (406) 656-0040
F: (406) 655-6015

NEBRASKA
Mr. William H. Sydow
Director
Oil & Gas Conservation
Commission
922 Illinois
P.O. Box 399
Sidney, NE 69162
P: (308) 254-6919
F: (308) 254-6922
E: bsydow@nogcc.ne.gov

NEW JERSEY
Mr. James P. Giuliano
Director
Division of Reliability &
Security
Board of Public Utilities
2 Gateway Center, 8th Floor
Newark, NJ 07102
P: (973) 648-3875
F: (201) 648-2242
E: james.giuliano
   @bpu.state.nj.us

Oil & Gas Regulation

NEW MEXICO
Mr. David Catanach
Division Director
Oil Conservation Division
1220 South St. Francis Drive
Santa Fe, NM 87505
P: (505) 476-3460
F: (505) 476-3462

NEW YORK
Mr. Joe Martens
Commissioner
Department of Environmental
Conservation
625 Broadway, 14th Floor
Albany, NY 12233
P: (518) 402-8540
F: (518) 402-8541
E: joemartens
    @gw.dec.state.ny.us

NORTH DAKOTA
Mr. Lynn D. Helms
Director
Oil & Gas Division
Industrial Commission,
Department 405
600 East Boulevard Avenue
Bismarck, ND 58505
P: (701) 328-8020
F: (701) 328-8022
E: lhelms@nd.gov

OHIO
Mr. Andre T. Porter
Chair
Department of Commerce
180 East Broad Street
Columbus, OH 43215
P: (614) 466-3016
F: (614) 466-7366
E: andre.porter
    @puc.state.oh.us

OKLAHOMA
Mr. Ron Dunkin
Director
Oil & Gas Division
Corporation Commission
P.O. Box 52000
Oklahoma City, OK 73152
P: (405) 521-2302

OREGON
Mr. Robert A. Houston
Oil, Gas and Geothermal
Specialist
Mineral Land Regulation &
Reclamation Program
229 Broadalbin Street,
Southwest
Albany, OR 97321
P: (541) 967-2080
F: (541) 967-2075
E: Robert.A.Houston
    @mlrr.oregongeology.com

PENNSYLVANIA
Mr. Scott Perry
Deputy Secretary
Office of Oil & Gas
Management
P.O. Box 8765
Harrisburg, PA 17105
P: (717) 772-2199

PUERTO RICO
Mr. Jose Maeso Gonzalez
Executive Director
Energy Affairs Administration
P.O. Box 41314
San Juan, PR 00940
P: (787) 999-2200 Ext. 2888
F: (787) 999-2246
E: jose.maeso@aae.pr.gov

RHODE ISLAND
Ms. Margaret E. Curran
Chair
Public Utilities Commission
89 Jefferson Boulevard
Warwick, RI 02888
P: (401) 780-2100
F: (401) 941-1691
E: margaret.curran
    @puc.ri.gov

SOUTH CAROLINA
Mr. Joe Gellici
Section Chief
Hydrology Section
Department of Natural
Resources
1000 Assembly Street
Columbia, SC 29201
P: (803) 734-6428
F: (803) 734-9200
E: gellicij@dnr.sc.gov

TENNESSEE
Mr. Mike Burton
Assistant Supervisor
Board of Water Quality, Oil &
Gas
401 Church Street
L & C Tower
Nashville, TN 37243
P: (615) 532-0166
F: (615) 532-1517
E: Michael.K.Burton
    @state.tn.us

UTAH
Mr. John R. Baza
Director
Division of Oil, Gas & Mining
1594 West North Temple, Suite
1210
P.O. Box 145801
Salt Lake City, UT 84114
P: (801) 538-5334
F: (801) 359-3940
E: johnbaza@utah.gov

VERMONT
Ms. Deborah L. Markowitz
Secretary
Agency of Natural Resources
103 South Main Street, Center
Building
Waterbury, VT 05671
P: (802) 241-3808
F: (802) 244-1102
E: deb.markowitz
    @state.vt.us

VIRGINIA
Mr. Conrad T. Spangler III
Director
Department of Mines, Minerals
& Energy
Washington Building, 8th Floor
1100 Bank Street
Richmond, VA 23219
P: (804) 692-3202
F: (804) 692-3237
E: conrad.spangler
    @dmme.virginia.gov

WEST VIRGINIA
Mr. James Martin
Chief
Office of Oil & Gas
601 57th Street, Southeast
Charleston, WV 25304
P: (304) 926-0499
F: (304) 926-0452
E: James.A.Martin@wv.gov

WISCONSIN
Mr. Jeff Ripp
Administrator
Gas & Electric Division
P.O. Box 7854
Madison, WI
P: (608) 266-0699
F: (608) 267-1381
E: Jeffrey.Ripp
    @wisconsin.gov

WYOMING
Mr. Mark Watson
Agency Supervisor
Oil & Gas Conservation
Commission
2211 King Boulevard
P.O. Box 2640
Casper, WY 82602
P: (307) 234-7147
F: (307) 234-5306

Ombudsman

Investigates citizens' complaints about the administrative acts of any state agency.

ALABAMA
Ms. Pam Bye
Director of Constituent Services
Office of the Governor
600 Dexter Avenue
Montgomery, AL 36130
P: (334) 242-7100
F: (334) 353-0004
E: pam.bye
 @governor.alabama.gov

ALASKA
Ms. Linda Lord-Jenkins
Ombudsman
Office of the Ombudsman
State Legislature
P.O. Box 101140
Anchorage, AK 99510
P: (907) 269-5290
F: (907) 269-5291
E: linda.lord-jenkins
 @akleg.gov

ARIZONA
Mr. Dennis Wells
Ombudsman-Citizens' Aide
Office of the Ombudsman -
Citizen's Aide
3737 North 7th Street, Suite 209
Phoenix, AZ 85014
P: (602) 277-7292
F: (602) 277-7312
E: ombuds@azoca.org

CALIFORNIA
Hon. Elaine M. Howle
State Auditor
Bureau of State Audits
621 Capitol Mall, Suite 1200
Sacramento, CA 95814
P: (916) 445-0255 Ext. 342
F: (916) 323-0913
E: elaineh@bsa.ca.gov

COLORADO
Ms. Karen Schaefer
Lead Mediator
State Employee Assistance
Program
Department of Personnel &
Administration
1525 Sherman Street, Suite 117
Denver, CO 80202
P: (303) 866-4314
F: (303) 866-4388
E: karen.schaefer
 @state.co.us

DELAWARE
Ms. Jennifer Hill
Director, Constituent Relations
Office of the Governor
150 Martin Luther King Jr.
Blvd., South
2nd Floor
Dover, DE 19901
P: (302) 744-4101
F: (302) 739-2775

DISTRICT OF COLUMBIA
Mr. Chris Taylor
Director of Community
Relations and Services
Mayor's Office of Community
Relations & Services
1350 Pennsylvania Avenue,
Northwest
Suite 211
Washington, DC 20004
P: (202) 727-8195
F: (202) 727-5931
E: chris.taylor@dc.gov

FLORIDA
Mr. Warren Davis
Director of Citizen Services
Office of the Governor
400 South Monroe Street
Tallahassee, FL 32399
P: (850) 717-9418
F: (850) 487-0801
E: Warren.Davis
 @eog.myflorida.com

HAWAII
Mr. Robin K. Matsunaga
Ombudsman
Office of the Ombudsman
465 South King Street, 4th Floor
Honolulu, HI 96813
P: (808) 587-0770
F: (808) 587-0773
E: complaints
 @ombudsman.hawaii.gov

IOWA
Ms. Ruth H. Cooperrider
Ombudsman
Office of Citizen's
Aide/Ombudsman
Ola Babcock Miller Building
1112 East Grand
Des Moines, IA 50319
P: (515) 281-3592
F: (515) 242-6007
E: ruth.cooperrider
 @legis.iowa.gov

KENTUCKY
Mr. Edward C. Monahan
Public Advocate
Department of Public Advocacy
100 Fair Oaks Lane, Suite 302
Frankfort, KY 40601
P: (502) 564-8006
F: (502) 564-7890

MAINE
Ms. Patricia A. Condon
Director of Constituent Services
Office of the Governor
#1 State House Station
Augusta, ME 04333
P: (207) 287-3531
F: (207) 287-1034

MARYLAND
Mr. Jeremy C. Rosendale
Director
Correspondence & Constituent
Services
Office of the Governor
State House
Annapolis, MD 21401
P: (410) 974-3591
F: (410) 974-3275
E: Jeremy.Rosendale
 @maryland.gov

MISSISSIPPI
Ms. Anniece McLemore
State LTC Ombudsman
Division of Aging & Adult
Services
Department of Human Services
750 North State Street
Jackson, MS 39202
P: (601) 359-4929
E: aging@mdhs.ms.gov

MISSOURI
Hon. Peter Kinder (R)
Lieutenant Governor
Office of the Lieutenant
Governor
State Capitol, Room 224
Jefferson City, MO 65101
P: (573) 751-4727
F: (573) 751-9422
E: ltgovinfo@mail.mo.gov

MONTANA
Mr. John Malia
Citizens' Advocate
Citizens' Advocate Office
State Capitol, Room 232
P.O. Box 200803
Helena, MT 59620
P: (406) 444-3468
E: citizensadvocate@mt.gov

NEBRASKA
Mr. Marshall Lux
Ombudsman
State Legislature
Room 807, State Capitol
P.O. Box 94604
Lincoln, NE 68509
P: (402) 471-2035
F: (402) 471-4277
E: mlux@leg.ne.gov

NEW HAMPSHIRE
Mr. Charles H. Weatherill
Ombudsman
Department of Health & Human
Services
105 Pleasant Street
Concord, NH 03301
P: (603) 271-6941
F: (603) 271-4632
E: cweather
 @dhhs.state.nh.us

NORTH DAKOTA
Ms. Barb Peske
Director
Constituent Services
Office of the Governor
600 East Boulevard Avenue
Bismarck, ND 58505
P: (701) 328-2208
F: (701) 328-2205
E: bapeske@nd.gov

NORTHERN MARIANA
ISLANDS
Mr. James Benedetto
Office of the Attorney General
P.O. Box 502452
Saipan, MP 96950
P: (670) 664-2333
F: (670) 664-2349
E: ombudsman@federal.com

PUERTO RICO
Ms. Iris Miriam Ruiz Class
Prosecutor
Office of the Ombudsman
P.O. Box 41088
San Juan, PR 00940
P: (787) 724-7373
F: (787) 724-7386
E: irismiriam.ruiz
 @opc.gobierno.pr

SOUTH DAKOTA
Ms. Grace Kessler
Director of Constituent Services
Office of the Governor
500 East Capitol Avenue
Pierre, SD 57501
P: (605) 773-3212
F: (605) 773-4711

Ombudsman

TEXAS
Mr. Gregory S. Davidson
Director
Constituent Communication
Division
Office of the Governor
P.O. Box 12428
Austin, TX 78711
P: (512) 463-1800
F: (512) 463-1849

U.S. VIRGIN ISLANDS
Mr. Julien Harley
St. John Administrator
Office of the Governor
21-22 Kongens Gade
Charlotte Amalie
St. Thomas, VI 00802
P: (340) 774-0001
F: (340) 693-4309

UTAH
Ms. Gloria Hunt
Constituent Services Director
Office of the Governor
350 North State Street, Suite
200
P.O. Box 142220
Salt Lake City, UT 84114
P: (801) 538-1178
F: (801) 538-1528
E: GHUNT@utah.gov

WEST VIRGINIA
Ms. Patricia Burdette
Director of Constituent Services
Office of the Governor
1900 Kanawha Boulevard, East
Charleston, WV 25305
P: (304) 558-2000
F: (304) 342-7025
E: Patricia.A.Burdette
  @wv.gov

Parks and Recreation

Manages the state's parks, historical sites and recreational areas.

Information provided by:

National Association of State Park Directors
Philip McKnelly
Executive Director
8829 Woodyhill Road
Raleigh, NC 27613
P: (919) 676-8365
F: (919) 676-8365
NASPD@me.com
www.naspd.org

ALABAMA
Mr. Greg Lein
Director
State Parks Division
64 North Union Street
Montgomery, AL 36130
P: (334) 242-3334
E: greg.lein
@dcnr.alabama.gov

ALASKA
Mr. Ben Ellis
Director
Division of Parks & Outdoor
Recreation
Department of Natural
Resources
550 West 7th Avenue, Suite 1380
Anchorage, AK 99501
P: (907) 269-8700
F: (907) 269-8907
E: ben.ellis@alaska.gov

ARIZONA
Ms. Sue Black
Executive Director
State Parks
1300 West Washington
Phoenix, AZ 85007
P: (602) 542-4174
F: (602) 542-4188

ARKANSAS
Mr. Greg Butts
Director
State Parks
One Capitol Mall, Suite 900
Little Rock, AR 72201
P: (501) 682-7743
F: (501) 682-1364
E: greg.butts@arkansas.gov

CALIFORNIA
Ms. Lisa Mangat
Director
Department of Parks &
Recreation
1416 Ninth Street
P.O. Box 942896
Sacramento, CA 95814
P: (916) 653-6995
F: (916) 654-6374
E: info@parks.ca.gov

COLORADO
Mr. Bob Broscheid
Director
Division of Parks & Wildlife
1313 Sherman Street, 6th Floor
Denver, CO 80203
P: (303) 866-3203
F: (303) 866-3206
E: bob.broscheid
@state.co.us

CONNECTICUT
Mr. Tom Tyler
Director
DEP, State Parks Division
79 Elm Street
Hartford, CT 06106
P: (860) 424-3099
F: (860) 424-4070
E: tom.tyler@ct.gov

DELAWARE
Mr. Raymond E. Bivens
Director
Division of Parks & Recreation
89 Kings Highway
Dover, DE 19901
P: (302) 739-9200
F: (302) 739-3817
E: raymond.bivens
@state.de.us

FLORIDA
Mr. Donald Forgione
Director
State Parks, Department of
Environmental Protection
3900 Commonwealth Boulevard
Tallahassee, FL 32399
P: (850) 245-2157
F: (850) 245-3041
E: donald.forgione
@dep.state.fl.us

GEORGIA
Ms. Becky Kelley
Director
State Parks, Recreation &
Historic Sites Division
2600 Highway 155, Southwest
Suite C
Stockbridge, GA 30281
P: (404) 656-2770
F: (770) 389-7402

HAWAII
Mr. Dan S. Quinn
Administrator
Division of State Parks
Department of Land & Natural
Resources
1151 Punchbowl Street Room
310
Honolulu, HI 96813
P: (808) 587-0300
F: (808) 587-0311

IDAHO
Mr. David Langhorst
Director
Department of Parks &
Recreation
5657 Warm Springs Avenue
P.O. Box 83720
Boise, ID 83720
P: (208) 334-4187
F: (208) 334-5232
E: david.langhorst
@idpr.idaho.gov

ILLINOIS
Mr. Ronald House
Director
Office of Land Management &
Education
One Natural Resources Way, 3rd
Floor
Springfield, IL 62702
P: (217) 782-6752
F: (217) 524-5612

INDIANA
Mr. Daniel W. Bortner
Director
Division of State Parks &
Reservoirs
Department of Natural
Resources
402 West Washington Street,
Room W298
Indianapolis, IN 46204
P: (317) 232-4136
F: (317) 232-4132
E: dbortner@dnr.IN.gov

IOWA
Mr. Todd Coffelt
Bureau Chief
State Parks
Department of Natural
Resources
Wallace State Office Building
Des Moines, IA 50319
P: (515) 281-8674
F: (515) 281-6794
E: todd.coffelt
@dnr.iowa.gov

KANSAS
Mr. Robin Jennison
Secretary
Department of Wildlife, Parks &
Tourism
1020 South Kansas Avenue,
Room 200
Topeka, KS 66612
P: (785) 296-2281
F: (785) 296-6953

KENTUCKY
Ms. Elaine Walker
Commissioner
State Parks
500 Mero Street, 10th Floor
Frankfort, KY 40601
P: (502) 564-2172
F: (502) 564-9015
E: elaine.walker@ky.gov

LOUISIANA
Mr. Dwight Landreneau
Assistant Secretary
Office of State Parks
P.O. Box 44426
Baton Rouge, LA 70804
P: (225) 342-8111
F: (225) 342-8107
E: parks@crt.la.gov

MAINE
Mr. Doug Denico
Director
Bureau of Parks & Lands
22 State House Station
18 Elkins Lane (AMHI Campus)
Augusta, ME 04333
P: (207) 287-3821
F: (207) 287-6170
E: Doug.Denico@maine.gov

MARYLAND
Ms. Nita Settina
Superintendent
Park Service
580 Taylor Avenue
Tawes State Office Building E-3
Annapolis, MD 21401
P: (410) 260-8186
F: (410) 260-8191
E: nsettina@dnr.state.md.us

MASSACHUSETTS
Ms. Priscilla H. Geigis
Director
Division of State Parks &
Recreation
Department of Conservation &
Recreation
251 Causeway Street, 9th Floor
Boston, MA 02114
P: (617) 626-4986
F: (617) 626-1351

Parks and Recreation

MICHIGAN
Mr. Ronald Olson
Chief
Parks & Recreation Division
P.O. Box 30257
Lansing, MI 48909
P: (517) 284-7275
F: (517) 373-4625
E: OLSONR@michigan.gov

MINNESOTA
Ms. Erika Rivers
Director
Division of Parks & Trails
500 Lafayette Road
St. Paul, MN 55155
P: (651) 259-5591
F: (651) 297-1157
E: erika.rivers@state.mn.us

MISSISSIPPI
Ms. Libby Hartfield
Director
State Parks
P.O. Box 451
Jackson, MS 39205
P: (601) 432-2218
F: (601) 432-2236

MISSOURI
Mr. Bill Bryan
Director
Division of State Parks
1659 East Elm Street
Jefferson City, MO 65102
P: (573) 751-1010
F: (573) 526-7716
E: Bill.Bryan@dnr.mo.gov

MONTANA
Mr. Chas Van Genderen
Administrator
State Parks
1420 East Sixth Avenue
P.O. Box 200701
Helena, MT 59620
P: (406) 444-3750
F: (406) 444-4952
E: fwpgen@mt.gov

NEBRASKA
Ms. Nikki Krause
Division Administrator
Parks Division
Game & Parks Commission
2200 North 33rd Street
Lincoln, NE 68503
P: (402) 471-5550
F: (402) 471-5528
E: Nikki.Krause
    @nebraska.gov

NEVADA
Mr. Eric Johnson
Administrator
Division of State Parks
901 South Stewart Street, Suite 5005
Carson City, NV 89701
P: (775) 684-2771
F: (775) 684-2777

NEW HAMPSHIRE
Ms. Gail Wolek
Administrator
Division of Parks & Recreation
172 Pembroke Road
P.O. Box 1856
Concord, NH 03302
P: (603) 271-3556
F: (603) 271-3553
E: gail.wolek@DRED.NH.GOV

NEW JERSEY
Mr. Mark Texel
Director
Division of Parks & Forestry
P.O. Box 404
Trenton, NJ 08625
P: (609) 292-2733
F: (609) 984-0503

NEW MEXICO
Mr. Tommy Mutz
Director
State Park Division
1220 South St. Francis Drive
Santa Fe, NM 87505
P: (505) 476-3355
F: (505) 476-3361
E: tommy.mutz@state.nm.us

NEW YORK
Ms. Rose Harvey
State Historic Preservation
Officer & Commissioner
Office of Parks, Recreation &
Historic Preservation
Empire State Plaza
Albany, NY 12238
P: (518) 474-0443
F: (518) 474-4492

NORTH CAROLINA
Mr. Mike Murphy
Director
State Parks System
217 West Jones Street
1615 Mail Service Center
Raleigh, NC 27699
P: (919) 707-9300
F: (919) 715-3085
E: mike.murphy@ncparks.gov

NORTH DAKOTA
Mr. Mark Zimmerman
Director
Parks & Recreation Department
1600 East Century Avenue,
Suite # 3
Bismarck, ND 58503
P: (701) 328-5361
F: (710) 328-5363

OHIO
Mr. Gary Obermiller
Chief
Division of Parks & Recreation
2045 Morse Road, Building C-3
Columbus, OH 43229
P: (614) 265-6511
F: (614) 261-8407

OKLAHOMA
Ms. Kris Marek
Director
State Parks, Resorts & Golf
P.O. Box 52002
Oklahoma City, OK 73152
P: (405) 521-3790
F: (405) 521-2428

OREGON
Ms. Lisa Sumption
Director
Parks & Recreation Department
725 Summer Street, Northeast,
Suite C
Salem, OR 97301
P: (503) 986-0719
F: (503) 986-0794
E: lisa.sumption@oregon.gov

PENNSYLVANIA
Mr. David Kemmerer
Director
Bureau of State Parks
P.O. Box 8551
Harrisburg, PA 17105
P: (717) 787-6640

RHODE ISLAND
Mr. Robert Paquette
Chief
Division of Parks & Recreation
2321 Hartford Avenue
Johnson, RI 02919
P: (401) 222-2632
F: (401) 934-0610

SOUTH CAROLINA
Mr. Phil Gaines
Director
State Park Service
1205 Pendleton Street
Columbia, SC 29201
P: (803) 734-0345
F: (803) 734-1017
E: pgaines@scprt.com

SOUTH DAKOTA
Mr. Doug Hofer
Director
Division of Parks & Recreation
Game, Fish & Parks
523 East Capitol Avenue
Pierre, SD 57501
P: (605) 773-3391
F: (605) 773-6245
E: doug.hofer@state.sd.us

TENNESSEE
Mr. Brock Hill
Deputy Commissioner
Bureau of Parks & Conservation
401 Church Street
7th Floor, L&C Annex
Nashville, TN 37243
P: (615) 532-0001
F: (615) 741-8858

TEXAS
Mr. Carter P. Smith
Executive Director
State Parks
4200 Smith School Road
Austin, TX 78744
P: (512) 389-4802
F: (512) 389-4960

UTAH
Mr. Fred Hayes
Director
Division of State Parks &
Recreation
Department of Natural
Resources
1594 West North Temple, Suite
116
Salt Lake City, UT 84116
P: (801) 538-7336
F: (801) 538-7378
E: fredhayes@utah.gov

VERMONT
Mr. Craig Whipple
Director
Division of State Parks
Forests, Parks & Recreation
1 National Life Drive, Davis 2
Montpelier, VT 05620
P: (802) 343-5318
F: (802) 828-1399
E: craig.whipple
    @state.vt.us

VIRGINIA
Mr. Craig Seaver
Director
Division of State Parks
203 Governor Street, Suite 306
Richmond, VA 23219
P: (804) 786-5055
F: (804) 786-9294
E: craig.seaver
   @dcr.virginia.gov

WASHINGTON
Mr. Don Hoch
Director
State Parks & Recreation
Commission
P.O. Box 42650
Olympia, WA 98504
P: (360) 902-8501
F: (360) 902-8681

WEST VIRGINIA
Mr. Kenneth Caplinger
Chief
Parks & Recreation
324 4th Avenue
South Charleston, WV 25303
P: (304) 558-2764
F: (304) 558-0077
E: Ken.K.Caplinger@wv.gov

WISCONSIN
Mr. Dan Schuller
Director
Bureau of Parks & Recreation
P.O. Box 7921
Madison, WI 53707
P: (608) 264-6035
F: (607) 267-7474
E: daniel.schuller
   @wisconsin.gov

WYOMING
Mr. Domenic Bravo
Administrator
State Parks & Historic Sites
2301 Central Avenue
Barrett Building, 4th Floor
Cheyenne, WY 82002
P: (307) 777-6323
F: (307) 777-6005

Parole and Probation (Adult)

Determines whether paroles should be granted or revoked and supervises adult parolees and probationers.

For more information contact:
American Probation & Parole Association
Carl Wicklund
Executive Director
P.O. Box 11910
Lexington, KY 40578
P: (859) 244-8203
F: (859) 244-8001
cwicklund@csg.org
www.appa-net.org

ALABAMA
Ms. Cynthia S. Dillard
Executive Director
Board of Pardons & Paroles
301 South Ripley Street
P.O. Box 302405
Montgomery, AL 36130
P: (334) 353-7771
F: (334) 242-1809
E: cynthia.dillard
   @alabpp.gov

ALASKA
Mr. Jeffrey Edwards
Director
Parole Board
Department of Corrections
550 West Seventh Avenue, Suite 601
Anchorage, AK 99501
P: (907) 269-4642
F: (907) 269-4697
E: jeffrey.edwards
   @alaska.gov

AMERICAN SAMOA
Mr. William E. Haleck
Commissioner
Department of Public Safety
American Samoa Government
P.O. Box 1086
Pato Pato, AS 96799
P: (684) 633-1111
F: (684) 633-7296
E: commissioner@dps.as.gov

ARIZONA
Mr. Terry Ardiance
Executive Director
Board of Executive Clemency
1645 West Jefferson Street, Suite 101
Phoenix, AZ 85007
P: (602) 542-5656
F: (602) 542-5680

ARKANSAS
Ms. Sheila Sharp
Deputy Director, Parole & Probation
Department of Community Correction
105 West Capitol Avenue
Little Rock, AR 72201
P: (501) 682-9581
F: (501) 682-9513
E: sheila.sharp
   @arkansas.gov

COLORADO
Mr. Brandon C. Shaffer
Chair
State Board of Parole
1600 West 24th Street, Building 54
Pueblo, CO 81003
P: (719) 583-5800
E: brandon.shaffer
   @state.co.us

CONNECTICUT
Mr. Richard Sparaco
Executive Director
Board of Pardons & Paroles
55 West Main Street
Waterbury, CT 06702
P: (203) 805-6605
F: (203) 805-6652
E: richard.sparaco
   @po.state.ct.us

DELAWARE
Mr. David Henderson
Chairperson
Board of Parole
820 North French Street
Carvel State Office Building, 5th Floor
Wilmington, DE 19801
P: (302) 577-5233
F: (302) 577-3501

DISTRICT OF COLUMBIA
Ms. Nancy M. Ware
Director
Court Services & Offender Supervision Agency
633 Indiana Avenue, Northwest
Washington, DC 20004
P: (202) 220-5300
F: (202) 220-5350

FLORIDA
Ms. Tena M. Pate
Chair
Parole Commission
4070 Esplanade Way
Tallahassee, FL 32399
P: (850) 487-1980
F: (850) 414-2627
E: tenapate@fpc.state.fl.us

GEORGIA
Mr. James E. Donald
Chair
Board of Pardons & Paroles
2 Martin Luther King Jr. Drive Southeast
5th Floor, East
Atlanta, GA 30334
P: (404) 651-6597
F: (404) 651-8502

GUAM
Mr. Edward A. Alvarez
Chief Probation Officer
Probation Services Division
Superior Court of Guam
120 West O'Brien Drive
Hagatna, GU 96910
P: (671) 475-3448
F: (671) 477-4944

HAWAII
Mr. Bert Y. Matsuoka
Chair
Paroling Authority
1177 Alakea Street, Ground Floor
Honolulu, HI 96813
P: (808) 587-1300
F: (808) 587-1314

IDAHO
Ms. Olivia Craven
Executive Director
Commission of Pardons & Parole
P.O. Box 83720
Statehouse Mail
Boise, ID 83720
P: (208) 334-2520
F: (208) 334-3501
E: ocraven@idoc.idaho.gov

ILLINOIS
Mr. Jesse Montgomery
Chief of Parole
Parole Division
1301 Concordia Court
P.O. Box 19277
Springfield, IL 62794
P: (309) 755-4511

INDIANA
Ms. Gwen Horth
Chair
Parole Board
402 West Washington Street, Room W466
Indianapolis, IN 46204
P: (317) 232-5673

IOWA
Ms. Dot Faust
Deputy Director, Offender Services
Department of Corrections
Jessie Parker Building
510 East 12th Street
Des Moines, IA 50319
P: (515) 725-5713
E: dorothy.faust@iowa.gov

KANSAS
Mr. Dave Riggin
Chair
Prisoner Review Board
714 Southwest Jackson, Suite 300
Topeka, KS 66603
P: (785) 296-3469
F: (785) 296-7949
E: prb@doc.ks.gov

KENTUCKY
Ms. Shannon Jones
Chair
Parole Board
P.O. Box 2400
Frankfort, KY 40602
P: (502) 564-3620
F: (502) 564-8995

LOUISIANA
Mr. Gerald Starks
Director
Division of Probation & Parole
504 Mayflower Street, Building 6
P.O. Box 94304
Baton Rouge, LA 70804
P: (225) 342-6609
F: (225) 342-3087

MAINE
Ms. Cynthia Brann
Associate Commissioner
Adult Community Corrections
Department of Corrections
State House Station 111
Augusta, ME 04333
P: (207) 287-4340

MARYLAND
Mr. Patrick McGee
Director
Division of Parole & Probation
6776 Reisterstown Road, Suite 305
Baltimore, MD 21215
P: (410) 585-3525
F: (410) 764-4091
E: pmcgee@dpscs.state.md.us

MICHIGAN
Mr. Thomas Combs
Chair
Parole Board
P.O. Box 30003
Lansing, MI 48909
P: (517) 373-0270
F: (517) 335-0039

MINNESOTA
Mr. Tom Roy
Commissioner
Department of Corrections
1450 Energy Park Drive, Suite 200
St. Paul, MN 55108
P: (651) 361-7200
F: (651) 642-0414
E: tom.roy@state.mn.us

MISSISSIPPI
Mr. Steve Pickett
Chair
State Parole Board
660 North Street, Suite 100A
Jackson, MS 39202
P: (601) 576-3520
F: (601) 576-3528

MISSOURI
Ms. Julie Kempker
Chief State Supervisor
Division of Parole & Probation
3400 Knipp Drive
Jefferson City, MO 65109
P: (573) 751-8488
F: (573) 751-8501

MONTANA
Mr. Fern Osler Johnson
Executive Director
Board of Pardons & Parole
1002 Hollenbeck Road
Deer Lodge, MT 59722
P: (406) 846-1404
F: (406) 846-3512

NEBRASKA
Ms. Rosalyn Cotton
Chair
Board of Parole
P.O. Box 94661
State House Station
Lincoln, NE 68509
P: (402) 471-2156
F: (402) 471-2453

NEVADA
Mr. Bernard W. Curtis
Division Administrator
Parole & Probation
1445 Old Hot Springs Road, Suite 104
Carson City, NV 89706
P: (775) 684-2605
F: (775) 684-2693

NEW HAMPSHIRE
Mr. Michael McAlister
Director
Division of Field Services
Department of Corrections
P.O. Box 1806
Concord, NH 03302
P: (603) 271-5652
E: michael.mcalister
    @nhdoc.state.nh.us

NEW JERSEY
Mr. David W. Thomas
Executive Director
State Parole Board
P.O. Box 862
Trenton, NJ 08625
P: (609) 292-4257
F: (609) 943-4769

NEW MEXICO
Ms. Sherry Stephens
Executive Director
Parole Board
45 Penitentiary Road
Santa Fe, NM 87508
P: (505) 827-8825
F: (505) 827-8933

NEW YORK
Ms. Tina M. Stanford
Chair
Board of Parole
1220 Washington Avenue, Building 2
Albany, NY 12226
P: (518) 473-9400
F: (212) 345-6670
E: nysparole
    @parole.state.ny.us

NORTH DAKOTA
Ms. Leann Bertsch
Director
Department of Corrections & Rehabilitation
3100 Railroad Avenue
P.O. Box 1898
Bismarck, ND 58502
P: (701) 328-6390
F: (701) 328-6186
E: lbertsch@asca.net

NORTHERN MARIANA ISLANDS
Ms. Ursula L. Aldan
Chief Probation Officer
Superior Court
P.O. Box 500307
Saipan, MP 96950
P: (670) 236-9865
F: (670) 236-9866
E: ualdan@hotmail.com

Mr. Eugene Villagomez
Chief Parole Officer
Board of Parole
P.O. Box 502641
Saipan, MP 95950
P: (670) 664-3300
F: (670) 664-3310
E: ualdan@hotmail.com

OKLAHOMA
Ms. Tracy George
Acting Director
Pardon & Parole Board
First National Center
120 North Robinson Avenue, Suite 900W
Oklahoma City, OK 73102
P: (405) 602-5863
F: (405) 602-6437
E: tracy.george
    @ppb.state.ok.us

OREGON
Ms. Brenda Carney
Executive Director
Board of Parole & Post-Prison Supervision
2575 Center Street, Northeast
Suite 100
Salem, OR 97301
P: (503) 945-0919
F: (503) 373-7558
E: brenda.k.carney
    @doc.state.or.us

PENNSYLVANIA
Mr. John Tuttle
Acting Chair
Board of Probation & Parole
1101 South Front Street
Harrisburg, PA 17104
P: (717) 787-5699

PUERTO RICO
Ms. Mercedes Peguero Moronta
President
Parole Board
Minillas Station
P.O. Box 40945
San Juan, PR 00940
P: (787) 754-8115
F: (787) 754-8181

RHODE ISLAND
Ms. Laura Pisaturo
Chair
Parole Board
Varley Building
40 Howard Avenue
Cranston, RI 02920
P: (401) 462-0900
F: (401) 462-0915
E: parolebd@doc.ri.gov

SOUTH CAROLINA
Ms. Kela E. Thomas
Director
Department of Probation, Parole & Pardon Services
2221 Devine Street, Suite 600
P.O. Box 50666
Columbia, SC 29250
P: (803) 734-9278
F: (803) 734-9440

SOUTH DAKOTA
Mr. Ed Ligtenberg
Executive Director
Department of Corrections
Board of Pardons & Paroles
1600 North Drive, P.O. Box 5911
Sioux Falls, SD 57117
P: (605) 367-5040
F: (605) 367-5115

TENNESSEE
Mr. Richard Montgomery
Chair
Board of Parole
404 James Robertson Parkway
Suite 1300
Nashville, TN 37243
P: (615) 741-1673
F: (615) 532-8581

TEXAS
Ms. Rissie L. Owens
Chair
Board of Pardons & Paroles
P. O. Box 13401
Austin, TX 78711
P: (512) 936-6351
F: (936) 291-8367
E: bpp-pio@tdcj.texas.gov

Parole and Probation (Adult)

U.S. VIRGIN ISLANDS
Hon. Michael C. Dunston
Presiding Judge
Superior Court
5400 Veteran's Drive
P.O. Box 70
St. Thomas, VI 00804
P: (340) 774-6680
F: (340) 777-8187

Mr. Chesley Roebuck
Chair
Board of Parole
P.O. Box 2668
St. Thomas, VI 00802
P: (340) 778-2036
F: (340) 778-1637

UTAH
Ms. Geri Miller-Fox
Division Director
Adult Probation & Parole
Department of Corrections
14717 South Minuteman Drive
Draper, UT 84020
P: (801) 545-5500
F: (801) 545-5911
E: gmiller@utah.gov

VERMONT
Ms. Sue Blair
Director
Parole Board
Department of Corrections
103 South Main Street
Waterbury, VT 05671
P: (802) 652-6536
F: (802) 652-6538

VIRGINIA
Mr. William W. Muse
Chair
Parole Board
6900 Atmore Drive
Richmond, VA 23225
P: (804) 674-3081
F: (804) 674-3284
E: william.muse
    @vadoc.virginia.gov

WASHINGTON
Ms. Lynne DeLano
Chair
Indeterminate Sentence Review
Board
4317 6th Avenue, Southeast
P.O. Box 40907
Olympia, WA 98504
P: (360) 407-2400
F: (360) 493-9287
E: lndelano@doc1.wa.gov

WEST VIRGINIA
Ms. Benita F. Murphy
Chair
Parole Board
1356 Hansford Street, Suite B
Charleston, WV 25301
P: (304) 558-6366
F: (304) 558-5678
E: bmurphy1@mail.wvnet.edu

WISCONSIN
Ms. Denise Symdon
Administrator
Division of Community
Corrections
P.O. Box 7925
Madison, WI 53707
P: (608) 240-5300
F: (608) 240-3330

WYOMING
Mr. Daniel M. Fetsco
Executive Director
Board of Parole
3120 Old Faithful Road, Suite
300
Cheyenne, WY 82002
P: (307) 777-5444
F: (307) 777-5386
E: daniel.fetsco@wyo.gov

Personnel

Formulates, implements, and enforces personnel management policies and procedures for the state.

Information provided by:

National Association of State Personnel Executives
Leslie Scott
Association Manager
P.O. Box 11910
Lexington, KY 40578
P: (859) 244-8182
F: (859) 244-8001
lscott@csg.org
www.naspe.net

ALABAMA
Jackie Graham
State Personnel Director
State Personnel Department
313 Folsom Administration Building
64 North Union Street, Suite 300
Montgomery, AL 36130
P: (334) 242-3711
F: (334) 353-3320
E: jackie.graham
@personnel.alabama.gov

ALASKA
Ms. Kate Sheehan
Director
Division of Personnel & Labor Relations
Department of Administration
P.O. Box 110201
Juneau, AK 99811
P: (907) 465-4429
E: kate.sheehan@alaska.gov

AMERICAN SAMOA
Mr. Puni Penei H. Sewell
Director
Department of Human Resources
American Samoa Government
Pago Pago, AS 96799
P: (684) 633-4485
F: (684) 633-1139
E: sewells_1@hotmail.com

ARIZONA
Ms. Marie Isaacson
Human Resources Director
Human Resource Division
Department of Administration
100 North 15th Avenue, Suite 261
Phoenix, AZ 85007
P: (602) 542-5482
F: (602) 542-2796
E: marie.isaacson@azdoa.gov

ARKANSAS
Ms. Kay Barnhill Terry
State Personnel Administrator
Office of Personnel Management
Department of Finance & Administration
1509 West 7th Street
Little Rock, AR 72201
P: (501) 682-5122
F: (501) 682-5104
E: kay.terry
@dfa.state.ar.us

CALIFORNIA
Ms. Suzanne M. Ambrose
Executive Officer
State Personnel Board
801 Capitol Mall
Sacramento, CA 95814
P: (916) 653-1028
F: (916) 653-8147
E: sambrose@spb.ca.gov

Mr. Richard Gillihan
Director
California CalHR
1515 S Street, Suite 400
Sacramento, CA 96814
P: (916) 327-4024
E: richard.gillihan
@calhr.ca.gov

COLORADO
Ms. Kim Burgess
Chief Human Resources Officer
Division of Human Resources
Department of Personnel & Administration
1525 Sherman Street
Denver, CO 80203
P: (303) 866-2171
F: (303) 866-2021
E: kim.burgess@state.co.us

CONNECTICUT
Dr. Pamela L. Libby
Director
Human Resource Management
165 Capitol Avenue, Room 411
Hartford, CT 06106
P: (860) 713-5204
F: (860) 622-2965
E: pamela.libby
@po.state.ct.us

DELAWARE
Ms. Amy Bonner
Deputy Director
State Human Resource Management
Office of Management & Budget
Haslet Armory, 122 William Penn Street
Dover, DE 19801
P: (302) 739-4195
F: (302) 739-7984
E: amy.bonner@state.de.us

Ms. Brenda Lakeman
Director
Human Resource Management
Office of Budget & Management
Haslet Armory, 122 William Penn Street
Dover, DE 19901
P: (302) 739-4195
F: (302) 739-7984
E: brenda.lakeman
@state.de.us

DISTRICT OF COLUMBIA
Ms. Shawn Stokes
Director
Department of Human Resources
441 4th Street Northwest, Suite 300S
Washington, DC 20001
P: (202) 442-9700
F: (202) 727-0154
E: dchr@dc.gov

FLORIDA
Ms. Sharon Larson
Director
Division of Human Resources
Department of Management Services
4050 Esplanade Way, Suite 235
Tallahassee, FL 32399
P: (850) 413-8725
F: (850) 922-6642
E: sharon.larson
@dms.myflorida.com

GEORGIA
Ms. Candy Sarvis
Deputy Commissioner
Human Resources Administration
West Tower, Room 504
2 Martin Luther King Jr. Drive Southwest
Atlanta, GA 30334
P: (404) 657-0591
F: (404) 656-5979
E: candy.sarvis@doas.ga.gov

GUAM
Ms. Benita A. Manglona
Director
Department of Administration
P.O. Box 884
Hagatna, GU 96932
P: (671) 475-1101
F: (671) 477-6788

HAWAII
Mr. James Hashimoto
Director
Department of Human Resources Development
State Office Tower
235 South Beretania Street, 14th Floor
Honolulu, HI 96813
P: (808) 587-1100
E: james.k.hashimoto
@hawaii.gov

IDAHO
Mr. David Fulkerson
Administrator
Department of Human Resources
P.O. Box 83720
700 West State Street
Boise, ID 83720
P: (208) 854-3077
E: david.fulkerson
@dhr.idaho.gov

ILLINOIS
Ms. Elizabeth Whitehorn
Chief of Staff, Bureau of Personnel
Department of Central Management Services
503 William G. Stratton Building
Springfield, IL 62706
P: (217) 524-8773
E: elizabeth.whitehorn
@illinois.gov

INDIANA
Mr. Denny Darrow
Director
State Personnel Department
402 West Washington Street, Room W161
Indianapolis, IN 46204
P: (317) 232-3065
E: jdarrow@spd.in.gov

IOWA
Ms. Karin Gregor
Chief Operating Officer
Department of Administrative Services
Human Resources Enterprise
Hoover State Office Building
Des Moines, IA 50319
P: (515) 281-5064
E: karin.gregor@iowa.gov

Personnel

KANSAS
Mr. Kraig Knowlton
Director
Division of Personnel Services
Landon State Office Building
900 Southwest Jackson, Room 251
Topeka, KS 66612
P: (785) 296-4278
F: (785) 296-6793
E: kraig.knowlton@da.ks.gov

KENTUCKY
Ms. Mary Elizabeth Bailey
Commissioner, Human Resources Administration
Personnel Cabinet
State Office Building
501 High Street, Third Floor
Frankfort, KY 40601
P: (502) 564-7571
E: marye.bailey@ky.gov

Mr. Timothy Longmeyer
Secretary
Personnel Cabinet
State Office Building, 3rd Floor
501 High Street
Frankfort, KY 40601
P: (502) 564-7430
F: (502) 564-7603
E: timothy.longmeyer@ky.gov

LOUISIANA
Ms. Shannon Templet
Director
Department of State Civil Service
1201 North Third Street, Suite 3-280
P.O. Box 94111
Baton Rouge, LA 70804
P: (225) 342-8272
F: (225) 342-0966
E: shannon.templet@la.gov

MAINE
Ms. Joyce Oreskovich
Director
Bureau of Human Resources
Administrative & Financial Services
4 State House Station
Augusta, ME 04333
P: (207) 624-7761
F: (207) 287-4414
E: joyce.a.oreskovich
@maine.gov

MARYLAND
Ms. Cynthia Kollner
Executive Director
Office of Personnel Services & Benefits
Department of Budget & Management
301 West Preston Street, Room 609
Baltimore, MD 21201
P: (410) 767-4715
F: (410) 333-5262
E: ckollner@dbm.state.md.us

MASSACHUSETTS
Mr. Paul Dietl
Chief Human Resources Officer
Human Resources Division
1 Ashburton Palce, Room 301
Boston, MA 02108
P: (617) 878-9703
F: (617) 727-1175
E: Paul.d.Dietl
@MassMail.State.MA.US

MICHIGAN
Ms. Jan Winters
State Personnel Director
Civil Service Commission
P.O. Box 30002
400 South Pine Street
Lansing, MI 48909
P: (517) 373-3020

MINNESOTA
Ms. Ann O'Brien
Assistant Commissioner
Division of Human Resource Management
Department of Management & Budget
658 Cedar Street
St. Paul, MN 55155
P: (651) 259-3636
F: (651) 296-8919
E: ann.o'brien@state.mn.us

MISSISSIPPI
Ms. Deanne Mosley
Executive Director
State Personnel Board
200 East Capitol Street, Suite 800
Jackson, MS 39201
P: (601) 359-2702
F: (601) 359-2729
E: Deanne.mosley
@mspb.ms.gov

MISSOURI
Ms. Nancy Johnston
Director, Division of Personnel
Office of Administration
301 West High Street, Suite 430
P.O. Box 388
Jefferson City, MO 65102
P: (573) 751-3053
F: (573) 522-8462
E: nancy.johnston@oa.mo.gov

MONTANA
Mr. Randy Morris
Acting Administrator
State Human Resources Division
Department of Administration
P.O. Box 200127
Helena, MT 59620
P: (406) 444-3894
F: (406) 444-0703
E: ramorris@mt.gov

NEBRASKA
Ms. Ruth Jones
Director
State Personnel Division
Department of Administrative Services
P.O. Box 94905
Lincoln, NE 68509
P: (402) 471-2075
F: (402) 471-3754
E: ruth.jones@nebraska.gov

NEVADA
Ms. Lee-Ann Easton
Administrator
Division of Human Resource Management
Department of Administration
100 North Stewart Street, Suite 200
Carson City, NV 89701
P: (775) 684-0101
F: (775) 684-0124
E: leaston@admin.nv.gov

NEW HAMPSHIRE
Ms. Sara J. Willingham
Director of Personnel
Division of Personnel
Department of Administrative Services
28 School Street
Concord, NH 03301
P: (603) 271-3262
F: (603) 271-1422
E: sara.willingham@nh.gov

NEW JERSEY
Mr. Robert M. Czech
Chair/Chief Executive Officer
State Civil Service Commission
P.O. Box 317
Trenton, NJ 08625
P: (606) 292-4125
E: robert.czech
@csc.state.nj.us

Ms. Grace Kelly
Deputy CEO
Civil Service Commission
P.O. Box 317
Trenton, NJ 08625
P: (606) 292-4125
E: grace.kelly
@csc.state.nj.us

NEW MEXICO
Mr. Justin Najaka
Director
State Personnel Office
2600 Cerrillos Road
Santa Fe, NM 87505
P: (505) 476-7751
F: (505) 476-7806
E: Justin.Najaka
@state.nm.us

NEW YORK
Ms. Lola Brabham
Commissioner
Department of Civil Service
Alfred E. Smith State Office Building
Albany, NY 12239
P: (518) 457-3701
E: lola.brabham
@cs.state.ny.us

NORTH CAROLINA
Mr. Neal Alexander
Director
Office of State Personnel
1331 Mail Service Center
Raleigh, NC 27699
P: (919) 807-4800
F: (919) 715-9750
E: neal.alexander
@osp.nc.gov

NORTH DAKOTA
Mr. Ken Purdy
Director
Human Resource Management Services
Office of Management & Budget
600 East Boulevard Avenue, Dept. 113
Bismarck, ND 58505
P: (701) 328-4735
E: kpurdy@state.nd.us

NORTHERN MARIANA ISLANDS

Mr. Norbert S. Sablan
Executive Assistant
Civil Services Commission
P.O. Box 5150, CHRB
Saipan, MP 96950
P: (670) 322-6954
F: (670) 322-3327
E: csc@saipan.com

OHIO

Ms. Stephanie Loucka
HRD Deputy Director
Human Resources Division
30 East Broad Street, 27th Floor
Columbus, OH 43215
P: (614) 466-3464
E: stephanie.m.loucka
    @das.state.oh.us

OKLAHOMA

Ms. Lucinda Meltabarger
Administrator
Human Capital Management
Division
2101 North Lincoln Boulevard,
Room G-80
Oklahoma City, OK 73105
P: (405) 521-3928
F: (405) 522-0694
E: lucinda.meltabarger
    @omes.ok.gov

OREGON

Ms. Madilyn Zike
Chief HR Officer
Human Resources Office
Department of Administrative
Services
155 Cottage Street, Northeast
Salem, OR 97301
P: (503) 378-3020
F: (503) 373-7684
E: madilyn.zike@state.or.us

PENNSYLVANIA

Mr. James A. Honchar
Deputy Secretary for Human
Resources & Management
State Human Resources &
Management
517 Finance Building
Harrisburg, PA 17110
P: (717) 787-5545
F: (717) 783-4429
E: jhonchar@pa.gov

PUERTO RICO

Ms. Marta Beltran
Administrator, Human
Resources Administrative Office
Central Labor Advisory
Ponce De Leon Avenue, Suite
1507
P.O. Box 8476
San Juan, PR 00910
P: (787) 706-5967
F: (787) 706-5697

RHODE ISLAND

Ms. Deborah Dawson
Human Resources Director
Office of Personnel
Administration
1 Capitol Hill
Providence, RI 02908
P: (401) 222-2160
F: (401) 222-6391
E: deborah.dawson@hr.ri.gov

SOUTH CAROLINA

Ms. Kim Aydlette
Director
Division of Human Resources
Department of Administration
8301 Parklane Road, Suite A220
Columbia, SC 29223
P: (803) 896-5300
F: (803) 896-5050

SOUTH DAKOTA

Ms. Laurie R. Gill
Commissioner
Bureau of Personnel
Capitol Building
500 East Capitol Avenue
Pierre, SD 57501
P: (605) 773-3148
F: (605) 773-4344
E: bhrinfo@state.sd.us

TENNESSEE

Ms. Rebecca R. Hunter
Commissioner
Department of Human
Resources
James K. Polk Building, 1st
Floor
505 Deaderick Street
Nashville, TN 37243
P: (615) 741-2958
F: (615) 741-7880
E: rebecca.hunter@tn.gov

U.S. VIRGIN ISLANDS

Mr. Kenneth L. Hermon Jr.
Commissioner
Division of Personnel
GERS Building, 3rd Floor
3438 Kronprindsens Gade
St. Thomas, VI 00802
P: (340) 774-8588
F: (340) 714-5040
E: info@dopusvi.net

UTAH

Ms. Debbie Cragun
Executive Director
Department of Human Resource
Management
2120 State Office Building
P.O. Box 141531
Salt Lake City, UT 84114
P: (801) 538-3403
F: (801) 538-3081
E: dcragun@utah.gov

VERMONT

Ms. Maribeth Spellman
Commissioner
Department of Human
Resources
110 State Street
Montpelier, VT 05620
P: (802) 828-3491
E: maribeth.spellman
    @state.vt.us

VIRGINIA

Mrs. Sara Redding Wilson
Director
Department of Human Resource
Management
101 North 14th Street, 12th
Floor
Richmond, VA 23219
P: (804) 225-2237
F: (804) 371-7401
E: sara.wilson
    @dhrm.virginia.gov

WASHINGTON

Mr. Glen Christopherson
Director
Office of State Human
Resources Director
128 10th Avenue, Southeast
P.O. Box 43113
Olympia, WA 98504
P: (360) 407-4104
F: (360) 753-1003
E: glen.christopherson
    @ofm.wa.gov

WEST VIRGINIA

Ms. Sara Walker
Director
State Division of Personnel
1900 Kanawha Boulevard, East
Charleston, WV 25305
P: (304) 558-3950
E: sara.p.walker@wv.gov

WISCONSIN

Mr. Gregory L. Gracz
Director
Office of State Employment
Relations
101 East Wilson Street
P.O. Box 7855
Madison, WI 53707
P: (608) 266-9820
F: (608) 267-1014
E: greg.gracz@wi.gov

WYOMING

Mr. David L. Urquidez
Administrator, Human
Resources Division
Department of Administration &
Information
Emerson Building
2001 Capitol Avenue, Room 128
Cheyenne, WY 82002
P: (307) 777-6722
F: (307) 777-6562
E: david.urquidez@wyo.gov

Port Authority

Agency housed under the department of transportation that oversees coastal transportation, international transportation, shipping, and all other acts involving state ports.

ALABAMA
Mr. James K. Lyons
Director/CEO
Port Authority
250 North Water Street
P.O. Box 1588
Mobile, AL 36633
P: (251) 441-7200
E: jlyons@asdd.com

ALASKA
Mr. Michael Lukshin
State Ports & Harbors Engineer
Department of Transportation
P.O. Box 112500
Juneau, AK 99811
P: (907) 465-3979
F: (907) 465-2460
E: michael.lukshin
    @alaska.gov

GEORGIA
Mr. Curtis Foltz
Executive Director
Ports Authority
P.O. Box 2406
Savannah, GA 31402
P: (912) 964-3874
F: (912) 966-3615
E: cfoltz@gaports.com

HAWAII
Mr. Davis K. Yogi
Administrator
Harbors Division
Hale Awa Ku Moku Building
79 South Nimitz Highway,
Room 310
Honolulu, HI 96813
P: (808) 587-1928
F: (808) 587-1984
E: Davis.Yogi@hawaii.gov

INDIANA
Mr. Rich Cooper
Chief Executive Officer
Ports of Indiana
150 West Market Street, Suite
100
Indianapolis, IN 46204
P: (317) 232-9200
F: (317) 232-0137
E: rcooper
    @portsofindiana.com

KANSAS
Mr. Mike King
Secretary of Transportation
Department of Transportation
Eisenhower State Office
Building
700 Southwest Harrison
Topeka, KS 66603
P: (785) 296-3461
F: (785) 296-1095

MAINE
Mr. John H. Henshaw
Executive Director
Port Authority
16 State House Station
Augusta, ME 04333
P: (207) 624-3564
F: (207) 624-3099
E: john.h.henshaw@maine.gov

MARYLAND
Mr. James J. White
Executive Director
Port Administration
World Trade Center
401 East Pratt Street
Baltimore, MD 21202
P: (410) 385-4401
E: jjwhite
    @marylandports.com

MASSACHUSETTS
Mr. Thomas P. Glynn Jr.
Chief Executive Officer
Port Authority
One Harborside Drive, Suite
200S
East Boston, MA 02128
P: (617) 568-5000

MINNESOTA
Mr. Charles A. Zelle
Commissioner
Department of Transportation
Transportation Building
395 John Ireland Boulevard
St. Paul, MN 55155
P: (651) 366-4800
F: (651) 366-4795
E: charlie.zelle
    @state.mn.us

MISSISSIPPI
Mr. Mark L. McAndrews
Port Director
Pascagoula Port Authority
P.O. Box 70
Pascagoula, MS 39568
P: (228) 762-4041
F: (228) 762-7476
E: info
    @portofpascagoula.com

NEW HAMPSHIRE
Mr. Geno Marconi
Director of Ports & Harbors
Division of Ports & Harbors
555 Market Street
Portsmouth, NH 03801
P: (603) 436-8500
F: (603) 436-2780
E: g.marconi@peasedev.org

NEW YORK
Mr. Patrick Foye
Executive Director
The Port Authority of New York
& New Jersey
225 Park Avenue South
New York, NY 10003
P: (212) 435-7000

NORTH CAROLINA
Mr. Jeff Miles
Acting Executive Director
State Ports Authority
2202 Burnett Boulevard
P.O. Box 9002
Wilmington, NC 28402
P: (910) 343-6430
F: (910) 763-6440
E: Jeff.Miles@ncports.com

NORTHERN MARIANA ISLANDS
Ms. MaryAnn Q. Lizama
Acting Executive Director
Commonwealth Ports Authority
P.O. Box 501055
Saipan, MP 96950
P: (670) 237-6500
F: (670) 234-5962

OHIO
Mr. Jerry Wray
Director
Department of Transportation
1980 West Broad Street
Columbus, OH 43223
P: (614) 466-2335
F: (614) 466-8662
E: Terri.Barnhart
    @dot.state.oh.us

OKLAHOMA
Mr. Robert W. Portiss
Director
Tulsa Port of Catoosa
5350 Cimarron Road
Catoosa, OK 74015
P: (918) 266-2291
F: (918) 266-7678
E: bob@tulsaport.com

Mr. Scott Robinson
Director
The Port of Muskogee
P.O. Box 2819
Muskogee, OK 74402
P: (918) 682-7886
F: (918) 683-4811
E: Scott@muskogeeport.com

SOUTH CAROLINA
Mr. James I. Newsome III
President and CEO
State Ports Authority
176 Concord Street
P.O.Box 22287
Charleston, SC 29413
P: (843) 577-8600
E: scspainfo@scspa.com

U.S. VIRGIN ISLANDS
Mr. Carlton Dowe
Executive Director
Port Authority
8074 Lindbergh Bay
P.O. Box 301707
St. Thomas, VI 00803
P: (340) 774-1629
F: (340) 774-0025
E: info@viport.com

UTAH
Mr. Chad Sheppick
Director
Motor Carriers Division
Department of Transportation
4501 South 2700 West, P.O. Box
148240
Salt Lake City, UT 84114
P: (801) 965-4156
F: (801) 965-4847
E: csheppick@utah.gov

VIRGINIA
Mr. John F. Reinhart
CEO & Executive Director
Port Authority
600 World Trade Center
Norfolk, VA 23510
P: (757) 683-8000
F: (757) 683-8500
E: jreinhart
    @portofvirginia.com

WEST VIRGINIA
Mr. Charles Neal Vance
Director
Public Port Authority
1900 Kanawha Boulevard, East
Building 5, Room A-137
Charleston, WV 25305
P: (304) 558-0330
F: (304) 558-0333
E: Charles.N.Vance@wv.gov

Public Defender

Represents indigent criminal defendants who desire to appeal their convictions to the state's intermediate appellate court or court of last resort.

ALASKA
Mr. Quinlan Steiner
Public Defender
Public Defender Agency
Department of Administration
900 West 5th Avenue, Suite 200
Anchorage, AK 99501
P: (907) 334-4400
F: (907) 269-5476
E: quinlan.steiner
  @alaska.gov

ARKANSAS
Ms. Didi Sallings
Director
Public Defender Commission
101 East Capitol, Suite 201
Little Rock, AR 72201
P: (501) 682-9070
F: (501) 682-9073

CALIFORNIA
Mr. Michael J. Hersek
State Public Defender
Office of the State Public
Defender
1111 Broadway, 10th Floor
Oakland, CA 94607
P: (510) 267-3300
F: (510) 452-8712

COLORADO
Mr. Douglas Wilson
State Public Defender
Office of the State Public
Defender
1300 Broadway, Suite 400
Denver, CO 80203
P: (303) 764-1400
F: (303) 764-1478
E: doug.wilson
  @coloradodefenders.us

CONNECTICUT
Ms. Susan O. Storey
Chief Public Defender
Division of Public Defender
Services
30 Trinity Street, 4th Floor
Hartford, CT 06106
P: (860) 509-6429
F: (860) 509-6495
E: susan.storey@jud.ct.gov

DELAWARE
Mr. Brendan O'Neill
Public Defender
Office of the Public Defender
Carvel State Office Building
820 North French Street, 3rd
Floor
Wilmington, DE 19801
P: (302) 577-5200
F: (302) 577-3995

DISTRICT OF COLUMBIA
Ms. Avis Buchanan
Director
Public Defender Service
633 Indiana Avenue, Northwest
Washington, DC 20004
P: (202) 628-1200
F: (202) 824-2423
E: abuchanan@pdsdc.org

FLORIDA
Mr. Sheldon Gusky
Executive Director
Public Defender Association
103 North Gadsden Street
P.O. Box 11057
Tallahassee, FL 32302
P: (850) 488-6850
F: (850) 488-4720
E: sgusky@st.flpda.org

GEORGIA
Hon. Sam S. Olens (R)
Attorney General
Office of the Attorney General
40 Capitol Square, Southwest
Atlanta, GA 30334
P: (404) 656-3300
F: (404) 657-8733
E: AGOlens@law.ga.gov

GUAM
Mr. Eric D. Miller
Executive Director
Public Defender Service
Corporation
779 Route 4
Sinajana, GU 96910
P: (671) 475-3100
F: (671) 477-5844
E: emiller@guampdsc.net

HAWAII
Mr. John M. Tonaki
Public Defender
Office of the Public Defender
1130 North Nimitz Highway
Suite A-254
Honolulu, HI 96817
P: (808) 586-2200
F: (808) 322-1949

IDAHO
Ms. Sara B. Thomas
State Appellate Public Defender
Appellate Public Defender
3050 North Lake Harbor Lane,
Suite 100
Boise, ID 83703
P: (208) 334-2712
F: (208) 334-2985
E: sthomas@sapd.state.id.us

ILLINOIS
Mr. Michael J. Pelletier
State Appellate Defender
Office of the State Appellate
Defender
400 West Monroe, Suite 202
P.O. Box 5240
Springfield, IL 62705
P: (217) 782-7203
F: (217) 782-5385
E: Michael.Pelletier
  @osad.state.il.us

IOWA
Mr. Samuel P. Langholz
State Public Defender
State Public Defender Office
Lucas Building, 4th Floor
321 East 12th Street
Des Moines, IA 50319
P: (515) 242-6158
F: (515) 281-7289
E: slangholz
  @spd.state.ia.us

KANSAS
Ms. Patricia A. Scalia
Executive Director
Board of Indigents' Defense
Services
714 Southwest Jackson, Suite
200
Topeka, KS 66603
P: (785) 296-4505
F: (785) 291-3082

KENTUCKY
Mr. Edward C. Monahan
Public Advocate
Department of Public Advocacy
100 Fair Oaks Lane, Suite 302
Frankfort, KY 40601
P: (502) 564-8006
F: (502) 564-7890

LOUISIANA
Mr. James T. Dixon Jr.
State Public Defender
Public Defender Board
5000 Laurel Street, Suite 300
Baton Rouge, LA 70801
P: (225) 219-9305
F: (225) 219-9326

MARYLAND
Mr. Paul B. DeWolfe Jr.
Public Defender
Public Defender System
William Donald Schefer Tower
6 St. Paul Street, Suite 1400
Baltimore, MD 21202
P: (410) 767-8479
F: (410) 333-8496
E: jsehorn@opd.state.md.us

MASSACHUSETTS
Mr. Anthony J. Benedetti
Chief Counsel
Administrative Office
Committee for Public Counsel
Services
44 Bromfield Street
Boston, MA 02108
P: (617) 988-8305
F: (617) 988-8495

MICHIGAN
Ms. Dawn Van Hoek
Director
State Appellate Defender Office
Suite 3300, Penobscot Building
645 Griswald
Detroit, MI 48226
P: (313) 256-9833
F: (313) 965-0372
E: dvanhoek@sado.org

MINNESOTA
Mr. John Stuart
State Public Defender
Board of Public Defense
331 Second Avenue South, Suite
900
Minneapolis, MN 55401
P: (612) 279-3512
E: john.stuart
  @pubdef.state.mn.us

MISSOURI
Mr. Michael Barrett
State Public Defender
Office of the State Public
Defender
Woodrail Centre
1000 West Nifong, Building 7,
Suite 100
Columbia, MO 65203
P: (573) 777-9977
F: (573) 777-9976
E: public.defender
  @mspd.mo.gov

MONTANA
Mr. William F. Hooks
Chief Public Defender
Office of the State Public
Defender
44 West Park Street
Butte, MT 59701
P: (406) 496-6080
F: (406) 496-6098

Public Defender

NEBRASKA
Mr. James R. Mowbray
Chief Counsel
Commission on Public
Advocacy
The Apothecary Building, Suite
270
140 North 8th Street, P.O. Box
98932
Lincoln, NE 68509
P: (402) 471-7774
F: (402) 471-8087
E: jmowbray@ncpa.ne.gov

NEVADA
Ms. Diane Crow
State Public Defender
Office of the Public Defender
Department of Health & Human
Services
511 East Robinson Street, #1
Carson City, NV 89701
P: (775) 687-4880
F: (775) 687-4993
E: drcrow
    @govmail.state.nv.us

NEW HAMPSHIRE
Mr. Christopher Keating
Executive Director
Public Defender
10 Ferry Street, Suite 202
Concord, NH 03301
P: (603) 224-1236
F: (603) 227-9367
E: ckeating@nhpd.org

NEW JERSEY
Mr. Joseph E. Krakora
Public Defender
Office of the Public Defender
25 Market Street, 1st Floor
N-Wing
P.O. Box 850
Trenton, NJ 08625
P: (609) 292-7087
F: (609) 777-1795
E: thedefenders
    @opd.state.nj.us

NEW MEXICO
Mr. Jorge A. Alvarado
Chief Public Defender
Public Defender Department
301 North Guadalupe Street
Santa Fe, NM 87501
P: (505) 395-2888
F: (505) 827-3999

NORTH CAROLINA
Mr. Thomas K. Maher
Executive Director
Office of Indigent Defense
Services
123 West Main Street
Suite 400
Durham, NC 27701
P: (919) 354-7200
F: (919) 354-7201
E: Thomas.K.Maher
    @nccourts.org

NORTH DAKOTA
Hon. Wayne Stenehjem (R)
Attorney General
Office of the Attorney General
State Capitol
600 East Boulevard Avenue
Bismarck, ND 58505
P: (701) 328-2210
F: (701) 328-2226
E: wstenehjem@nd.gov

**NORTHERN MARIANA
ISLANDS**
Mr. Doug Hartig
Chief Public Defender
Office of the Public Defender
Civic Center Complex
P.O. Box 5010007
Saipan, MP 96950
P: (670) 234-6503
F: (670) 234-1009
E: hartigd1@gmail.com

OHIO
Mr. Timothy Young
Director
Office of the Public Defender
250 East Broad Street, Suite
1400
Columbus, OH 43215
P: (614) 466-5394
F: (614) 644-9972

OKLAHOMA
Mr. Joe P. Robertson
Executive Director
Indigent Defense System
P.O. Box 926
Norman, OK 73070
P: (405) 801-2601

OREGON
Ms. Nancy Cozine
Executive Director
Office of Public Defense
Services
1175 Court Street, Northeast
Salem, OR 97301
P: (503) 378-3349
F: (503) 378-4462
E: Nancy.Cozine
    @opds.state.or.us

RHODE ISLAND
Ms. Mary S. McElroy
Public Defender
Office of the Public Defender
160 Pine Street
Providence, RI 02903
P: (401) 222-3492
F: (401) 222-5225
E: Information@ripd.org

SOUTH DAKOTA
Hon. Marty J. Jackley (R)
Attorney General
Office of the Attorney General
1302 East Highway 14, Suite 1
Pierre, SD 57501
P: (605) 773-3215
F: (605) 773-4106
E: atghelp@state.sd.us

U.S. VIRGIN ISLANDS
Omodare Jupiter
Federal Public Defender
Office of the Federal Public
Defender
P.O. Box 3450
Christiansted
St. Croix, VI 00820
P: (340) 773-3585
F: (340) 773-3742

VERMONT
Mr. Matthew F. Valerio
Defender General
Office of the Defender General
6 Baldwin Street, 4th Floor
Montpelier, VT 05633
P: (802) 828-3168
F: (802) 828-3163
E: matthew.valerio
    @state.vt.us

VIRGINIA
Mr. David J. Johnson
Executive Director
Indigent Defense Commission
1604 Santa Rosa Road, Suite
200
Henrico, VA 23229
P: (804) 662-7249
F: (804) 662-7359
E: djohnson
    @idc.virginia.gov

WASHINGTON
Ms. Joanne Moore
Director
State Office of Public Defense
711 Capitol Way South, Suite
106
Evergreen Plaza Building, P.O.
Box 40957
Olympia, WA 98504
P: (360) 586-3164, Ext. 112
F: (360) 586-8165
E: opd@opd.wa.gov

WEST VIRGINIA
Ms. Dana F. Eddy
Executive Director
Public Defender Services
One Players Club Drive, Suite
301
Charleston, WV 25311
P: (304) 558-3905
F: (304) 558-1098
E: Dana.F.Eddy@wv.gov

WISCONSIN
Ms. Kelli Thompson
State Public Defender
Office of the State Public
Defender
315 North Henry, 2nd Floor
P.O. Box 7923
Madison, WI 53707
P: (608) 266-0087
F: (608) 267-0584
E: ThompsonK@opd.wi.gov

WYOMING
Ms. Diane M. Lozano
State Public Defender
Office of the State Public
Defender
Rogers Building
316 West 22nd Street
Cheyenne, WY 82002
P: (307) 777-7519
F: (307) 777-8742
E: diane.lozano@wyo.gov

Public Lands

Manages state-owned lands.

ALABAMA
Ms. Patti Powell
Director
State Lands Division
Conservation & Natural
Resources
64 North Union Street, Suite 468
Montgomery, AL 36130
P: (334) 242-3484
F: (334) 242-0999
E: patti.powell
    @dcnr.alabama.gov

ALASKA
Mr. Brent Goodrum
Director
Division of Mining, Land &
Water
Department of Natural
Resources
550 West Seventh Avenue, Suite
1070
Anchorage, AK 99501
P: (907) 269-8600
F: (907) 269-8904
E: brent.goodrum@alaska.gov

ARIZONA
Ms. Lisa Atkins
State Land Commissioner
State Land Department
1616 West Adams Street
Phoenix, AZ 85007
P: (602) 542-4621

ARKANSAS
Hon. John Thurston
Commissioner
Commissioner of State Lands
109 State Capitol
Little Rock, AR 72201
P: (501) 324-9422
F: (501) 324-9421
E: land@cosl.org

CALIFORNIA
Mr. Jim Abbott
Acting Director
Bureau of Land Management
2800 Cottage Way, Suite
W-1623
Sacramento, CA 95825
P: (916) 978-4600
F: (916) 978-4416
E: Jim_Abbott@blm.gov

Ms. Kari Lewis
Supervising Biologist
Lands Program
1812 9th Street
Sacramento, CA 95811
P: (916) 445-3789
F: (916) 445-4058
E: Kari.Lewis
    @wildlife.ca.gov

COLORADO
Mr. Bill Ryan
Director
Board of Land Commissioners
Department of Natural
Resources
1127 Sherman Street, Suite 300
Denver, CO 80203
P: (303) 866-3454
F: (303) 866-3152
E: bill.ryan@state.co.us

CONNECTICUT
Mr. Robert J. Klee
Commissioner
Department of Energy &
Environmental Protection
79 Elm Street
Hartford, CT 06106
P: (860) 424-3001
F: (860) 424-4051
E: deep.commissioner@ct.gov

DELAWARE
Mr. Raymond E. Bivens
Director
Division of Parks & Recreation
89 Kings Highway
Dover, DE 19901
P: (302) 739-9200
F: (302) 739-3817
E: raymond.bivens
    @state.de.us

DISTRICT OF COLUMBIA
Dr. Sharia Shanklin
Interim Director
Department of Parks &
Recreation
1250 U Street, Northwest
Washington, DC 20009
P: (202) 673-7647
F: (202) 673-2087

GEORGIA
Mr. Mark Williams
Commissioner
Department of Natural
Resources
2 Martin Luther King Jr. Drive
Southeast
Suite 1252, East Tower
Atlanta, GA 30334
P: (404) 656-3500
F: (404) 656-0770

HAWAII
Ms. Suzanne D. Case
Chairperson
Department of Land & Natural
Resources
Kalanimoku Building
1151 Punchbowl Street
Honolulu, HI 96813
P: (808) 587-0400
F: (808) 587-0390
E: dlnr@hawaii.gov

IDAHO
Mr. Tom Schultz
Director
Department of Lands
300 North 6th Street, Suite 103
P.O. Box 83720
Boise, ID 83720
P: (208) 334-0242
F: (208) 334-5342
E: tschultz@idl.idaho.gov

ILLINOIS
Mr. Ronald House
Director
Office of Land Management &
Education
One Natural Resources Way, 3rd
Floor
Springfield, IL 62702
P: (217) 782-6752
F: (217) 524-5612

INDIANA
Mr. Mitch Zoll Jr.
Division Director
Historic Preservation &
Archaeology
Department of Natural
Resources
402 West Washington Street,
W274
Indianapolis, IN 46204
P: (317) 232-3492
F: (317) 232-0693
E: mzoll@dnr.in.gov

IOWA
Mr. Chuck Gipp
Director
Department of Natural
Resources
4th Floor, Wallace Building
502 East 9th Street
Des Moines, IA 50319
P: (515) 281-5817
F: (515) 281-8895
E: chuck.gipp@dnr.iowa.gov

KANSAS
Mr. Robin Jennison
Secretary
Department of Wildlife, Parks &
Tourism
1020 South Kansas Avenue,
Room 200
Topeka, KS 66612
P: (785) 296-2281
F: (785) 296-6953

KENTUCKY
Mr. Benjy T. Kinman
Deputy Commissioner
Department of Fish & Wildlife
Resources
One Sportsman's Lane
Frankfort, KY 40601
P: (502) 564-3400
F: (502) 564-0506

LOUISIANA
Mr. Spencer Robinson
Public Lands Administrator
Office of State Lands
Division of Administration
P.O. Box 44124
Baton Rouge, LA 70804
P: (225) 342-4578
F: (225) 342-5458
E: Spencer.Robinson@la.gov

MAINE
Mr. Will Harris
Director
Bureau of Parks & Lands
22 State House Station
18 Elkins Lane (AMHI Campus)
Augusta, ME 04333
P: (207) 287-3821
F: (207) 287-6170
E: Will.Harris@maine.gov

MARYLAND
Ms. Kristin Saunders
Assistant Secretary for Land
Resources
Department of Natural
Resources
Tawes State Office Building, C4
580 Taylor Avenue
Annapolis, MD 21401
P: (410) 260-8106
F: (410) 260-8111
E: ksaunders
    @dnr.state.md.us

MASSACHUSETTS
Ms. Carol Sanchez
Commissioner
Department of Conservation &
Recreation
251 Causeway Street, Suite 900
Boston, MA 02114
P: (617) 626-1250
F: (617) 626-1351

Public Lands

MICHIGAN
Mr. Ronald Olson
Chief
Parks & Recreation Division
P.O. Box 30257
Lansing, MI 48909
P: (517) 284-7275
F: (517) 373-4625
E: OLSONR@michigan.gov

MINNESOTA
Mr. Tom Landwehr
Commissioner
Department of Natural
Resources
500 Lafayette Road
St. Paul, MN 55155
P: (651) 259-5022
F: (651) 296-4799
E: Tom.Landwehr@state.mn.us

MISSISSIPPI
Mr. Gerald McWhorter
Assistant Secretary of State
Public Lands Division
125 South Congress Street
P.O. Box 136
Jackson, MS 39205
P: (601) 359-5156
F: (601) 359-1461
E: gmcwhorter
    @sos.state.ms.us

MISSOURI
Mr. Bill Bryan
Director
Division of State Parks
1659 East Elm Street
Jefferson City, MO 65102
P: (573) 751-1010
F: (573) 526-7716
E: Bill.Bryan@dnr.mo.gov

MONTANA
Mr. John Tubbs
Director
Department of Natural
Resources & Conservation
1625 Eleventh Avenue
P.O. Box 201601
Helena, MT 59620
P: (406) 444-2074
F: (406) 444-2684

NEBRASKA
Mr. Jim Fuller
Assistant Division Administrator
Parks Division
Game & Parks Commission
2200 North 33rd Street
Lincoln, NE 68503
P: (402) 471-5550
F: (402) 471-5528
E: Jim.Fuller@nebraska.gov

NEW HAMPSHIRE
Mr. Brad W. Simpkins
Interim Director/State Forester
Division of Forests & Lands
P.O. Box 1856
Concord, NH 03302
P: (603) 271-2214
F: (603) 271-6488
E: brad.simpkins
    @dred.state.nh.us

NEW JERSEY
Mr. Dave Chanda
Director
Division of Fish & Wildlife
P.O. Box 400
Trenton, NJ 08625
P: (609) 292-9410
F: (609) 292-8207

NEW MEXICO
Hon. Aubrey Dunn (R)
Commissioner
State Land Office
310 Old Santa Fe Trail
P.O. Box 1148
Santa Fe, NM 87504
P: (505) 827-5760
F: (505) 827-5766
E: commissioner
    @slo.state.nm.us

NEW YORK
Mr. Joe Martens
Commissioner
Department of Environmental
Conservation
625 Broadway, 14th Floor
Albany, NY 12233
P: (518) 402-8540
F: (518) 402-8541
E: joemartens
    @gw.dec.state.ny.us

NORTHERN MARIANA
ISLANDS
Mr. Pedro A. Tenorio
Acting Secretary
Department of Public Lands
P.O. Box 500380
Saipan, MP 96950
P: (670) 234-3751
F: (670) 234-3755

OHIO
Mr. James J. Zehringer
Director
Department of Natural
Resources
2045 Morse Road, Building D
Columbus, OH 43229
P: (614) 265-6565
F: (614) 261-9601

OKLAHOMA
Ms. Kelly Dixon
Division Director
Land Protection Division
Department of Environmental
Quality
P.O. Box 1677
Oklahoma City, OK 73101
P: (405) 702-5100
F: (405) 702-5101
E: kelly.dixon@deq.ok.gov

OREGON
Ms. Mary Abrams
Director
Department of State Lands
775 Summer Street, Northeast,
Suite 100
Salem, OR 97301
P: (503) 986-5224
F: (503) 378-4844
E: mary.m.abrams
    @dsl.state.or.us

PENNSYLVANIA
Mr. David Kemmerer
Director
Bureau of State Parks
P.O. Box 8551
Harrisburg, PA 17105
P: (717) 787-6640

RHODE ISLAND
Ms. Janet Coit
Director
Department of Environmental
Management
235 Promenade Street, 4th Floor
Providence, RI 02908
P: (401) 222-2771
F: (401) 222-6802
E: janet.coit@dem.ri.gov

SOUTH DAKOTA
Hon. Ryan Brunner (R)
Commissioner
Department of School & Public
Lands
500 East Capitol Avenue
Pierre, SD 57501
P: (605) 773-3303
F: (605) 773-5520
E: ryan.brunner@state.sd.us

TENNESSEE
Mr. Julius Johnson
Commissioner
Department of Agriculture
Melrose Station
P.O. Box 40627
Nashville, TN 37204
P: (615) 837-5100
F: (615) 837-5333

TEXAS
Mr. Carter P. Smith
Executive Director
Parks & Wildlife Department
4200 Smith School Road
Austin, TX 78744
P: (512) 389-4802
F: (512) 389-4960

U.S. VIRGIN ISLANDS
Ms. Alicia Barnes
Department of Planning &
Natural Resources
Dronningens Gade 71&72A,
Kongens Quarter
Charlotte Amalie, VI 00802
P: (340) 774-3320
F: (340) 773-1082

Mr. Carlton Dowe
Executive Director
Port Authority
8074 Lindbergh Bay
P.O. Box 301707
St. Thomas, VI 00803
P: (340) 774-1629
F: (340) 774-0025
E: info@viport.com

Ms. Lynn A. Millin Maduro
Commissioner
Property & Procurement
Division
Building No. 1, Third Floor,
Subbase
St. Thomas, VI 00802
P: (340) 774-0828 Ext. 295
F: (340) 777-9587

UTAH
Mr. Brian Cottham
State Forester/Director
Division of Forestry, Fire &
State Lands
1594 West North Temple, Suite
3520
P.O. Box 145703
Salt Lake City, UT 84114
P: (801) 538-5504
F: (801) 533-4111
E: briancottham@utah.gov

VERMONT
Ms. Deborah L. Markowitz
Secretary
Agency of Natural Resources
103 South Main Street, Center
Building
Waterbury, VT 05671
P: (802) 241-3808
F: (802) 244-1102
E: deb.markowitz
    @state.vt.us

VIRGINIA
Mr. Richard F. Sliwoski
Director
Department of General Services
1100 Bank Street, Suite 420
Richmond, VA 23219
P: 804-786-3311
F: 804-371-8305
E: richard.sliwoski
   @dgs.virginia.gov

WASHINGTON
Hon. Peter J. Goldmark (D)
Commissioner of Public Lands
Department of Natural
Resources
1111 Washington Street,
Southeast
P.O. Box 47000
Olympia, WA 98504
P: (360) 902-1000
F: (360) 902-1775
E: cpl@dnr.wa.gov

WEST VIRGINIA
Mr. Joe T. Scarberry
Supervisor
Office of Land & Streams
Building 74, Room 228
324 Fourth Avenue
South Charleston, WV 25303
P: (304) 558-3225
F: (304) 558-6048
E: Joe.T.Scarberry@wv.gov

WISCONSIN
Ms. Tia Nelson
Executive Secretary
Board of Commissioners of
Public Lands
101 East Wilson Street, 2nd
Floor
P.O. Box 8943
Madison, WI 53708
P: (608) 266-8369
F: (608) 267-2787
E: Tia.Nelson@wisconsin.gov

WYOMING
Ms. Bridget Hill
Director
Office of State Lands &
Investments
Herschler Building, 3 West
122 West 25th Street
Cheyenne, WY 82002
P: (307) 777-6629
F: (307) 777-5400
E: bridget.hill1@wyo.gov

Public Safety

Provides information and services to insure the protection and safety of citizens and property.

ALABAMA
Mr. Spencer Collier
Director
Law Enforcement Agency
301 South Ripley Street
P.O. Box 1511
Montgomery, AL 36102
P: (334) 242-4394
F: (334) 242-0512

ALASKA
Mr. Gary Folger
Commissioner
Department of Public Safety
5700 East Tudor Road
Anchorage, AK 99507
P: (907) 269-5086
F: (907) 269-4543
E: gary.folger@alaska.gov

AMERICAN SAMOA
Mr. William E. Haleck
Commissioner
Department of Public Safety
American Samoa Government
P.O. Box 1086
Pato Pato, AS 96799
P: (684) 633-1111
F: (684) 633-7296
E: commissioner@dps.as.gov

ARIZONA
Mr. Frank Milstead
Director
Department of Public Safety
P.O. Box 6638
Phoenix, AZ 85005
P: (602) 223-2000
F: (602) 223-2917

ARKANSAS
Colonel Bill Bryant
Director
State Police
1 State Police Plaza Drive
Little Rock, AR 72209
P: (501) 618-8299
F: (501) 618-8710
E: info@asp.arkansas.gov

CALIFORNIA
Mr. John Isaacson
Branch Chief
Public Safety Branch
Governor's Office of Emergency
Services
3650 Schriever Avenue
Mather, CA 95655
P: (916) 845-8644
F: (916) 636-3764
E: john.isaacson
    @calema.ca.gov

COLORADO
Mr. Stan Hilkey
Executive Director
Department of Public Safety
700 Kipling Street, #1000
Denver, CO 80215
P: (303) 239-4400
F: (303) 239-4670
E: stan.hilkey@state.co.us

CONNECTICUT
Ms. Dora B. Schriro
Commissioner
Department of Emergency
Services & Public Protection
1111 Country Club Road
Middletown, CT 06457
P: (860) 685-8000
F: (860) 685-8354
E: dora.schriro@ct.gov

DELAWARE
Mr. Lewis D. Schiliro
Cabinet Secretary
Department of Safety &
Homeland Security
303 Transportation Circle
P.O. Box 818
Dover, DE 19903
P: (302) 744-2680
F: (302) 739-4874

DISTRICT OF COLUMBIA
Ms. Cathy L. Lanier
Chief of Police
Metropolitan Police Department
300 Indiana Avenue, Northwest
Room 5059
Washington, DC 20001
P: (202) 727-9099
F: (202) 727-4106
E: mpd@dc.gov

FLORIDA
Mr. Rick Swearingen
Commissioner
Department of Law
Enforcement
2331 Phillips Road
P.O. Box 1489
Tallahassee, FL 32302
P: (850) 410-7001
E: RickSwearingen
    @fdle.state.fl.us

GEORGIA
Colonel Mark W. McDonough
Commissioner
Department of Public Safety
P.O. Box 1456
Atlanta, GA 30371
P: (404) 624-7477
F: (404) 624-7788

GUAM
Mr. Fred E. Bordallo Jr.
Chief of Police
Police Department
#13-16A Mariner Avenue
P.O. Box 23909
Tiyan, GU 96913
P: (671) 475-8508
F: (671) 472-4036
E: chief@gpd.guam.gov

HAWAII
Mr. Nolan Espinda
Director
Department of Public Safety
919 Ala Moana Boulevard,
Room 400
Honolulu, HI 96814
P: (808) 587-1350
F: (808) 587-1282
E: psd.
    office.of.the.director
    @hawaii.gov

ILLINOIS
Mr. Brad Curry
Chief Public Safety Officer
Department of Corrections
1301 Concordia Court
P.O. Box 19277
Springfield, IL 62794
P: (217) 558-2200

INDIANA
Mr. Douglas G. Carter
Superintendent
State Police
Indiana Government Center
North
100 North Senate Avenue
Indianapolis, IN 46204
P: (317) 232-8248
E: ISP@isp.in.gov

IOWA
Mr. Larry L. Noble
Commissioner
Department of Public Safety
215 East 7th Street
Des Moines, IA 50319
P: (515) 725-6182
E: noble@dps.state.ia.us

KANSAS
Maj. Gen. Lee E.
    Tafanelli (R)
Adjutant General
Adjutant General's Department
2800 Southwest Topeka
Boulevard
Topeka, KS 66611
P: (785) 274-1001
F: (785) 274-1682
E: lee.tafanelli
    @us.army.mil

KENTUCKY
Mr. J. Michael Brown
Secretary
Justice & Public Safety Cabinet
125 Holmes Street
Frankfort, KY 40601
P: (502) 564-7554
F: (502) 564-4840

LOUISIANA
Col. Michael D. Edmonson
Deputy Secretary
State Police
Public Safety Services
7919 Independence Boulevard
Baton Rouge, LA 70806
P: (225) 925-6118
F: (225) 925-6006

MAINE
Mr. John E. Morris
Commissioner
Department of Public Safety
45 Commerce Drive, Suite 1
104 State House Station
Augusta, ME 04333
P: (207) 626-3800
F: (207) 287-3042
E: john.e.morris@maine.gov

MARYLAND
Mr. Stephen Moyer
Secretary
Department of Public Safety &
Correctional Services
300 East Joppa Road, Suite 1000
10th Floor
Towson, MD 21286
P: (410) 339-5000

MASSACHUSETTS
Mr. Matthew Carlin
Commissioner
Department of Public Safety
One Ashburton Place, Room
1301
Boston, MA 02108
P: (617) 727-3200
F: (617) 727-5732

MICHIGAN
Colonel Kriste Kibbey Etue
Director
State Police
333 South Grand Avenue
P.O. Box 30634
Lansing, MI 48909
P: (517) 332-2521
F: (517) 241-0409
E: EtueK@michigan.gov

MINNESOTA
Ms. Ramona Dohman
Commissioner
Department of Public Safety
445 Minnesota Street, Suite 1000
St. Paul, MN 55101
P: (651) 201-7160
F: (651) 297-5728
E: Mona.Dohman@state.mn.us

MISSISSIPPI
Mr. Albert Santa Cruz
Commissioner
Department of Public Safety
P.O. Box 958
Jackson, MS 39205
P: (601) 987-1212
F: (601) 987-1488
E: commissioner
@mdps.state.ms.us

MISSOURI
Mr. Lane Roberts
Director
Department of Public Safety
Office of the Director
P.O. Box 749
Jefferson City, MO 65102
P: (573) 751-4905
F: (573) 751-5399

MONTANA
Mr. Ed Tinsley
Administrator
Department of Disaster &
Emergency Services
P.O. Box 4789
Fort Harrison, MT 59636
P: (406) 324-4777
F: (406) 324-4790
E: edtinsley@mt.gov

NEBRASKA
Colonel Bradley Rice
Superintendent of Law
Enforcement & Public Safety
State Patrol
P.O. Box 94907
Lincoln, NE 68509
P: (402) 471-4545
F: (402) 479-4002
E: bradley.rice
@nebraska.gov

NEVADA
Mr. James Wright
Director
Department of Public Safety
555 Wright Way
Carson City, NV 89711
P: (775) 684-4808
F: (775) 684-4809

NEW HAMPSHIRE
Mr. John J. Barthelmes
Commissioner
Department of Safety
James H. Hayes Safety Building
33 Hazen Drive
Concord, NH 03305
P: (603) 223-3889
F: (603) 271-3903
E: john.barthelmes
@dos.nh.gov

NEW JERSEY
Col. Rick Fuentes
Superintendent
State Police
P.O. Box 7068
West Trenton, NJ 08628
P: (609) 882-2000
F: (609) 530-4383

NEW MEXICO
Mr. Gregory J. Fouratt Jr.
Cabinet Secretary
Department of Public Safety
4491 Cerrillos Road
P.O. Box 1628
Santa Fe, NM 87504
P: (505) 827-3370
F: (505) 827-3434

NEW YORK
Mr. Michael C. Green
Executive Deputy Commissioner
Division of Criminal Justice Services
4 Tower Place, 10th Floor
Albany, NY 12203
P: (518) 457-5837
F: (518) 473-1271

NORTH CAROLINA
Mr. Frank L. Perry
Secretary
Department of Public Safety
512 North Salisbury Street
4201 Mail Service Center
Raleigh, NC 27699
P: (919) 733-2126
F: (919) 715-8477
E: frank.perry@ncdps.gov

NORTH DAKOTA
Colonel James Prochniak
Superintendent
Highway Patrol
600 East Boulevard Avenue
Department 504
Bismarck, ND 58505
P: (701) 328-2455
F: (701) 328-1717
E: jprochni@nd.gov

NORTHERN MARIANA ISLANDS
Mr. James C.
Deleon Guerrero
Commissioner
Department of Public Safety
Jose M. Sablan Building
Caller Box 10007
Saipan, MP 96950
P: (670) 664-9022
F: (670) 664-9070

OHIO
Colonel John Born
Director
Department of Public Safety
1970 West Broad Street
P.O. Box 182081
Columbus, OH 43218
P: (614) 466-3383
F: (614) 466-0433

OKLAHOMA
Mr. Michael C. Thompson
Commissioner
Department of Public Safety
P.O. Box 11415
Oklahoma City, OK 73136
P: (405) 425-2424
E: mike.thompson
@dps.state.ok.us

OREGON
Mr. Eriks Gabliks
Director
Department of Public Safety
Standards & Training
4190 Aumsville Highway, Southeast
Salem, OR 97317
P: (503) 378-2332
F: (503) 378-2043
E: eriks.gabliks
@state.or.us

PENNSYLVANIA
Colonel Marcus L. Brown
Acting Commissioner
State Police
1800 Elmerton Avenue
Harrisburg, PA 17110
P: (717) 783-5517
F: (717) 783-7690

PUERTO RICO
Mr. Hector Pesquera
Superintendent
Puerto Rico Police
P.O. Box 70166
San Juan, PR 00936
P: (787) 793-1234
F: (787) 781-0080

RHODE ISLAND
Colonel Steven G. O'Donnell
Commissioner & Superintendent
Department of Public Safety
311 Danielson Pike
North Scituate, RI 02857
P: (401) 444-1000
F: (401) 444-1105
E: sodonnell
@risp.state.ri.us

SOUTH CAROLINA
Mr. Leroy Smith
Director
Department of Public Safety
10311 Wilson Boulevard
P.O. Box 1993
Blythewood, SC 29016
P: (803) 896-7979
F: (803) 896-7881

SOUTH DAKOTA
Mr. Trevor Jones
Secretary
Department of Public Safety
118 West Capitol Avenue
Pierre, SD 57501
P: (605) 773-3178
F: (605) 773-3018
E: DPSInfo@state.sd.us

TENNESSEE
Mr. Bill Gibbons
Commissioner
Department of Safety &
Homeland Security
1150 Foster Avenue
P.O. Box 945
Nashville, TN 37202
P: (615) 251-5166
E: email.safety@tn.gov

TEXAS
Captain Ruben Galindo
Captain
Patrol & Security Operations
Department of Public Safety
5805 North Lamar
Austin, TX 78752
P: (512) 475-4821
F: (512) 305-9136

Public Safety

U.S. VIRGIN ISLANDS
Mr. Rodney F. Querrard
Commissioner
Police Department
Alexander Farrelly Criminal
Justice Ctr.
Charlotte Amalie
St. Thomas, VI 00802
P: (340) 715-5605
F: (340) 715-5517

UTAH
Mr. Keith D. Squires
Commissioner
Department of Public Safety
4501 South 2700 West
Salt Lake City, UT 84114
P: (801) 965-4062
F: (801) 965-4608
E: ksquires@utah.gov

VIRGINIA
Mr. Brian J. Moran
Secretary of Public Safety &
Homeland Security
Office of the Secretary of Public
Safety & Homeland Security
1111 East Broad Street
Patrick Henry Building
Richmond, VA 23219
P: (804) 786-5351
F: (804) 371-6381
E: brian.moran
    @governor.virginia.gov

WASHINGTON
Mr. John R. Batiste
Chief
State Patrol
General Administration Building
P.O. Box 42600
Olympia, WA 98504
P: (360) 596-4000
E: john.batiste@wsp.wa.gov

WEST VIRGINIA
Mr. Joe Thornton
Cabinet Secretary
Department of Military Affairs
& Public Safety
Building 1, Room W-400
1900 Kanawha Boulevard, East
Charleston, WV 25305
P: (304) 558-2930
F: (304) 558-6221
E: joseph.c.thornton@wv.gov

WISCONSIN
Mr. David S. Matthews
Administrator
Division of Criminal
Investigation
Department of Justice
P.O. Box 7857
Madison, WI 53707
P: (608) 266-1671

WYOMING
Colonel John Butler
Administrator
Highway Patrol
5300 Bishop Boulevard
Cheyenne, WY 82009
P: (307) 777-4301
F: (307) 777-3897

Public Utility Regulation

Supervises and regulates the electric, gas, telephone and water utilities in the state.

Information provided by:

National Association of Regulatory Utility Commissioners
Charles D. Gray
Executive Director
1101 Vermont Avenue NW, Suite 200
Washington, DC 20005
P: (202) 898-2208
F: (202) 898-2213
cgray@naruc.org
www.naruc.org

ALABAMA
Ms. Twinkle Andress
    Cavanaugh (R)
President
Public Service Commission
100 North Union Street, Suite 850
P.O. Box 304260
Montgomery, AL 36130
P: (334) 242-5203
F: (334) 242-0509
E: twinkle.cavanaugh
    @psc.alabama.gov

ALASKA
Mr. Robert Pickett
Chairman
Regulatory Commission
701 West 8th Avenue, Suite 300
Anchorage, AK 99501
P: (907) 276-6222
F: (907) 276-0160
E: bob.pickett@alaska.gov

ARIZONA
Hon. Bob Stump (R)
Chair
Corporation Commission
1200 West Washington Street
Phoenix, AZ 85007
P: (602) 542-3935
F: (602) 542-0752
E: bstump@azcc.gov

ARKANSAS
Mr. Ted J. Thomas
Chair
Public Service Commission
1000 Center Building
P.O. Box 400
Little Rock, AR 72203
P: (501) 682-2051
F: (501) 682-5731
E: tthomas@psc.state.ar.us

CALIFORNIA
Mr. Paul Clanon
Executive Director
Public Utilities Commission
California State Building
505 Van Ness Avenue
San Francisco, CA 94102
P: (415) 703-3808
F: (415) 703-1758
E: pac@cpuc.ca.gov

COLORADO
Mr. Joshua Epel
Chair
Public Utilities Commission
1560 Broadway, Suite 250
Denver, CO 80202
P: (303) 894-2007
F: (303) 894-2065
E: joshua.epel@state.co.us

CONNECTICUT
Mr. Arthur H. House
Chair
Public Utilties Regulatory Authority
10 Franklin Square
New Britain, CT 06051
P: (860) 827-2807
F: (860) 827-2806
E: arthur.house@ct.gov

Mr. Robert J. Klee
Commissioner
Department of Energy & Environmental Protection
79 Elm Street
Hartford, CT 06106
P: (860) 424-3001
F: (860) 424-4051
E: deep.commissioner@ct.gov

DELAWARE
Mr. Dallas Winslow
Chair
Public Service Commission
861 Silver Lake Boulevard
Cannon Building, Suite 100
Dover, DE 19904
P: (302) 736-7500
F: (302) 739-4849
E: dallaswinslow@yahoo.com

DISTRICT OF COLUMBIA
Ms. Betty Ann Kane
Chair
Public Service Commission
1333 H Street, Northwest
2nd Floor, West Tower
Washington, DC 20005
P: (202) 626-5125
F: (202) 626-9212
E: bakane@psc.dc.gov

FLORIDA
Mr. Art Graham
Chair
Public Service Commission
2540 Shumard Oak Boulevard
Gerald Gunter Building
Tallahassee, FL 32399
P: (850) 413-6040
F: (850) 413-6025
E: agraham@psc.state.fl.us

GEORGIA
Mr. Chuck Eaton
Chair
Public Service Commission
244 Washington Street
Atlanta, GA 30334
P: (404) 657-2020
F: (404) 657-2010
E: ceaton@psc.state.ga.us

GUAM
Mr. Jeffrey C. Johnson
Chair
Public Utilities Commission
414 West Soledad Avenue, Suite 207
GCIC Building, P.O. Box 862
Hagatna, GU 96910
P: (671) 472-1907
F: (671) 472-1917
E: jjohnson@guampuc.com

HAWAII
Ms. Hermina M. Morita
Chair
Public Utilities Commission
465 South King Street
Kekuanao'a Building, Room 103
Honolulu, HI 96813
P: (808) 586-2020
F: (808) 586-2066
E: hermina.m.morita
    @hawaii.gov

IDAHO
Mr. Paul Kjellander
President
Public Utilities Commission
472 West Washington Street
P.O. Box 83720
Boise, ID 83720
P: (208) 334-2898
F: (208) 334-3762
E: paul.kjellander
    @puc.idaho.gov

ILLINOIS
Mr. Brien J. Sheahan
Chair
Commerce Commission
160 North LaSalle Street, Suite C-800
Chicago, IL 60601
P: (312) 814-2850
F: (312) 814-1818
E: bsheahan
    @icc.illinois.gov

INDIANA
Ms. Carol A. Stephan
Chair
Utility Regulatory Commission
PNC Center, Suite 1500 East
101 West Washington Street
Indianapolis, IN 46204
P: (317) 234-4715
F: (317) 232-6758
E: cstephan@urc.in.gov

KANSAS
Ms. Shari Feist Albrecht
Chair
Corporation Commission
1500 Southwest Arrowhead Road
Topeka, KS 66604
P: (785) 271-3350
F: (785) 271-3354
E: s.feist.albrecht
    @kcc.ks.gov

KENTUCKY
Mr. David Armstrong
Chair
Public Service Commission
211 Sower Boulevard
P.O. Box 615
Frankfort, KY 40602
P: (502) 782-2551
F: (502) 564-8992
E: david.armstrong@ky.gov

LOUISIANA
Mr. Lambert C.
    Boissiere III
Commissioner
Public Service Commission
602 North Fifth Street
P.O. Box 91154
Baton Rouge, LA 70821
P: (504) 680-9529
F: (504) 680-9536
E: cesily.roberts@la.gov

MAINE
Mr. Mark Vannoy
Chair
Public Utilities Commission
18 State House Station
Augusta, ME 04333
P: (207) 287-1360
F: (207) 287-1039
E: mark.vannoy@maine.gov

Public Utility Regulation

MARYLAND
Mr. W. Kevin Hughes
Chair
Public Service Commission
6 St. Paul Street, 16th Floor
Baltimore, MD 21202
P: (410) 767-8073
F: (410) 333-6495
E: kevin.hughes
  @maryland.gov

MASSACHUSETTS
Ms. Angela M. O'Connor
Chair
Department of Public Utilities
One South Station
Boston, MA 02110
P: (617) 305-3654
F: (617) 345-9102
E: angie.oconnor
  @state.ma.us

Ms. Karen Charles Peterson
Commissioner
Department of
Telecommunications & Cable
1000 Washington Street, Suite
820
Boston, MA 02118
P: (617) 368-1116
F: (617) 988-8217
E: karen.c.peterson
  @state.ma.us

MICHIGAN
Mr. John D. Quackenbush
Chair
Public Service Commission
7109 West Saginaw Highway
P.O. Box 30221
Lansing, MI 48909
P: (517) 284-8060
F: (517) 284-8293
E: quackenbushj
  @michigan.gov

MINNESOTA
Ms. Beverly Jones Heydinger
Chair
Public Utilities Commission
121 7th Place East, Suite 350
St. Paul, MN 55101
P: (651) 201-2250
F: (651) 297-7073
E: beverly.haydinger
  @state.mn.us

Mr. Mike Rothman
Commissioner
Department of Commerce
85 East 7th Place, Suite 500
St. Paul, MN 55101
P: (651) 539-1638
F: (651) 296-4328
E: commerce.commissioner
  @state.mn.us

MISSISSIPPI
Mr. Lynn Posey
Chair
Public Service Commission
501 North West Street
Woolfolk State Office Building
Jackson, MS 39201
P: (800) 356-6430
F: (601) 961-5824
E: lynn.posey
  @psc.state.ms.us

MISSOURI
Mr. Robert S. Kenney
Chair
Public Service Commission
200 Madison Street
P.O. Box 360
Jefferson City, MO 65102
P: (573) 751-4132
F: (573) 526-7341
E: robert.kenney@psc.mo.gov

MONTANA
Hon. Brad Johnson (R)
Chair
Public Service Commission
1701 Prospect Avenue
P.O. Box 202601
Helena, MT 59620
P: (406) 444-6169
F: (406) 444-7618
E: bjohnson@mt.gov

NEBRASKA
Mr. Frank E. Landis Jr.
Chair
Public Service Commission
300 The Atrium, 1200 N Street
P.O. Box 94927
Lincoln, NE 68509
P: (402) 471-0229
F: (402) 471-0233
E: frank.landis
  @nebraska.gov

Mr. Stephen Lichter
Chair
Power Review Board
301 Centennial Mall, South
P.O. Box 94713
Lincoln, NE 68509
P: (402) 471-2301
F: (402) 471-3715
E: stephen.lichter
  @eadengineering.com

NEVADA
Ms. Alaina C. Burtenshaw
Chair
Public Utilities Commission
9075 West Diablo Drive, Suite
250
Las Vegas, NV 89148
P: (702) 486-7234
F: (702) 486-7206
E: aburtens@puc.nv.gov

NEW HAMPSHIRE
Ms. Debra A. Howland
Executive Director
Public Utilities Commission
21 South Fruit Street, Suite 10
Concord, NH 03301
P: (603) 271-2431
F: (603) 271-3878
E: debra.howland@puc.nh.gov

NEW JERSEY
Mr. Richard S. Mroz
President
Board of Public Utilities
44 South Clinton Avenue
P.O. Box 350
Trenton, NJ 08625
P: (609) 777-3310
F: (609) 777-3330
E: richard.mroz
  @bpu.state.nj.us

NEW MEXICO
Ms. Valerie Espinoza
Vice Chair
Public Regulation Commission
1120 Paseo De Peralta
P.O. Box 1269
Santa Fe, NM 87504
P: (505) 827-4533
F: (505) 476-0161
E: valerie.espinoza
  @state.nm.us

NEW YORK
Ms. Joan McDonald
Commissioner
Department of Transportation
50 Wolf Road, 6th Floor
Albany, NY 12232
P: (518) 457-4422
F: (518) 457-5583
E: joan.mcdonald@dot.ny.gov

Ms. Audrey Zibelman
Chair
Public Service Commission
Three Empire State Plaza
Albany, NY 12223
P: (518) 474-2523
F: (518) 473-2838
E: audrey.zibelman
  @dps.ny.gov

NORTH CAROLINA
Mr. Edward S. Finley Jr.
Chair
Utilities Commission
430 North Salisbury Street
4325 Mail Service Center
Raleigh, NC 27699
P: (919) 733-6067
F: (919) 715-5970
E: finley@ncuc.net

NORTH DAKOTA
Hon. Brian Kalk (R)
Chair
Public Service Commission
600 East Boulevard Avenue
Department 408
Bismarck, ND 58505
P: (701) 328-4195
F: (701) 328-2410
E: bkalk@nd.gov

OHIO
Mr. Andre T. Porter
Chair
Public Utilities Commission
180 East Broad Street
Columbus, OH 43215
P: (614) 466-3016
F: (614) 466-7366
E: andre.porter
  @puc.state.oh.us

OKLAHOMA
Hon. Bob Anthony (R)
Chair
Corporation Commission
2101 North Lincoln Boulevard
P.O. Box 52000
Oklahoma City, OK 73152
P: (405) 521-2261
F: (405) 521-4532
E: b.anthony@occemail.com

OREGON
Ms. Susan K. Ackerman
Chair
Public Utility Commission
3930 Fairview Industrial Drive
Southeast
P.O. Box 1088
Salem, OR 97302
P: (503) 378-6611
F: (503) 378-5505
E: susan.ackerman
@state.or.us

PENNSYLVANIA
Ms. Gladys Brown
Chair
Public Utility Commission
400 North Street
Commonwealth Keystone
Building
Harrisburg, PA 17120
P: (717) 787-1031
F: (717) 783-0698
E: gmb@pa.gov

PUERTO RICO
Mr. Omar E. Negron Judice
Chair
Public Service Commission
P.O. Box 190870
San Juan, PR 00919
P: (787) 756-1919
F: (787) 756-8086
E: onegron@csp.pr.gov

Mr. Javier Rua Jovet
President
Telecommunications Regulatory
Board
500 Avenue Roberto H. Todd
(Pda. 18-Santurce)
San Juan, PR 00907
P: (787) 281-9393
F: (787) 756-0814
E: javier.rua@jrtpr.pr.gov

RHODE ISLAND
Ms. Margaret E. Curran
Chair
Public Utilities Commission
89 Jefferson Boulevard
Warwick, RI 02888
P: (401) 780-2100
F: (401) 941-1691
E: margaret.curran
@puc.ri.gov

SOUTH CAROLINA
Ms. Nikki M. Hall
Chair
Public Service Commission
101 Executive Center Drive
P.O. Drawer 11649
Columbia, SC 29211
P: (803) 896-5180
F: (803) 896-5188
E: nikki.hall@psc.sc.gov

SOUTH DAKOTA
Hon. Gary W. Hanson (R)
Chair
Public Utilities Commission
State Capitol, 500 East Capitol
Avenue
Pierre, SD 57501
P: (605) 773-3201
F: (866) 757-6031
E: gary.hanson@state.sd.us

TENNESSEE
Mr. James Allison
Chair
Regulatory Authority
502 Deaderick Street, 4th Floor
Nashville, TN 37243
P: (615) 741-2904
F: (615) 741-5015
E: jim.allison@tn.gov

Mr. Bill Johnson
President & Chief Executive
Officer
Tennessee Valley Authority
400 West Summit Hill Drive
Knoxville, TN 37902
P: (865) 632-2101
E: admin@naruc.org

TEXAS
Ms. Donna L. Nelson
Chair
Public Utility Commission
1701 North Congress Avenue
P.O. Box 13326
Austin, TX 78711
P: (512) 936-7015
F: (512) 936-7018
E: donna.nelson
@puc.texas.gov

U.S. VIRGIN ISLANDS
Mr. Johann A. Clendinen
Chair
Public Service Commission
P.O. Box 40
Charlotte Amalie
St. Thomas, VI 00804
P: (304) 244-4362
F: (340) 774-4879
E: sport@iclogistics.com

VERMONT
Mr. Christopher Recchia
Commissioner
Department of Public Service
Department of Public Service
112 State Street
Montpelier, VT 05620
P: (802) 828-2321
F: (802) 828-2342
E: chris.recchia
@state.vt.us

Mr. James Volz
Chair
Public Service Board
112 State Street, 4th Floor
Montpelier, VT 05620
P: (802) 828-1655
F: (802) 828-3351
E: james.volz@state.vt.us

VIRGINIA
Ms. Judith W. Jagdmann
Chair
State Corporation Commission
1300 East Main Street
P.O. Box 1197
Richmond, VA 23218
P: (804) 371-9608
F: (804) 371-9376
E: commissioners
@scc.virginia.gov

WASHINGTON
Mr. David W. Danner
Chair
Utilities & Transportation
Commission
1300 South Evergreen Park
Drive
P.O. Box 47250
Olympia, WA 98504
P: (360) 664-1208
F: (360) 586-1150
E: ddanner@utc.wa.gov

WEST VIRGINIA
Mr. Michael A. Albert
Chair
Public Service Commission
201 Brooks Street
P.O. Box 812
Charleston, WV 25323
P: (304) 340-0306
F: (304) 340-3758
E: malbert@psc.state.wv.us

WISCONSIN
Ms. Ellen Nowak
Chair
Public Service Commission
610 North Whitney Way
P.O. Box 7854
Madison, WI 53707
P: (608) 267-7899
F: (608) 266-1401
E: ellen.nowak
@wisconsin.gov

WYOMING
Mr. Alan B. Minier
Chair
Public Service Commission
2515 Warren Avenue, Suite 300
Cheyenne, WY 82002
P: (307) 777-5725
F: (307) 777-5700
E: al.minier@wyo.gov

Purchasing

Central screening and acquisition point for supplies, equipment, and/or services for state agencies.

ALABAMA
Mr. Michael Jones
State Purchasing Director
Division of Purchasing
Department of Finance
100 North Union Street, Suite 192
Montgomery, AL 36104
P: (334) 242-7250
F: (334) 242-4419
E: michael.jones
    @purchasing.alabama.gov

ALASKA
Mr. Tom Mayer
Director
Division of General Services
P.O. Box 110210, State Office Building
Floor 7, 333 Willoughby Avenue
Juneau, AK 99811
P: (907) 465-5677
F: (907) 465-2189
E: tom.mayer@alaska.gov

ARIZONA
Ms. Barbara Corella
State Procurement Administrator
State Procurement Office
100 North 15th Avenue, Suite 201
Phoenix, AZ 85007
P: (602) 542-9146
F: (602) 542-5508
E: barbara.corella
    @azdoa.gov

ARKANSAS
Ms. Camber Thompson
Director
Office of State Procurement
Department of Finance & Administration
1509 West 7th Street, Floor 3
Little Rock, AR 72201
P: (501) 324-9312
E: camber.thompson
    @dfa.arkansas.gov

CALIFORNIA
Mr. Jim Butler
Chief Procurement Officer
Procurement Division
Department of General Services
707 Third Street, Floor 2
West Sacramento, CA 95605
P: (916) 375-4417
F: (916) 375-4421
E: jim.butler@dgs.ca.gov

COLORADO
Ms. Cindy Lombardi
State Purchasing & Contracts Director
Department of Personnel & Administration
1525 Sherman Street, Floor 3
Denver, CO 80203
P: (303) 866-6212
F: (303) 894-7445
E: cindy.lombardi
    @state.co.us

CONNECTICUT
Ms. Carol Wilson
Director of Procurement
Procurement Programs & Services
165 Capitol Avenue, Floor 5 South
Hartford, CT 06106
P: (860) 713-5093
F: (860) 622-2904
E: carol.wilson@ct.gov

DELAWARE
Mr. Dean W. Stotler
Director
Government Support Services
Office of Management & Budget
100 Enterprise Place, Suite 4
Dover, DE 19904
P: (302) 857-4501
F: (302) 739-2564
E: dean.stotler@state.de.us

DISTRICT OF COLUMBIA
Mr. George Schutter
Acting Chief Procurement Officer
Office of Contracting & Procurement
441 4th Street, Northwest
Suite 700S
Washington, DC 20001
P: (202) 724-4242
E: george.schutter@dc.gov

FLORIDA
Ms. Rosalyn Ingram
Director of State Purchasing
Division of State Purchasing
4050 Esplanade Way, Suite 360
Tallahassee, FL 32399
P: (850) 488-8440
E: rosalyn.ingram
    @dms.myflorida.com

GEORGIA
Ms. Leslie Lowe
Deputy Commissioner for Procurement
State Purchasing Division
200 Piedmont Avenue, Suite 1302
West Tower
Atlanta, GA 30334
P: (404) 656-0934
F: (404) 344-4903
E: leslie.lowe@doas.ga.gov

HAWAII
Ms. Sarah Allen
Procurement Administrator
State Procurement Office
1151 Punchbowl Street, Room 230A
Honolulu, HI 96813
P: (808) 587-4700
E: sarah.allen@hawaii.gov

IDAHO
Mr. Bill Burns
Administrator
Division of Purchasing
650 West State Street, Room B15
Boise, ID 83702
P: (208) 332-1610
F: (208) 327-7320
E: bill.burns@adm.idaho.gov

ILLINOIS
Mr. Matt Brown
Chief Procurement Officer
Chief Procurement Office for General Services
401 South Spring Street
Stratton Building, Room 712
Springfield, IL 62706
P: (217) 558-2231
F: (217) 558-2164
E: matt.brown@illinois.gov

INDIANA
Ms. Debra Walker
Deputy Commissioner, Procurement Division
Department of Administration
402 West Washington Street
Room W468
Indianapolis, IN 46204
P: (317) 234-5584
F: (317) 232-7312
E: dwalker@idoa.in.gov

IOWA
Mr. Kelly Green
Chief Operations Officer
Central Procurement Enterprise
Hoover State Office Building, Floor 3
1305 East Walnut Street
Des Moines, IA 50319
P: (515) 725-2272
E: kelly.green@iowa.gov

KANSAS
Mr. Tracy Diel
Director of Procurement & Contracts
Office of Procurement & Contracts
Department of Administration
900 Southwest Jackson, Suite 451-S
Topeka, KS 66612
P: (785) 296-2376
F: (785) 296-7240
E: tracy.diel@da.ks.gov

KENTUCKY
Mr. Donald Speer
Executive Director
Office of Procurement Services
Finance & Administration Cabinet
702 Capitol Annex, Room 096
Frankfort, KY 40601
P: (502) 564-4510
E: don.speer@ky.gov

MAINE
Mr. Mark Lutte
Director
Division of Purchases
Burton M. Cross Building, Floor 4
9 State House Station, 111 Sewall Street
Augusta, ME 04330
P: (207) 624-7332
F: (207) 287-6578
E: mark.lutte@maine.gov

MARYLAND
Ms. Nancy Hevey
Director of General Services
Office of Procurement & Logistics
State Office Building, Room M-6
301 West Preston Street
Baltimore, MD 21201
P: (410) 767-4045
F: (410) 333-5986
E: Nancy.hevey@maryland.gov

MASSACHUSETTS
Mr. Gary Lambert
Assistant Secretary for
Operational Services
Operational Services Division
Office for Administration &
Finance
One Ashburton Place, Room
1017
Boston, MA 02108
P: (617) 720-3330
F: (617) 727-4527
E: gary.lambert@state.ma.us

MICHIGAN
Mr. Jeff Brownlee
Chief Procurement Officer
Department of Technology,
Management & Budget -
Procurement
525 West Allegan Street
Lansing, MI 48913
P: (517) 284-7012
F: (517) 335-0046
E: brownleej@michigan.gov

MINNESOTA
Ms. Betsy Hayes
Acting Chief Procurement
Officer
Materials Management Division
Department of Administration
50 Sherburne Avenue, Suite 112
St. Paul, MN 55155
P: (651) 201-2407
F: (651) 297-3996
E: betsy.hayes@state.mn.us

MISSISSIPPI
Ms. Monica Ritchie
Director of Purchasing, Travel &
Fleet Management
Office of Purchasing, Travel &
Fleet Management
701 Woolfolk Building, Suite A
501 North West Street
Jackson, MS 39201
P: (601) 359-6603
F: (601) 359-3910
E: monica.ritchie
    @dfa.ms.gov

MISSOURI
Ms. Karen Boeger
Director of Purchasing
Division of Purchasing &
Materials Management
301 West High Street, Room
630
Harry S. Truman Building
Jefferson City, MO 65101
P: (573) 751-1699
F: (573) 526-9815
E: karen.boeger@oa.mo.gov

MONTANA
Mr. Brad Sanders
Chief Procurement Officer
State Procurement Bureau
General Services Division
125 North Roberts Street, Room
165
Helena, MT 59601
P: (406) 444-1459
F: (406) 444-2529
E: bsanders@mt.gov

NEBRASKA
Ms. Brenda Pape
State Procurement Manager
State Purchasing Bureau
1526 K Street, Suite 130
Lincoln, NE 68508
P: (402) 471-0970
F: (402) 471-2089
E: Brenda.Pape@Nebraska.gov

NEVADA
Mr. Greg Smith
Administrator
Purchasing Division
Department of Administration
515 East Musser Street, Suite
300
Carson City, NV 89701
P: (775) 684-0170
F: (775) 684-0188
E: gmsmith@admin.nv.gov

NEW HAMPSHIRE
Mr. Robert Stowell
Administrator
Bureau of Purchase & Property
25 Capitol Street, Room 102
Concord, NH 03301
P: (603) 271-3606
F: (603) 271-2700
E: robert.stowell@nh.gov

NEW JERSEY
Jignasa Desai-McCleary
Director
Division of Purchase & Property
Department of Treasury
33 West State Street, 8th Floor
Trenton, NJ 08608
P: (609) 292-4886
F: (609) 984-2575
E: Julie.Weaver
    @treas.nj.gov

NEW MEXICO
Mr. Lawrence Maxwell
Director of State Purchasing
State Purchasing Division
General Services Department
1100 St. Francis Drive, Room
2016
Santa Fe, NM 87505
P: (505) 827-0472
F: (505) 827-2484
E: Lawrence.Maxwell
    @state.nm.us

NEW YORK
Ms. Susan Filburn
Chief Procurement Officer
State Procurement
Corning Tower, Floor 38
Empire State Plaza
Albany, NY 12242
P: (518) 473-5291
E: susan.filburn@ogs.ny.gov

NORTH CAROLINA
Ms. Patricia Bowers
Director
Division of Purchase & Contract
116 West Jones Street
Raleigh, NC 27603
P: (919) 807-4550
F: (919) 807-4508
E: patti.bowers@doa.nc.gov

NORTH DAKOTA
Ms. Sherry Neas
Director
Central Services Division - SPO
Capitol Tower, Floor 14,
Department 012
600 East Boulevard Avenue
Bismarck, ND 58505
P: (701) 328-1726
F: (701) 328-1615
E: sneas@nd.gov

OHIO
Mr. Wayne McCulty
State Procurement Administrator
Office of Procurement Services
4200 Surface Road
Columbus, OH 43228
P: (614) 466-7066
F: (614) 485-1056
E: wayne.mcculty
    @das.state.oh.us

OKLAHOMA
Mr. Steve Hagar
State Purchasing Director
Central Purchasing Division
2401 North Lincoln Street,
Suite 116
Oklahoma City, OK 73105
P: (405) 521-2115
F: (405) 521-4475
E: steve.hagar@omes.ok.gov

OREGON
Ms. Dianne Lancaster
Chief Procurement Officer
Procurement Policy Group -
CFO
Department of Administrative
Services
155 Cottage Street, Northeast,
Floor 3
Salem, OR 97301
P: (503) 378-3529
F: (503) 373-1626
E: dianne.lancaster
    @oregon.gov

PENNSYLVANIA
Ms. Jennifer Doherty
Chief Procurement Officer
Bureau of Procurement
Department of General Services
555 Walnut Street, Floor 6
Harrisburg, PA 17101
P: (717) 787-5862
E: jedoherty@pa.gov

PUERTO RICO
Mr. Luis Castro-Agis
Administrator
General Services Administration
P.O. Box 195568
San Juan, PR 00919
P: (787) 759-7675
F: (787) 753-6160
E: lcagis@asg.gobierno.pr

RHODE ISLAND
Ms. Nancy McIntyre
Purchasing Agent
Division of Purchases
Department of Administration
One Capitol Hill, Floor 2
Providence, RI 02908
P: (401) 574-8126
F: (401) 574-8387
E: nancy.mcintyre
    @purchasing.ri.gov

Purchasing

SOUTH CAROLINA
Mr. Delbert Singleton
Assistant Executive Director &
Board Secretary
Budget & Control Board
1200 Senate Street
Columbia, SC 29201
P: (803) 734-2314
F: (803) 734-2117
E: delbert@oed.sc.gov

SOUTH DAKOTA
Mr. Steven Berg
Director of Procurement
Office of Procurement
Management
Bureau of Administration
523 East Capitol Avenue, PMB
01231
Pierre, SD 57501
P: (605) 773-5270
F: (605) 773-4840
E: steven.berg@state.sd.us

TENNESSEE
Mr. Mike Perry
Chief Procurement Officer
Central Procurement Office
WRS Tennessee Tower, Floor 3
312 Rosa L. Parks Avenue, Floor
3
Nashville, TN 37243
P: (615) 741-3625
E: mike.perry@tn.gov

TEXAS
Mr. Chuks Amajor
Interim Director, TPASS and
Strategic Sourcing
Comptroller of Public Accounts
1711 San Jacinto Boulevard
Austin, TX 78701
P: (512) 463-8476
E: chuks.amajor
   @cpa.texas.gov

UTAH
Mr. Kent Beers
Executive Director
Division of Purchasing &
General Services
3150 State Office Building,
Capitol Hill
P.O. Box 141061
Salt Lake City, UT 84114
P: (801) 538-3143
F: (801) 538-3882
E: kbeers@utah.gov

VERMONT
Ms. Deb Damore
Director
Department of Buildings &
General Services
Office of Purchasing &
Contracting
10 Baldwin Street
Montpelier, VT 05633
P: (802) 828-5784
F: (802) 828-2222
E: deborah.damore
   @state.vt.us

VIRGINIA
Mr. Robert Gleason
Director
Division of Purchases & Supply
1111 East Broad Street
Richmond, VA 23219
P: (804) 786-3846
F: (804) 371-7877
E: robert.gleason
   @dgs.virginia.gov

WASHINGTON
Ms. Christine Warnock
Chief Procurement Officer
Master Contracts & Consulting,
Department of Enterprise
Services
1500 Jefferson Street, Southeast
Floor 6, P.O. Box 41411
Olympia, WA 98501
P: (360) 407-9398
F: (360) 586-2426
E: christine.warnock
   @des.wa.gov

WEST VIRGINIA
Mr. David R. Tincher
Director
Purchasing Division
Department of Administration
2019 Washington Street, East
Charleston, WV 25305
P: (304) 558-2538
F: (304) 558-0006
E: david.tincher@wv.gov

WISCONSIN
Mr. Rick Hughes
Bureau Director
Bureau of Procurement
101 East Wilson Street, Floor 6
P.O. Box 7867
Madison, WI 53707
P: (608) 266-1558
F: (608) 267-0600
E: rick.hughes
   @wisconsin.gov

WYOMING
Ms. Lori Galles
Interim Procurement Manager
Department of Administration &
Information
General Services Division
700 West 21st Street
Cheyenne, WY 82002
P: (307) 777-6707
F: (307) 777-5852
E: lori.galles@wyo.gov

Recycling

Responsible for promoting and implementing state oversight of municipal solid waste recycling, source reduction and recycling within state government and industry.

ALABAMA
Mr. Lance R. LeFleur
Director
Department of Environmental Management
P.O. Box 301463
Montgomery, AL 36130
P: (334) 271-7710
F: (334) 279-3043

ALASKA
Mr. Bob Blankenburg
Program Manager
Solid Waste Program
Department of Environmental Health
555 Cordova Street
Anchorage, AK 99501
P: (907) 269-7802
F: (907) 269-7600
E: bob.blankenburg
    @alaska.gov

ARIZONA
Ms. Laura L. Malone
Waste Programs Division
Director
Department of Environmental Quality
1110 West Washington Street
Phoenix, AZ 85007
P: (602) 771-4567
F: (602) 771-2302
E: malone.laura@azdeq.gov

CALIFORNIA
Ms. Caroll Mortensen
Director
Department of Resources, Recycling & Recovery
1001 I Street
P.O. Box 4025
Sacramento, CA 95812
P: (916) 322-4025
F: (916) 319-7227
E: Caroll.Mortensen
    @calrecycle.ca.gov

COLORADO
Mr. Gary Baughman
Director
Hazardous Materials & Waste Management Division
Public Health & Environment
4300 Cherry Creek Drive, South
Denver, CO 80246
P: (303) 692-3338
F: (303) 759-5355
E: gary.baughman
    @state.co.us

CONNECTICUT
Ms. Yvonne Bolton
Bureau Chief
Bureau of Materials Management & Compliance Assurance
Energy & Environmental Protection
79 Elm Street
Hartford, CT 06106
P: (860) 424-3021
F: (860) 424-4060
E: yvonne.bolton@ct.gov

DELAWARE
Mr. Richard P. Watson
Chief Executive Officer
Solid Waste Authority
1128 South Bradford Street
P.O. Box 455
Dover, DE 19903
P: (302) 739-5361
F: (302) 739–4287
E: info@dswa.com

DISTRICT OF COLUMBIA
Mr. William O. Howland Jr.
Director
Department of Public Works
2000 14th Street, Northwest
Washington, DC 20009
P: (202) 673-6833
F: (202) 671-0642
E: dpw@dc.gov

FLORIDA
Mr. Jorge Caspary
Director
Division of Waste Management
Department of Environmental Protection
2600 Blair Stone Road
Tallahassee, FL 32399
P: (850) 245-8693
E: jorge.caspary
    @dep.state.fl.us

GEORGIA
Mr. Kevin Clark
Executive Director
Environmental Finance Authority
233 Peachtree Street, Northwest
Harris Tower, Suite 900
Atlanta, GA 30303
P: (404) 584-1000
F: (404) 584-1069

GUAM
Mr. Carl V. Dominguez
Director
Department of Public Works
542 North Marine Corp Drive
Tamuning, GU 96913
P: (671) 646-3131
F: (671) 649-6178
E: carl.dominguez
    @dpw.guam.gov

HAWAII
Mr. Gary L. Gill
Deputy Director for Environmental Health
Environmental Health Administration
1250 Punchbowl Street
Honolulu, HI 96813
P: (808) 586-4424
F: (808) 586-4444
E: gary.gill@doh.hawaii.gov

IDAHO
Mr. Curt Fransen
Director
Department of Environmental Quality
1410 North Hilton
Boise, ID 83706
P: (208) 373-0240
F: (208) 373-0417
E: curt.fransen
    @deq.idaho.gov

ILLINOIS
Mr. Jim Schultz
Director
Department of Commerce & Economic Opportunity
100 West Randolph Street, Suite 3-400
Chicago, IL 60601
P: (312) 814-2811
E: Jim.Schultz@Illinois.gov

INDIANA
Ms. Monica Hartke-Tarr
Branch Chief
Office of Planning & Assessment
Department of Environmental Management
100 North Senate Avenue, Room IGCN 1101
Indianapolis, IN 46204
P: (317) 233-5431
F: (317) 233-6647
E: mhartke@idem.in.gov

KANSAS
Mr. William L. Bider
Director
Bureau of Waste Management
1000 Southwest Jackson Street
Suite 320
Topeka, KS 66612
P: (785) 296-1600
F: (785) 296-8909
E: wbider@kdheks.gov

KENTUCKY
Mr. Anthony R. Hatton
Division Director
Division of Waste Management
Department for Environmental Protection
200 Fair Oaks Lane, 2nd Floor
Frankfort, KY 40601
P: (502) 564-6716
F: (502) 564-4049
E: tony.hatton@ky.gov

LOUISIANA
Ms. Lourdes Iturralde
Administrator
Public Participation & Permits Support Services
Department of Environmental Quality
P.O. Box 4313
Baton Rouge, LA 70821
P: (225) 219-3180
F: (225) 219-3309

MAINE
Mr. George MacDonald
Team Director
Waste Management & Recycling Program
State Planning Office
38 State House Station
Augusta, ME 04333
P: (207) 624-6245
F: (207) 287-6489
E: George.MacDonald
    @maine.gov

Recycling

MARYLAND
Ms. Hilary Miller
Acting Director
Land Management
Administration
Department of the Environment
1800 Washington Boulevard
Baltimore, MD 21230
P: (410) 537-3304
F: (410) 537-3321
E: hilary.miller
  @maryland.gov

MASSACHUSETTS
Mr. Matthew A. Beaton
Secretary of Energy and
Environmental Affairs
Executive Office of Energy &
Environmental Affairs
100 Cambridge Street, Suite 900
Boston, MA 02114
P: (614) 626-1000
F: (614) 626-1181

MICHIGAN
Ms. Amy A. Butler
Chief
Environmental Science &
Services Division
525 West Allegan Street
P.O. Box 30473
Lansing, MI 48909
P: (517) 241-0490
E: BUTLERA1@michigan.gov

MINNESOTA
Mr. Matt Massman
Commissioner
Department of Administration
116 Veterans Service Building
20 West 12 Street
St. Paul, MN 55155
P: (651) 201-3421
E: Matt.Massman@state.mn.us

MISSISSIPPI
Mr. John D. Burns
State Recycling Coordinator
Recycling & Solid Waste
Reduction Program
515 East Amite Street
P.O. Box 2261
Jackson, MS 39225
P: (601) 961-5005
F: (601) 961-5703
E: John_D_Burns
  @deg.state.ms.us

MISSOURI
Mr. Chris Nagel
Program Director
Solid Waste Management
Program
P.O. Box 176
Jefferson City, MO 65102
P: (573) 751-5401
F: (573) 526-3902
E: swmp@dnr.mo.gov

MONTANA
Hon. Sheila Hogan
Director
Department of Administratoin
P.O. Box 200101
Helena, MT 59620
P: (406) 444-3033
F: (406) 444-6194
E: shogan@mt.gov

NEBRASKA
Mr. Jim Macy
Director
Department of Environmental
Quality
1200 N Street, Suite 400
Lincoln, NE 68508
P: (402) 471-3585
F: (402) 471-2909
E: Jim.Macy@nebraska.gov

NEVADA
Mr. Eric Noack
Bureau Chief
Bureau of Waste Management
Division of Environmental
Protection
901 South Stewart Street, Suite
4001
Carson City, NV 89701
P: (775) 687-9366
F: (775) 687-5856
E: enoack@ndep.nv.gov

NEW HAMPSHIRE
Mr. Thomas S. Burack
Commissioner
Department of Environmental
Services
Six Hazen Drive
Concord, NH 03301
P: (603) 271-2958
F: (603) 271-2867
E: thomas.burack@des.nh.gov

NEW JERSEY
Mr. Guy Watson
Bureau Chief
Bureau of Recycling & Planning
Departmant of Environmental
Protection
P.O. Box 402
Trenton, NJ 08625
P: (609) 984-3438
F: (609) 633-1112
E: Guy.Watson
  @dep.state.nj.us

NEW MEXICO
Ms. Auralie Ashley-Marx
Bureau Chief
Solid Waste Bureau
Harold Runnels Building, Room
N2150
1190 St. Francis Drive, P.O. Box
5469
Santa Fe, NM 87502
P: (505) 827-0197
F: (505) 827-2902
E: auralie.ashley-marx
  @state.nm.us

NEW YORK
Mr. Salvatore Ervolina
Director
Division of Materials
Management
625 Broadway
Albany, NY 12233
P: (518) 402-8651
F: (518) 402-9024
E: dshm@gw.dec.state.ny.us

NORTH DAKOTA
Mr. Scott Radig
Director
Division of Waste Management
Department of Health
918 East Divide Avenue, 3rd
Floor
Bismark, ND 58501
P: (701) 328-5166
F: (701) 328-5200
E: sradig@nd.gov

**NORTHERN MARIANA
ISLANDS**
Mr. Martin C. Sablan
Secretary
Department of Public Works
Caller Box 10007, Capitol Hill
Saipan, MP 96950
P: (670) 235-5827
F: (670) 235-6346

OHIO
Mr. James J. Zehringer
Director
Department of Natural
Resources
2045 Morse Road, Building D
Columbus, OH 43229
P: (614) 265-6565
F: (614) 261-9601

OKLAHOMA
Ms. Kelly Dixon
Division Director
Land Protection Division
Department of Environmental
Quality
P.O. Box 1677
Oklahoma City, OK 73101
P: (405) 702-5100
F: (405) 702-5101
E: kelly.dixon@deq.ok.gov

OREGON
Mr. George M. Naughton
Chief Operating Officer
Department of Administrative
Services
155 Cottage Street, Northeast,
U10
Salem, OR 97301
P: (503) 378-5460
F: (503) 373-7643
E: george.m.naughton
  @oregon.gov

PENNSYLVANIA
Mr. Kenneth R. Reisinger
Bureau Director
Bureau of Waste Management
Department of Environmental
Protection
P.O. Box 69170
Harrisburg, PA 17106
P: (717) 783-2388
F: (717) 787-1904
E: ra-epwaste@pa.gov

PUERTO RICO
Mr. Augustine F. Carbo Lugo
Director
Solid Waste Management
Authority
P.O. Box 40285
San Juan, PR 00918
P: (787) 765-7575
F: (787) 753-2220

Mr. Jose Maeso Gonzalez
Executive Director
Energy Affairs Administration
P.O. Box 41314
San Juan, PR 00940
P: (787) 999-2200 Ext. 2888
F: (787) 999-2246
E: jose.maeso@aae.pr.gov

RHODE ISLAND
Mr. Michael O'Connell
Executive Director
Resource Recovery Corporation
65 Shun Pike
Johnston, RI 02919
P: (401) 942-1430
F: (401) 942-3280
E: moconnell@rirrc.org

SOUTH CAROLINA
Ms. Daphne G. Neel
Bureau Chief
Bureau of Land & Waste
Management
Dept. of Health &
Environmental Control
2600 Bull Street
Columbia, SC 29201
P: (803) 896-4007
F: (803) 896-4001
E: neeldg@dhec.sc.gov

SOUTH DAKOTA
Mr. Andrew McCloud
Environmental Scientist
Department of Environment &
Natural Resources
Waste Management Program
523 East Capitol Avenue
Pierre, SD 57501
P: (605) 773-3153
F: (605) 773-6035

TENNESSEE
Mr. Robert J. Martineau Jr.
Commissioner
Department of Environment &
Conservation
William R. Snodgrass Tennessee
Tower
312 Rosa L. Parks Avenue, 2nd
Floor
Nashville, TN 37243
P: (615) 532-0106
F: (615) 532-0120

TEXAS
Ms. Gayla D. Davis
Manager
State Leasing Services
Facilities Commission
P.O. Box 13047
Austin, TX 78711
P: (512) 463-3331
F: (512) 239-5533
E: Gayla.Davis
  @tfc.state.tx.us

U.S. VIRGIN ISLANDS
Mr. Darryl A. Smalls
Commissioner
Department of Public Works
6002 Estate Anna's Hope
Christiansted, VI 00820
P: (340) 776-4844
F: (340) 773-1290

UTAH
Ms. Donna Spangler
Communications Director
Office of Planning & Public
Affairs
Department of Environmental
Quality
P.O. Box 144810
Salt Lake City, UT 84114
P: (801) 536-4484
F: (801) 536-4480
E: dspangler@utah.gov

VERMONT
Mr. Marc Roy
Section Chief
Technical Services/Underground
Storage Tanks/Salvage Yards
Waste Management &
Prevention Division
1 National Life Drive - Davis 1
Montpelier, VT 05620
P: (802) 522-0275
F: (802) 828-1011
E: marc.roy@state.vt.us

VIRGINIA
Mr. David K. Paylor
Director
Department of Environmental
Quality
629 East Main Street
Richmond, VA 23219
P: (804) 698-4390
F: (804) 698-4019
E: david.paylor
  @deq.virginia.gov

WASHINGTON
Ms. Laurie G. Davies
Program Manager
Waste 2 Resources Program
Department of Ecology
P.O. Box 47600
Olympia, WA 98504
P: (360) 407-6103
F: (360) 407-6102
E: laurie.davies@ecy.wa.gov

WEST VIRGINIA
Mr. Richard P. Cooke
Director
Solid Waste Management Board
601 57th Street, Southeast
Charleston, WV 25304
P: (304) 926-0448
F: (304) 926-0472
E: Richard.P.Cooke@wv.gov

WISCONSIN
Mr. Michael Prager
Land Recycling Team Leader
Divison of Air, Waste,
Remediation & Redevelopment
101 South Webster
Madison, WI 53703
P: (608) 261-4927
E: Michael.Prager
  @wisconsin.gov

WYOMING
Mr. Todd Parfitt
Director
Department of Environmental
Quality
122 West 25th Street
Herschler Building
Cheyenne, WY 82002
P: (307) 777-7937
F: (307) 777-7682
E: todd.parfitt@wyo.gov

Revenue

Administers state tax laws and the collection and processing of state taxes.

ALABAMA
Ms. Julie P. MaGee
Commissioner
Department of Revenue
50 North Ripley Street
Montgomery, AL 36104
P: (334) 242-1175

ALASKA
Mr. Randall Hoffbeck
Commissioner
Department of Revenue
P.O. Box 110400
Juneau, AK 99501
P: (907) 465-2300
F: (907) 465-2389
E: randall.hoffbeck
    @alaska.gov

AMERICAN SAMOA
Hon. Falema'o M. Pili
Treasurer
Office of the Treasurer
American Samoa Government
Pago Pago, AS 96799
P: (684) 633-4155
F: (684) 633-4100

ARIZONA
Mr. David Raber
Director
Department of Revenue
1600 West Monroe
Phoenix, AZ 85007
P: (602) 716-6090
F: (602) 542-2072

ARKANSAS
Mr. John H. Theis
Assistant Commissioner, Policy
and Legal
Department of Finance &
Administration
Ledbetter Building
1816 West 7th Street, Suite 2440
Little Rock, AR 72201
P: (501) 682-7000
F: (501) 683-1161
E: john.theis
    @dfa.arkansas.gov

CALIFORNIA
Mr. Selvi Stanislaus
Executive Officer
Franchise Tax Board
P.O. Box 1468
Sacramento, CA 95812
P: (916) 845-4543
F: (916) 845-3191
E: selvi.stanislaus
    @ftb.ca.gov

COLORADO
Ms. Barbara Brohl
Executive Director
Department of Revenue
1375 Sherman Street
P.O. Box 17087
Denver, CO 80217
P: (303) 866-5610
F: (303) 866-2400
E: barbara.brohl
    @state.co.us

CONNECTICUT
Mr. Kevin B. Sullivan
Commissioner
Department of Revenue
Services
25 Sigourney Street, Suite 2
Hartford, CT 06106
P: (860) 297-5962
F: (860) 297-5698
E: kevin.b.sullivan
    @po.state.ct.us

DELAWARE
Mr. Patrick T. Carter
Director
Division of Revenue
Carvel State Office Building
820 North French Street
Wilmington, DE 19801
P: (302) 577-8686
F: (302) 577-8202
E: patrick.carter
    @state.de.us

DISTRICT OF COLUMBIA
Mr. Stephen M. Cordi
Deputy Chief Financial Officer
Office of Tax & Revenue
1101 4th Street, Southwest
Suite 270 West
Washington, DC 20024
P: (202) 727-4829
F: (202) 442-6890
E: stephen.cordi@dc.gov

FLORIDA
Mr. Marshall Stranburg
Executive Director
Department of Revenue
5050 West Tennessee Street
Tallahassee, FL 32399
P: (850) 617-8600
E: EMailDOR@dor.state.fl.us

GEORGIA
Ms. Lynnette Riley
Revenue Commissioner
Department of Revenue
1800 Century Center Boulevard
Atlanta, GA 30345
P: (404) 417-2100

GUAM
Mr. Artemio B. Ilagan
Banking & Insurance
Commissioner
Department of Revenue &
Taxation
Department of Revenue &
Taxation
P.O. Box 23607
GMF Barrigada, GU 96921
P: (671) 635-1817
F: (671) 633-2643
E: art.ilagan@revtax.gov.gu

HAWAII
Ms. Maria E. Zielinski
Director
Department of Taxation
P.O. Box 259
Honolulu, HI 96809
P: (808) 587-1540
F: (808) 587-1560
E: Tax.Directors.Office
    @hawaii.gov

IDAHO
Mr. Rich Jackson
Chair
Tax Commission
P.O. Box 36
Boise, ID 83722
P: (208) 334-7660
E: tax-commissioners
    @tax.idaho.gov

ILLINOIS
Ms. Connie Beard
Director
Department of Revenue
101 West Jefferson Street
Springfield, IL 62702
P: (217) 782-3336
F: (217) 782-6337

INDIANA
Mr. Mike Alley
Commissioner
Department of Revenue
100 North Senate Avenue, Room
248N
Indianapolis, IN 46204
P: (317) 232-8039
F: (317) 232-2103
E: MAlley@dor.IN.gov

IOWA
Ms. Courtney M. Kay-Decker
Director
Department of Revenue
Hoover State Office Building
1305 East Walnut Street
Des Moines, IA 50319
P: (515) 281-3204
E: courtney.decker@iowa.gov

KANSAS
Mr. Nick Jordan
Secretary
Department of Revenue
Docking State Office Building,
2nd Floor
915 Southwest Harrison Street
Topeka, KS 66612
P: (785) 296-3909
F: (785) 296-7928

KENTUCKY
Mr. Thomas B. Miller
Commissioner
Department of Revenue
501 High Street
11th Floor, Station #1
Frankfort, KY 40601
P: (502) 564-3226
F: (502) 564-3875

LOUISIANA
Mr. Tim Barfield
Secretary of Revenue
Department of Revenue
617 North Third Street
P.O. Box 201
Baton Rouge, LA 70821
P: (855) 307-3893
F: (225) 219-2708
E: Krissy.Thomas@la.gov

MAINE
Mr. Jerome D. Gerard
Executive Director
Revenue Services
24 State House Station
51 Commerce Drive
Augusta, ME 04333
P: (207) 624-9620
E: Jerome.D.Gerard
    @maine.gov

MARYLAND
Mr. Wayne Green
Director
Revenue Administration
Division
Comptroller of Maryland
110 Carroll Street, Room 105
Annapolis, MD 21411
P: (410) 260-7445
E: wgreen@comp.state.md.us

MASSACHUSETTS
Mr. Mark Nunnelly
Commissioner
Department of Revenue
100 Cambridge Street, 8th Floor
Boston, MA 02114
P: (617) 626-2201
F: (617) 626-2299

MICHIGAN
Mr. Jay Wortley
Chief Economist & Director
Office of Revenue & Tax
Analysis
Richard H. Austin Building
430 West Allegan Street
Lansing, MI 48922
P: (517) 373-2158
F: (517) 335-3298
E: WortleyJ1@michigan.gov

MISSISSIPPI
Mr. Ed Morgan
Commissioner
Department of Revenue
P.O. Box 1033
Jackson, MS 39215
P: (601) 923-7000
F: (601) 923-7423

MONTANA
Mr. Mike Kadas
Director
Department of Revenue
P.O. Box 5805
Helena, MT 59604
P: (406) 444-6900
F: (406) 444-3696

NEBRASKA
Mr. Leonard Sloup
Acting Tax Commissioner
Department of Revenue
P.O. Box 94818
Lincoln, NE 68509
P: (402) 471-5805
F: (402) 471-5608
E: len.sloup@nebraska.gov

NEVADA
Mr. Christopher G. Nielsen
Executive Director
Department of Taxation
1550 College Parkway, Suite
115
Carson City, NV 89706
P: (775) 684-2000
F: (775) 684-2020

NEW HAMPSHIRE
Mr. John T. Beardmore
Commissioner
Department of Revenue
Administration
Governor Hugh Gallen State
Office Park
109 Pleasant Street
Concord, NH 03302
P: (603) 230-5000
F: (603) 271-6121
E: john.beardmore
　@dra.nh.gov

Ms. Kathryn E. Skouteris
Assistant Commissioner
Department of Revenue
Administration
Governor Hugh Gallen State
Office Park
109 Pleasant Street
Concord, NH 03302
P: (603) 230-5000
F: (603) 271-6121
E: kathryn.skouteris
　@dra.nh.gov

NEW JERSEY
Mr. Michael J. Bryan
Director
Division of Taxation
P.O. Box 281
Trenton, NJ 08695
P: (609) 292-5185

NEW MEXICO
Ms. Demesia Padilla
Secretary
Taxation & Revenue
Department
1100 South St. Francis Drive
Santa Fe, NM 87504
P: (505) 827-0700
F: (505) 827-0331

NEW YORK
Mr. Thomas H. Mattox
Commissioner
Department of Taxation &
Finance
W.A. Harriman Campus,
Building 9
Albany, NY 12227

NORTH CAROLINA
Mr. Lyons Gray
Secretary
Department of Revenue
501 North Wilmington Street
P.O. Box 25000
Raleigh, NC 27640
P: (919) 814-1006
F: (919) 733-0023
E: lyons.gray@dornc.com

NORTH DAKOTA
Hon. Ryan
　Rauschenberger (R)
Commissioner
Office of the State Tax
Commissioner
600 East Boulevard Avenue
Department 127
Bismarck, ND 58505
P: (701) 328-7088
F: (701) 328-3700
E: rrauschenberger@nd.gov

**NORTHERN MARIANA
ISLANDS**
Ms. Larissa Larson
Secretary
Department of Finance
P.O. Box 5234, CHRB
Saipan, MP 96950
P: (670) 664-1000
F: (670) 664-1115
E: revtax@gtepacifica.net

OHIO
Mr. Joseph W. Testa
Tax Commissioner
Department of Taxation
P.O. Box 530
Columbus, OH 43216
P: (614) 466-2166
F: (614) 466-6401
E: contactthecommissioner
　@tax.state.oh.us

OKLAHOMA
Mr. Thomas Kemp Jr.
Chair
Tax Commission
2501 North Lincoln Boulevard
Oklahoma City, OK 73194
P: (405) 521-3160
F: (405) 522-0074

OREGON
Mr. James C. Bucholz
Director
Department of Revenue
Room 457, Revenue Building
Salem, OR 97301
P: (503) 945-8214
F: (503) 945-8290
E: james.c.bucholz
　@oregon.gov

PENNSYLVANIA
Ms. Eileen McNulty
Secretary
Department of Revenue
Strawberry Square
Harrisburg, PA 17128
P: (717) 783-3683
F: (717) 787-3990

RHODE ISLAND
Mr. David Sullivan
Acting Director of Revenue
Department of Revenue
One Capitol Hill
Providence, RI
P: (401) 574-8999
F: (401) 574-8997

SOUTH CAROLINA
Mr. William M. Blume Jr.
Director
Department of Revenue
P.O. Box 125
Columbia, SC 29214
P: (803) 898-5040
E: Director@sctax.org

SOUTH DAKOTA
Mr. Andy Gerlach
Secretary
Department of Revenue
445 East Capital Avenue
Pierre, SD 57501
P: (605) 773-3311
F: (605) 773-5129

TENNESSEE
Mr. Richard H. Roberts
Commissioner
Department of Revenue
500 Deaderick Street
Andrew Jackson Building
Nashville, TN 37242
P: (615) 741-2461
F: (615) 741-2883

TEXAS
Hon. Glenn Hegar (R)
Comptroller of Public Accounts
Office of the Comptroller of
Public Accounts
LBJ State Office Building, 1st
Floor
111 East 17th Street
Austin, TX 78774
P: (512) 463-4444
F: (512) 463-4902
E: glenn.hegar
　@cpa.state.tx.us

U.S. VIRGIN ISLANDS
Ms. Claudette J.
　Watson-Anderson
Director
Bureau of Internal Revenue
6115 Estate Smith Bay, Suite
225
St. Thomas, VI 00802
P: (340) 715-1040
F: (340) 774-2672

Revenue

UTAH

Mr. Barry C. Conover
Executive Director
State Tax Commission
210 North 1950 West
Salt Lake City, UT 84134
P: (801) 297-3820
F: (801) 297-6358
E: bconover@utah.gov

VERMONT

Mr. James B. Reardon
Commissioner
Department of Finance &
Management
109 State Street
Montpelier, VT 05609
P: (802) 828-2376
F: (802) 828-2428
E: jim.reardon@state.vt.us

VIRGINIA

Mr. Craig M. Burns
Tax Commissioner
Department of Taxation
Main Street Centre
600 East Main Street, 23rd Floor
Richmond, VA 23219
P: (804) 786-3301
F: (804) 786-4208
E: craig.burns
    @tax.virginia.gov

WASHINGTON

Ms. Vikki Smith
Director
Department of Revenue
Executive Office
P.O. Box 47450
Olympia, WA 98504
P: (360) 534-1605

WEST VIRGINIA

Mr. Robert S. Kiss
Cabinet Secretary
Department of Revenue
State Capitol
Building 1, W-300
Charleston, WV 25305
P: (304) 558-1017
F: (304) 558-2324
E: Robert.S.Kiss@wv.gov

WISCONSIN

Mr. Richard G. Chandler
Secretary
Department of Revenue
2135 Rimrock Road
P.O. Box 8933, Mail Stop 624-A
Madison, WI 53713
P: (608) 266-2772
F: (608) 267-0834
E: Richard.Chandler
    @revenue.wi.gov

WYOMING

Mr. Dan Noble
Director
Department of Revenue
122 West 25th Street, 2nd Floor
West
Cheyenne, WY 82002
P: (307) 777-5287
F: (307) 777-7722
E: DirectorofRevenue
    @wyo.gov

Savings and Loan

Administers laws regulating the operation of savings and loan associations in the state.

ALABAMA
Mr. John D. Harrison
Superintendent
Banking Department
P.O. Box 4600
Montgomery, AL 36103
P: (334) 242-3452
F: (334) 242-3500
E: john.harrison
    @banking.alabama.gov

ALASKA
Ms. Kevin Anselm
Director
Division of Banking &
Securities
Division of Banking &
Securities
P.O. Box 110807
Juneau, AK 99811
P: (907) 465-2521
F: (907) 465-2549
E: kevin.anselm@alaska.gov

ARIZONA
Mr. Lauren W. Kingry
Superintendent of Financial
Institutions
Department of Financial
Institutions
2910 North 44th Street, Suite
310
Phoenix, AZ 85018
P: (602) 771-2770
F: (602) 381-1225
E: lkingry@azdfi.gov

ARKANSAS
Mr. B. Edmond Waters
Securities Commissioner
Securities Department
Heritage West Building, Suite
300
201 East Markham Street
Little Rock, AR 72201
P: (501) 324-9260
F: (501) 324-9268
E: ewaters
    @securities.arkansas.gov

CALIFORNIA
Ms. Jan Lynn Owen
Commissioner
Department of Business
Oversight
1515 K Street, Suite 200
Sacramento, CA 95814
P: (866) 275-2677
F: (916) 322-1559

COLORADO
Mr. Mark Valente
Acting Commissioner
Division of Financial Services
Department of Regulatory
Agencies
1560 Broadway, Room 950
Denver, CO 80202
P: (303) 894-7742
E: mark.valente@state.co.us

DELAWARE
Mr. Robert A. Glen
Commissioner
Office of State Bank
Commissioner
555 East Lockerman Street
Dover, DE 19901
P: (302) 739-4235
F: (302) 739-3609
E: Dawn.Hollinger
    @state.de.us

DISTRICT OF COLUMBIA
Mr. Chester A. McPherson
Acting Commissioner
Department of Insurance,
Securities & Banking
Government of the District of
Columbia
810 First Street Northeast, Suite
701
Washington, DC 20002
P: (202) 727-8000
F: (202) 535-1196
E: disb@dc.gov

GEORGIA
Mr. Kevin Hagler
Commissioner
Department of Banking &
Finance
2990 Brandywine Road, Suite
200
Atlanta, GA 30341
P: (770) 986-1633
F: (770) 986-1654
E: khagler@dbf.state.ga.us

HAWAII
Ms. Iris Ikeda Catalani
Commissioner
Division of Financial
Institutions
King Kalakaua Building
335 Merchant Street, Room 221
Honolulu, HI 96813
P: (808) 586-2820
F: (808) 586-2818
E: dfi@dcca.hawaii.gov

IDAHO
Mr. Gavin M. Gee
Director
Department of Finance
800 Park Boulevard, Suite 200
P.O. Box 83720
Boise, ID 83720
P: (208) 332-8010
F: (208) 332-8097
E: gavin.gee
    @finance.idaho.gov

ILLINOIS
Mr. Michael Mannion
Division Director
Division of Banking
100 West Randolph, 9th Floor
Chicago, IL 60601
P: (312) 793-3000
F: (312) 793-0756

INDIANA
Mr. Dennis L. Bassett
Public Finance Director
Department of Financial
Institutions
One North Capitol, Suite 900
Indianapolis, IN 46204
P: (317) 233-4332
F: (317) 232-6786
E: DeBassett@ifa.IN.gov

IOWA
Mr. James M. Schipper
Superintendent
Division of Banking
200 East Grand Avenue, Suite
300
Des Moines, IA 50309
P: (515) 281-4014
F: (515) 281-4862
E: jschipper
    @idob.state.ia.us

KANSAS
Mr. Deryl Schuster
Commissioner
Office of the State Banking
Commissioner
700 Jackson, Suite 300
Topeka, KS 66603
P: (785) 296-2266
F: (785) 296-0168

KENTUCKY
Mr. Charles A. Vice
Commissioner
Department of Financial
Institutions
1025 Capital Center Drive, Suite
200
Frankfort, KY 40601
P: (502) 573-3390
F: (502) 573-8787
E: charles.vice@ky.gov

LOUISIANA
Mr. Sidney E. Seymour
Chief Examiner
Office of Financial Institutions
8660 United Plaza Boulevard,
Suite 200
P.O. Box 94095
Baton Rouge, LA 70804
P: (225) 925-4660
F: (225) 925-4524
E: sseymour@ofi.la.gov

MAINE
Mr. Lloyd P. LaFountain III
Superintendent
Bureau of Financial Institutions
Professional & Financial
Regulation
36 State House Station
Augusta, ME 04333
P: (207) 624-8570
F: (207) 624-8590
E: lloyd.p.lafountain.III
    @maine.gov

MARYLAND
Mr. Gordon Cooley
Acting Commissioner of
Financial Regulation
Division of Financial
Regulation
500 North Calvert Street, Room
402
Baltimore, MD 21202
P: (410) 230-6001
F: (410) 333-0475
E: gordon.cooley
    @maryland.gov

MASSACHUSETTS
Mr. David Cotney
Commissioner
Division of Banks
1000 Washington Street,
10th Floor
Boston, MA 02118
P: (617) 956-1500
F: (617) 956-1599

Savings and Loan

MICHIGAN
Ms. Ann Flood
Director
Department of Insurance &
Financial Services
611 West Ottawa, 3rd Floor
P.O. Box 30220
Lansing, MI 48909
P: (517) 373-0220
F: (517) 335-4978
E: difs-info@michigan.gov

MINNESOTA
Mr. Mike Rothman
Commissioner
Department of Commerce
85 East 7th Place, Suite 500
St. Paul, MN 55101
P: (651) 539-1638
F: (651) 296-4328
E: commerce.commissioner
    @state.mn.us

MISSOURI
Ms. Debbie Hardman
Acting Commissioner of Finance
Division of Finance
Truman State Office Building,
Room 630
P.O. Box 716
Jefferson City, MO 65102
P: (573) 751-3242
F: (573) 751-9192
E: finance@dof.mo.gov

MONTANA
Ms. Melanie Hall
Commissioner
Division of Banking &
Financial Institutions
301 South Park, Suite 316
P.O. Box 200546
Helena, MT 59620
P: (406) 841-2920
F: (406) 841-2930
E: mghall@mt.gov

NEBRASKA
Mr. Mark Quandahl
Director
Department of Banking &
Finance
1230 O Street, Suite 400
P.O. Box 95006
Lincoln, NE 68509
P: (402) 471-2845
E: mark.quandahl
    @nebraska.gov

NEVADA
Mr. George E. Burns
Commissioner
Financial Institutions Division
Department of Business &
Industry
2785 East Desert Inn Road, Suite
180
Las Vegas, NV 89121
P: (702) 486-4120
F: (702) 486-4563
E: gburns@fid.state.nv.us

NEW HAMPSHIRE
Mr. Glenn A. Perlow
Commissioner
Banking Department
53 Regional Drive, Suite 200
Concord, NH 03301
P: (603) 271-3561
F: (603) 271-1090
E: nhbd@banking.state.nh.us

NEW JERSEY
Mr. Kenneth E. Kobylowski
Commissioner
Department of Banking &
Insurance
State of New Jersey
20 West State Street, P.O. Box
325
Trenton, NJ 08625
P: (609) 292-7272
F: (609) 984-5273
E: commissioner
    @dobi.state.nj.us

NORTH DAKOTA
Mr. Robert J. Entringer
Commissioner
Department of Financial
Institutions
2000 Schafer Street, Suite G
Bismarck, ND 58501
P: (701) 328-9933
F: (701) 328-0290
E: rentring@nd.gov

OHIO
Mr. Charles J. Dolezal
Superintendent
Division of Financial
Institutions
Department of Commerce
77 South High Street, 21st Floor
Columbus, OH 43215
P: (614) 728-8400
F: (614) 728-0380
E: webdfi-cf
    @com.state.oh.us

OKLAHOMA
Mr. Mick Thompson
Commissioner
State Banking Department
2900 North Lincoln Boulevard
Oklahoma City, OK 73105
P: (405) 521-2782
F: (405) 522-2993
E: mick.thompson
    @banking.ok.gov

OREGON
Mr. David C. Tatman
Division Administrator
Division of Finance &
Corporate Securities
Consumer & Business Services
350 Winter Street, Northeast,
Room 410
Salem, OR 97301
P: (503) 947-7475
F: (503) 947-7862
E: david.c.tatman
    @oregon.gov

PENNSYLVANIA
Ms. Robin Weissmann
Secretary
Department of Banking &
Securities
17 North 2nd Street, Suite 1300
Harrisburg, PA 17101
P: (717) 787-2665

SOUTH CAROLINA
Mr. Louie A. Jacobs
Commissioner of Banking
Office of the Commissioner of
Banking
1205 Pendleton Street, Suite 305
Columbia, SC 29201
P: (803) 734-2001
F: (803) 734-2013

SOUTH DAKOTA
Mr. Bret Afdahl
Director
Division of Banking
Department of Labor &
Regulation
1601 North Harrison Avenue,
Suite 1
Pierre, SD 57501
P: (605) 773-3421
F: (866) 326-7504
E: banking@state.sd.us

TENNESSEE
Mr. Greg Gonzales
Commissioner
Department of Financial
Institutions
414 Union Street, Suite 1000
Nashville, TN 37219
P: (615) 741-5603
F: (615) 253-6306
E: Greg.Gonzales@tn.gov

TEXAS
Ms. Caroline Jones
Commisssioner
Department of Savings &
Mortgage Lending
2601 North Lamar Boulevard,
Suite 201
Austin, TX 78705
P: (512) 475-1038
F: (512) 475-1360

UTAH
Mr. G. Edward Leary
Commissioner
Department of Financial
Institutions
324 South State Street, Suite
201
P.O. Box 146800
Salt Lake City, UT 84114
P: (801) 538-8830
F: (801) 538-8894
E: ELEARY@utah.gov

VERMONT
Ms. Susan L. Donegan
Commissioner
Department of Financial
Regulation
89 Main Street
Montpelier, VT 05620
P: (802) 828-3301
F: (802) 828-3306
E: susan.donegan
    @state.vt.us

VIRGINIA
Mr. E. Joseph Face Jr.
Commissioner of Financial
Institutions
Bureau of Financial Institutions
1300 East Main Street, Suite
800
P.O. Box 640
Richmond, VA 23218
P: (804) 371-9657
F: (804) 371-9416
E: joe.face
    @scc.virginia.gov

WASHINGTON
Mr. Rick Riccobono
Director of Banks
Division of Banks
Department of Financial
Institutions
P.O. Box 41200
Olympia, WA 98504
P: (360) 902-8704
F: (360) 704-6904

WEST VIRGINIA
Ms. Sara M. Cline
Commissioner of Banking
Division of Financial
Institutions
900 Pennsylvania Avenue, Suite
306
Charleston, WV 25302
P: (304) 558-2294
F: (304) 558-0442
E: scline@wvdob.org

WISCONSIN
Mr. Michael Mach
Administrator
Division of Banking
P.O. Box 7876
Madison, WI 53707
P: (608) 261-7578
F: (608) 267-6889
E: Mike.Mach
    @dfi.wisconsin.gov

Secretary of State

Statewide official who oversees a variety of electoral, registration, publication, and legislative duties for the state.

Information provided by:

National Association of Secretaries of State
Leslie Reynolds
Executive Director
444 North Capitol Street, NW
Suite 401
Washington, DC 20001
P: (202) 624-3525
F: (202) 624-3527
reynolds@sso.org
www.nass.org

ALABAMA
Hon. John Merrill (R)
Secretary of State
Office of the Secretary of State
P.O. Box 5616
Montgomery, AL 36103
P: (334) 242-7200
F: (334) 242-4993
E: john.merrill
    @sos.alabama.gov

ALASKA
Hon. Byron Mallot (I)
Lieutenant Governor
Office of the Lieutenant
Governor
550 West 7th Street, Suite 1700
Anchorage, AK 99501
P: (907) 269-7460
F: (907) 269-0263

AMERICAN SAMOA
Hon. Lemanu Peleti
    Mauga (I)
Lieutenant Governor
Office of the Lieutenant
Governor
Territory of American Samoa
Pago Pago, AS 96799
P: (684) 633-4116
F: (684) 633-2269

ARIZONA
Hon. Michele Reagan (R)
Secretary of State
Office of the Secretary of State
Capitol Executive Tower, 7th
Floor
1700 West Washington
Phoenix, AZ 85007
P: (602) 542-4285
F: (602) 542-1575
E: sosadmin@azsos.gov

ARKANSAS
Hon. Mark Martin (R)
Secretary of State
Office of the Secretary of State
256 State Capitol Building
Little Rock, AR 72201
P: (501) 682-1010
F: (501) 682-3510
E: info@sos.arkansas.gov

CALIFORNIA
Hon. Alex Padilla (D)
Secretary of State
Office of the Secretary of State
1500 11th Street
Sacramento, CA 95814
P: (916) 653-7244
F: (916) 653-4795
E: secretarypadilla
    @sos.ca.gov

COLORADO
Hon. Wayne Williams (R)
Secretary of State
Office of the Secretary of State
1700 Broadway, Suite 200
Denver, CO 80290
P: (303) 894-2200
F: (303) 869-4860
E: secretary
    @sos.state.co.us

CONNECTICUT
Hon. Denise W. Merrill (D)
Secretary of State
Office of the Secretary of State
State Capitol Building, Room
104
Hartford, CT 06106
P: (860) 509-6200
F: (860) 509-6209
E: denise.merrill@ct.gov

DELAWARE
Hon. Jeffrey Bullock (D)
Secretary of State
Office of the Secretary of State
Townsend Building
401 Federal Street, Suite 3
Dover, DE 19901
P: (302) 739-4111
F: (302) 739-3811
E: kathy.bradford
    @state.de.us

DISTRICT OF COLUMBIA
Hon. Lauren C. Vaughn
    (appointed)
Secretary of the District
Office of the Secretary of State
1350 Pennsylvania Avenue,
Northwest
Suite 419
Washington, DC 20004
P: (202) 727-6306
F: (202) 727-3582
E: secretary@dc.gov

FLORIDA
Hon. Kenneth Detzner (R)
    (appointed)
Secretary of State
Office of the Secretary of State
500 South Bronough Street
Tallahassee, FL 32399
P: (850) 245-6500
F: (850) 245-6125
E: dossecretaryofstate
    @dos.myflorida.com

GEORGIA
Hon. Brian Kemp (R)
Secretary of State
Office of the Secretary of State
214 State Capitol
Atlanta, GA 30334
P: (404) 656-2881
F: (404) 656-0513
E: soscontact@sos.ga.gov

GUAM
Hon. Ray Tenorio (R)
Lieutenant Governor
Office of the Lieutenant
Governor
R.J. Bordallo Governor's
Complex
P.O. Box 2950
Hagatna, GU 96932
P: (671) 475-9380
F: (671) 477-2007
E: webmaster
    @guamletgovernor.net

HAWAII
Hon. Shan S. Tsutsui (D)
Lieutenant Governor
Office of the Lieutenant
Governor
Executive Chambers
State Capitol
Honolulu, HI 96813
P: (808) 586-0255
F: (808) 586-0231
E: shan.tsutsui@hawaii.gov

IDAHO
Hon. Lawrence Denney (R)
Secretary of State
Office of the Secretary of State
P.O. Box 83720
Boise, ID 83720
P: (208) 334-2300
F: (208) 334-2282
E: ldenney@sos.idaho.gov

ILLINOIS
Hon. Jesse White (D)
Secretary of State
Office of the Secretary of State
213 State Capitol
Springfield, IL 62756
P: (217) 782-2201
F: (217) 785-0358
E: jessewhite@ilsos.net

INDIANA
Hon. Connie Lawson (R)
Secretary of State
Office of the Secretary of State
201 State House
Indianapolis, IN 46204
P: (317) 232-6536
F: (317) 233-3283
E: sos@sos.in.gov

IOWA
Hon. Paul Pate (R)
Secretary of State
Office of the Secretary of State
Lucas Building, 1st Floor
321 East 12th Street
Des Moines, IA 50319
P: (515) 281-8993
F: (515) 242-5952
E: sos@sos.iowa.gov

KANSAS
Hon. Kris Kobach (R)
Secretary of State
Office of the Secretary of State
120 Southwest 10th Avenue
Memorial Hall, 1st Floor
Topeka, KS 66612
P: (785) 296-4575
F: (785) 368-8033
E: sos@sos.ks.gov

KENTUCKY
Hon. Alison Lundergan
    Grimes (D)
Secretary of State
Office of the Secretary of State
700 Capital Avenue, Suite 152
Frankfort, KY 40601
P: (502) 564-3490
F: (502) 564-5687
E: sos.secretary@ky.gov

LOUISIANA
Hon. Tom Schedler (R)
Secretary of State
Office of the Secretary of State
P.O. Box 94125
Baton Rouge, LA 70804
P: (225) 922-2880
F: (225) 922-2003
E: admin@sos.la.gov

MAINE
Hon. Matthew Dunlap (D)
Secretary of State
Office of the Secretary of State
148 State House Station
Augusta, ME 04333
P: (207) 626-8400
F: (207) 287-8598
E: sos.office@maine.gov

MARYLAND
Hon. John C. Wobensmith
(appointed)
Secretary of State
Office of the Secretary of State
16 Francis Street
Annapolis, MD 21401
P: (410) 974-5521
F: (410) 841-5527
E: mdsos@sos.state.md.us

MASSACHUSETTS
Hon. William Francis
Galvin (D)
Secretary of the Commonwealth
Office of the Secretary of the
Commonwealth
State House, Room 337
Boston, MA 02133
P: (617) 727-9180
F: (617) 742-4722
E: cis@sec.state.ma.us

MICHIGAN
Hon. Ruth Johnson (R)
Secretary of State
Office of the Secretary of State
430 West Allegan Street
Lansing, MI 48918
P: (517) 373-2510
F: (517) 373-0727
E: secretary@michigan.gov

MINNESOTA
Hon. Steve Simon (DFL)
Secretary of State
Office of the Secretary of State
180 State Office Building
100 Martin Luther King Jr.
Boulevard
St. Paul, MN 55155
P: (651) 201-1328
F: (651) 269-9073
E: secretary.state
@state.mn.us

MISSISSIPPI
Hon. C. Delbert
Hosemann Jr. (R)
Secretary of State
Office of the Secretary of State
125 South Congress Street
Jackson, MS 39205
P: (601) 359-1350
F: (601) 359-6700
E: delbert.hosemann
@sos.ms.gov

MISSOURI
Hon. Jason Kander (D)
Secretary of State
Office of the Secretary of State
600 West Main
P.O. Box 1767
Jefferson City, MO 65101
P: (573) 751-4936
F: (573) 526-4903
E: info@sos.mo.gov

MONTANA
Hon. Linda McCulloch (D)
Secretary of State
Office of the Secretary of State
P.O. Box 202801
Helena, MT 59620
P: (406) 444-2034
F: (406) 444-4249
E: sos@mt.gov

NEBRASKA
Hon. John A. Gale (R)
Secretary of State
Office of the Secretary of State
P.O. Box 94608
Lincoln, NE 68509
P: (402) 471-2554
F: (402) 471-3237
E: Sos.info@nebraska.gov

NEVADA
Hon. Barbara Cegavske (R)
Secretary of State
Office of the Secretary of State
101 North Carson Stree, Suite 3
Carson City, NV 89701
P: (775) 684-5708
F: (775) 684-5724
E: sosexec@sos.nv.gov

NEW HAMPSHIRE
Hon. William M. Gardner (D)
(elected by the Legislature)
Secretary of State
Office of the Secretary of State
State House, Room 204
Concord, NH 03301
P: (603) 271-3242
F: (603) 271-6316
E: kladd@sos.state.nh.us

NEW JERSEY
Hon. Kim Guadagno (R)
(appointed)
Lieutenant Governor
Office of the Lieutenant
Governor
P.O. Box 001
Trenton, NJ 08625
P: (609) 292-6000
F: (609) 292-3454
E: lt.governor
@gov.state.nj.us

NEW MEXICO
Hon. Dianna J. Duran (R)
Secretary of State
Office of the Secretary of State
325 Don Gaspar, Suite 300
Capitol Annex
Santa Fe, NM 87501
P: (505) 827-3600
F: (505) 827-8081
E: diannaj.duran
@state.nm.us

NEW YORK
Hon. Cesar A. Perales
(appointed)
Secretary of State
Office of the Secretary of State
One Commerce Plaza
99 Washington Avenue, Suite
1100
Albany, NY 12231
P: (518) 486-9846
F: (518) 474-4797
E: info@dos.ny.gov

NORTH CAROLINA
Hon. Elaine F. Marshall (D)
Secretary of State
Office of the Secretary of State
P.O. Box 29622
Raleigh, NC 27626
P: (919) 807-2005
F: (919) 807-2010
E: emarshal@sosnc.com

NORTH DAKOTA
Hon. Alvin A. Jaeger (R)
Secretary of State
Office of the Secretary of State
600 East Boulevard
Department 108
Bismarck, ND 58505
P: (701) 328-2900
F: (701) 328-1690
E: ajaeger@nd.gov

OHIO
Hon. Jon Husted (R)
Secretary of State
Office of the Secretary of State
180 East Broad Street
Columbus, OH 43215
P: (614) 466-2655
F: (614) 644-0649
E: jhusted
@ohiosecretaryofstate.gov

OKLAHOMA
Hon. Chris Benge (R)
(appointed)
Secretary of State
Office of the Secretary of State
2300 North Lincoln Boulevard,
Suite 101
Oklahoma City, OK 73105
P: (405) 521-3912
F: (405) 521-2031
E: webmaster@sos.ok.gov

OREGON
Hon. Jeanne Atkins
Secretary of State
Office of the Secretary of State
136 State Capitol
Salem, OR 97310
P: (503) 986-1523
F: (503) 986-1616
E: oregon.sos@state.or.us

PENNSYLVANIA
Hon. Pedro A. Cortes (D)
(appointed)
Acting Secretary of the
Commonwealth
Office of the Secretary of State
302 North Office Building
Harrisburg, PA 17120
P: (717) 787-6458
F: (717) 787-1734
E: ST-PRESS@pa.gov

PUERTO RICO
Hon. David Bernier (PDP)
(appointed)
Secretary of State
Office of the Secretary of State
Department of State
Box 9023271
San Juan, PR 00902
P: (787) 722-2121
F: (787) 722-2684

Secretary of State

RHODE ISLAND
Hon. Nellie Gorbea (D)
  (elected by the Legislature)
Secretary of State
Office of the Secretary of State
82 Smith Street
217 State House
Providence, RI 02903
P: (401) 222-2357
F: (401) 222-1356
E: nmgorbea@sos.ri.gov

SOUTH CAROLINA
Hon. Mark Hammond (R)
Secretary of State
Office of the Secretary of State
1205 Pendleton Street, Suite 525
Columbia, SC 29201
P: (803) 734-2170
F: (803) 734-1661
E: rdaggerhart@sos.sc.gov

SOUTH DAKOTA
Hon. Shantel Krebs (R)
Secretary of State
Office of the Secretary of State
500 East Capitol Avenue, Suite
204
Pierre, SD 57501
P: (605) 773-3537
F: (605) 773-6580
E: shantel.krebs
  @state.sd.us

TENNESSEE
Hon. Tre Hargett (R)
  (elected by the Legislature)
Secretary of State
Office of the Secretary of State
First Floor, State Capitol
Nashville, TN 37243
P: (615) 741-2819
F: (615) 741-5962
E: tre.hargett@tn.gov

TEXAS
Hon. Carlos Cascos
  (appointed)
Secretary of State
Office of the Secretary of State
1100 Congress Avenue
Austin, TX 78701
P: (512) 463-5770
F: (512) 475-2761
E: secretary@sos.texas.gov

UTAH
Hon. Spencer J. Cox (R)
Lieutenant Governor
Office of the Lieutenant
Governor
P.O. Box 142325
Salt Lake City, UT 84114
P: (801) 538-1041
F: (801) 538-1133

VERMONT
Hon. Jim Condos (D)
Secretary of State
Office of the Secretary of State
128 State Street
Montpelier, VT 05633
P: (802) 828-2148
F: (802) 828-2496
E: jim.condos
  @sec.state.vt.us

VIRGINIA
Hon. Levar Stoney
  (appointed)
Secretary of the Commonwealth
Office of the Secretary of the
Commonwealth
P.O. Box 2454
Richmond, VA 23218
P: (804) 786-2441
F: (804) 371-0017
E: socmail
  @governor.virginia.gov

WASHINGTON
Hon. Kim Wyman (R)
Secretary of State
Office of the Secretary of State
P.O. Box 40220
Olympia, WA 98504
P: (360) 902-4151
F: (360) 586-5629
E: kim.wyman@sos.wa.gov

WEST VIRGINIA
Hon. Natalie Tennant (D)
Secretary of State
Office of the Secretary of State
Building 1, Suite-157K
1900 Kanawha Boulevard, East
Charleston, WV 25305
P: (304) 558-6000
F: (304) 558-0900
E: wvsos@wvsos.com

WISCONSIN
Hon. Douglas J.
  La Follette (D)
Secretary of State
Office of the Secretary of State
P.O. Box 7848
Madison, WI 53707
P: (608) 266-8888
F: (608) 266-3159
E: doug.lafollette
  @sos.state.wi.us

WYOMING
Hon. Ed Murray (R)
Secretary of State
Office of the Secretary of State
State Capitol Building, Room
106
200 West 24th Street
Cheyenne, WY 82002
P: (307) 777-7378
F: (307) 777-6217
E: secofstate@wyo.gov

Securities

Regulates the sale of securities and registers securities prior to public sale.

ALABAMA
Mr. Joseph P. Borg
Director
Securities Commission
401 Adams Avenue, Suite 280
P.O. Box 304700
Montgomery, AL 36130
P: (334) 242-2984
F: (334) 242-0240
E: Joseph.Borg
   @asc.alabama.gov

ALASKA
Ms. Kevin Anselm
Director
Division of Banking &
Securities
Division of Banking &
Securities
P.O. Box 110807
Juneau, AK 99811
P: (907) 465-2521
F: (907) 465-2549
E: kevin.anselm@alaska.gov

ARIZONA
Mr. Matthew J. Neubert
Director
Securities Division
Corporation Commission
1300 West Washington, 3rd
Floor
Phoenix, AZ 85007
P: (602) 542-4242
F: (602) 388-1335
E: securitiesdiv@azcc.gov

ARKANSAS
Mr. B. Edmond Waters
Securities Commissioner
Securities Department
Heritage West Building, Suite
300
201 East Markham Street
Little Rock, AR 72201
P: (501) 324-9260
F: (501) 324-9268
E: ewaters
   @securities.arkansas.gov

CALIFORNIA
Ms. Jan Lynn Owen
Commissioner
Department of Business
Oversight
1515 K Street, Suite 200
Sacramento, CA 95814
P: (866) 275-2677
F: (916) 322-1559

COLORADO
Mr. Gerald Rome
Securities Commissioner
Division of Securities
1560 Broadway, Suite 900
Denver, CO 80202
P: (303) 894-2320
F: (303) 861-2126
E: gerald.rome@state.co.us

CONNECTICUT
Mr. Eric J. Wilder
Division Director
Securities & Business
Investments Division
Department of Banking
260 Constitution Plaza
Hartford, CT 06103
P: (860) 240-8230
F: (860) 240-8295
E: eric.wilder@ct.gov

DISTRICT OF COLUMBIA
Mr. Theodore A. Miles
Associate Commissioner,
Securities
Department of Insurance,
Securities & Banking
Securities Bureau
810 First Street Northeast, Suite
701
Washington, DC 20002
P: (202) 442-7800
F: (202) 354-1092

FLORIDA
Ms. Pam Epting
Director, Division of Securities
Office of Financial Regulation
200 East Gaines Street
Tallahassee, FL 32399
P: (850) 410-9500
F: (850) 410-9748

GEORGIA
Noula Zaharis
Securities Division Director
Office of the Secretary of State,
Division of Securities
Two Martin Luther King, Jr.
Drive, SE
802 West Tower, Suite 313
Atlanta, GA 30334
P: (404) 654-6023

HAWAII
Ms. Ty Nohara
Commissioner of Securities
Business Registration Division
Commerce & Consumer Affairs
P.O. Box 40
Honolulu, HI 96810
P: (808) 586-2744
F: (808) 586-3977

IDAHO
Mr. Jim Burns
Acting Securities Bureau Chief
Department of Finance
800 Park Boulevard, Suite 200
Boise, ID 83712
P: (208) 332-8004
F: (208) 332-8099

ILLINOIS
Ms. Tanya Solov
Director of Securities
Securities Department
Office of the Secretary of State
69 West Washington Street, Suite
1220
Chicago, IL 60602
P: (312) 793-3384
F: (312) 793-1202

INDIANA
Mr. Alex Glass
Securities Commissioner
Securities Division
Office of the Secretary of State
302 West Washington, Room
E111
Indianapolis, IN 46204
P: (317) 232-6681
F: (317) 233-3675
E: aglass@sos.in.gov

IOWA
Ms. Rosanne Mead
Securities Administrator
Insurance Division
Securities Bureau
601 Locust, 4th Floor
Des Moines, IA 50309
P: (515) 281-5705
F: (515) 281-3059

KANSAS
Mr. Josh Ney
Securities Commissioner
Office of the Securities
Commissioner
109 Southwest 9th Street, Suite
600
Topeka, KS 66612
P: (785) 296-3307
F: (785) 296-6872
E: josh.ney@ksc.ks.gov

KENTUCKY
Ms. Shonita Bossier
Director, Division of Securities
Department of Financial
Institutions
1025 Capital Center Drive, Suite
200
Frankfort, KY 40601
P: (502) 573-3390
F: (502) 573-2182

LOUISIANA
Ms. Rhonda Reeves
Deputy Commissioner of
Securities
Securities Commission
Office of Financial Institutions
8660 United Plaza Boulevard,
2nd Floor
Baton Rouge, LA 70809
P: (225) 925-4512
F: (225) 925-4511
E: rreeves@ofi.la.gov

MAINE
Ms. Judith M. Shaw
Securities Administrator
Department of Professional &
Financial Regulation
Office of Securities
121 State House Station
Augusta, ME 04333
P: (207) 624-8551
F: (207) 624-8590
E: judith.m.shaw@maine.gov

MARYLAND
Ms. Melanie Senter Lubin
Securities Commissioner
Division of Securities
Office of the Attorney General
200 Saint Paul Place
Baltimore, MD 21202
P: (410) 576-6360
F: (410) 576-6532
E: mlubin@oag.state.md.us

MASSACHUSETTS
Mr. Bryan Lantagne
Director
Securities Division
One Ashburton Place, Room
1701
Boston, MA 02108
P: (617) 727-3548
F: (617) 248-0177
E: securities
   @sec.state.ma.us

MICHIGAN
Mr. Alan J. Schefke
Bureau Director
Corporations, Securities &
Commercial Licensing Bureau
Licensing & Regulatory Affairs
P.O. Box 30018
Lansing, MI 48909
P: (517) 241-9202

Securities

MINNESOTA
Mr. Mike Rothman
Commissioner
Department of Commerce
85 East 7th Place, Suite 500
St. Paul, MN 55101
P: (651) 539-1638
F: (651) 296-4328
E: commerce.commissioner
   @state.mn.us

MISSISSIPPI
Ms. Cheryn Netz
Assistant Secretary of State
Securities Division
Office of the Secretary of State
125 South Congress Street, P.O.
Box 136
Jackson, MS 39205
P: (601) 359-1334
F: (601) 359-9070

MISSOURI
Mr. Andrew Hartnett
Commissioner of Securities
Securities Division
Office of the Secretary of State
600 West Main Street, P.O. Box
1276
Jefferson City, MO 65102
P: (573) 522-3686
F: (573) 526-3124
E: securities@sos.mo.gov

MONTANA
Ms. Lynne Egan
Deputy Securities Commissioner
Commissioner of Securities &
Insurance, State Auditor's Office
Securities Department
840 Helena Avenue
Helena, MT 59601
P: (406) 444-2040
F: (406) 444-5558

NEBRASKA
Mr. Jack E. Herstein
Assistant Director, Bureau of
Securities
Department of Banking &
Finance
1526 K Street, Suite 300
Lincoln, NE 68508
P: (402) 471-3445
E: jack.herstein
   @nebraska.gov

NEVADA
Ms. Diana Foley
Securities Administrator
Securities Division
Office of the Secretary of State
555 East Washington Avenue,
Suite 5200
Las Vegas, NV 89101
P: (702) 486-2440
F: (702) 486-2452

NEW HAMPSHIRE
Mr. Barry L. Glennon
Director of Securities Regulation
Bureau of Securities Regulation
Department of State
107 North Main Street, # 204
Concord, NH 03301
P: (603) 271-1463
F: (603) 271-7933
E: securities@sos.nh.gov

NEW JERSEY
Ms. Laura Posner
Bureau Chief
Bureau of Securities
Department of Law & Public
Safety
153 Halsey Street, 6th Floor
Newark, NJ 07102
P: (973) 504-3600
F: (973) 504-3601

NEW MEXICO
Mr. Alan Wilson
Director of Securities
Securities Division
Regulation & Licensing
Department
P.O Box 25101
Santa Fe, NM 87505
P: (505) 476-4608
F: (505) 984-0617
E: Alan.Wilson@state.nm.us

NEW YORK
Mr. Chad Johnson
Bureau Chief
Investor Protection Bureau
Office of the Attorney General
120 Broadway, 23rd Floor
New York, NY 10271
P: (212) 416-8222
F: (212) 416-8816

NORTH CAROLINA
Mr. David S. Massey
Deputy Securities Administrator
Department of the Secretary of
State
Securities Division
2 South Salisbury Street
Raleigh, NC 27601
P: (919) 733-3924
F: (919) 807-2183
E: dmassey@sosnc.com

NORTH DAKOTA
Ms. Karen Tyler
Commissioner
Securities Commission
600 East Boulevard Avenue
State Capitol, 5th Floor
Bismarck, ND 58505
P: (701) 328-2910
F: (701) 328-2946
E: ktyler@nd.gov

OHIO
Ms. Andrea L. Seidt
Commissioner
Division of Securities
77 South High Street, 22nd
Floor
Columbus, OH 43215
P: (614) 644-7381
F: (614) 466-3316
E: securitiesgeneral.
   questions@com.state.oh.us

OKLAHOMA
Mr. Irving L. Faught
Administrator
Securities Commission
1st National Center, Suite 860
120 North Robinson
Oklahoma City, OK 73102
P: (405) 280-7700
F: (405) 280-7742

OREGON
Mr. David C. Tatman
Division Administrator
Division of Finance &
Corporate Securities
Consumer & Business Services
350 Winter Street, Northeast,
Room 410
Salem, OR 97301
P: (503) 947-7475
F: (503) 947-7862
E: david.c.tatman
   @oregon.gov

PENNSYLVANIA
Ms. Robin Weissmann
Secretary
Department of Banking &
Securities
17 North 2nd Street, Suite 1300
Harrisburg, PA 17101
P: (717) 787-2665

PUERTO RICO
Mr. Damaris Mendoza-Roman
Securities Administrator
Commissioner of Financial
Institutions
P.O. Box 11855
San Juan, PR 00910
P: (787) 723-3131
F: (787) 723-4225

RHODE ISLAND
Ms. Maria D'Alessandro
Deputy Director of Securities,
Commercial Licensing, Racing
& Athletics
Department of Business
Regulation
1511 Pontiac Avenue, Building
69-1
Cranston, RI 02920
P: (401) 462-9506
F: (401) 462-9532

SOUTH CAROLINA
Mr. Stephen Lynch
Deputy Securities Commissioner
Office of the Attorney General,
Securities Division
Rembert C. Dennis Building,
Suite 501
1000 Assembly Street, P.O. Box
11549
Columbia, SC 29211
P: (803) 734-9916
F: (803) 734-3677

SOUTH DAKOTA
Mr. Michael J. Youngberg
Director
Division of Securities
124 South Euclid Avenue, Suite
104
Pierre, SD 57501
P: (605) 773-4823
F: (605) 773-5953
E: drr.securities
   @state.sd.us

TENNESSEE
Ms. Daphne D. Smith
Assistant Commissioner for
Securities
Department of Commerce &
Insurance, Securities Division
Davy Crockett Tower, Suite 680
500 James Robertson Parkway
Nashville, TN 37243
P: (615) 741-2947
F: (615) 532-8375

TEXAS
Mr. John Morgan
Securities Commissioner
State Securities Board
208 East 10th Street, 5th Floor
P.O. Box 13167
Austin, TX 78711
P: (512) 305-8300
F: (512) 305-8310

U.S. VIRGIN ISLANDS
Ms. Deverita Sturdivant
Chief of Securities Regulation
Division of Banking &
Insurance
18 Kongens Gade
St. Thomas, VI 00802
P: (340) 774-7166
F: (340) 774-9458

UTAH
Mr. Keith Woodwell
Director
Department of Commerce,
Division of Securities
160 East 300 South, 2nd Floor
P.O. Box 146760
Salt Lake City, UT 84114
P: (801) 530-6600
F: (801) 530-6980
E: kwoodwell@utah.gov

VERMONT
Mr. Michael Pieciak
Deputy Commissioner of
Securities
Department of Financial
Regulation
89 Main Street, 3rd Floor
Montpelier, VT 05620
P: (802) 828-3420
F: (802) 828-2896
E: michael.pieciak
    @state.vt.us

VIRGINIA
Mr. Ronald W. Thomas
Director
State Corporation Commission,
Division of Securities & Retail
Franchising
1300 East Main Street, 9th Floor
P.O. Box 1197
Richmond, VA 23218
P: (804) 371-9051
F: (804) 371-9911
E: ron.thomas
    @scc.virginia.gov

WASHINGTON
Mr. William Beatty
Securities Administrator
Department of Financial
Institutions, Securities Division
P.O. Box 9033
Olympia, WA 98507
P: (360) 902-8760
F: (360) 902-0524

WEST VIRGINIA
Ms. Lisa Hopkins
Senior Deputy Commissioner of
Securities
Securities Division, Office of
the State Auditor
1900 Kanawha Boulevard, East
Building 1, Room W-100
Charleston, WV 25305
P: (304) 558-2251
F: (304) 558-4211
E: securities@wvsao.gov

WISCONSIN
Ms. Patricia D. Struck
Administrator
Department of Financial
Institutions, Division of
Securities
201 West Washington Avenue,
Suite 300
P.O. Box 1768
Madison, WI 53701
P: (608) 266-1064
F: (608) 264-7979
E: patricia.struck
    @dfi.wisconsin.gov

WYOMING
Ms. Karen Wheeler
Division Director
Compliance Division
State Capitol Building, Room
106
200 West 24th Street
Cheyenne, WY 82002
P: (307) 777-5347
F: (307) 777-6217

Small and Minority Business Assistance

Provides assistance and information on financing and government procurement opportunities to small and minority business ventures.

ALABAMA
Mr. Greg Canfield
Secretary
Department of Commerce
P.O. Box 304106
Montgomery, AL 36130
P: (334) 242-0421
F: (334) 242-5669
E: greg.canfield
@commerce.alabama.gov

ALASKA
Ms. Lorene Palmer
Director
Department of Commerce,
Community & Economic
Development
Office of Economic
Development
P.O. Box 110804
Juneau, AK 99811
P: (907) 465-2625
F: (907) 465-3767
E: lorene.palmer@alaska.gov

AMERICAN SAMOA
Mr. Keniseli Lafaele
Director
Department of Commerce
American Samoa Government
Executive Office Building,
Utulei
Pago Pago, AS 96799
P: (684) 633-5155
F: (684) 633-4195
E: keniseli.lafaele@doc.as

ARIZONA
Ms. Sandra Watson
President & CEO
Commerce Authority
333 North Central Avenue, Suite
1900
Phoenix, AZ 85004
P: (602) 845-1200
F: (602) 845-1201
E: commerce@azcommerce.com

ARKANSAS
Ms. Patricia Nunn Brown
Director of Minority Business
Economic Development
Commission
900 West Capitol Avenue, Suite
400
Little Rock, AR 72201
P: (501) 682-2559
F: (501) 682-7394
E: pbrown@arkansasedc.com

COLORADO
Ms. Kelly Manning
Director
Small Business Development
Center
1625 Broadway, Suite 2700
Denver, CO 80202
P: (303) 892-3864
F: (303) 892-3848
E: kelly.manning
@state.co.us

Mr. LeRoy Romero
Manager
Office of Economic
Development & International
Trade
Minority Business Office
1625 Broadway, Suite 2700
Denver, CO 80202
P: (303) 892-3840
F: (303) 892-3848
E: leroy.romero@state.co.us

DISTRICT OF COLUMBIA
Ms. Monica Palacio
Director
Office of Human Rights
441 4th Street, Northwest
Suite 570 North
Washington, DC 20001
P: (202) 727-4559
F: (202) 727-9589
E: ohr@dc.gov

GEORGIA
Mr. Chris Carr
Commissioner
Department of Economic
Development
75 Fifth Street, Northwest
Suite 1200
Atlanta, GA 30308
P: (404) 962-4000
F: (404) 962-4009

HAWAII
Mr. Luis P. Salaveria
Director
Department of Business,
Economic Development &
Tourism
250 South Hotel Street
P.O. Box 2359
Honolulu, HI 96804
P: (808) 586-2355
F: (808) 586-2377
E: director
@dbedt.hawaii.gov

IDAHO
Mr. Jeffery Sayer
Director
Department of Commerce
700 West State Street
P.O. Box 83720
Boise, ID 83720
P: (208) 334-2470
F: (208) 334-2631
E: jeffery.sayer
@commerce.idaho.gov

ILLINOIS
Mr. Jim Schultz
Director
Department of Commerce &
Economic Opportunity
100 West Randolph Street, Suite
3-400
Chicago, IL 60601
P: (312) 814-2811
E: Jim.Schultz@Illinois.gov

INDIANA
Ms. Terrie F. Daniel
Deputy Commissioner
Minority & Women's Business
Enterprises
Department of Administration
402 West Washington Street,
Room W469
Indianapolis, IN 46204
P: (317) 232-3061
F: (317) 233-6921
E: TDaniel@idoa.IN.gov

IOWA
Ms. Debi Durham
Director
Economic Development
Authority
200 East Grand Avenue
Des Moines, IA 50309
P: (515) 725-3022
F: (515) 725-3010
E: debi.durham@iowa.gov

KANSAS
Ms. Rhonda F. Harris
Director
Office of Minority & Women
Business Development
Suite 100, Curtis State Office
Building
1000 Southwest Jackson Street
Topeka, KS 66612
P: (785) 296-3425
F: (785) 296-3490
E: rharris
@kansascommerce.com

KENTUCKY
Mr. Mark Johnson
Assistant Director
Division of Small Business
Services
Cabinet for Economic
Development
Old Capitol Annex, 300 West
Broadway
Frankfort, KY 40601
P: (502) 564-2064
F: (502) 564-3256
E: markl.johnson@ky.gov

LOUISIANA
Mr. Stephen Grissom
Secretary
Economic Development
1051 North Third Street
Baton Rouge, LA 70802
P: (225) 342-5478
F: (225) 342-9095
E: sgrissom@la.gov

MAINE
Mr. George C. Gervais
Commissioner
Department of Economic &
Community Development
59 State House Station
Augusta, ME 04333
P: (207) 624-9800

MARYLAND
Celester Hall
Manager
Small Business
Business & Economic
Development
401 East Pratt Street
Baltimore, MD 21202
P: (410) 767-6356
E: LHall@choosemaryland.org

MASSACHUSETTS
Ms. Sandra E. Borders
Director
Office of Diversity & Equal
Opportunity
One Ashburton Place, Room 213
Boston, MA 02108
P: (617) 727-7441
F: (617) 878-9830

Small and Minority Business Assistance

MICHIGAN
Mr. Michael A. Finney
President & CEO
Economic Development
Corporation
300 North Washington Square
Lansing, MI 48913
P: (517) 241-1400
F: (517) 241-3683
E: michael@michigan.org

MINNESOTA
Mr. Matt Massman
Commissioner
Department of Administration
116 Veterans Service Building
20 West 12 Street
St. Paul, MN 55155
P: (651) 201-3421
E: Matt.Massman@state.mn.us

MISSISSIPPI
Mr. Brent L. Christensen
Executive Director
Development Authority
501 North West Street
P.O. Box 849
Jackson, MS 39205
P: (601) 359-3449
F: (601) 359-3832
E: bchristensen
    @mississippi.org

MISSOURI
Mr. Walter Pearson
Interim Director
Office of Equal Opportunity
301 West High Street, Room
630
P.O. Box 809
Jefferson City, MO 65102
P: (573) 751-8130
F: (573) 522-8078

MONTANA
Ms. Meg O'Leary
Director
Department of Commerce
301 South Park Avenue
P.O. Box 200501
Helena, MT 59620
P: (406) 841-2700
F: (406) 841-2701

NEBRASKA
Ms. Brenda Hicks-Sorensen
Director
Department of Economic
Development
550 South 16th Street
Lincoln, NE 68508
P: (402) 471-3125
E: brenda.hicks-sorensen
    @nebraska.gov

NEVADA
Mr. Richard Boulware
Chair
Commission on Minority Affairs
Department of Business &
Industry
555 East Washington Avenue,
Suite 4900
Las Vegas, NV 89101
P: (702) 486-2750
F: (702) 486-2758
E: biinfo@dbi.state.nv.us

NEW HAMPSHIRE
Mr. Jack Donovan
Executive Director
Business Finance Authority
2 Pillsbury Street, Suite 201
Concord, NH 03301
P: (603) 415-0191
F: (603) 415-0194
E: JackD@nhbfa.com

NEW JERSEY
Ms. Michele Brown
Chief Executive Officer
Economic Development
Authority
36 West State Street
P.O. Box 990
Trenton, NJ 08625
P: (609) 292-1800
F: (609) 292-0885
E: njeda@njeda.com

NEW MEXICO
Mr. Jon Barela
Secretary
Economic Development
Department
1100 South Saint Francis Drive
P.O. Box 20003
Santa Fe, NM 87504
P: (505) 827-0305
F: (505) 827-0328
E: Jon.Barela@state.nm.us

NEW YORK
Mr. Kenneth Adams
President & CEO
Empire State Development
633 Third Avenue
New York, NY 10017
P: (212) 803-3700
F: (212) 803-3715

NORTH CAROLINA
Mr. Scott Daugherty
Executive Director
Small Business & Technology
Development Center
5 West Hargett Street, Suite 600
Raleigh, NC 27601
P: (919) 715-7272
F: (919) 715-7777
E: sdaugherty
    @nccommerce.com

NORTH DAKOTA
Mr. Al Anderson
Commissioner
Department of Commerce
1600 East Century Avenue,
Suite 2
P.O. Box 2057
Bismarck, ND 58503
P: (701) 328-7284
F: (701) 328-5320
E: alrandeson@nd.gov

**NORTHERN MARIANA
ISLANDS**
Mr. Manuel A. Sablan
Executive Director
Commonwealth Development
Authority
P.O. Box 502149
Saipan, MP 96950
P: (670) 234-6245
F: (670) 235-7147
E: administration
    @cda.gov.mp

OKLAHOMA
Ms. Vikki Dearing
Director, Employer Workforce
Services & Rapid Response
Coordinator
Department of Commerce
900 North Stiles Avenue
Oklahoma City, OK 73104
P: (405) 815-5114
F: (405) 605-2811
E: vikki_dearing
    @okcommerce.gov

PENNSYLVANIA
Mr. Dennis Davin
Secretary
Department of Community &
Economic Development
Commonwealth Keystone
Building
400 North Street, 4th Floor
Harrisburg, PA 17120
P: (866) 466-3972
F: (717) 783-4662

RHODE ISLAND
Mr. Charles C. Newton
Administrator
Minority Business Enterprise
One Capitol Hill, 2nd Floor
Providence, RI 02908
P: (401) 574-8670
F: (401) 574-8387
E: Charles.Newton
    @doa.ri.gov

SOUTH CAROLINA
Mr. Stanley Foreman
Director
Office of Small & Minority
Business Assistance
1205 Pendleton Street, Suite 474
Columbia, SC 29201
P: (803) 734-5010
F: (803) 734-0548
E: sforeman@oepp.sc.gov

SOUTH DAKOTA
Mr. Pat Costello
Commissioner
Governor's Office of Economic
Development
711 East Wells Avenue
Pierre, SD 57501
P: (800) 872-6190
F: (605) 773-3256
E: goedinfo@state.sd.us

TENNESSEE
Mr. Randy Bell
Commissioner
Department of Economic &
Community Development
312 Rosa L. Parks Avenue, 11th
Floor
Nashville, TN 37243
P: (615) 741-1888
F: (615) 741-7306
E: Randy.Bell@tn.gov

TEXAS
Mr. Harvey Hilderbran
Executive Director
Facilities Commission
1711 San Jacinto
P.O. Box 13047
Austin, TX 78711
P: (512) 463-3446
E: Harvey.Hilderbran
    @tfc.state.tx.us

Small and Minority Business Assistance

U.S. VIRGIN ISLANDS
Mr. Percival Clouden
Chief Executive Officer
Economic Development
Authority
8000 Nisky Shopping Center,
Suite 620
P.O. Box 305038
St. Thomas, VI 00802
P: (340) 714-1700
F: (340) 773-6499

UTAH
Mr. Spencer Peterson Eccles
Executive Director
Governor's Office of Economic
Development
60 East South Temple, 3rd Floor
Salt Lake City, UT 84111
P: (801) 538-8769
F: (801) 538-8888
E: speccles@utah.gov

VIRGINIA
Ms. Ida McPherson
Director
Department of Minority
Business Enterprise
1100 East Main Street, Suite 300
Richmond, VA 23219
P: (804) 371-6228
F: (804) 371-7359
E: ida.mcpherson
    @dmbe.virginia.gov

WASHINGTON
Mr. Brian Bonlender
Director
Department of Commerce
1011 Plum Street, Southeast
P.O. Box 42525
Olympia, WA 98504
P: (360) 725-4000

WEST VIRGINIA
Mr. J. Keith Burdette
Cabinet Secretary
Department of Commerce
Capitol Complex Building 6,
Room 525
1900 Kanawha Boulevard East
Charleston, WV 25305
P: (304) 558-2234
F: (304) 558-1189
E: J.Keith.Burdette@wv.gov

WISCONSIN
Mr. Reed Hall
CEO & Secretary
Economic Development
Corporation
201 West Washington Avenue
P.O. Box 1687
Madison, WI 53701
P: (608) 267-4417
E: Reed.Hall@wedc.org

WYOMING
Ms. Kristie Langley
Administrator
Child Support Enforcement
2300 Capitol Avenue, 5th Floor
Hathaway Building
Cheyenne, WY 82002
P: (307) 777-6948
F: (307) 777-5588

Mr. Shawn Reese
Chief Executive Officer
Business Council
214 West 15th Street
Cheyenne, WY 82002
P: (307) 777-2862
F: (307) 777-2837
E: shawn.reese@wyo.gov

Social Services

Responsible for the delivery of services to children, disabled, and elderly.

ALABAMA
Ms. Nancy T. Buckner
Commissioner
Department of Human
Resources
Gordon Persons Building, Suite 2104
50 North Ripley Street
Montgomery, AL 36130
P: (334) 242-1310
F: (334) 353-1115
E: Nancy.Buckner
   @dhr.alabama.gov

ALASKA
Ms. Valerie Davidson
Commissioner
Department of Health & Social
Services
350 Main Street, Room 404
P.O. Box 110601
Juneau, AK 99811
P: (907) 465-3030
F: (907) 465-3068
E: valerie.davidson
   @alaska.gov

AMERICAN SAMOA
Dr. Taeaoafua Meki Solomona
Director
Department of Human & Social
Services
P.O. Box 997534
Pago Pago, AS 96799
P: (684) 633-1664
F: (684) 633-7449
E: mtsolomona@dhss.as

ARIZONA
Mr. Timothy Jeffries
Director
Department of Economic
Security
1717 West Jefferson Street
Phoenix, AZ 85007
P: (602) 542-4791

ARKANSAS
Ms. Delia Anderson
Director
Division of County Operations
P.O. Box 1437, Slot S301
Little Rock, AR 72203
P: (501) 682-8375
F: (501) 682-8367
E: delia.anderson
   @arkansas.gov

CALIFORNIA
Mr. Will Lightbourne
Director
Department of Social Services
744 P Street
Sacramento, CA 95814
P: (916) 657-2598
F: (916) 651-6569

COLORADO
Mr. Reginald L. Bicha
Executive Director
Department of Human Services
1575 Sherman Street
Denver, CO 80203
P: (303) 866-3475
F: (303) 866-2606
E: reggie.bicha@state.co.us

CONNECTICUT
Mr. Roderick L. Bremby
Commissioner
Department of Social Services
55 Farmington Avenue
Hartford, CT 06105
P: (860) 424-5024
E: commis.dss@ct.gov

DELAWARE
Ms. Rita M. Landgraf
Secretary
Department of Health & Social
Services
Main Building
1901 North DuPont Highway
New Castle, DE 19720
P: (302) 255-9040
F: (302) 255-4429

DISTRICT OF COLUMBIA
Mr. David A. Berns
Director
Department of Human Services
64 New York Avenue, Northeast
6th Floor
Washington, DC 20002
P: (202) 671-4200
F: (202) 671-4326
E: dhs@dc.gov

FLORIDA
Mr. Mike Carroll
Secretary
Department of Children &
Families
1317 Winewood Boulevard
Building 1, Room 202
Tallahassee, FL 32399
P: (850) 487-1111
F: (850) 922-2993
E: mike_carroll
   @dcf.state.fl.us

GEORGIA
Mr. Keith Horton
Commissioner
Department of Human Services
2 Peachtree Street, Northwest
Suite 29-250
Atlanta, GA 30303
P: (404) 656-5680
F: (404) 651-8669

HAWAII
Dr. Rachael Wong
Director
Department of Human Services
1390 Miller Street, Room 209
P.O. Box 339
Honolulu, HI 96809
P: (808) 586-4997
F: (808) 586-4890
E: dhs@dhs.hawaii.gov

IDAHO
Mr. Robert B. Luce
Administrator
Division of Family &
Community Services
450 West State Street, 5th Floor
Cenarrusa Building, P.O. Box 83720
Boise, ID 83720
P: (208) 334-0641
F: (208) 332-7331
E: brownd3@dhw.idaho.gov

ILLINOIS
Mr. Richard Calica
Director
Department of Children &
Family Services
406 East Monroe Street
Springfield, IL 62701
P: (217) 785-2509
F: (217) 785-1052

INDIANA
Ms. Adrienne Shields
Director of Family Resources
Family & Social Services
Administration
402 West Washington Street,
Room W392
Indianapolis, IN 46204
P: (317) 234-2373
F: (317) 232-4490
E: Adrienne.Shields
   @fssa.IN.gov

IOWA
Ms. Sally Titus
Deputy Director
Department of Human Services
Hoover Building
1305 East Walnut
Des Moines, IA 50319
P: (515) 281-6360
F: (515) 281-4597
E: stitus@dhs.state.ia.us

KANSAS
Ms. Phyllis Gilmore
Secretary
Department for Children &
Families
915 Southwest Harrison Street
Topeka, KS 66612
P: (785) 296-3274
F: (785) 296-2173

KENTUCKY
Ms. Audrey Tayse Haynes
Secretary
Cabinet for Health & Family
Services
275 East Main Street, 5W-A
Frankfort, KY 40621
P: (502) 564-7042
F: (502) 564-7091

LOUISIANA
Ms. Suzy Sonnier
Secretary
Department of Children &
Family Services
P.O. Box 3776
Baton Rouge, LA 70821
P: (225) 342-0286
F: (225) 342-8636
E: Suzy.Sonnier@dcfs.la.gov

MAINE
Ms. Mary Mayhew
Commissioner
Department of Health & Human
Services
221 State Street
Augusta, ME 04333
P: (207) 287-3707
F: (207) 287-3005
E: mary.mayhew@maine.gov

MARYLAND
Mr. Sam Malhotra
Secretary
Department of Human
Resources
311 West Saratoga Street
Baltimore, MD 21201
P: (410) 767-7109
F: (410) 333-0099
E: sam.malhotra
   @maryland.gov

MASSACHUSETTS
Ms. Linda Spears
Commissioner
Department of Children &
Families
600 Washington Street
Boston, MA 02111
P: (617) 748-2000

Social Services

MICHIGAN
Ms. Maura D. Corrigan
Director
Department of Human Services
235 South Grand Avenue
P.O. Box 30037
Lansing, MI 48909
P: (313) 456-4887
F: (517) 335-6101
E: dhsweb@michigan.gov

MISSISSIPPI
Mr. Derra Dukes
Director
Office of Social Services Block
Grant
Department of Human Services
750 North State Street
Jackson, MS 39202
P: (601) 359-4658

MISSOURI
Mr. Brian Kinkade
Director
Department of Social Services
Broadway State Office Building
P.O. Box 1527
Jefferson City, MO 65102
P: (573) 751-4815
F: (573) 751-3203

NEBRASKA
Mr. Tony Green
Acting Director
Division of Children & Family
Services
P.O. Box 95026
Lincoln, NE 60509
P: (402) 471-9272
E: Tony.Green@nebraska.gov

NEW HAMPSHIRE
Mr. Nicholas A. Toumpas
Commissioner
Department of Health & Human
Services
129 Pleasant Street
Concord, NH 03301
P: (603) 271-9200
F: (603) 271-4912
E: ntoumpas
   @dhhs.state.nh.us

NEW JERSEY
Ms. Jennifer Velez
Commissioner
Department of Human Services
222 South Warren Street
P.O. Box 700
Trenton, NJ 08625
P: (609) 292-3717

NEW MEXICO
Mr. Brent Earnest
Cabinet Secretary
Human Services Department
P.O. Box 2348
Santa Fe, NM 87504
P: (505) 827-7750

Ms. Veronica Gonzales
Secretary
Department of Cultural Affairs
407 Galisteo, Suite 260
Santa Fe, NM 87501
P: (505) 827-6364

NEW YORK
Ms. Kristin M. Proud
Commissioner
Office of Temporary &
Disability Assistance
40 North Pearl Street
Albany, NY 12243
P: (518) 473-1090

NORTH CAROLINA
Mr. Wayne E. Black
Director
Division of Social Services
McBryde Building, 820 South
Boylan Ave.
2401 Mail Service Center
Raleigh, NC 27699
P: (919) 527-6335
F: (919) 334-1018
E: wayne.black@dhhs.nc.gov

NORTH DAKOTA
Ms. Maggie D. Anderson
Executive Director
Department of Human Services
State Capitol, Judicial Wing
600 East Boulevard Avenue,
Dept. 325
Bismarck, ND 58505
P: (701) 328-2538
F: (701) 328-1545
E: manderson@nd.gov

Ms. Carol K. Olson
Executive Director
Department of Human Services
State Capitol, Judicial Wing
600 East Boulevard Avenue,
Dept. 325
Bismarck, ND 58505
P: (701) 328-2538
F: (701) 328-1545
E: colson@nd.gov

**NORTHERN MARIANA
ISLANDS**
Mr. Joseph P. Villagomez
Secretary of Public Health
Department of Public Health
P.O. Box 500409
Saipan, MP 96950
P: (670) 234-8950
F: (670) 234-8930
E: jkvsaipan@aol.com

OHIO
Ms. Cynthia J. Dungey
Director
Department of Job & Family
Services
30 East Broad Street, 32nd Floor
Columbus, OH 43215
P: (614) 466-9195
F: (614) 466-2815

OREGON
Ms. Erinn L. Kelley-Siel
Director
Department of Human Services
500 Summer Street, Northeast,
E-15
Salem, OR 97301
P: (503) 945-7001
F: (503) 378-2897
E: erinn.kelley-siel
   @state.or.us

PENNSYLVANIA
Mr. Theodore Dallas
Secretary
Department of Human
Resources
P.O. Box 2675
Harrisburg, PA 17105
P: (717) 787-2600

PUERTO RICO
Ms. Idalia Columbus Rondon
Secretary
Department of the Family
P.O. Box 11398
Hato Rey, PR 00917
P: (787) 294-4900
F: (787) 294-0732

RHODE ISLAND
Ms. Melba Depena Affigne
Director
Department of Human Services
600 New London Avenue
Cranston, RI
F: (401) 462-3677
E: Director@dhs.ri.gov

SOUTH CAROLINA
Ms. V. Susan Alford
Director
Department of Social Services
1535 Confederate Avenue
Extension
P.O. Box 1520
Columbia, SC 29202
P: (803) 898-7360
F: (803) 898-7277

SOUTH DAKOTA
Ms. Lynne A. Valenti
Cabinet Secretary
Department of Social Services
700 Governors Drive
Pierre, SD 57501
P: (605) 773-3165
F: (605) 773-4855
E: DSSInfo@state.sd.us

TENNESSEE
Dr. Raquel Hatter
Commissioner
Department of Human Services
400 Deaderick Street, 15th Floor
Nashville, TN 37243
P: (615) 313-4700
F: (615) 741-4165
E: raquel.hatter@tn.gov

TEXAS
Ms. Stephanie Muth
Deputy Executive Commissioner
for Social Services
Health & Human Services
Commission
4900 North Lamar Boulevard
P.O.Box 13247
Austin, TX 78711
P: (512) 424-6767
F: (512) 491-1967

U.S. VIRGIN ISLANDS
Mr. Christopher E. Finch
Commissioner
Department of Human Services
Knud Hansen Complex,
Building A
1303 Hospital Ground
St. Thomas, VI 00802
P: (340) 774-0930
F: (340) 773-2980

UTAH
Ms. Ann S. Williamson
Executive Director
Department of Human Services
195 North 1950 West
Salt Lake City, UT 84116
P: (801) 538-4017
F: (801) 538-4016
E: annwilliamson@utah.gov

VIRGINIA
Ms. Margaret Schultze
Commissioner
Department of Social Services
801 East Main Street
Richmond, VA 23219
P: (804) 726-7000
E: margaret.schultze
    @dss.virginia.gov

WASHINGTON
Mr. Kevin W. Quigley
Secretary
Department of Social & Health
Services
P.O. Box 45130
Olympia, WA 98504
P: (360) 902-7800

WEST VIRGINIA
Ms. Karen L. Bowling
Cabinet Secretary
Department of Health & Human
Resources
One Davis Square, Suite 100
East
Charleston, WV 25301
P: (304) 558-0684
F: (304) 558-1130
E: DHHRSecretary@wv.gov

WYOMING
Dr. Steve Corsi
Director
Department of Family Services
Hathaway Building, 3rd Floor
2300 Capitol Avenue
Cheyenne, WY 82002
P: (307) 777-7561
F: (307) 777-7747
E: steve.corsi@wyo.gov

State Data Center

Center that acts as an information clearinghouse for the Census Bureau and other data sources within the state.

ALABAMA
Ms. Carolyn Trent
Socioeconomic Analyst
State Data Center
Center for Business & Economic Research
University of Alabama, Box 870221
Tuscaloosa, AL 35487
P: (205) 348-6191
E: ctrent@cba.ua.edu

ALASKA
Ms. Heidi Drygas
Commissioner
Department of Labor & Workforce Development
P.O. Box 111149
Juneau, AK 99811
P: (907) 465-2700
F: (907) 465-2784
E: heidi.drygas@alaska.gov

AMERICAN SAMOA
Mr. Etuale Tuileta
Chief Statistician
Research & Statistics Division
Department of Commerce
Executive Office Building, Utulei
Pago Pago, AS 96799
P: (684) 633-5155
E: etuale.tuileta@doc.as

ARIZONA
Mr. Allen L. Barnes
State Data Center Lead
Office of Employment & Population Statistics
Commerce Authority
1700 West Washington Street, Suite 600
Phoenix, AZ 85007
P: (602) 542-5746
F: (602) 771-1207
E: AllenB@azcommerce.com

ARKANSAS
Ms. Phyllis Poche
Director
Census State Data Center
UALR Institute for Economic Advancement
2801 South University Avenue
Little Rock, AR 72204
P: (501) 569-8530
F: (501) 569-8538
E: pnpoche@ualr.edu

CALIFORNIA
Mr. William Schooling
Chief
Demographic Research Unit
915 L Street
Sacramento, CA 95814
P: (916) 323-4086
F: (916) 327-0222
E: bill.schooling
@dof.ca.gov

COLORADO
Ms. Elizabeth Garner
State Demographer
Demography Office
Department of Local Affairs
1313 Sherman Street, Room 521
Denver, CO 80203
P: (303) 864-7750
F: (303) 864-7759
E: elizabeth.garner
@state.co.us

CONNECTICUT
Mr. Michael Howser
Director
State Data Center, University of Connecticut
Homer Babbidge Library
369 Fairfield Road, Unit 1005M
Storrs, CT 06269
P: (860) 570-9028
E: ctsdc@uconn.edu

DELAWARE
Ms. Miriam Pomilio
Planner/GIS Coordinator
Office of State Planning Coordination
Office of Management & Budget
122 Martin Luther King Jr. Blvd., South
Dover, DE 19901
P: (302) 739-3090
E: miriam.pomilio
@state.de.us

DISTRICT OF COLUMBIA
Ms. Joy E. Phillips
Associate Director
State Data Center
1100 4th Street, Southwest
Suite E650
Washington, DC 20024
P: (202) 442-7600
F: (202) 442-7638

FLORIDA
Mr. David W. Taylor
Executive Director & Chief Information Officer
Agency for Enterprise Information Technology
4030 Esplanade Way, Suite 135
Tallahassee, FL 32399
P: (850) 922-7502
F: (850) 487-9937
E: David.Taylor
@aeit.myflorida.com

GEORGIA
Mr. Robert Giacomini
Director of Research
Governor's Office of Planning & Budget
270 Washington Street, Southwest
8th Floor
Atlanta, GA 30334
P: (404) 656-3820
F: (404) 656-3828
E: robert.giacomini
@opb.state.ga.us

GUAM
Ms. Lorilee T. Crisostomo
Administrator
Bureau of Statistics & Plans
548 North Marine Corps Drive
Tamuning, GU 96913
P: (671) 646-4361
F: (671) 477-9402
E: lorilee.crisostomo
@epa.guam.gov

HAWAII
Dr. Eugene Tian
Administrator
Research & Economic Analysis Division
State Data Center
P.O. Box 2359
Honolulu, HI 96804
P: (808) 586-2355
F: (808) 586-8449
E: xtian@dbedt.hawaii.gov

IDAHO
Mr. Jeffery Sayer
Director
Department of Commerce
700 West State Street
P.O. Box 83720
Boise, ID 83720
P: (208) 334-2470
F: (208) 334-2631
E: jeffery.sayer
@commerce.idaho.gov

ILLINOIS
Mr. Kevin Harrison
Coordinator
Office of Information Technology Management
Commerce & Economic Opportunity
607 East Adams, Floor 3, Room 3
Springfield, IL 62701
P: (217) 558-0424
F: (217) 524-4876

INDIANA
Mr. Jacob Speer
Director & State Librarian
State Library
State Library
140 North Senate Avenue
Indianapolis, IN 46204
P: (317) 232-3693
E: jspeer1@library.in.gov

IOWA
Mr. Gary Krob
Data Warehouse Analyst
State Data Center
Ola Babcock Miller Building
1112 East Grand Avenue
Des Moines, IA 50319
P: (515) 281-6618
F: (515) 242-6543
E: gary.krob
@lib.state.ia.us

KENTUCKY
Dr. Janet Kelly
Executive Director
State Data Center
University of Louisville
426 West Bloom Street
Louisville, KY 40208
P: (502) 852-2435
F: (502) 852-7386
E: janet.kelly
@louisville.edu

MAINE
Ms. Amanda Rector
State Economist
State Planning Office
38 State House Station
19 Union Street
Augusta, ME 04333
P: (207) 624-6206
F: (207) 287-6489
E: amanda.k.rector
@maine.gov

MARYLAND
Ms. Jane Traynham
Manager
Research & State Data Center
Department of Planning
301 West Preston Street
Baltimore, MD 21201
P: (410) 767-4450
F: (410) 767-4480
E: jane.traynham
@maryland.gov

MASSACHUSETTS
Mr. John Gaviglio
Data Manager
State Data Center
UMASS Donahue Institute
100 Venture Way, Suite 9
Hadley, MA 01035
P: (413) 545-0176
F: (413) 545-3420
E: jgaviglio
@donahue.umassp.edu

MICHIGAN
Mr. David Behen
Chief Information Officer &
Department Director
Department of Technology,
Management & Budget
320 South Walnut Street, 2nd
Floor
P.O. Box 30026
Lansing, MI 48909
P: (517) 373-3209
E: behend@michigan.gov

MINNESOTA
Mr. Matt Massman
Commissioner
Department of Administration
116 Veterans Service Building
20 West 12 Street
St. Paul, MN 55155
P: (651) 201-3421
E: Matt.Massman@state.mn.us

MISSISSIPPI
Mr. John J. Green
Director
Center for Population Studies
302 Leavell Hall
P.O. Box 1848
University, MS 38677
P: (662) 915-7295
F: (662) 915-7736
E: jjgreen@olemiss.edu

MISSOURI
Terry Blauvelt
Statistical Research Analyst
Census Data Center
State Library
P.O. Box 387
Jefferson City, MO 65101
P: (417) 895-6331
E: Terry.Blauvelt
@sos.mo.gov

MONTANA
Mr. Ron Baldwin
Chief Information Officer
Information Technology
Services Division
125 North Roberts Street
P.O. Box 200113
Helena, MT 59620
P: (406) 444-2777
F: (406) 444-2701

NEBRASKA
Mr. Jerome Deichart
Director & Senior Research
Associate
Center for Public Affairs
Research
CPACS Building, Room 108
6001 Dodge Street
Omaha, NE 68182
P: (402) 554-2134
F: (402) 554-4946
E: jdeicher@unomaha.edu

NEVADA
Mr. William D. Anderson
Chief Economist
Department of Employment,
Training & Rehabilitation
Research & Analysis Bureau
500 East Third Street
Carson City, NV 89713
P: (775) 684-0387
F: (775) 684-3850
E: wdanderson@nvdetr.org

NEW HAMPSHIRE
Mr. Ken Gallager
State Data Center
Johnson Hall, 3rd Floor
107 Pleasant Street
Concord, NH 03301
P: (603) 271-1773
F: (603) 271-2615
E: ken.gallager@nh.gov

NEW JERSEY
Mr. Len Preston
Director
State Data Center
P.O. Box 388
Trenton, NJ 08625
P: (609) 984-2595
F: (609) 984-6833
E: lpreston@dol.state.nj.us

NEW MEXICO
Ms. Elizabeth Davis
Research & Marketing Director
Economic Development
Department
Joseph Montoya Building
1100 South Saint Francis Drive
Santa Fe, NM 87505
P: (505) 827-0333
F: (505) 827-0328
E: Elizabeth.Davis
@state.nm.us

NEW YORK
Ms. Laura Close
State Data Center
30 South Pearl Street
Albany, NY 12207
P: (518) 292-5300
E: Laura.Close@labor.ny.gov

NORTH CAROLINA
Ms. Jennifer Song
State Demographer
Department of State Budget &
Management
Demographic & Economic
Analysis
116 West Jones Street
Raleigh, NC 27603
P: (919) 807-4700
E: jennifer.song
@osbm.nc.gov

NORTH DAKOTA
Mr. Paul T. Govig
Director
Division of Community
Services
1600 East Century Avenue,
Suite 2
P.O. Box 2057
Bismarck, ND 58502
P: (701) 328-4499
F: (701) 328-2308
E: pgovig@nd.gov

Mr. Mike J. Ressler
Chief Information Officer
Information Technology
Department
4201 Normandy Street
Bismarck, ND 58503
P: (701) 328-1000
F: (701) 328-1075
E: mressler@nd.gov

OKLAHOMA
Ms. Deidre Myers
Division Director
Research, Economic Analysis &
Policy Services
Department of Commerce
900 North Stiles Avenue
Oklahoma City, OK 73104
P: (405) 815-5383
F: (405) 605-2807
E: deidre_myers
@okcommerce.gov

OREGON
Ms. Julie M. Bozzi
Administrator
Enterprise Technology Services
530 Airport Road
Salem, OR 97301
P: (503) 378-4578
F: (503) 378-2736
E: julie.bozzi@oregon.gov

PENNSYLVANIA
Ms. Sue Copella
Director
State Data Center
777 West Harrisburg Pike
Middletown, PA 17057
P: (717) 948-6427
F: (717) 948-6754
E: sdc3@psu.edu

PUERTO RICO
Mr. Carlos Quinones Rivas
Director
Office of Management &
Budget
P.O. Box 9023228
San Juan, PR 00902
P: (787) 725-9420
F: (787) 722-0299

State Data Center

SOUTH CAROLINA
Mr. Frank Rainwater
Executive Director
Revenue and Fiscal Affairs
Office
1000 Assembly Street
Suite 402
Columbia, SC 29201

TENNESSEE
Mr. Mark Bengel
Chief Information Officer
Office for Information
Resources
Department of Finance &
Administration
312 Rosa L. Parks Avenue
Nashville, TN 37343
P: (615) 741-7951
F: (615) 532-0471

TEXAS
Mr. Todd Kimbriel
Interim Executive Director &
CIO
Department of Information
Resources
300 West 15th Street, Suite 1300
P.O. Box 13564
Austin, TX 78711
P: (512) 475-0579
F: (512) 475-4759

U.S. VIRGIN ISLANDS
Stevie Henry
Principal Investigator
Conservation Data Center
#2 John Brewer's Bay
St. Thomas, VI 00802
P: (340) 693-1033
F: (340) 693-1025
E: shenry@uvi.edu

UTAH
Ms. Kristen Cox
Executive Director
Governor's Office of
Management & Budget
State Capitol, Suite 150
P.O. Box 132210
Salt Lake City, UT 84114
P: (801) 538-1027
F: (801) 538-1547
E: kristencox@utah.gov

VIRGINIA
Ms. Ellen Marie Hess
Commissioner
Employment Commission
703 East Main Street
Richmond, VA 23219
E: ellen.hess
   @vec.virginia.gov

WEST VIRGINIA
Mr. J. Keith Burdette
Cabinet Secretary
Department of Commerce
Capitol Complex Building 6,
Room 525
1900 Kanawha Boulevard East
Charleston, WV 25305
P: (304) 558-2234
F: (304) 558-1189
E: J.Keith.Burdette@wv.gov

WISCONSIN
Mr. Phil Wells
Program & Policy
Analyst-Advanced
Demographic Services Center
101 East Wilson, 9th Floor
P.O. Box 8944
Madison, WI 53708
P: (608) 266-1927
F: (608) 267-6917
E: philip.wells
   @wisconsin.gov

State and Public Libraries

Serves the information and research needs of state executive and legislative branch officials. Also oversees the development of public libraries in the state and federal programs related to such libraries.

ALABAMA
Ms. Nancy Pack
Director
Public Library Service
6030 Monticello Drive
Montgomery, AL 36130
P: (334) 213-3901
F: (334) 213-3993
E: npack@apls.state.al.us

ALASKA
Ms. Linda Thibodeau
State Librarian & Director
Division of Libraries, Archives
& Museums
P.O. Box 110571
Juneau, AK 99811
P: (907) 465-2911
F: (907) 465-2151
E: linda.thibodeau
    @alaska.gov

ARIZONA
Ms. Joan Clark
State Librarian
State of Arizona
State Capitol, Room 200
1700 West Washington
Phoenix, AZ 85007
P: (602) 926-4035
F: (602) 256-7983
E: jclark@azlibrary.gov

ARKANSAS
Ms. Carolyn Ashcraft
State Librarian
State Library
900 West Capital
Suite 100
Little Rock, AR 72201
P: (501) 682-1526
F: (501) 682-1899
E: carolyn
    @library.arkansas.gov

CALIFORNIA
Mr. Greg Lucas
Librarian
State of California
P.O. Box 942837
Sacramento, CA 94237
P: (916) 323-9759
E: Greg.Lucas
    @library.ca.gov

COLORADO
Mr. Gene Hainer
Assistant Commissioner
State Library
201 East Colfax Avenue, Room 309
Denver, CO 80203
P: (303) 594-4780
F: (303) 866-6940
E: ehainer2@gmail.com

CONNECTICUT
Mr. Kendall F. Wiggin
State Librarian
State Library
231 Capitol Avenue
Hartford, CT 06106
P: (860) 757-6510
F: (860) 757-6503
E: kendall.wiggin@ct.gov

DELAWARE
Dr. Anne E.C. Norman
Director & State Librarian
Division of Libraries
121 Duke of York Street
Dover, DE 19901
P: (302) 739-4748
F: (302) 739-6787
E: annie.norman@state.de.us

DISTRICT OF COLUMBIA
Mr. Richard Reyes-Gavilan
Executive Director
District of Columbia
901 G Street, Northwest
Suite 400
Washington, DC 20001
P: (202) 727-1101
E: rrg@dc.gov

FLORIDA
Ms. Amy Johnson
Director
Division of Library &
Information Services
R.A. Gray Building
Tallahassee, FL 32399
P: (850) 245-6622
F: (850) 245-6643
E: amy.johnson
    @dos.myflorida.com

GEORGIA
Ms. Julie Walker
State Librarian
Public Library Service
1800 Century Place, Northeast
Suite 150
Atlanta, GA 30345
P: (404) 406-4519
F: (404) 235-7201
E: jwalker
    @georgialibraries.org

HAWAII
Ms. Stacey A. Aldrich
State Librarian
State Public Library System
44 Merchant Street
Honolulu, HI 96813
P: (717) 783-2466
F: (717) 772-3265
E: stacey.aldrich
    @librarieshawaii.org

IDAHO
Ms. Ann Joslin
State Librarian
Commission for Libraries
325 West State Street
Boise, ID 83702
P: (208) 334-2150
F: (208) 334-4016
E: ann.joslin
    @libraries.idaho.gov

ILLINOIS
Ms. Anne Craig
Director
State Library
300 South Second Street
Gwendolyn Brooks Building
Springfield, IL 62701
P: (217) 782-2994
F: (217) 785-4326
E: acraig@ilsos.net

INDIANA
Mr. Jacob Speer
Director & State Librarian
State of Indiana
State Library
140 North Senate Avenue
Indianapolis, IN 46204
P: (317) 232-3693
E: jspeer1@library.in.gov

IOWA
Mr. Michael Scott
Chief Library Officer
State of Iowa
State Library
1112 East Grand Avenue
Des Moines, IA 50319
P: (515) 281-4105
F: (515) 242-6543
E: michael.scott
    @lib.state.ia.us

KANSAS
Ms. Jo Budler
State Librarian
State Library
Capitol Building, Room 343-N
300 Southwest 10th Avenue
Topeka, KS 66612
P: (785) 506-4563
F: (785) 368-7291
E: jo.budler@library.ks.gov

KENTUCKY
Mr. Wayne Onkst
State Librarian & Commissioner
Department for Libraries &
Archives
P.O. Box 537
Frankfort, KY 40602
P: (502) 564-8300, Ext. 312
F: (502) 564-5773
E: wayne.onkst@ky.gov

LOUISIANA
Ms. Rebecca Hamilton
State Librarian
State Library
P.O. Box 131
Baton Rouge, LA 70821
P: (225) 342-4923
F: (225) 219-4804
E: rhamilton@crt.la.gov

MAINE
Mr. James Ritter
State Librarian
State Library
64 State House Station
Augusta, ME 04333
P: (207) 287-5604
F: (207) 287-5624
E: james.ritter@maine.gov

MARYLAND
Ms. Irene M. Padilla
Assistant State Superintendent
for Libraries
Division of Library
Development & Services
200 West Baltimore Street
Baltimore, MD 21201
P: (410) 767-0435
F: (410) 333-2507
E: ipadilla
    @msde.state.md.us

MASSACHUSETTS
Ms. Dianne Carty
Director
Board of Library
Commissioners
98 North Washington Street,
Suite 401
Boston, MA 02114
P: (617) 725-1860 Ext. 222
E: dianne.carty@state.ma.us

State and Public Libraries

MICHIGAN
Mr. Randy Riley
State Librarian
State Library & Historical
Center
P.O. Box 30007
Lansing, MI 48909
P: (517) 373-5860
F: (517) 373-4480
E: rileyr1@michigan.gov

MINNESOTA
Ms. Jennifer Nelson
State Librarian & Director
State Library Services
Department of Education
1500 Highway 36 West
Roseville, MN 55113
P: (651) 582-8791
E: Jennifer.R.Nelson
    @state.mn.us

MISSISSIPPI
Ms. Susan Cassagne
Executive Director
Library Commission
3881 Eastwood Drive
Jackson, MS 39211
P: (601) 432-4038
E: susan@mlc.lib.ms.us

MISSOURI
Ms. Barbara Reading
State Librarian
State Library
P.O. Box 387
Jefferson City, MO 65102
P: (573) 526-4783
E: Barbara.reading
    @sos.mo.gov

MONTANA
Ms. Jennie Stapp
State Librarian
State Librarian's Office
1515 East 6th Avenue
P.O. Box 201800
Helena, MT 59620
P: (406) 444-4799
F: (406) 444-0266
E: jstapp2@mt.gov

NEBRASKA
Mr. Rod Wagner
Director
Library Commission
The Atrium
1200 N Street, Suite 120
Lincoln, NE 68508
P: (402) 471-4001
F: (402) 471-2083
E: rod.wagner@nebraska.gov

NEVADA
Ms. Daphne DeLeon
Division Administrator & State
Librarian
State Library & Archives
100 North Stewart Street
Carson City, NV 89701
P: (775) 684-3315
F: (775) 684-3311
E: ddeleon@admin.nv.gov

NEW HAMPSHIRE
Mr. Michael York
State Librarian
State Library
20 Park Street
Concord, NH 03301
P: (603) 271-2397
F: (603) 271-6826
E: michael.york@dcr.nh.gov

NEW JERSEY
Ms. Mary Chute
State Librarian
State of New Jersey
185 West State Street
Trenton, NJ 08625
P: (609) 278-2640 Ext. 101
F: (609) 278-2647
E: mchute@njstatelib.org

NEW MEXICO
Mr. Michael Delello
Department of Cultural Affairs
407 Galisteo Street
Santa Fe, NM 87507
P: (505) 827-6354
F: (505) 476-9701
E: Michael.Delello
    @state.nm.us

NEW YORK
Mr. Bernard A. Margolis
State Librarian & Assistant
Commissioner for Libraries
State Library
Cultural Education Center
10C34
Albany, NY 12230
P: (518) 474-5930
F: (518) 486-6880
E: bmargolis@mail.nysed.gov

NORTH CAROLINA
Ms. Cal Shepard
State Librarian
State Library
4640 Mail Service Center
Raleigh, NC 27699
P: (919) 807-7410
F: (919) 733-8748
E: cal.shepard@ncdcr.gov

NORTH DAKOTA
Ms. Mary Soucie
State Librarian
State of North Dakota
604 East Boulevard Avenue
Department 250
Bismarck, ND 58505
P: (701) 328-4654
F: (701) 328-2040
E: msoucie@nd.gov

OHIO
Ms. Beverly Cain
State Librarian
State Library
274 East 1st Avenue, Suite 100
Columbus, OH 43201
P: (614) 644-6843
F: (614) 466-3584
E: bcain@library.ohio.gov

OKLAHOMA
Ms. Susan C. McVey
State Librarian
Department of Libraries
200 Northeast 18th Street
Oklahoma City, OK 73105
P: (405) 522-3173
F: (405) 521-1077
E: smcvey
    @oltn.odl.state.ok.us

OREGON
Ms. MaryKay Dahlgreen
State Librarian
State Library
250 Winter Street, Northeast
Salem, OR 97301
P: (503) 378-4367
F: (503) 585-8059
E: marykay.dahlgreen
    @state.or.us

PENNSYLVANIA
Mr. Brian Dawson
Director
Department of Education
Forum Building, Room 200
607 South Drive
Harrisburg, PA 17120
P: (717) 787-8007
F: (717) 772-0044
E: bridawson@pa.gov

RHODE ISLAND
Ms. Karen Mellor
Acting Chief Library Officer
Office of Library & Information
Services
1 Capitol Hill, Floor 2
Providence, RI 02908
P: (401) 574-9304
E: Karen.Mellor@olis.ri.gov

SOUTH CAROLINA
Ms. Leesa Benggio
State of South Carolina
P.O. Box 11469
Columbia, SC 29211
P: (803) 734-8668
F: (803) 734-0822
E: lbenggio
    @statelibrary.sc.gov

SOUTH DAKOTA
Ms. Daria Bossman
State Librarian
State of South Dakota
MacKay Building
800 Governors Drive
Pierre, SD 57501
P: (605) 773-3131
E: daria.bossman
    @state.sd.us

TENNESSEE
Mr. Charles A. Sherrill
State Librarian & Archivist
State Library & Archives
403 7th Avenue, North
Nashville, TN 37243
P: (615) 741-7996
F: (615) 532-9293
E: Chuck.Sherrill@tn.gov

TEXAS
Mr. Mark Smith
Director & State Librarian
State Library & Archives
P.O. Box 12516
Austin, TX 78711
P: (512) 463-5460
E: msmith@tsl.state.tx.us

U.S. VIRGIN ISLANDS
Ms. Ingrid Bough
Territorial Director of Libraries,
Archives & Museums
Territory of the Virgin Islands
C/o Florence Williams Public
Library
1122 King Street, Christiansted
St. Croix, VI 00820
P: (304) 773-5715
F: (304) 773-5327
E: ingrid.bough@dpnr.vi.gov

UTAH
Ms. Donna Jones Morris
State Librarian
State Library
250 North 1950 West, Suite A
Salt Lake City, UT 84116
P: (801) 715-6770
F: (801) 715-6767
E: dmorris@utah.gov

VERMONT
Ms. Martha Reid
State Librarian
Department of Libraries
109 State Street
Montpelier, VT 05609
P: (802) 828-3265
F: (802) 828-2199
E: martha.reid@state.vt.us

VIRGINIA
Ms. Sandra Treadway
State Librarian
The Library of Virginia
800 East Broad Street
Richmond, VA 23219
P: (804) 692-3535
F: (804) 692-3594
E: Sandra.Treadway
   @lva.virginia.gov

WASHINGTON
Mr. Rand Simmons
State Librarian
State Library
Office of the Secretary of State
P.O. Box 42460
Tumwater, WA 98504
P: (360) 570-5585
F: (360) 586-7575
E: rand.simmons@sos.wa.gov

WEST VIRGINIA
Ms. Karen E. Goff
Secretary
State of West Virginia
1900 Kanawha Boulevard, East
Cultural Center
Charleston, WV 25305
P: (304) 558-2041
F: (304) 558-2044
E: karen.e.goff@wv.gov

WISCONSIN
Mr. Kurt Kiefer
State Librarian
Division for Libraries,
Technology & Community
Learning
Department of Public Instruction
P.O. Box 7841
Madison, WI 53707
P: (608) 266-2205
F: (608) 266-8770
E: Kurt.Kiefer@dpi.wi.gov

WYOMING
Ms. Lesley D. Boughton
State Librarian
State Library
2800 Central Avenue
Cheyenne, WY 82002
P: (307) 777-5911
F: (307) 777-5920
E: lesley.boughton@wyo.gov

State Police

Patrols the state's highways and enforces the motor vehicle laws of the state.

ALABAMA
Mr. Spencer Collier
Director
Law Enforcement Agency
301 South Ripley Street
P.O. Box 1511
Montgomery, AL 36102
P: (334) 242-4394
F: (334) 242-0512

ALASKA
Mr. Gary Folger
Commissioner
Department of Public Safety
5700 East Tudor Road
Anchorage, AK 99507
P: (907) 269-5086
F: (907) 269-4543
E: gary.folger@alaska.gov

AMERICAN SAMOA
Mr. William E. Haleck
Commissioner
Department of Public Safety
American Samoa Government
P.O. Box 1086
Pato Pato, AS 96799
P: (684) 633-1111
F: (684) 633-7296
E: commissioner@dps.as.gov

ARIZONA
Mr. Frank Milstead
Director
Department of Public Safety
P.O. Box 6638
Phoenix, AZ 85005
P: (602) 223-2000
F: (602) 223-2917

ARKANSAS
Colonel Bill Bryant
Director
State Police
1 State Police Plaza Drive
Little Rock, AR 72209
P: (501) 618-8299
F: (501) 618-8710
E: info@asp.arkansas.gov

CALIFORNIA
Mr. Joseph A. Farrow
Commissioner
Highway Patrol
601 North 7th Street
P.O. Box 942898
Sacramento, CA 94298
P: (916) 843-3001
F: (916) 843-3266

COLORADO
Colonel Scott G. Hernandez
Chief
State Patrol
Department of Public Safety
700 Kipling Street
Lakewood, CO 80215
P: (303) 239-4403
F: (303) 239-4481
E: scott.hernandez
 @state.co.us

CONNECTICUT
Ms. Dora B. Schriro
Commissioner
Department of Emergency
Services & Public Protection
1111 Country Club Road
Middletown, CT 06457
P: (860) 685-8000
F: (860) 685-8354
E: dora.schriro@ct.gov

DELAWARE
Colonel Nathaniel McQueen
Commissioner
State Police
1441 North DuPont Highway
P.O. Box 430
Dover, DE 19903
P: (302) 739-5291

DISTRICT OF COLUMBIA
Ms. Cathy L. Lanier
Chief of Police
Metropolitan Police Department
300 Indiana Avenue, Northwest
Room 5059
Washington, DC 20001
P: (202) 727-9099
F: (202) 727-4106
E: mpd@dc.gov

FLORIDA
Mr. Rick Swearingen
Commissioner
Department of Law
Enforcement
2331 Phillips Road
P.O. Box 1489
Tallahassee, FL 32302
P: (850) 410-7001
E: RickSwearingen
 @fdle.state.fl.us

GEORGIA
Colonel Mark W. McDonough
Commissioner
Department of Public Safety
P.O. Box 1456
Atlanta, GA 30371
P: (404) 624-7477
F: (404) 624-7788

ILLINOIS
Mr. Hiram Grau
State Director
State Police
801 South 7th Street, Suite 1100
– S
Springfield, IL 62703
P: (217) 782-7263
E: hiram.grau@illinois.gov

INDIANA
Mr. Douglas G. Carter
Superintendent
State Police
Indiana Government Center
North
100 North Senate Avenue
Indianapolis, IN 46204
P: (317) 232-8248
E: ISP@isp.in.gov

IOWA
Col. Patrick J. Hoye
Colonel
State Patrol Division
Department of Public Safety
215 East 7th Street
Des Moines, IA 50319
P: (515) 725-6101
E: hoye@dps.state.ia.us

KANSAS
Mr. Mark Bruce
Superintendent
Highway Patrol
122 Southwest 7th Street
Topeka, KS 66603
P: (785) 296-6800
F: (785) 296-3049

KENTUCKY
Mr. Rodney Brewer
Commissioner
State Police
919 Versailles Road
Frankfort, KY 40601
P: (502) 782-1800
F: (502) 573-1479

LOUISIANA
Col. Michael D. Edmonson
Deputy Secretary
State Police
Public Safety Services
7919 Independence Boulevard
Baton Rouge, LA 70806
P: (225) 925-6118
F: (225) 925-6006

MAINE
Colonel Robert A. Williams
Chief
State Police
42 State House Station
45 Commerce Drive
Augusta, ME 04333
P: (207) 624-7200
E: robert.a.williams
 @maine.gov

MARYLAND
Colonel William Pallozzi
Superintendent
Department of State Police
1201 Reisterstown Road
Pikesville, MD 21208
P: (410) 653-4219
E: msp.superintendent
 @maryland.gov

MASSACHUSETTS
Colonel Richard D. McKeon
Superintendent
State Police
470 Worcester Road
Framingham, MA 01702
P: (508) 820-2300
F: (617) 727-6874

MICHIGAN
Colonel Kriste Kibbey Etue
Director
State Police
333 South Grand Avenue
P.O. Box 30634
Lansing, MI 48909
P: (517) 332-2521
F: (517) 241-0409
E: EtueK@michigan.gov

MINNESOTA
Colonel Kevin Daly
Chief
State Patrol
445 Minnesota Street
St. Paul, MN 55101
P: (651) 201-7100
F: (651) 296-5937
E: kevin.daly@state.mn.us

MISSISSIPPI
Lt. Col. Larry Waggoner
Director
Bureau of Investigation
P.O. Box 958
Jackson, MS 39205
P: (601) 987-1573
F: (601) 987-1488
E: lwaggoner
 @mdps.state.ms.us

State Police

MISSOURI
Colonel J. Bret Johnson
Superintendent
State Highway Patrol
1510 East Elm Street
Jefferson City, MO 65101
P: (573) 751-3313

MONTANA
Hon. Tim Fox (R)
Attorney General
Department of Justice
Justice Building
215 North Sanders
Helena, MT 59620
P: (406) 444-2026
F: (406) 444-3549
E: contactdoj@mt.gov

NEBRASKA
Colonel Bradley Rice
Superintendent of Law
Enforcement & Public Safety
State Patrol
P.O. Box 94907
Lincoln, NE 68509
P: (402) 471-4545
F: (402) 479-4002
E: bradley.rice
@nebraska.gov

NEVADA
Mr. Bernard W. Curtis
Division Administrator
Parole & Probation
1445 Old Hot Springs Road,
Suite 104
Carson City, NV 89706
P: (775) 684-2605
F: (775) 684-2693

NEW HAMPSHIRE
Colonel Robert L. Quinn
Director
Division of State Police
Department of Safety
33 Hazen Drive
Concord, NH 03305
P: (603) 223-8813
F: (603) 271-1153
E: SPHeadquarters
@dos.nh.gov

NEW JERSEY
Col. Rick Fuentes
Superintendent
State Police
P.O. Box 7068
West Trenton, NJ 08628
P: (609) 882-2000
F: (609) 530-4383

NEW MEXICO
Mr. Pete N. Kassetas
Chief of Police
Department of Public Safety
4491 Cerrillos Road
P.O. Box 1628
Santa Fe, NM 87504
P: (505) 827-9002
F: (505) 827-3394
E: NMSP.Chief@state.nm.us

NEW YORK
Mr. Joseph D'Amico
Superintendent
State Police
1220 Washington Avenue,
Building 22
Albany, NY 12226
P: 518) 457-6721

NORTH CAROLINA
Colonel William J. Grey
Commander
State Highway Patrol
4702 Mail Service Center
Raleigh, NC 27699
P: (919) 733-7952
F: (919) 733-1189

NORTH DAKOTA
Colonel James Prochniak
Superintendent
Highway Patrol
600 East Boulevard Avenue
Department 504
Bismarck, ND 58505
P: (701) 328-2455
F: (701) 328-1717
E: jprochni@nd.gov

NORTHERN MARIANA ISLANDS
Mr. James C.
Deleon Guerrero
Commissioner
Department of Public Safety
Jose M. Sablan Building
Caller Box 10007
Saipan, MP 96950
P: (670) 664-9022
F: (670) 664-9070

OHIO
Colonel Paul A. Pride
Superintendent
State Highway Patrol
1970 West Broad Street
P.O. Box 182074
Columbus, OH 43223
P: (614) 466-2990

OKLAHOMA
Mr. Michael C. Thompson
Commissioner
Department of Public Safety
P.O. Box 11415
Oklahoma City, OK 73136
P: (405) 425-2424
E: mike.thompson
@dps.state.ok.us

PENNSYLVANIA
Colonel Marcus L. Brown
Acting Commissioner
State Police
1800 Elmerton Avenue
Harrisburg, PA 17110
P: (717) 783-5517
F: (717) 783-7690

PUERTO RICO
Mr. Hector Pesquera
Superintendent
Puerto Rico Police
P.O. Box 70166
San Juan, PR 00936
P: (787) 793-1234
F: (787) 781-0080

RHODE ISLAND
Colonel Steven G. O'Donnell
Commissioner & Superintendent
Department of Public Safety
311 Danielson Pike
North Scituate, RI 02857
P: (401) 444-1000
F: (401) 444-1105
E: sodonnell
@risp.state.ri.us

SOUTH CAROLINA
Colonel Michael Oliver
Commander
Highway Patrol
10311 Wilson Boulevard
P.O. Box 1993
Blythewood, SC 29016
P: (803) 896-7920
F: (803) 896-7922

SOUTH DAKOTA
Colonel Craig Price
Superintendent
Highway Patrol
Department of Public Safety
118 West Capitol Avenue
Pierre, SD 57501
P: (605) 773-3105
F: (605) 773-6046

TENNESSEE
Mr. Bill Gibbons
Commissioner
Department of Safety &
Homeland Security
1150 Foster Avenue
P.O. Box 945
Nashville, TN 37202
P: (615) 251-5166
E: email.safety@tn.gov

TEXAS
Mr. Steve McCraw
Director
Department of Public Safety
5805 North Lamar Boulevard
P.O. Box 4087
Austin, TX 78773
P: (512) 424-2000
F: (512) 483-5708

U.S. VIRGIN ISLANDS
Mr. Rodney F. Querrard
Commissioner
Police Department
Alexander Farrelly Criminal
Justice Ctr.
Charlotte Amalie
St. Thomas, VI 00802
P: (340) 715-5605
F: (340) 715-5517

UTAH
Col. Daniel Fuhr
Superintendent
Department of Public Safety
Utah Highway Patrol
4501 South 2700 West, P.O. Box
141100
Salt Lake City, UT 84114
P: (801) 965-4518
F: (801) 965-4716
E: dfuhr@utah.gov

VERMONT
Colonel Thomas J.
L'Esperance
Director
State Police
103 South Main Street
Waterbury, VT 05671
P: (802) 875-2112
E: Tom.LEsperance
@state.vt.us

State Police

VIRGINIA
Col. W. Steven Flaherty
Superintendent
Department of State Police
7700 Midlothian Turnpike
P.O. Box 27472
Richmond, VA 23235
P: (804) 674-2087
F: (804) 674-2132
E: steve.flaherty
   @vsp.virginia.gov

WASHINGTON
Mr. John R. Batiste
Chief
State Patrol
General Administration Building
P.O. Box 42600
Olympia, WA 98504
P: (360) 596-4000
E: john.batiste@wsp.wa.gov

WEST VIRGINIA
Colonel Jay Smithers
Superintendent
State Police
725 Jefferson Road
South Charleston, WV 25309
P: (304) 746-2115
F: (304) 746-2230
E: Jay.Smithers@wvsp.gov

WISCONSIN
Mr. Stephen Fitzgerald
Superintendent
Division of State Patrol
4802 Sheboygan Avenue, Room
551
P.O. Box 7912
Madison, WI 53707
P: (608) 266-3212
F: (608) 267-4495
E: Stephen.Fitzgerald
   @dot.wi.gov

WYOMING
Colonel John Butler
Administrator
Highway Patrol
5300 Bishop Boulevard
Cheyenne, WY 82009
P: (307) 777-4301
F: (307) 777-3897

State Security

Develops and oversees operations to insure the safety of state citizens from threats of violence and terrorism.

ALABAMA
Mr. Art Faulkner
Director
Emergency Management
Agency
5898 County Road 41
P.O. Box 2160
Clanton, AL 35046
P: (205) 280-2201
F: (205) 280-2410
E: art.faulkner
    @ema.alabama.gov

ALASKA
Maj. Gen. Thomas H. Katkus
Adjutant General
Department of Military &
Veterans Affairs
P.O. Box 5800
Fort Richardson, AK 99505
P: (907) 428-6003
F: (907) 428-6019
E: thomas.katkus
    @us.army.mil

AMERICAN SAMOA
Mr. William E. Haleck
Commissioner
Department of Public Safety
American Samoa Government
P.O. Box 1086
Pato Pato, AS 96799
P: (684) 633-1111
F: (684) 633-7296
E: commissioner@dps.as.gov

ARIZONA
Mr. Frank Milstead
Director
Department of Public Safety
P.O. Box 6638
Phoenix, AZ 85005
P: (602) 223-2000
F: (602) 223-2917

ARKANSAS
Mr. David Maxwell
Director
Department of Emergency
Management
Building 9501
Camp Joseph T. Robinson
North Little Rock, AR 72199
P: (501) 683-7834
F: (501) 683-7890
E: david.maxwell
    @adem.arkansas.gov

CALIFORNIA
Mr. Joseph A. Farrow
Commissioner
Highway Patrol
601 North 7th Street
P.O. Box 942898
Sacramento, CA 94298
P: (916) 843-3001
F: (916) 843-3266

Mr. Mark Ghilarducci
Director
Governor's Office of Emergency
Services
3650 Schriever Avenue
Mather, CA 95655
P: (916) 845-8506
F: (916) 845-8511
E: mark.ghilarducci
    @caloes.ca.gov

COLORADO
Ms. Karin McGowan
Interim Director
Office of Emergency
Preparedness & Response
4300 Cherry Creek Drive, South
Denver, CO 80246
P: (303) 692-3473
F: (303) 691-7811
E: karin.mcgowan
    @state.co.us

CONNECTICUT
Ms. Dora B. Schriro
Commissioner
Department of Emergency
Services & Public Protection
1111 Country Club Road
Middletown, CT 06457
P: (860) 685-8000
F: (860) 685-8354
E: dora.schriro@ct.gov

DELAWARE
Mr. Lewis D. Schiliro
Cabinet Secretary
Department of Safety &
Homeland Security
303 Transportation Circle
P.O. Box 818
Dover, DE 19903
P: (302) 744-2680
F: (302) 739-4874

DISTRICT OF COLUMBIA
Ms. Cathy L. Lanier
Chief of Police
Metropolitan Police Department
300 Indiana Avenue, Northwest
Room 5059
Washington, DC 20001
P: (202) 727-9099
F: (202) 727-4106
E: mpd@dc.gov

FLORIDA
Mr. Rick Swearingen
Commissioner
Department of Law
Enforcement
2331 Phillips Road
P.O. Box 1489
Tallahassee, FL 32302
P: (850) 410-7001
E: RickSwearingen
    @fdle.state.fl.us

GEORGIA
Colonel Mark W. McDonough
Commissioner
Department of Public Safety
P.O. Box 1456
Atlanta, GA 30371
P: (404) 624-7477
F: (404) 624-7788

GUAM
Maj. Gen. Benny M. Paulino
Adjutant General
National Guard
430 Army Drive, Building 300
Barrigada, GU 96913
P: (671) 735-0406
F: (671) 734-4081
E: benny.m.paulino
    @us.army.mil

HAWAII
Maj. Gen. Darryl D.M. Wong
Adjutant General
Department of Defense
3949 Diamond Head Road
Honolulu, HI 96816
P: (808) 733-4246
F: (808) 733-4499
E: darryll.wong
    @hickarm.af.mil

IDAHO
Maj. Gen. Gary L. Sayler
Adjutant General
Military Division
4040 West Guard Street
Boise, ID 83705
P: (208) 422-5242
F: (208) 422-6179
E: gary.sayler@ang.af.mil

ILLINOIS
Mr. Hiram Grau
State Director
State Police
801 South 7th Street, Suite 1100
– S
Springfield, IL 62703
P: (217) 782-7263
E: hiram.grau@illinois.gov

Mr. James Joseph
Director
State Emergency Management
Agency
2200 South Dirksen Parkway
Springfield, IL 62703
P: (217) 782-2700
E: james.joseph
    @illinois.gov

INDIANA
Mr. Douglas G. Carter
Superintendent
State Police
Indiana Government Center
North
100 North Senate Avenue
Indianapolis, IN 46204
P: (317) 232-8248
E: ISP@isp.in.gov

IOWA
Mr. Mark J. Schouten
Director
Homeland Security &
Emergency Management
Department
7900 Hickmand Road, Suite 500
Windsor Heights, IA 50324
P: (515) 725-3223
F: (515) 725-3260
E: mark.schouten@iowa.gov

KANSAS
Maj. Gen. Lee E.
    Tafanelli (R)
Adjutant General
Adjutant General's Department
2800 Southwest Topeka
Boulevard
Topeka, KS 66611
P: (785) 274-1001
F: (785) 274-1682
E: lee.tafanelli
    @us.army.mil

KENTUCKY
Maj. Gen. Edward W. Tonini
Adjutant General
Department of Military Affairs
100 Minuteman Parkway
Frankfort, KY 40601
P: (502) 607-1558
F: (502) 607-1271
E: edward.tonini
    @us.army.mil

State Security

LOUISIANA
Mr. Kevin Davis
Director
Governor's Office of Homeland
Security & Emergency
Preparedness
7667 Independence Boulevard
Baton Rouge, LA 70608
P: (225) 922-1503
F: (225) 925-7501
E: kevin.davis@la.gov

MAINE
Mr. Bruce Fitzgerald
Director
State Emergency Management
Agency
45 Commerce Drive, Suite #2
Augusta, ME 04333
P: (207) 624-4400
F: (207) 287-3178
E: Bruce.F.Fitzgerald
   @maine.gov

MARYLAND
Mr. Andrew Lauland
Homeland Security Advisor
Governor's Office of Homeland
Security
6 St. Paul Street
24th Floor, Schaefer Tower
Baltimore, MD 21201
P: (410) 974-2389
E: Andy.Lauland
   @maryland.gov

MASSACHUSETTS
Mr. Daniel Bennett
Secretary
Executive Office of Public
Safety & Security
One Ashburton Place, Suite
2133
Boston, MA 02108
P: (617) 727-7775
F: (617) 727-4764

MICHIGAN
Colonel Kriste Kibbey Etue
Director
State Police
333 South Grand Avenue
P.O. Box 30634
Lansing, MI 48909
P: (517) 332-2521
F: (517) 241-0409
E: EtueK@michigan.gov

Captain Chris A. Kelenske
Director
State Emergency Management
& Homeland Security Division
State Police
4000 Collins Road
Lansing, MI 48910
P: (517) 333-5043
F: (517) 333-4987
E: kelenskec@michigan.gov

MINNESOTA
Ms. Ramona Dohman
Commissioner
Department of Public Safety
445 Minnesota Street, Suite
1000
St. Paul, MN 55101
P: (651) 201-7160
F: (651) 297-5728
E: Mona.Dohman@state.mn.us

MISSISSIPPI
Mr. Robert Latham
Director
Emergency Management
Agency
#1 MEMA Drive
P.O. Box 5644
Pearl, MS 39288
P: (601) 933-6882
F: (601) 933-6810
E: rlatham@mema.ms.gov

MISSOURI
Mr. Lane Roberts
Director
Department of Public Safety
Office of the Director
P.O. Box 749
Jefferson City, MO 65102
P: (573) 751-4905
F: (573) 751-5399

MONTANA
Mr. Ed Tinsley
Administrator
Department of Disaster &
Emergency Services
P.O. Box 4789
Fort Harrison, MT 59636
P: (406) 324-4777
F: (406) 324-4790
E: edtinsley@mt.gov

NEBRASKA
Colonel Bradley Rice
Superintendent of Law
Enforcement & Public Safety
State Patrol
P.O. Box 94907
Lincoln, NE 68509
P: (402) 471-4545
F: (402) 479-4002
E: bradley.rice
   @nebraska.gov

NEVADA
Mr. Christopher B. Smith
Director
Division of Emergency
Management
Public Safety
2478 Fairview Drive
Carson City, NV 89701
P: (775) 687-0300
F: (775) 687-0322
E: cbsmith@dps.state.nv.us

NEW HAMPSHIRE
Colonel Robert L. Quinn
Director
Division of State Police
Department of Safety
33 Hazen Drive
Concord, NH 03305
P: (603) 223-8813
F: (603) 271-1153
E: SPHeadquarters
   @dos.nh.gov

NEW JERSEY
Mr. Edward Dickson
Director
Office of Homeland Security &
Preparedness
P.O. Box 091
Trenton, NJ 08625
P: (609) 584-4000
F: (609) 631-4916

NEW MEXICO
Mr. Jay Mitchell
Director
State Department of Homeland
Security & Emergency
Management
P.O. Box 27111
Santa Fe, NM 87502
P: (505) 476-9655
E: jay.mitchell@state.nm.us

NEW YORK
Mr. Jerome Hauer
Commissioner
Division of Homeland Security
& Emergency Services
1220 Washington Avenue,
Building 22
Suite 101
Albany, NY 12226
P: (518) 242-5058
F: (518) 322-4978
E: hauer@dhses.ny.gov

NORTH CAROLINA
Mr. Frank L. Perry
Secretary
Department of Public Safety
512 North Salisbury Street
4201 Mail Service Center
Raleigh, NC 27699
P: (919) 733-2126
F: (919) 715-8477
E: frank.perry@ncdps.gov

NORTH DAKOTA
Ms. Debbie LaCombe
State Director
Homeland Security Division
Fraine Barracks Lane, Building
35
P.O. Box 5511
Bismarck, ND 58504
P: (701) 328-8100
F: (701) 328-8181
E: dlacombe@nd.gov

Colonel James Prochniak
Superintendent
Highway Patrol
600 East Boulevard Avenue
Department 504
Bismarck, ND 58505
P: (701) 328-2455
F: (701) 328-1717
E: jprochni@nd.gov

**NORTHERN MARIANA
ISLANDS**
Mr. Marvin P. Seman
Director
Office of Homeland Security
Office of the Governor
Caller Box 10007
Saipan, MP 95950
P: (670) 664-2216
F: (670) 664-2211
E: marvin.seman@gmail.com

OHIO
Colonel John Born
Director
Department of Public Safety
1970 West Broad Street
P.O. Box 182081
Columbus, OH 43218
P: (614) 466-3383
F: (614) 466-0433

OKLAHOMA
Mr. Michael C. Thompson
Commissioner
Department of Public Safety
P.O. Box 11415
Oklahoma City, OK 73136
P: (405) 425-2424
E: mike.thompson
    @dps.state.ok.us

PENNSYLVANIA
Mr. Richard Flinn Jr.
Director
State Emergency Management
Agency
2605 Interstate Drive
Harrisburg, PA 17110
P: (717) 651-2007
E: rflinn@pa.gov

PUERTO RICO
Mr. Hector Pesquera
Superintendent
Puerto Rico Police
P.O. Box 70166
San Juan, PR 00936
P: (787) 793-1234
F: (787) 781-0080

RHODE ISLAND
Maj. Gen. Kevin R. McBride
Adjutant General
National Guard
645 New London Avenue
Cranston, RI 02920
P: (401) 275-4102
F: (401) 275-4338
E: kevin.r.mcbride
    @us.army.mil

SOUTH CAROLINA
Mr. Mark A. Keel
Chief
State Law Enforcement Division
4400 Broad River Road
P.O. Box 21398
Columbia, SC 29221
P: (803) 896-9223
F: (803) 896-7041

SOUTH DAKOTA
Mr. Trevor Jones
Secretary
Department of Public Safety
118 West Capitol Avenue
Pierre, SD 57501
P: (605) 773-3178
F: (605) 773-3018
E: DPSInfo@state.sd.us

Mr. Stefan Pluta
Homeland Security Director
Office of Homeland Security
Department of Public Safety
118 West Capitol Avenue
Pierre, SD 57501
P: (605) 773-3450
F: (605) 773-6631
E: stefan.pluta@state.sd.us

TENNESSEE
Mr. Bill Gibbons
Commissioner
Department of Safety &
Homeland Security
1150 Foster Avenue
P.O. Box 945
Nashville, TN 37202
P: (615) 251-5166
E: email.safety@tn.gov

TEXAS
Mr. Steve McCraw
Director
Department of Public Safety
5805 North Lamar Boulevard
P.O. Box 4087
Austin, TX 78773
P: (512) 424-2000
F: (512) 483-5708

U.S. VIRGIN ISLANDS
Mr. Renaldo Rivera
Adjutant General
National Guard
4031 La Grande Princess, Lot
1B
Christiansted, VI 00820
P: (340) 712-7710
F: (340) 712-7709
E: renaldo.rivera
    @us.army.mil

UTAH
Mr. Kris J. Hamlet
Director
Division of Emergency
Management
1110 State Office Building
Salt Lake City, UT 84114
P: (801) 538-9553
F: (801) 965-4608
E: krishamlet@utah.gov

WASHINGTON
Maj. Gen. Timothy J.
    Lowenberg
Adjutant General
Military Department
One Militia Drive, Building One
Camp Murray, WA 98430
P: (253) 512-8201
F: (253) 512-8497
E: timothy.lowenberg
    @us.army.mil

WEST VIRGINIA
Mr. Joe Thornton
Cabinet Secretary
Department of Military Affairs
& Public Safety
Building 1, Room W-400
1900 Kanawha Boulevard, East
Charleston, WV 25305
P: (304) 558-2930
F: (304) 558-6221
E: joseph.c.thornton@wv.gov

WISCONSIN
Mr. Brian M. Satula
Director
Division of Emergency
Management
2400 Wright Street
P.O. Box 7865
Madison, WI 53704
P: (608) 242-3210
F: (608) 242-3247
E: brian.satula
    @wisconsin.gov

WYOMING
Mr. Guy Cameron
Director
Office of Homeland Security
5500 Bishop Boulevard
East Door
Cheyenne, WY 82002
P: (307) 777-8511
F: (307) 635-6017
E: guy.cameron@wyo.gov

Telecom-munications

Responsible for communications planning and organizing a statewide plan for total communications, especially with local government emergency matters.

ALABAMA
Mr. Andy Cannon
Assistant Director, Network & Operations
Information Services Division
Folsom Administrative Building
64 North Union Street, Suite 200
Montgomery, AL 36130
P: (334) 242-3045
F: (334) 242-7002
E: andy.cannon
  @isd.alabama.gov

ALASKA
Mr. Jim Bates
Director & Chief Information Officer
Division of Enterprise Technology Services
Department of Administration
P.O. Box 110206
Juneau, AK 99811
P: (907) 269-4744
F: (907) 465-3450
E: jim.bates@alaska.gov

ARIZONA
Mr. Donald Hennington
Chief Operations Officer
State Data Center
Department of Administration
100 North 15th Avenue, Suite 400
Phoenix, AZ 85007
P: (602) 542-1422
F: (602) 542-0120

ARKANSAS
Mr. Don McDaniel
Administrator, Enterprise Network Services
Department of Information Services
One Capitol Mall, 3rd Floor
Little Rock, AR 72201
P: (501) 682-5027
F: (501) 682-4316
E: don.mcdaniel
  @arkansas.gov

CALIFORNIA
Ms. Barbara Garrett
Deputy Director
Statewide Telecommunications & Network Division
P.O. Box 1810
Rancho Cordova, CA 95741
P: (916) 464-3400
E: barbara.garrett
  @state.ca.gov

COLORADO
Ms. Kelley Eich
Interim End User Services Leader
Office of Information Technology
601 East 18th Avenue, Suite 250
Denver, CO 80203
P: (303) 764-7700
F: (303) 764-7725
E: kelley.eich@state.co.us

CONNECTICUT
Mr. Bernard O'Donnell
Director
Communication Services
Enterprise Systems & Technology
101 East River Drive
East Hartford, CT 06108
P: (860) 622-2444
F: (860) 622-4900
E: bernard.odonnell@ct.gov

DELAWARE
Ms. Colleen Gause
Team Leader
Department of Technology & Information
William Penn Building
801 Silver Lake Boulevard
Dover, DE 19904
P: (302) 739-9644
F: (302) 677-7002
E: Colleen.Gause
  @state.de.us

GEORGIA
Mr. Tom Fruman
Director
Enterprise Governance & Planning
Georgia Technology Authority
47 Trinity Avenue, Southwest
Atlanta, GA 30334
P: (404) 463-2300
F: (404) 463-2380
E: tfruman@gta.ga.gov

HAWAII
Ms. Sharon Wong
Acting Administrator
Information & Communications Services Division
Accounting & General Services
1151 Punchbowl Street
Honolulu, HI 96813
P: (808) 586-1920
F: (808) 586-1922
E: ICSD.Administration
  @hawaii.gov

ILLINOIS
Mr. Jonelle Brent
Chief of Staff
Bureau of Communications & Computer Services
120 West Jefferson Street, 3rd Floor
Springfield, IL 62702
P: (217) 557-3337
E: rich_fetter
  @cms.state.il.us

INDIANA
Mr. William Pierce
Broadband Executive
Office of Technology
100 North Senate Avenue, Room N-551
Indianapolis, IN 46204
P: (317) 233-2009
F: (317) 232-0748
E: bpierce@iot.in.gov

IOWA
Mr. Ric Lumbard
Executive Director
Iowa Communications Network
400 East 14th Street
Des Moines, IA 50319

KANSAS
Mr. Jay Coverdale
Deputy Director
Bureau of Telecommunications
Information Technology Services
900 Southwest Jackson, Room 751-S
Topeka, KS 66612
P: (785) 296-3937
E: jay.coverdale@ks.gov

LOUISIANA
Ms. Jane Patterson
Director
Office of Telecommunications Management
Division of Administration
P.O. Box 94280
Baton Rouge, LA 70804
P: (225) 342-7701
F: (225) 342-6867
E: otm@la.gov

MAINE
Ms. Ellen Lee
Director, Vendor Management Office
Department of Administrative & Financial Services
Office of Information Technology
145 State House Station
Augusta, ME 04333
P: (207) 624-8800
F: (207) 287-4563
E: ellen.lee@maine.gov

MASSACHUSETTS
Mr. Charlie Desourdy
Acting Chief Information Officer
Information Technology Division
One Ashburton Place, Room 804
Boston, MA 02108
P: (617) 626-4434
F: (617) 626-4411

MICHIGAN
Mr. David Behen
Chief Information Officer & Department Director
Department of Technology, Management & Budget
320 South Walnut Street, 2nd Floor
P.O. Box 30026
Lansing, MI 48909
P: (517) 373-3209
E: behend@michigan.gov

MINNESOTA
Mr. Dan Oehmke
Systems Supervisor
MN.IT Services Office
Centennial Building, 658 Cedar Street
St. Paul, MN 55155
P: (651) 201-1037
F: (651) 297-5368
E: Dan.Oehmke@state.mn.us

MISSISSIPPI
Mr. Steven Walker
Telecom Services Director
Information Technology Services
3771 Eastwood Drive
Jackson, MS 39211
P: (601) 432-8004
F: (601) 713-6380
E: Steven.Walker@its.ms.gov

Telecommunications

MONTANA
Kris Harrison
Chief, Network Technology
Services Bureau
Department of Administration
125 North Roberts, Room 229
P.O. Box 200113
Helena, MT 59620
P: (406) 444-3344

NEBRASKA
Ms. Jayne Scofield
Network Services Manager
Office of the Chief Information
Officer
501 South 14th Street
Lincoln, NE 68509
P: (402) 471-3454
F: (402) 471-3339
E: jayne.scofield
    @cio.ne.gov

NEVADA
Mr. Ken Adams
Chief IT Manager,
Telecommunications
Enterprise IT Services
100 North Stewart Street, Suite
100
Carson City, NV 89701
P: (775) 684-5800
F: (775) 684-7345

NEW JERSEY
Mr. E. Steven Emanuel
Chief Information Officer
Office of Information
Technology
200/300 Riverview Plaza
P.O. Box 212
Trenton, NJ 08625
P: (609) 777-5865
F: (609) 633-9100
E: steven.emanuel
    @oit.state.nj.us

NEW MEXICO
Ms. Jacqueline Miller
Deputy Secretary
Department of Information
Technology
Department of General Services
715 Alta Vista Street, P.O. Box
22550
Santa Fe, NM 87502
P: (505) 827-0000
F: (505) 827-2998
E: jacque.miller
    @state.nm.us

NEW YORK
Mr. Peter J. Arment
First Deputy Director
Division of Telecommunications
Empire State Building
Corning Tower Building, 27th
Floor
Albany, NY 12242
P: (518) 402-2324
F: (518) 473-7145
E: peter.arment
    @oft.state.ny.us

NORTH CAROLINA
Mr. Steve Stoneman
Executive Director
Client & Network Services
Support
4101 Mail Service Center
P.O. Box 17209
Raleigh, NC 27699
P: (919) 754-6465
F: (919) 850-2827
E: steve.stoneman@nc.gov

NORTH DAKOTA
Mr. Mike J. Ressler
Chief Information Officer
Information Technology
Department
4201 Normandy Street
Bismarck, ND 58503
P: (701) 328-1000
F: (701) 328-1075
E: mressler@nd.gov

OHIO
Mr. Spencer Wood
Chief Operating Officer
Infrastructure Services Division
Office of Information
Technology
1320 Arthur E. Adams Drive
Columbus, OH 43221
P: (614) 644-9245
F: (614) 466-7345
E: spencer.wood
    @das.ohio.gov

OREGON
Mr. Al Grapoli
Voice Services Manager
State Data Center
Department of Administrative
Services
955 Center Street, Northeast
U510
Salem, OR 97383
P: (503) 378-3338
F: (503) 378-8333
E: al.grapoli@state.or.us

Mr. Alex Pettit
Chief Information Officer
Office of State Finance
Executive Building
155 Cottage Street Northeast, 4th
Floor
Salem, OR 97301
P: (503) 378-3175
F: (503) 378-3795
E: alex.pettit
    @das.state.or.us

PENNSYLVANIA
Mr. John MacMillan
Deputy Secretary for
Information Technology & Chief
Information Officer
Office for Information
Technology
Governor's Office of
Administration
209 Finance Building
Harrisburg, PA 17120
P: (717) 787-5440
F: (717) 787-4523
E: cio@pa.gov

RHODE ISLAND
Mr. Clarence Bussius
Enterprise Telecommunications
Manager
Division of Information
Technology
6 Harrington Road
Cranston, RI 02920
P: (401) 462-1432
E: clarence.bussius
    @doit.ri.gov

SOUTH CAROLINA
Mr. Kyle Herron
Chief Operating Officer
Division of Technology
P.O. Box 12444
Columbia, SC 29211
P: (803) 896-0222
E: kherron@cio.sc.gov

SOUTH DAKOTA
Mr. Dennis Nincehelser
Director of Telecommunications
Bureau of Information &
Telecommunications
700 Governors Drive
Pierre, SD 57501
P: (605) 773-4165
F: (605) 773-3741
E: dennis.nincehelser
    @state.sd.us

TENNESSEE
Mr. Mark Bengel
Chief Information Officer
Office for Information
Resources
Department of Finance &
Administration
312 Rosa L. Parks Avenue
Nashville, TN 37343
P: (615) 741-7951
F: (615) 532-0471

TEXAS
Mr. John Hoffman
Director
Communications Technology
Services
Department of Information
Resources
300 West 15th Street, Suite 1300
Austin, TX 78701
P: (512) 936-2501
F: (512) 475-4759
E: john.hoffman
    @dir.texas.gov

UTAH
Mr. Mark VanOrden
Chief Information Officer
Department of Technology
Services
1 State Office Buidling, Floor 6
Salt Lake City, UT 84114
P: (801) 538-3298
F: (801) 538-3622
E: mvanorden@utah.gov

VERMONT
Mr. Richard Boes
Commissioner & Chief
Information Officer
Department of Information &
Innovation
Agency of Administration
133 State Street
Montpelier, VT 05633
P: (802) 828-4141
F: (802) 828-3398
E: richard.boes@state.vt.us

VIRGINIA
Ms. Debbie Dodson
Director, Internal Technology &
Portfolio Management
Information Technologies
Agency
110 South 7th Street
Richmond, VA 23219
P: (804) 416-6209
E: debbie.dodson
    @vita.virginia.gov

Telecommunications

WASHINGTON
Mr. William Weinman
Assistant Director
Telecommunication Services
Division
1300 South Evergreen Park
Drive
Southwest
Olympia, WA 98504
P: (360) 664-1109

WEST VIRGINIA
Mr. John Dunlap
Director of Infrastructure
Office of Technology
1900 Kanawha Boulevard, East
Capitol Complex, Building 5,
10th Floor
Charleston, WV 25305
P: (304) 957-6864
F: (304) 558-0136
E: John.D.Dunlap@wv.gov

WISCONSIN
Mr. Tim Herbert
Assistant Bureau Director
Bureau of Infrastructure Support
101 East Wilson Street
Madison, WI 53707
P: (608) 261-8550
E: tim.herbert
    @wisconsin.gov

WYOMING
Mr. Rick Imbrogno
Administrator
Information Technology
Division
Emerson Building, Room 237
2001 Capitol Avenue
Cheyenne, WY 82002
P: (307) 777-5840
F: (307) 777-6725

Tourism

Coordinates promotional and advertising programs for the tourism industry in the state.

ALABAMA
Mr. Lee Sentell
Director
Tourism Department
401 Adams Avenue
P.O. Box 4927
Montgomery, AL 36103
P: (334) 242-4413
E: Lee.Sentell
@tourism.alabama.gov

ALASKA
Ms. Caryl McConkie
Tourism Development Specialist
Division of Economic
Development
P.O. Box 110804
Juneau, AK 99811
P: (907) 465-5478
F: (907) 465-3767
E: caryl_mcconkie
@commerce.state.ak.us

AMERICAN SAMOA
Mr. Keniseli Lafaele
Director
Department of Commerce
American Samoa Government
Executive Office Building,
Utulei
Pago Pago, AS 96799
P: (684) 633-5155
F: (684) 633-4195
E: keniseli.lafaele@doc.as

Ms. Virginia Samuelu
Deputy Director
Office of Tourism, Department
of Commerce
American Samoa Government
PO Box 1147
Pago Pago, AS 96799
P: (684) 699-9411
F: (684) 699-9414
E: amsamoa
@amerikasamoa.info

ARIZONA
Ms. Sherry Henry
Executive Director
Office of Tourism
1110 West Washington Street,
Suite 155
Phoenix, AZ 85007
P: (602) 364-3717
F: (602) 364-3701
E: shenry@azot.gov

ARKANSAS
Mr. Richard Davies
Executive Director
Department of Parks & Tourism
#1 Capitol Mall, Room 4A900
Little Rock, AR 72201
P: (501) 682-2535
F: (501) 682-2383
E: richard.davies
@arkansas.gov

CALIFORNIA
Ms. Caroline Beteta
Executive Director
California Tourism
P.O. Box 1499
Sacramento, CA 95812
P: (916) 444-4429
F: (916) 322-3402
E: cbeteta@commerce.ca.gov

COLORADO
Mr. Al White
Director
Tourism Office
1625 Broadway, Suite 2700
Denver, CO 80202
P: (303) 892-3856
F: (303) 892-3885
E: Al.White@state.co.us

CONNECTICUT
Mr. Randy Fiveash
Director of Tourism
Offices of Culture & Tourism
One Constitution Plaza, 2nd
Floor
Hartford, CT 06103
P: (860) 256-2769
F: (860) 256-2811
E: Randall.Fiveash@ct.gov

FLORIDA
Mr. Karl Blischke
Director
Division of Strategic Business
Development
Department of Economic
Opportunity
107 East Madison St., Caldwell
Building
Tallahassee, FL 32399
P: (850) 245-7105
F: (850) 921-3223
E: karl.blischke
@deo.myflorida.com

GEORGIA
Mr. Kevin Langston
Deputy Commissioner of
Tourism
Department of Economic
Development
75 Fifth Street, Northwest
Suite 1200
Atlanta, GA 30308
P: (404) 962-4000
F: (404) 962-4093
E: klangston@georgia.org

GUAM
Ms. Joann G. Camacho
General Manager
Visitor's Bureau
401 Pale San Vitores Road
Tumon, GU 96913
P: (671) 646-5278
F: (671) 646-8861

IDAHO
Ms. Diane Norton
Tourism Manager
Department of Commerce
700 West State Street
P.O. Box 83720
Boise, ID 83720
P: (208) 334-2650 Ext. 2149
F: (208) 334-2631
E: diane.norton
@tourism.idaho.gov

ILLINOIS
Mr. Jim Schultz
Director
Department of Commerce &
Economic Opportunity
100 West Randolph Street, Suite
3-400
Chicago, IL 60601
P: (312) 814-2811
E: Jim.Schultz@Illinois.gov

INDIANA
Hon. Sue Ellspermann (R)
Lieutenant Governor
Office of the Lieutenant
Governor
State Capitol, Room 333
Indianapolis, IN 46204
P: (317) 232-4545
F: (317) 232-4788

IOWA
Ms. Shawna Lode-Myers
Manager
Tourism Office
200 East Grand Avenue
Des Moines, IA 50309
P: (515) 725-3090
F: (515) 242-4718
E: shawna.lode-myers
@iowa.gov

KANSAS
Ms. Becky Blake
Director
Department of Wildlife, Parks &
Tourism
KDWPT - 2nd Floor
1020 S. Kansas Ave.
Topeka, KS 66612
P: (785) 296-8478
F: (785) 296-6988
E: Becky.Blake@travelks.com

KENTUCKY
Mr. Mike Mangeot
Commissioner
Department of Travel &
Tourism
500 Mero Street, 22nd Floor
Frankfort, KY 40601
P: (502) 564-4930
F: (502) 564-5695
E: michael.mangeot@ky.gov

Mr. Bob Stewart
Secretary
Tourism, Arts & Heritage
Cabinet
24th Floor, Capital Plaza Tower
500 Mero Street
Frankfort, KY 40601
P: (502) 564-4270
F: (502) 564-1512

LOUISIANA
Hon. Jay Dardenne (R)
Lieutenant Governor
Office of the Lieutenant
Governor
1051 North 3rd Street
Capitol Annex Building, P.O.
Box 44243
Baton Rouge, LA 70804
P: (225) 342-7009
F: (225) 342-1949
E: ltgov@crt.la.gov

MAINE
Ms. Carolann Ouellette
Director
Office of Tourism
#59 State House Station
Augusta, ME 04333
P: (888) 624-6345
F: (207) 287-8070
E: Carolann.Ouellette
@maine.gov

Tourism

MARYLAND
Mr. R. Michael Gill
Secretary
Department of Business &
Economic Development
World Trade Center
401 East Pratt Street
Baltimore, MD 21202
P: (410) 767-6301
F: (410) 333-8628
E: Mike.Gill@maryland.gov

MASSACHUSETTS
Ms. Betsy Wall
Executive Director
Office of Travel & Tourism
10 Park Plaza, Suite 3730
Boston, MA 02116
P: (617) 973-8500
F: (617) 973-8525

MICHIGAN
Mr. George Zimmerman
Vice President
Marketing, Communications, &
Travel Michigan
300 North Washington Square
Lansing, MI 48913
P: (517) 335-4590
E: zimmermanng@michigan.gov

MINNESOTA
Mr. John Edman
Director
Explore Minnesota Tourism
121 7th Place East
Metro Square, Suite 100
St. Paul, MN 55101
P: (651) 757-1844
F: (651) 296-7095
E: john.edman@state.mn.us

MISSISSIPPI
Ms. Mary Beth Wilkerson
Director
Division of Tourism
P.O. Box 849
Jackson, MS 39205
P: (601) 359-3297
F: (601) 359-5757
E: mwilkerson
@mississippi.org

MONTANA
Ms. Jeri Duran
Division Administrator
Office of Tourism
301 South Park Avenue
P.O. Box 200533
Helena, MT 59620
P: (406) 841-2870
F: (406) 841-2871

NEBRASKA
Ms. Brenda Hicks-Sorensen
Director
Department of Economic
Development
550 South 16th Street
Lincoln, NE 68508
P: (402) 471-3125
E: brenda.hicks-sorensen
@nebraska.gov

NEVADA
Mr. Larry Friedman
Chief Deputy
Commission on Tourism
401 North Carson Street
Carson City, NV 89701
P: (775) 687-4322
F: (775) 687-6779
E: lfriedman
@travelnevada.com

NEW HAMPSHIRE
Ms. Lori Harnois
Director
Department of Resources &
Economic Development
Division of Travel & Tourism
P.O. Box 1856
Concord, NH 03302
P: (603) 271-2665
F: (603) 271-6870
E: travel@dred.nh.gov

NEW MEXICO
Ms. Rebecca Latham
Cabinet Secretary
Tourism Department
491 Old Santa Fe Trail
Santa Fe, NM 87501
P: (505) 827-7469
F: (505) 827-3985

NEW YORK
Mr. Kenneth Adams
President & CEO
Empire State Development
633 Third Avenue
New York, NY 10017
P: (212) 803-3700
F: (212) 803-3715

NORTH CAROLINA
Mr. Wit Tuttell
Acting Assistant Secretary
Division of Tourism, Film &
Sports Development
Department of Commerce
4324 Mail Service Center
Raleigh, NC 27699
P: (919) 733-7472
F: (919) 733-8582
E: wtuttell@nccommerce.com

NORTH DAKOTA
Ms. Sarah Otte-Coleman
Director
Tourism Division
1600 East Century Avenue,
Suite 2
Century Center, P.O. Box 2057
Bismarck, ND 58502
P: (701) 328-2525
F: (701) 328-4878
E: socoleman@nd.gov

**NORTHERN MARIANA
ISLANDS**
Mr. Perry P. Tenorio
Managing Director
Visitor's Authority
P.O. Box 500861
Saipan, MP 96950
P: (670) 664-3200
F: (670) 664-3237
E: gov.wia1@gtepacifica.net

OHIO
Ms. Mary Cusick
Director
Tourism Ohio
P.O. Box 1001
Columbus, OH 43216
P: (614) 466-8844
F: (614) 466-6744

OREGON
Mr. Todd Davidson
Chief Executive Officer
Tourism Commission
250 Church Street, Southeast
Suite 100
Salem, OR 97301
P: (503) 967-1568
F: (503) 967-1579
E: Todd@TravelOregon.com

PENNSYLVANIA
Ms. Debbie Bowman
Executive Director
Tourism Office
Commonwealth Keystone
Building
400 North Street, 4th Floor
Harrisburg, PA 17120
P: (717) 346-7791
E: debowman@pa.gov

PUERTO RICO
Mr. Mario Gonzalez Lafuente
Director
Puerto Rico Tourism Company
P.O. Box 9023960
San Juan, PR 00901
P: (787) 721-2400
F: (787) 722-6238

RHODE ISLAND
Mr. Mark Brodeur
Director of Tourism
Economic Development
Corporation
315 Iron Horse Way, Suite 101
Providence, RI 02908
P: (401) 278-9100 Ext. 102
F: (401) 273-8270
E: mbrodeur@commerceri.com

SOUTH CAROLINA
Mr. Duane Parrish
Director
Department of Parks, Recreation
& Tourism
1205 Pendleton Street
Columbia, SC 29201
P: (803) 734-0166
F: (803) 734-1409
E: dparrish@scprt.com

SOUTH DAKOTA
Mr. James D. Hagen
Secretary of Tourism
Office of Tourism
711 East Wells Avenue
Pierre, SD 57501
P: (605) 773-3301
F: (605) 773-5977
E: sdinfo@state.sd.us

TENNESSEE
Ms. Susan Whitaker
Commissioner
Department of Tourist
Development
William Snodgrass/Tennessee
Tower
312 Rosa L. Parks Avenue
Nashville, TN 37243
P: (615) 741-9001
F: (615) 532-0477
E: Susan.Whitaker@tn.gov

TEXAS
Mr. Brad Smyth
Director
Texas Tourism
Office of the Governor
P.O. Box 12428
Austin, TX 78711
P: (512) 936-0101
F: (512) 936-0303

U.S. VIRGIN ISLANDS
Ms. Beverly Nicholson Doty
Commissioner
Department of Tourism
Elainco Building
78 Contant 1-2-3
St. Thomas, VI 00802
P: (340) 774-8784
F: (340) 773-0495

UTAH
Ms. Vicki Varela
Managing Director
Governor's Office of Economic
Office
Office of Tourism
Council Hall, 300 North State
Street
Salt Lake City, UT 84040
P: (801) 538-1370
F: (801) 538-1399
E: vvarela@utah.gov

VERMONT
Ms. Megan M. Smith
Commissioner
Department of Tourism &
Marketing
Commerce & Community
Development
One National Life Drive, 6th
Floor
Montpelier, VT 05620
P: (802) 505-5800
F: (802) 828-3366
E: megan.smith@state.vt.us

VIRGINIA
Ms. Rita McClenny
President & CEO
Tourism Corporation
901 East Byrd Street, 19th Floor
Richmond, VA 23219
P: (804) 545-5532
F: (804) 545-5501
E: president@virginia.org

WEST VIRGINIA
Ms. Amy Shuler Goodwin
Commissioner
Division of Tourism
90 MacCorkle Avenue,
Southwest
South Charleston, WV 25303
P: (304) 957-9345
E: amy.s.goodwin@wv.gov

WISCONSIN
Ms. Stephanie Klett
Secretary
Department of Tourism
201 West Washington Avenue
P.O. Box 8690
Madison, WI 53708
P: (608) 266-2161
F: (608) 266-3403
E: sklett
@travelwisconsin.com

WYOMING
Ms. Diane Shober
Executive Director
Office of Tourism
5611 High Plains Road
Cheyenne, WY 82007
P: (307) 777-2808
F: (307) 777-2877
E: Diane.Shober@wyo.gov

Training and Development

Responsible for the training and development of state employees.

ALABAMA
Ms. Norma L. Taylor
Manager of Training
State Personnel Department
300 Folsom Administration Building
64 North Union Street
Montgomery, AL 36130
P: (334) 242-3494
F: (334) 242-1110

ALASKA
Ms. Kate Sheehan
Director
Division of Personnel & Labor Relations
Department of Administration
P.O. Box 110201
Juneau, AK 99811
P: (907) 465-4429
E: kate.sheehan@alaska.gov

AMERICAN SAMOA
Mr. Le'i S. Thompson
Director
Department of Human Resources
Executive Office Building
AP Lutali, 2nd Floor
Pago Pago, AS 96799
P: (684) 644-4485
F: (684) 633-1139
E: sonnythompson
    @samoatelco.com

CALIFORNIA
Ms. Jill McAloon
Acting Executive Director
Employment Training Panel
1100 J Street, Suite 400
Sacramento, CA 95814
P: (916) 327-5640
F: (916) 445-5972
E: jill.mcaloon@etp.ca.gov

COLORADO
Ms. Kim Burgess
Chief Human Resources Officer
Division of Human Resources
Department of Personnel & Administration
1525 Sherman Street
Denver, CO 80203
P: (303) 866-2171
F: (303) 866-2021
E: kim.burgess@state.co.us

CONNECTICUT
Ms. Melody A. Currey
Commissioner
Department of Administrative Services
165 Capitol Avenue
Hartford, CT 06106
P: (860) 713-5100
F: (860) 713-7481
E: Melody.Currey@ct.gov

DELAWARE
Ms. Lori Reeder
Director
Department of Labor
Division of Employment & Training
4425 North Market Street
Wilmington, DE 19802
P: (302) 761-8085
E: lori.reeder@state.de.us

DISTRICT OF COLUMBIA
Ms. Shawn Stokes
Director
Department of Human Resources
441 4th Street Northwest, Suite 300S
Washington, DC 20001
P: (202) 442-9700
F: (202) 727-0154
E: dchr@dc.gov

GEORGIA
Mr. James Anderson
Program Manager
Leadership Institute
Twin Towers (West)
2 Martin Luther King Jr. Drive Southeast
Atlanta, GA 30334
P: (404) 651-8717
F: (770) 357-9019
E: james.anderson
    @spa.ga.gov

GUAM
Ms. Benita A. Manglona
Director
Department of Administration
P.O. Box 884
Hagatna, GU 96932
P: (671) 475-1101
F: (671) 477-6788

HAWAII
Dr. James K. Nishimoto
Director
Department of Human Resources Development
235 South Beretania Street, Suite 1400
Honolulu, HI 96813
P: (808) 587-1100
F: (808) 587-1106

IDAHO
Mr. Jay E. Engstrom
Deputy Director, Programs
Workforce Development Division
Department of Labor
317 West Main Street
Boise, ID 83735
P: (208) 332-3570 Ext. 2121
F: (208) 334-6430
E: jay.engstrom
    @labor.idaho.gov

ILLINOIS
Ms. Roneta Taylor
Division Manager
Technical Services & Agency Training Division
Stratton Office Building, Room 504
401 South Spring
Springfield, IL 62706
P: (217) 557-0225

INDIANA
Nereida Williams
Employee Engagement Division
State Personnel Department
402 West Washington Street, Room W161
Indianapolis, IN 46204
P: (317) 234-3111
F: (317) 232-3089
E: NeWilliams@spd.IN.gov

KANSAS
Mr. Pat George
Secretary
Department of Commerce
1000 Southwest Jackson Street, Suite 100
Topeka, KS 66612
P: (785) 296-2741
F: (785) 296-5055
E: pgeorge
    @kansascommerce.com

KENTUCKY
Mr. Buddy Hoskinson
Executive Director
Office of Employment & Training
Education Cabinet
275 East Main Street, Mail Drop 2-EK
Frankfort, KY 40621
P: (502) 564-4440 Ext. 23437
F: (502) 564-6745
E: buddy.hoskinson@ky.gov

Mr. Timothy Longmeyer
Secretary
Personnel Cabinet
State Office Building, 3rd Floor
501 High Street
Frankfort, KY 40601
P: (502) 564-7430
F: (502) 564-7603
E: timothy.longmeyer@ky.gov

LOUISIANA
Ms. Dana LeBherz
Training Division Administrator
Comprehensive Public Training Program
Department of State Civil Service
P.O. Box 94111
Baton Rouge, LA 70804
P: (225) 342-8539
F: (225) 342-2386
E: Dana.LeBherz@La.Gov

MARYLAND
Ms. Cynthia Kollner
Executive Director
Office of Personnel Services & Benefits
Department of Budget & Management
301 West Preston Street, Room 609
Baltimore, MD 21201
P: (410) 767-4715
F: (410) 333-5262
E: ckollner@dbm.state.md.us

MASSACHUSETTS
Mr. Paul Dietl
Chief Human Resources Officer
Human Resources Division
1 Ashburton Palce, Room 301
Boston, MA 02108
P: (617) 878-9703
F: (617) 727-1175
E: Paul.d.Dietl
    @MassMail.State.MA.US

MICHIGAN
Ms. Janet McClelland
Acting State Personnel Director
State Civil Service Commission
400 South Pine Street
P.O. Box 30002
Lansing, MI 48909
P: (517) 373-3030
F: (517) 373-7690
E: mcclellandj@michigan.gov

MINNESOTA
Mr. Myron Frans
Commissioner
Management & Budget
658 Cedar Street, Suite 400
St. Paul, MN 55155
P: (651) 201-8011
F: (651) 797-1300
E: myron.frans@state.mn.us

MISSOURI
Mr. Bill Miller
Director
Division of Personnel
Office of Administration
P.O. Box 388
Jefferson City, MO 65101
P: (573) 751-4162
F: (573) 751-8641
E: persmail@oa.mo.gov

MONTANA
Hon. Sheila Hogan
Director
Department of Administration
P.O. Box 200101
Helena, MT 59620
P: (406) 444-3033
F: (406) 444-6194
E: shogan@mt.gov

NEBRASKA
Ms. Ruth Jones
Director
State Personnel Division
Department of Administrative
Services
P.O. Box 94905
Lincoln, NE 68509
P: (402) 471-2075
F: (402) 471-3754
E: ruth.jones@nebraska.gov

NEVADA
Ms. Patricia L. Hoppe
Employee Development
Manager
Office of Employee
Development
Division of Human Resource
Management
555 East Washington Avenue,
Suite 1400
Las Vegas, NV 89101
P: (702) 486-2928
F: (702) 486-2925
E: phoppe@admin.nv.gov

NEW HAMPSHIRE
Ms. Sara J. Willingham
Director of Personnel
Division of Personnel
Department of Administrative
Services
28 School Street
Concord, NH 03301
P: (603) 271-3262
F: (603) 271-1422
E: sara.willingham@nh.gov

NEW JERSEY
Mr. Dennis M. Bone
Chair
State Employment & Training
Commission
P.O. Box 940
Trenton, NJ 08625
P: (609) 633-0605
F: (609) 633-1359

NEW MEXICO
Mr. Justin Najaka
Director
State Personnel Office
2600 Cerrillos Road
Santa Fe, NM 87505
P: (505) 476-7751
F: (505) 476-7806
E: Justin.Najaka
@state.nm.us

NEW YORK
Mr. Jerry Boone
Commissioner
Department of Civil Service
Alfred E. Smith State Office
Building
Albany, NY 12239
P: (518) 457-3701
F: (518) 473-5696
E: jerry.boone
@cs.state.ny.us

NORTH CAROLINA
Ms. Paula Kukulinski
Director
Talent Management Division
Office of Human Resources
1331 Mail Service Center
Raleigh, NC 27699
P: (919) 733-8343
E: paula.kukulinski@nc.gov

NORTHERN MARIANA ISLANDS
Ms. Edith DeLeon Guerrero
Secretary
Workforce Investment Agency
Capitol Hill
Saipan, MP 96950
P: (670) 664-3196
F: (670) 664-3197
E: gov.wia1@gtepacifica.net

OKLAHOMA
Ms. Lisa Fortier
Director
Human Resource Development
Services Division
Human Capital Management
Division
2101 North Lincoln Boulevard
Oklahoma City, OK 73105
P: (405) 521-6345
F: (405) 524-6942
E: lisa.fortier@opm.ok.gov

OREGON
Mr. Twyla Dawn Lawson
Senior State Human Resource
Management Consultant
Chief Human Resource Office
Human Resource Policy
155 Cottage Street, Northeast,
U-30
Salem, OR 97301
P: (503) 373-7677
F: (503) 373-7684
E: Twyla.Lawson@Oregon.gov

PENNSYLVANIA
Ms. Sharon Minnich
Secretary
Governor's Office of
Administration
207 Finance Building
Harrisburg, PA 17102
P: (717) 772-5174
E: sminnich@pa.gov

PUERTO RICO
Ms. Marta Beltran
Administrator, Human
Resources Administrative Office
Central Labor Advisory &
Human Resources
Administrative Office
Ponce De Leon Avenue, Suite
1507
P.O. Box 8476
San Juan, PR 00910
P: (787) 706-5967
F: (787) 706-5697

Mr. Vance Thomas
Secretary
Department of Labor & Human
Resources
P.O. Box 195540
Hato Rey, PR 00918
P: (787) 754-2119
F: (787) 753-9550

RHODE ISLAND
Ms. Melissa Day
Assistant Administrative Officer
Office of Training &
Development
Department of Administration
One Capitol Hill
Providence, RI 02908
P: (401) 222-2178
F: (401) 222-6378
E: Melissa.Day@hr.ri.gov

SOUTH CAROLINA
Ms. Kim Aydlette
Director
Division of Human Resources
Department of Administration
8301 Parklane Road, Suite A220
Columbia, SC 29223
P: (803) 896-5300
F: (803) 896-5050

SOUTH DAKOTA
Ms. Ellen Zeller
Director of Training
Bureau of Human Resources -
Training
Becker-Hansen Building
700 East Broadway Avenue
Pierre, SD 57501
P: (605) 773-3461
F: (605) 773-5389
E: ctr@state.sd.us

TENNESSEE
Ms. Trish Holliday
Chief Learning Officer
Strategic Learning Solutions
James K. Polk Building
505 Deaderick Street
Nashville, TN 37243
P: (615) 741-4126
F: (615) 532-0728
E: Trish.Holliday@tn.gov

U.S. VIRGIN ISLANDS
Mr. Kenneth L. Hermon Jr.
Commissioner
Division of Personnel
GERS Building, 3rd Floor
3438 Kronprindsens Gade
St. Thomas, VI 00802
P: (340) 774-8588
F: (340) 714-5040
E: info@dopusvi.net

Training and Development

UTAH
Mr. J.J. Acker
Administrative Director
Department of Human Resource
Management
State Office Building, Room
2120
Salt Lake City, UT 84114
P: (801) 538-4297
F: (801) 538-3081
E: JACKER@utah.gov

VERMONT
Ms. Rose Lucenti
Director, Workforce
Development
Department of Labor
5 Green Mountain Drive
P.O. Box 488
Montpelier, VT 05601
P: (802) 828-4151
F: (802) 828-4374
E: rose.lucenti@state.vt.us

VIRGINIA
Mrs. Sara Redding Wilson
Director
Department of Human Resource
Management
101 North 14th Street, 12th
Floor
Richmond, VA 23219
P: (804) 225-2237
F: (804) 371-7401
E: sara.wilson
    @dhrm.virginia.gov

WASHINGTON
Mr. Glen Christopherson
Director
State Human Resources
Division
128 10th Avenue, Southeast
P.O. Box 43113
Olympia, WA 98504
P: (360) 407-4104
F: (360) 753-1003
E: glen.christopherson
    @ofm.wa.gov

WISCONSIN
Ms. Jeanette Johnson
Administrator
Division of Affirmative Action
101 East Wilson Street
P.O. Box 7855
Madison, WI 53707
P: (608) 266-3017
F: (608) 267-1020
E: oserdaa@wi.gov

WYOMING
Ms. Joan K. Evans
Director
Department of Workforce
Services
122 West 25th Street
Herschler Building, 2nd Floor
East
Cheyenne, WY 82002
P: (307) 777-8728
F: (307) 777-5857
E: joan.evans@wyo.gov

Transportation and Highways

Umbrella agency responsible for planning, designing, constructing and maintaining public transportation services, highways and facilities throughout the state.

ALABAMA
Mr. John R. Cooper
Transportation Director
Department of Transportation
1409 Coliseum Boulevard
P.O. Box 303050
Montgomery, AL 36130
P: (334) 242-6311
F: (334) 262-8041

ALASKA
Mr. Marc Luiken
Commissioner
Department of Transportation &
Public Facilities
3132 Channel Drive
P.O. Box 112500
Juneau, AK 99811
P: (907) 465-3901
F: (907) 586-8365

ARIZONA
Mr. John Halikowski
Director
Department of Transportation
206 South 17th Avenue
Phoenix, AZ 85007
P: (602) 712-7011
F: (602) 712-6941

ARKANSAS
Mr. Scott Bennett
Director of Highways &
Transportation
State Highway & Transportation
Department
10324 Interstate 30
P.O. Box 2261
Little Rock, AR 72203
P: (501) 569-2211
F: (501) 569-2400

CALIFORNIA
Mr. Malcolm Dougherty
Director
Department of Transportation
1120 N Street
P.O. Box 942873
Sacramento, CA 94273
P: (916) 654-5266
F: (916) 654-6608

COLORADO
Mr. Shailen Bhatt
Executive Director
Department of Transportation
4201 East Arkansas Avenue
Denver, CO 80222
P: (303) 757-9201
F: (303) 757-9656

CONNECTICUT
Mr. James Redeker
Commissioner
Department of Transportation
2800 Berlin Turnpike
P.O. Box 317546
Newington, CT 06131
P: (860) 594-3000
F: (860) 594-3008

DELAWARE
Mr. Scott Vien
Director
Division of Motor Vehicles
303 Transportation Circle
P.O. Box 698
Dover, DE 19903

DISTRICT OF COLUMBIA
Mr. Leif A. Dormsjo
Director of Transportation
Department of Transportation
55 M Street Southeast, #400
Washington, DC 20003
P: (202) 673-6813
F: (202) 671-0642

FLORIDA
Mr. Jim Boxold
Secretary
Department of Transportation
605 Suwannee Street
Tallahassee, FL 32399
P: (850) 414-5200
F: (850) 414-5201

GEORGIA
Mr. Russell McMurry
Commissioner
Department of Transportation
600 West Peachtree Street,
Northwest
Atlanta, GA 30308
P: (404) 631-1000
F: (404) 631-1022

HAWAII
Mr. Ford Fuchigami
Director
Department of Transportation
Aliiaimoku Building, Room 509
869 Punchbowl Street
Honolulu, HI 96813
P: (808) 587-2150
F: (808) 587-2167

IDAHO
Mr. Brian W. Ness
Director
Transportation Department
3311 West State Street
P.O. Box 7129
Boise, ID 83707
P: (208) 334-8820
F: (208) 334-3858

ILLINOIS
Mr. Randall S. Blankenhorn
Secretary
Department of Transportation
2300 South Dirksen Parkway
Springfield, IL 62764
P: (217) 782-5597
F: (217) 782-6828

INDIANA
Ms. Brandye Hendrickson
Commissioner
Department of Transportation
Indiana Government Center
North
100 North Senate Avenue, Room
N 758
Indianapolis, IN 46204
P: (317) 232-5525
F: (317) 232-0238

IOWA
Mr. Paul Trombino III
Director
Department of Transportation
800 Lincoln Way
Ames, IA 50010
P: (515) 239-1111
F: (515) 817-6508

KANSAS
Mr. Michael S. King
Secretary
Department of Transportation
Eisenhower State Office
Building
700 Harrison
Topeka, KS 66603
P: (785) 296-3461
F: (785) 296-1095

KENTUCKY
Mr. Mike Hancock
Secretary
Transportation Cabinet
200 Mero Street
Frankfort, KY 40622
P: (502) 564-4890
F: (502) 564-4809

LOUISIANA
Ms. Sherri LeBas
Secretary
Department of Transportation &
Development
1201 Capitol Access Road
P.O. Box 94245
Baton Rouge, LA 70804
P: (225) 379-1200
F: (225) 379-1851

MAINE
Mr. David Bernhardt
Commissioner
Department of Transportation
24 Child Street
16 State House Station
Augusta, ME 04333
P: (207) 624-3000
F: (207) 624-3001

MARYLAND
Mr. Pete K. Rahn
Secretary
Department of Transportation
Office of the Secretary, P.O.
Box 548
7201 Corporate Center Drive
Hanover, MD 21076
P: (888) 713-1414
F: (410) 865-1334

MASSACHUSETTS
Ms. Stephanie Pollack
Secretary of Transportation and
Public Works
Department of Transportation
10 Park Plaza, Suite 3170
Boston, MA 02116
P: (617) 973-7000
F: (617) 973-8031

MICHIGAN
Mr. Kirk T. Steudle
Director
Department of Transportation
Murray D. Van Wagoner
Building
425 West Ottawa Street, P.O.
Box 30050
Lansing, MI 48933
P: (517) 373-2114
F: (517) 373-8841
E: mdotdirector
  @michigan.gov

MINNESOTA
Mr. Charles A. Zelle
Commissioner
Department of Transportation
Transportation Building
395 John Ireland Boulevard
St. Paul, MN 55155
P: (651) 366-4800
F: (651) 366-4795
E: charlie.zelle
  @state.mn.us

Transportation and Highways

MISSISSIPPI
Ms. Melinda LittleJohn
McGrath
Executive Director
Department of Transportation
Administrative Office Building
401 North West Street, P.O. Box 1850
Jackson, MS 39215
P: (601) 359-7001
F: (601) 359-7050

MISSOURI
Ms. Roberta Broeker
Director
Department of Transportation
105 West Capitol Avenue
P.O. Box 270
Jefferson City, MO 65102
P: (573) 751-4622
F: (573) 751-6555

MONTANA
Mr. Michael T. Tooley
Director
Department of Transportation
2701 Prospect Avenue
P.O. Box 201001
Helena, MT 59620
P: (406) 444-6201
F: (406) 444-7643

NEBRASKA
Mr. Moe Jamshidi
Acting Director
Department of Roads
1500 Highway 2
P.O. Box 94759
Lincoln, NE 68509
P: (402) 479-4615
F: (402) 479-4325

NEVADA
Mr. Rudy Malfabon
Director
Department of Transportation
1263 South Stewart Street
Carson City, NV 89712
P: (775) 888-7440
F: (775) 888-7201

NEW HAMPSHIRE
Mr. Bill Cass
Acting Commissioner
Department of Transportation
John O. Morton Building
7 Hazen Drive, P.O. Box 483
Concord, NH 03302
P: (603) 271-3734
F: (603) 271-3914

NEW JERSEY
Mr. Jamie Fox
Commissioner
Department of Transportation
1035 Parkway Avenue
P.O. Box 600
Trenton, NJ 08625
P: (609) 530-3536
F: (609) 530-3894

NEW MEXICO
Mr. Tom Church
Cabinet Secretary
Department of Transportation
Joe M. Anaya Building
1120 Cerrilos Road, P.O. Box 1149
Santa Fe, NM 87504
P: (505) 827-5110
F: (505) 827-5469

NEW YORK
Ms. Joan McDonald
Commissioner
Department of Transportation
50 Wolf Road, 6th Floor
Albany, NY 12232
P: (518) 457-4422
F: (518) 457-5583
E: joan.mcdonald@dot.ny.gov

NORTH CAROLINA
Mr. Anthony Tata
Secretary
Department of Transportation
1507 Mail Service Center
1 South Wilmington Street
Raleigh, NC 27699
P: (919) 707-2800
F: (919) 733-9150

NORTH DAKOTA
Mr. Grant Levi
Director
Department of Transportation
608 East Boulevard Avenue
Bismarck, ND 58505
P: (701) 328-2581
F: (701) 328-0310
E: glevi@nd.gov

OHIO
Mr. Jerry Wray
Director
Department of Transportation
1980 West Broad Street
Columbus, OH 43223
P: (614) 466-2335
F: (614) 466-8662
E: Terri.Barnhart
@dot.state.oh.us

OKLAHOMA
Mr. J. Michael Patterson
Director
Department of Transportation
200 Northeast 21st Street
Oklahoma City, OK 73105
P: (405) 522-1800
F: (405) 522-1805

OREGON
Mr. Matthew Garrett
Director
Department of Transportation
355 Capitol Street, Northeast
Salem, OR 97301
P: (503) 986-3452
F: (503) 986-3432
E: Matthew.l.garrett
@odot.state.or.us

PENNSYLVANIA
Leslie S. Richards
Secretary
Department of Transportation
Keystone Building
400 North Street
Harrisburg, PA 17120
P: (717) 787-5574
F: (717) 787-5491

PUERTO RICO
Mr. Miguel A. Torres Diaz
Secretary of Transportation & Public Works
Department of Transportation & Public Works
Office of the Secretary
P.O. Box 41269, Minillas Station
San Juan, PR 00940
P: (787) 722-2929
F: (787) 728-1620

RHODE ISLAND
Mr. Peter Alviti
Director
Department of Transportation
State Office Building
2 Capitol Hill
Providence, RI 02903
P: (401) 222-2481
F: (401) 222-2086

SOUTH CAROLINA
Ms. Janet Oakley
Secretary of Transportation
Department of Transportation
Silas N. Pearman Building
955 Park Street
Columbia, SC 29201
P: (803) 737-2314
F: (803) 737-2038

SOUTH DAKOTA
Mr. Darin Bergquist
Secretary
Department of Transportation
700 East Broadway Avenue
Pierre, SD 57501
P: (605) 773-3265
F: (605) 773-3921

TENNESSEE
Mr. John Schroer
Commissioner
Department of Transportation
700 James K. Polk Building
505 Deaderick Street
Nashville, TN 37243
P: (615) 741-2848
F: (615) 741-2508

TEXAS
Mr. Joe Weber
Executive Director
Department of Transportation
Dewitt C. Greer Highway Building
125 East 11th Street
Austin, TX 78701
P: (512) 305-9501
F: (512) 305-9567

UTAH
Mr. Carlos Braceras
Executive Director
Department of Transportation
4501 South 2700, West
Salt Lake City, UT 84129
P: (801) 965-4000
F: (801) 965-4338

VERMONT
Ms. Sue Minter
Secretary of Transportation
Agency of Transportation
One National Life Drive
Montpelier, VT 05633
P: (802) 828-2657
F: (802) 828-3522

VIRGINIA
Mr. Charlie A. Kilpatrick
Commissioner
Department of Transportation
1401 East Broad Street
Richmond, VA 23219
P: (804) 786-2801
F: (804) 786-2940

Mr. Aubrey Layne Jr.
Secretary of Transportation
Department of Transportation
1401 East Broad Street
Richmond, VA 23219
P: (804) 786-2801
F: (804) 786-2940

WASHINGTON
Lynn Peterson
Secretary of Transportation
Department of Transportation
310 Maple Park Avenue,
Southeast
P.O. Box 47316
Olympia, WA 98504
P: (360) 705-7054
F: (360) 705-6800

WEST VIRGINIA
Mr. Paul A. Mattox Jr.
Secretary of
Transportation/Commissioner of
Highways
Department of Transportation
1900 Kanawha Boulevard, East
Building 5, Room 110
Charleston, WV 25305
P: (304) 558-0444
F: (304) 558-1004
E: Paul.A.Mattox@wv.gov

WISCONSIN
Mr. Mark Gottlieb
Secretary
Department of Transportation
4802 Sheboygan Avenue
P.O. Box 7910
Madison, WI 53707
P: (608) 266-1114
F: (608) 266-9912

WYOMING
Mr. John F. Cox
Director
Department of Transportation
5300 Bishop Boulevard
Cheyenne, WY 82009
P: (307) 777-4484
F: (307) 777-4163

Treasurer

The custodian of all state funds and securities belonging to and held in trust by the state.

ALABAMA
Hon. Young Boozer III (R)
State Treasurer
Office of the State Treasurer
600 Dexter Avenue
State Capitol, Room S-106
Montgomery, AL 36104
P: (334) 242-7501
F: (334) 242-7592
E: young.boozer
@treasury.alabama.gov

ALASKA
Hon. Pamela Leary
(appointed)
State Treasurer
Department of Revenue
P.O. Box 110400
Juneau, AK 99811
P: (907) 465-3669
F: (907) 465-2389
E: pam.leary@alaska.gov

AMERICAN SAMOA
Hon. Falema'o M. Pili
Treasurer
Office of the Treasury
American Samoa Government
Pago Pago, AS 96799
P: (684) 633-4155
F: (684) 633-4100

ARIZONA
Hon. Jeff De Wit (R)
State Treasurer
Office of the State Treasurer
1701 West Washington Street
Phoenix, AZ 85007
P: (602) 542-7800
F: (602) 542-7176

ARKANSAS
Mr. Dennis Milligan
State Treasurer
Office of the State Treasurer
220 State Capitol
Little Rock, AR 72201
P: (501) 682-5888
F: (501) 682-3842

CALIFORNIA
Hon. John Chiang (D)
State Treasurer
Office of the State Treasurer
915 Capitol Mall, Room 110
Sacramento, CA 95814
P: (916) 653-2995
F: (916) 653-3125

COLORADO
Hon. Walker Stapleton (R)
State Treasurer
Office of the State Treasurer
140 State Capitol Building
Denver, CO 80203
P: (303) 866-2441
F: (303) 866-2123
E: treasurer.stapleton
@state.co.us

CONNECTICUT
Hon. Denise L. Nappier (D)
State Treasurer
Office of State Treasurer
55 Elm Street, 7th Floor
Hartford, CT 06106
P: (860) 702-3010
F: (860) 702-3043
E: denise.nappier@ct.gov

DELAWARE
Hon. Ken Simpler (R)
State Treasurer
Office of the State Treasurer
820 Silver Lake Boulevard,
Suite 100
Dover, DE 19904
P: (302) 672-6700
F: (302) 739-5635

DISTRICT OF COLUMBIA
Mr. Jeffrey Barnette
(appointed)
Chief Financial Officer
Office of Finance & Treasury
1101 4th Street, Southwest
Suite 850
Washington, DC 20024
P: (202) 442-8200
F: (202) 442-8201

FLORIDA
Hon. Jeffrey H. Atwater (R)
Chief Financial Officer
Department of Financial
Services
200 East Gaines Street
Tallahassee, FL 32399
P: (850) 413-2850
F: (850) 413-2950
E: allison@jeffatwater.com

GEORGIA
Hon. Steve McCoy
(appointed)
Treasurer & Director
Office of the State Treasurer
200 Piedmont Avenue
Suite 1204, West Tower
Atlanta, GA 30334
P: (404) 656-2168
F: (404) 656-9048
E: OSTWeb@treasury.ga.gov

GUAM
Hon. Rose T. Fejeran
Treasurer
Department of Administration,
Treasury
P.O. Box 884
Hagatna, GU 96928
P: (671) 475-1101
F: (671) 477-6788
E: rtfejeran@doa.guam.gov

HAWAII
Hon. Wesley Machida
(appointed)
Director of Finance
Department of Budget &
Finance
P.O. Box 150
Honolulu, HI 96810
P: (808) 586-1518
F: (808) 586-1976
E: hi.budgetandfinance
@hawaii.gov

IDAHO
Hon. Ron G. Crane (R)
State Treasurer
Office of the State Treasurer
304 North 8th Street
Boise, ID 83720
P: (208) 334-3200
F: (208) 332-2959
E: ron.crane@sto.idaho.gov

ILLINOIS
Hon. Michael W.
Frerichs (D)
State Treasurer
Office of the State Treasurer
Statehouse
Executive Office 203
Springfield, IL 62706
P: (217) 782-2211
F: (217) 785-2777

INDIANA
Hon. Kelly Mitchell (R)
State Treasurer
Office of the State Treasurer
242 State House
Indianapolis, IN 46204
P: (317) 232-6386
F: (317) 233-1780

IOWA
Hon. Michael L.
Fitzgerald (D)
State Treasurer
Office of the State Treasurer
State Capitol Building
Des Moines, IA 50319
P: (515) 281-5368
F: (515) 281-7562
E: mike.fitzgerald@iowa.gov

KANSAS
Hon. Ron Estes (R)
State Treasurer
Office of the State Treasurer
900 Southwest Jackson Street,
Suite 201
Topeka, KS 66612
P: (785) 296-3171
F: (785) 296-7950
E: ron@treasurer.ks.gov

KENTUCKY
Hon. Todd Hollenbach (D)
State Treasurer
State Treasury
1050 U.S. Highway 127 South
Suite 100
Frankfort, KY 40601
P: (502) 564-4722
F: (502) 564-6545
E: todd.hollenbach@ky.gov

LOUISIANA
Hon. John Neely Kennedy (R)
State Treasurer
Office of the State Treasurer
P.O. Box 44154
Baton Rouge, LA 70804
P: (225) 342-0010
F: (225) 342-0046
E: jkennedy
@treasury.state.la.us

MAINE
Hon. Terry Hayes (I)
State Treasurer
Office of the State Treasurer
39 State House Station
Augusta, ME 04333
P: (207) 624-7477
F: (207) 287-2367
E: state.treasurer
@maine.gov

MARYLAND
Hon. Nancy K. Kopp (D)
(elected by the Legislature)
State Treasurer
Office of the State Treasurer
80 Calvert Street
Annapolis, MD 21401
P: (410) 260-7160
F: (410) 260-6056
E: nkopp
@treasurer.state.md.us

MASSACHUSETTS
Hon. Deb Goldberg (D)
State Treasurer
Office of the State Treasurer
State House, Room 227
Boston, MA 02133
P: (617) 367-3900
F: (617) 248-0372

MICHIGAN
Mr. Nick Khouri
    (appointed)
State Treasurer
Department of Treasury
430 West Allegan Street
Lansing, MI 48922
P: (517) 373-3223
F: (517) 335-1785

MINNESOTA
Mr. Myron Frans
Commissioner
Management & Budget
658 Cedar Street, Suite 400
St. Paul, MN 55155
P: (651) 201-8011
F: (651) 797-1300
E: myron.frans@state.mn.us

MISSISSIPPI
Hon. Lynn Fitch (R)
State Treasurer
Office of the State Treasurer
P.O. Box 138
Jackson, MS 39205
P: (601) 359-3600
F: (601) 576-4495

MISSOURI
Hon. Clint Zweifel (D)
State Treasurer
Office of the State Treasurer
State Capitol, Room 229
P.O. Box 210
Jefferson City, MO 65102
P: (573) 751-2411
F: (573) 751-9443
E: clint.zweifel
    @treasurer.mo.gov

MONTANA
Hon. Sheila Hogan
    (appointed)
Director
Department of Administration
P.O. Box 200101
Helena, MT 59620
P: (406) 444-3033
F: (406) 444-6194
E: shogan@mt.gov

NEBRASKA
Hon. Don B. Stenberg (R)
State Treasurer
Office of the State Treasurer
State Capitol, Room 2005
Lincoln, NE 68509
P: (402) 471-2455
F: (402) 471-4390
E: Don.Stenberg
    @nebraska.gov

NEVADA
Hon. Dan Schwartz (R)
State Treasurer
Office of the State Treasurer
101 North Carson Street, Suite 4
Carson City, NV 89701
P: (775) 684-7109
F: (775) 684-5623
E: statetreasurer
    @nevadatreasurer.gov

NEW HAMPSHIRE
Mr. William Dwyer
    (elected by the Legislature)
State Treasurer
State Treasury
25 Capitol Street
Concord, NH 03301
P: (603) 271-2621
F: (603) 271-3922

NEW JERSEY
Hon. Andrew P.
    Sidamon-Eristoff
    (appointed)
State Treasurer
Department of Treasury
State House, First Floor
P.O. Box 002
Trenton, NJ 08625
P: (608) 292-6748
F: (609) 984-3888

NEW MEXICO
Hon. Tim Eichenberg (D)
State Treasurer
Office of the State Treasurer
2055 South Pacheco Street,
Suite 100
Santa Fe, NM 85008
P: (505) 955-1172
F: (505) 955-1195

NEW YORK
Honourable Eric Mostert
    (appointed)
Deputy Commissioner &
Treasurer
Department of Taxation &
Finance
Division of the Treasury
P.O. Box 22119
Albany, NY 12201
P: (518) 474-4250
F: (518) 402-4118

NORTH CAROLINA
Hon. Janet Cowell (D)
State Treasurer
Department of State Treasurer
325 North Salisbury Street
Raleigh, NC 27603
P: (919) 508-5176
F: (919) 508-5167
E: janet.cowell
    @nctreasurer.com

NORTH DAKOTA
Hon. Kelly L. Schmidt (R)
State Treasurer
Office of State Treasurer
600 East Boulevard, Department
120
State Capital, 3rd Floor
Bismarck, ND 58505
P: (701) 328-2643
F: (701) 328-3002
E: treasurer@nd.gov

**NORTHERN MARIANA
ISLANDS**
Mr. Mark O. Rabauliman
Secretary of Commerce
Department of Commerce
Caller Box 10007 CK
Saipan, MP 96950
P: (670) 664-3000
F: (670) 664-3067

OHIO
Hon. Josh Mandel (R)
Treasurer of State
Office of the State Treasurer
30 East Broad Street
9th Floor
Columbus, OH 43215
P: (614) 466-2160
F: (614) 644-7313

OKLAHOMA
Hon. Ken Miller (R)
State Treasurer
Office of the State Treasurer
Room 217, State Capitol
Building
2300 North Lincoln Boulevard
Oklahoma City, OK 73105
P: (405) 521-3191
F: (405) 521-4994

OREGON
Hon. Ted Wheeler
State Treasurer
Office of the State Treasurer
900 Court Street, Room 159
Salem, OR 97301
P: (503) 378-4329
F: (503) 373-7051
E: Oregon.Treasurer
    @state.or.us

PENNSYLVANIA
Hon. Timothy Craig
State Treasurer
Treasury Department
129 Finance Building
Harrisburg, PA 17120
P: (717) 787-2465
F: (717) 783-9760

PUERTO RICO
Hon. Juan Zaragoza Gomez
Secretary of Treasury
Department of the Treasury
P.O. Box 9024140
San Juan, PR 00902
P: (787) 721-2020
F: (787) 723-6213

RHODE ISLAND
Hon. Seth Magaziner (D)
General Treasurer
Office of the General Treasurer
102 State House
Providence, RI 02903
P: (401) 222-2397
F: (401) 222-6140
E: generaltreasurer
    @treasury.ri.gov

SOUTH CAROLINA
Hon. Curtis Loftis (R)
State Treasurer
Office of the State Treasurer
P.O. Box 11778
Columbia, SC 29211
P: (803) 734-2101
F: (803) 734-2690
E: treasurer@sto.sc.gov

SOUTH DAKOTA
Hon. Rich L. Sattgast (R)
State Treasurer
Office of the State Treasurer
500 East Capitol Avenue
Pierre, SD 57501
P: (605) 773-3378
F: (605) 773-3115
E: rich.sattgast
    @state.sd.us

TENNESSEE
Hon. David H. Lillard Jr.
    (elected by the Legislature)
State Treasurer
Department of Treasury
State Capitol, First Floor
600 Charlotte Avenue
Nashville, TN 37243
P: (615) 741-2956
F: (615) 253-1591
E: david.lillard@tn.gov

Treasurer

TEXAS
Hon. Glenn Hegar (R)
Comptroller of Public Accounts
Office of the Comptroller of
Public Accounts
LBJ State Office Building, 1st
Floor
111 East 17th Street
Austin, TX 78774
P: (512) 463-4444
F: (512) 463-4902
E: glenn.hegar
   @cpa.state.tx.us

U.S. VIRGIN ISLANDS
Mr. Valdamier Collens
   (appointed)
Department of Finance
Treasury Division
2314 Kronprindsens Gade
St. Thomas, VI 00802
P: (340) 774-4750
F: (340) 776-4028

UTAH
Hon. Richard K. Ellis (R)
State Treasurer
Office of the State Treasurer
350 North State Street, Suite
180
P.O. Box 142315
Salt Lake City, UT 84114
P: (801) 538-1042
F: (801) 538-1465
E: sto@utah.gov

VERMONT
Hon. Elizabeth Pearce
State Treasurer
Office of the State Treasurer
109 State Street
Montpelier, VT 05609
P: (802) 828-3322
F: (802) 828-2772
E: Beth.Pearce@state.vt.us

VIRGINIA
Hon. Manju Ganeriwala
   (appointed)
State Treasurer
Department of the Treasury
P.O. Box 1879
Richmond, VA 23219
P: (804) 225-3131
F: (804) 786-0833
E: Manju.Ganeriwala
   @trs.virginia.gov

WASHINGTON
Hon. James L. McIntire (D)
State Treasurer
Office of the State Treasurer
Legislative Building
P.O. Box 40200
Olympia, WA 98504
P: (360) 902-9001
F: (360) 902-9044
E: watreas@tre.wa.gov

WEST VIRGINIA
Hon. John D. Perdue (D)
State Treasurer
Office of the State Treasurer
State Capitol Complex
Building 1, Room E-145
Charleston, WV 25305
P: (304) 558-5000
F: (304) 558-4097

WISCONSIN
Hon. Matt Adamczyk (R)
State Treasurer
Office of the State Treasurer
P.O. Box 2114
Madison, WI 53701
P: (608) 266-3714
F: (608) 266-2647
E: Matt.Adamczyk
   @wisconsin.gov

WYOMING
Hon. Mark Gordon
State Treasurer
Office of the State Treasurer
200 West 24th Street
Cheyenne, WY 82002
P: (307) 777-7408
F: (307) 777-5411
E: treasurer@wyo.gov

Tribal Affairs

Acts as a liaison between state and tribal officials and advances the concerns of Native Americans.

ALABAMA
Mr. Robert Russell Jr.
Executive Director
Indian Affairs Commission
771 South Lawrence Street
Suite 106
Montgomery, AL 36130
P: (334) 242-2831
F: (334) 240-3408

ARIZONA
Ms. Kristine M. FireThunder
Executive Director
Commission of Indian Affairs
State Capitol Building,
Executive Tower
1700 West Washington Street,
Suite 430
Phoenix, AZ 85007
P: (602) 542-4426
F: (602) 542-4428
E: iainfo@az.gov

CALIFORNIA
Mr. Cynthia Gomez
Executive Secretary
Native American Heritage
Commission
1550 Harbor Boulevard, Suite
100
West Sacramento, CA 95691
P: (916) 373-3710
F: (916) 373-5471
E: nahc@nahc.ca.gov

COLORADO
Hon. Joe Garcia (D)
Lieutenant Governor
Commission on Indian Affairs
130 State Capitol
Denver, CO 80203
P: (303) 866-2087
F: (303) 866-5469
E: josephagarcia
@state.co.us

CONNECTICUT
Mr. Ed W. Sarabia Jr.
Indian Affairs Coordinator
Indian Affairs
Energy & Environmental
Protection
79 Elm Street
Hartford, CT 06106
P: (860) 424-3066
F: (860) 424-4058
E: edward.sarabia@ct.gov

FLORIDA
Mr. Joe Quetone
Executive Director
Governor's Council on Indian
Affairs
1341 Cross Creek Circle
Tallahassee, FL 32301
P: (850) 488-0730
E: quetonej@fgcia.com

GEORGIA
Dr. David Crass
Division Director & Deputy
State Historic Preservation
Officer
Historic Preservation Division
254 Washington Street,
Southwest
Ground Level
Atlanta, GA 30334
P: (404) 656-2840
F: (404) 657-1368
E: david.crass
@dnr.state.ga.us

IOWA
Ms. Jill Avery
Board Administrator
Commission on Native
American Affairs
Lucas State Office Building
321 East 12th Street
Des Moines, IA 50319
P: (515) 242-6334
E: jill.avery@iowa.gov

KENTUCKY
Ms. Tressa Brown
Native American Heritage
Coordinator
State Heritage Council
State Historic Preservation
Office
300 Washington Street
Frankfort, KY 40601
P: (502) 564-7005 Ext. 125
F: (502) 564-5820
E: tressa.brown@ky.gov

LOUISIANA
Mr. Mark Ford
Director
Governor's Office of Indian
Affairs
150 North Third Street, Suite
713
P.O. Box 94004
Baton Rouge, LA 70804
P: (225) 219-8715
F: (225) 219-7551
E: Mark.ford@la.gov

MAINE
Mr. John
Dieffenbacher-Krall
Executive Director
Indian Tribal-State Commission
P.O. Box 241
Stillwater, ME 04489
P: (207) 817-3799
F: (207) 394-9230
E: mitsced@roadrunner.com

MARYLAND
Mr. E. Keith Colston
Assistant Director
Commission on Indian Affairs
301 West Preston Street, 15th
Floor
Baltimore, MD 21201
P: (410) 767-7631
F: (410) 333-7542
E: KColston
@goci.state.md.us

MICHIGAN
Ms. Donna Budnick
American Indian Specialist
Department of Civil Rights
110 West Michigan Avenue,
Suite 800
Lansing, MI 48933
P: (517) 335-3165
F: (517) 241-0546

MINNESOTA
Ms. Annamarie Hill
Executive Director
Indian Affairs Council
161 St. Anthony Avenue, Suite
919
St. Paul, MN 55103
P: (651) 296-0041
F: (651) 296-0309
E: annamarie.hill
@state.mn.us

MONTANA
Mr. Jason Smith
Director
Office of Indian Affairs
Capitol Building, 2nd Floor,
Room 202
P.O. Box 200801
Helena, MT 59620
P: (406) 444-3702
F: (406) 444-1350
E: oia@mt.gov

NEBRASKA
Ms. Judi M. Gaiashkibos
Executive Director
Commission on Indian Affairs
1445 K Street, 6th Floor, East
P.O. Box 94981
Lincoln, NE 68509
P: (402) 471-3475
E: judi.gaiashkibos
@nebraska.gov

NEVADA
Ms. Sherry L. Rupert
Executive Director
Indian Commission
5366 Snyder Avenue
Carson City, NV 89701
P: (775) 687-8333
F: (775) 687-8330
E: srupert
@govmail.state.nv.us

NEW JERSEY
Ms. Rowena Madden
Director
Commission on American
Indian Affairs
Office of the Secretary of State
P.O. Box 300
Trenton, NJ 08625
P: (609) 341-2740
F: (609) 777-1764
E: AmericanIndian
@sos.state.nj.us

NEW MEXICO
Ms. Kelly Zunie
Secretary
Indian Affairs Department
Wendell Chino Building, 2nd
Floor
1220 South St. Francies Drive
Santa Fe, NM 87505
P: (505) 476-1600
F: (505) 476-1601
E: kelly.zunie@state.nm.us

NORTH CAROLINA
Mr. Gregory A. Richardson
Executive Director
Commission of Indian Affairs
Department of Administration
1317 Mail Service Center
Raleigh, NC 27699
P: (919) 807-4440
F: (919) 807-4461
E: greg.richardson
@doa.nc.gov

NORTH DAKOTA
Mr. Scott J. Davis
Executive Director
Indian Affairs Commission
600 East Boulevard Avenue, 1st
Floor
Judicial Wing, Room #117
Bismarck, ND 58505
P: (701) 328-2432
F: (701) 328-1537
E: sjdavis@nd.gov

Tribal Affairs

OREGON
Ms. Karen Quigley
Executive Director
Legislative Commission on
Indian Services
167 State Capitol
Salem, OR 97310
P: (503) 986-1067
F: (503) 986-1071
E: karen.m.quigley
@state.or.us

SOUTH CAROLINA
Mr. Raymond Buxton
Commissioner
Human Affairs Commission
2611 Forest Drive, Suite 200
P.O. Box 4490
Columbia, SC 29204
P: (803) 737-7825
E: rbuxton@schac.sc.gov

SOUTH DAKOTA
Mr. Leroy J.R. LaPlante
Secretary of Tribal Relations
Department of Tribal
Governmental Relations
302 East Dakota
Pierre, SD 57501
P: (605) 773-3415
F: (605) 773-6592

UTAH
Ms. Shirlee Silversmith
Director
Division of Indian Affairs
Department of Community &
Culture
300 South Rio Grande Street
Salt Lake City, UT 84101
P: (801) 245-7209
F: (801) 521-4727
E: ssilversmith@utah.gov

WASHINGTON
Mr. Craig A. Bill
Executive Director
Governor's Office of Indian
Affairs
210 - 11th Avenue, Southwest,
Suite 415
P.O. Box 40909
Olympia, WA 98504
P: (360) 902-8826
F: (360) 902-8829
E: craig.bill@goia.wa.gov

WISCONSIN
Ms. Dawn Vick
Intergovernmental Services
Team Leader
State Tribal Relations Initiative
101 East Wilson Street, 9th
Floor
P.O. Box 8944
Madison, WI 53708
P: (608) 266-7043
F: (608) 267-6917
E: dawn.vick@wisconsin.gov

Unclaimed Property

Responsible for the marshaling, administration and disposition of unclaimed or abandoned property.

ALABAMA

Hon. Young Boozer III (R)
State Treasurer
Office of the State Treasurer
600 Dexter Avenue
State Capitol, Room S-106
Montgomery, AL 36104
P: (334) 242-7501
F: (334) 242-7592
E: young.boozer
      @treasury.alabama.gov

Ms. Daria Story
Assistant Treasurer/Chief
Operating Officer
State Treasury
600 Dexter Avenue, S-100
Montgomery, AL 36130
P: (334) 242-7500
F: (334) 353-4080
E: daria.story
      @treasury.alabama.gov

ALASKA

Hon. Pamela Leary
State Treasurer
Treasury Division
P.O. Box 110400
Juneau, AK 99811
P: (907) 465-3669
F: (907) 465-2389
E: pam.leary@alaska.gov

Ms. Rachel Lewis
Unclaimed Property Manager
Unclaimed Property Section
Department of Revenue,
Treasury Division
P.O. Box 110420
Juneau, AK 99811
P: (907) 465-5885
F: (907) 465-2394
E: rachel.lewis@alaska.gov

ARIZONA

Mr. John A. Greene
Director
Department of Revenue
1600 West Monroe
Phoenix, AZ 85007
P: (602) 716-6090
F: (602) 542-2072

Mr. Joshua Joyce
Administrator
Unclaimed Property
Department of Revenue
1600 West Monroe
Phoenix, AZ 85007
P: (602) 716-6033
F: (602) 716-7997
E: JJoyce@azdor.gov

ARKANSAS

Hon. Andrea Lea (R)
Auditor of State
Office of the Auditor of State
State Capitol Building, Room 230
Little Rock, AR 72201
P: (501) 682-6030
F: (501) 682-2521

Mr. Robert Scott
Unclaimed Property Division
Manager
State Auditor's Office
P.O. Box 251906
Little Rock, AR 72225
P: (501) 371-2124
F: (501) 683-4285
E: RobS@auditor.ar.gov

CALIFORNIA

Mr. Gary Qualset
Chief
Unclaimed Prpperty Division
State Controller's Office
10600 White Rock Road,
Building A
Rancho Cordova, CA 95670
P: (916) 464-6263
F: (916) 322-4404
E: GQualset@sco.ca.gov

COLORADO

Hon. Walker Stapleton (R)
State Treasurer
Office of the State Treasurer
140 State Capitol Building
Denver, CO 80203
P: (303) 866-2441
F: (303) 866-2123
E: treasurer.stapleton
      @state.co.us

Ms. Patty White
Program Director
Unclaimed Property Division
State Treasury
1580 Logan Street, Suite 500
Denver, CO 80203
P: (303) 866-6070
F: (303) 866-6154
E: patty.white@state.co.us

CONNECTICUT

Ms. Maria M. Greenslade
Assistant Deputy Treasurer
Unclaimed Property
State Treasury
55 Elm Street
Hartford, CT 06106
P: (860) 702-3125
E: maria.greenslade
      @po.state.ct.us

Hon. Denise L. Nappier (D)
State Treasurer
Office of State Treasurer
55 Elm Street, 7th Floor
Hartford, CT 06106
P: (860) 702-3010
F: (860) 702-3043
E: denise.nappier@ct.gov

DELAWARE

Mr. Patrick T. Carter
Director
Division of Revenue
Carvel State Office Building
820 North French Street
Wilmington, DE 19801
P: (302) 577-8686
F: (302) 577-8202
E: patrick.carter
      @state.de.us

Mr. Thomas J. Cook
Secretary of Finance
Department of Finance
Carvel State Building, 8th Floor
820 North French Street
Wilmington, DE 19801
P: (302) 577-8987
F: (302) 577-8982
E: tom.cook@state.de.us

DISTRICT OF COLUMBIA

Hon. Lasana K. Mack
Treasurer & Deputy CFO
Office of Finance & Treasury
1101 4th Street, Southwest,
Suite W850
Washington, DC 20024
P: (202) 727-6055
F: (202) 727-6049
E: lasana.mack@dc.gov

Mr. Gracie B. Musher
Manager, Unclaimed Property
Office of Finance & Treasury
1101 4th Street, Southwest
Suite W 800-B
Washington, DC 20024
P: (202) 442-8195
F: (202) 442-8180
E: gracie.musher@dc.gov

FLORIDA

Hon. Jeffrey H. Atwater (R)
Chief Financial Officer
Department of Financial
Services
200 East Gaines Street
Tallahassee, FL 32399
P: (850) 413-2850
F: (850) 413-2950
E: allison@jeffatwater.com

Mr. Walter Graham
Chief of Unclaimed Property
Department of Financial
Services
200 East Gaines Street
353 Fletcher Building
Tallahassee, FL 32399
P: (850) 413-5522
F: (850) 413-3017
E: Walter.Graham
      @myfloridacfo.com

GEORGIA

Ms. Lynnette Riley
Revenue Commissioner
Department of Revenue
1800 Century Center Boulevard
Atlanta, GA 30345
P: (404) 417-2100

HAWAII

Mr. Scott Kami
Administrator
Financial Administration
Division
Department of Budget &
Finance
P.O. Box 150
Honolulu, HI 96810
P: (808) 586-1612
F: (808) 586-1644
E: scott.a.kami@hawaii.gov

Hon. Wesley Machida
Director of Finance
Department of Budget &
Finance
P.O. Box 150
Honolulu, HI 96810
P: (808) 586-1518
F: (808) 586-1976
E: hi.budgetandfinance
      @hawaii.gov

IDAHO

Hon. Ron G. Crane (R)
State Treasurer
State Treasurer's Office
304 North 8th Street
Boise, ID 83720
P: (208) 334-3200
F: (208) 332-2959
E: ron.crane@sto.idaho.gov

Unclaimed Property

Ms. Cozette Walters
Administrator
Unclaimed Property
State Treasurer's Office
P.O. Box 83720
Boise, ID 83720
P: (208) 332-2979
F: (208) 332-2970
E: cozette.walters
    @sto.idaho.gov

ILLINOIS
Hon. Michael W.
    Frerichs (D)
State Treasurer
Office of the State Treasurer
Statehouse
Executive Office 203
Springfield, IL 62706
P: (217) 782-2211
F: (217) 785-2777

INDIANA
Ms. Becky Yuan
Director
Unclaimed Property Division
Office of the Attorney General
P.O. Box 2504
Greenwood, IN 46142
P: (317) 883-4537
F: (317) 883-4520
E: byuan@atg.in.gov

Hon. Greg Zoeller (R)
Attorney General
Office of the Attorney General
Indiana Government Center
South
302 West Washington Street, 5th
Floor
Indianapolis, IN 46204
P: (317) 232-6201
F: (317) 232-7979
E: Constituent@atg.in.gov

IOWA
Ms. Karen Austin
Deputy Treasurer
Office of the State Treasurer
Lucas State Office Building
321 East 12th Street
Des Moines, IA 50319
P: (515) 281-7677
F: (515) 281-6962
E: karen.austin@iowa.gov

Hon. Michael L.
    Fitzgerald (D)
State Treasurer
State Treasurer's Office
State Capitol Building
Des Moines, IA 50319
P: (515) 281-5368
F: (515) 281-7562
E: mike.fitzgerald@iowa.gov

KANSAS
Hon. Ron Estes (R)
State Treasurer
Office of the State Treasurer
900 Southwest Jackson Street,
Suite 201
Topeka, KS 66612
P: (785) 296-3171
F: (785) 296-7950
E: ron@treasurer.ks.gov

Ms. Rita Mohr
Director of Unclaimed Property
State Treasury
900 Southwest Jackson, Suite
201
Topeka, KS 66612
P: (785) 291-3171
F: (785) 296-7950
E: rita@treasurer.ks.gov

KENTUCKY
Hon. Todd Hollenbach (D)
State Treasurer
Office of the State Treasurer
1050 U.S. Highway 127 South
Suite 100
Frankfort, KY 40601
P: (502) 564-4722
F: (502) 564-6545
E: todd.hollenbach@ky.gov

Ms. Brenda L. Owens
Director
Unclaimed Property Division
State Treasury
1050 U.S. Highway 127 South,
Suite 100
Frankfort, KY 40601
P: (502) 564-4722
F: (502) 564-4200
E: brenda.owens@ky.gov

LOUISIANA
Hon. John Neely Kennedy (R)
State Treasurer
Department of the Treasury
P.O. Box 44154
Baton Rouge, LA 70804
P: (225) 342-0010
F: (225) 342-0046
E: jkennedy
    @treasury.state.la.us

Ms. Kathleen Lobell
Director of Unclaimed Property
State Treasury
P.O. Box 44154
Baton Rouge, LA 70804
P: (225) 219-9400
E: klobell
    @treasury.state.la.us

MAINE
Hon. Terry Hayes (I)
State Treasurer
Office of the State Treasurer
39 State House Station
Augusta, ME 04333
P: (207) 624-7477
F: (207) 287-2367
E: state.treasurer
    @maine.gov

MARYLAND
Ms. Tamarra Eaton
Manager
Unclaimed Property
Comptroller's Office
301 West Preston Street, Room
310
Baltimore, MD 21201
P: (410) 767-1705
E: teaton@comp.state.md.us

Hon. Peter Franchot (D)
Comptroller
Office of the Comptroller
L.L. Goldstein Treasury
Building
P.O. Box 466
Annapolis, MD 21404
P: (410) 260-7801
F: (410) 974-3808
E: mdcomptroller
    @comp.state.md.us

MASSACHUSETTS
Mr. Mark W. Bracken
Director of Abandoned Property
State Treasury
One Ashburton Place, 12th Floor
Boston, MA 02108
P: (617) 367-0400
F: (617) 367-3645
E: mwbracken
    @tre.state.ma.us

Hon. Deb Goldberg (D)
State Treasurer
Office of the State Treasurer
State House, Room 227
Boston, MA 02133
P: (617) 367-3900
F: (617) 248-0372

MICHIGAN
Mr. Gonzalo G. Llano
Administrator
Unclaimed Property Division
State Treasury
P.O. Box 30756
Lansing, MI 48909
P: (517) 636-5307
F: (517) 322-5986
E: llanog@michigan.gov

MINNESOTA
Mr. Robert Commodore
Senior Director
Consumer & Industry Services
Department of Commerce
85 7th Place East, Suite 500
St. Paul, MN 55101
P: (651) 296-2508
E: Robert.Commodore
    @state.mn.us

Mr. Mike Rothman
Commissioner
Department of Commerce
85 East 7th Place, Suite 500
St. Paul, MN 55101
P: (651) 539-1638
F: (651) 296-4328
E: commerce.commissioner
    @state.mn.us

Ms. Amy Trumper
Administrator
Department of Commerce
85 7th Place East, Suite 500
St. Paul, MN 55101
P: (651) 282-5087
F: (651) 296-4328
E: Amy.Trumper@state.mn.us

MISSISSIPPI
Hon. Lynn Fitch (R)
State Treasurer
Office of the State Treasurer
P.O. Box 138
Jackson, MS 39205
P: (601) 359-3600
F: (601) 576-4495

MISSOURI
Mr. Scott Harper
Director of Unclaimed Property
& General Services
Division of Unclaimed Property
State Treasury
P.O. Box 1272
Jefferson City, MO 65102
P: (573) 751-2082
F: (573) 526-6027
E: scott.harper
    @treasurer.mo.gov

Hon. Clint Zweifel (D)
State Treasurer
Office of the State Treasurer
State Capitol, Room 229
P.O. Box 210
Jefferson City, MO 65102
P: (573) 751-2411
F: (573) 751-9443
E: clint.zweifel
    @treasurer.mo.gov

Unclaimed Property

MONTANA

Mr. Mike Kadas
Director
Department of Revenue
P.O. Box 5805
Helena, MT 59604
P: (406) 444-6900
F: (406) 444-3696

Mr. Jim McKeon
Unit Manager
Department of Revenue
P.O. Box 5805
Helena, MT 59604
P: (406) 444-1940
F: (406) 444-4091
E: jmckeon@mt.gov

NEBRASKA

Ms. Meaghan Aguirre
Unclaimed Property Coordinator
State Treasury
809 P Street
Lincoln, NE 68509
P: (402) 471-1089
F: (402) 471-1167
E: meaghan.aguirre
    @nebraska.gov

Hon. Don B. Stenberg (R)
State Treasurer
Office of the State Treasurer
State Capitol, Room 2005
Lincoln, NE 68509
P: (402) 471-2455
F: (402) 471-4390
E: Don.Stenberg
    @nebraska.gov

NEVADA

Hon. Dan Schwartz (R)
State Treasurer
Office of the State Treasurer
101 North Carson Street, Suite 4
Carson City, NV 89701
P: (775) 684-7109
F: (775) 684-5623
E: statetreasurer
    @nevadatreasurer.gov

NEW HAMPSHIRE

Hon. Catherine Provencher
State Treasurer
State Treasury
25 Capitol Street, Room 121
Concord, NH 03301
P: (603) 271-2621
F: (603) 271-3922
E: cprovencher
    @treasury.state.nh.us

Mr. Brian Regan
Director
Abandoned Property Division
State Treasury
25 Capitol Street, Room 205
Concord, NH 03301
P: (603) 271-1499
F: (603) 271-2730
E: bregan
    @treasury.state.nh.us

NEW JERSEY

Mr. Steven Harris
Chief of Unclaimed Property
Operations
Division of Taxation
P.O. Box 214
50 Barrack Street, 6th Floor
Trenton, NJ 08695
P: (609) 777-4655
F: (609) 984-0595
E: steven.harris
    @treas.state.nj.us

Hon. Andrew P.
    Sidamon-Eristoff
State Treasurer
Department of Treasury
State House, First Floor
P.O. Box 002
Trenton, NJ 08625
P: (608) 292-6748
F: (609) 984-3888

NEW MEXICO

Ms. Stephanie Dennis
Tax Compliance Specialist
Supervisor
Taxation & Revenue
Department
P.O. Box 25123
Santa Fe, NM 87504
P: (505) 827-0762
F: (505) 827-1759
E: stephanie.dennis
    @state.nm.us

Ms. Demesia Padilla
Secretary
Taxation & Revenue
Department
1100 South St. Francis Drive
Santa Fe, NM 87504
P: (505) 827-0700
F: (505) 827-0331

NEW YORK

Hon. Thomas P. DiNapoli (D)
Comptroller
Office of the State Comptroller
110 State Street
Albany, NY 12236
P: (518) 474-4040
F: (518) 474-3004
E: tdinapoli
    @osc.state.ny.us

Mr. Lawrence Schantz
Director
Office of Unclaimed Funds
State Comptroller's Office
110 State Street, 8th Floor
Albany, NY 12236
P: (518) 473-6318
F: (518) 474-7016
E: lschantz@osc.state.ny.us

NORTH CAROLINA

Hon. Janet Cowell (D)
State Treasurer
Department of State Treasurer
325 North Salisbury Street
Raleigh, NC 27603
P: (919) 508-5176
F: (919) 508-5167
E: janet.cowell
    @nctreasurer.com

Ms. Shirley Fowler
Administrator
Unclaimed Property Division
Department of State Treasurer
325 North Salisbury Street
Raleigh, NC 27603
P: (919) 508-5929
F: (919) 508-5181
E: shirley.fowler
    @nctreasurer.com

NORTH DAKOTA

Ms. Linda Fisher
Administrator
Department of Trust Lands
P.O. Box 5523
Bismarck, ND 58506
P: (701) 328-2800
F: (701) 328-3650
E: llfisher@nd.gov

Mr. Lance Gaebe
Land Commissioner
State Land Department
P.O. Box 5523
Bismarck, ND 58506
P: (701) 328-2800
F: (701) 328-3650
E: lancegaebe@nd.gov

OHIO

Mr. Yaw Obeng
Superintendent
Division of Unclaimed Funds
Department of Commerce
77 South High Street, 20th Floor
Columbus, OH 43266
P: (614) 644-6094
F: (614) 752-5078
E: Yaw.O'Beng
    @com.state.oh.us

OKLAHOMA

Ms. Kathy Janes
Director of Unclaimed Property
State Treasurer's Office
2401 Northwest 23rd Street,
Suite 42
Oklahoma City, OK 73107
P: (405) 522-6743
F: (405) 521-2677
E: Kathy.Janes
    @treasurer.ok.gov

Hon. Ken Miller (R)
State Treasurer
Office of the State Treasurer
Room 217, State Capitol
Building
2300 North Lincoln Boulevard
Oklahoma City, OK 73105
P: (405) 521-3191
F: (405) 521-4994

OREGON

Mr. Patrick Tate
Unclaimed Property Manager
Finance & Administration
Department of State Lands
775 Summer Street, Northeast,
Suite 100
Salem, OR 97301
P: (503) 986-5248
F: (503) 378-4844
E: patrick.tate@state.or.us

PENNSYLVANIA

Hon. Timothy Craig
State Treasurer
Office of the State Treasurer
129 Finance Building
Harrisburg, PA 17120
P: (717) 787-2465
F: (717) 783-9760

Mr. Frederick Stollsteimer
Director
Bureau of Unclaimed Property
State Treasury
Room 127, Finance Building
Harrisburg, PA 17120
P: (717) 783-5926
F: (717) 772-0970
E: fstollsteimer
    @patreasury.org

Unclaimed Property

PUERTO RICO
Ms. Hilda Enid Davila
Assistant Commissioner,
Administration
Office of the Commissioner of
Financial Institutions
Unclaimed Property
P.O. Box 11855
San Juan, PR 00910
P: (787) 723-3131
F: (787) 723-4225
E: enidd@ocif.gobierno.pr

Mr. Alfredo Padilla
Commissioner of Financial
Institutions
Office of the Commissioner of
Financial Institutions
Commonwealth of Puerto Rico
P.O. Box 11855
San Juan, PR 00910
P: (787) 723-3131
F: (787) 723-4042
E: comisionado
    @ocif.gobierno.pr

RHODE ISLAND
Hon. Seth Magaziner (D)
General Treasurer
Office of the General Treasurer
102 State House
Providence, RI 02903
P: (401) 222-2397
F: (401) 222-6140
E: generaltreasurer
    @treasury.ri.gov

SOUTH CAROLINA
Hon. Curtis Loftis (R)
State Treasurer
Office of the State Treasurer
P.O. Box 11778
Columbia, SC 29211
P: (803) 734-2101
F: (803) 734-2690
E: treasurer@sto.sc.gov

SOUTH DAKOTA
Ms. Lee DeJabet
Unclaimed Property
Administrator
State Treasury
State Capitol Building, Suite
212
500 East Capitol Avenue
Pierre, SD 57501
P: (605) 773-3900
F: (605) 773-3115
E: Lee.DeJabet@state.sd.us

Hon. Rich L. Sattgast (R)
State Treasurer
Office of the State Treasurer
500 East Capitol Avenue
Pierre, SD 57501
P: (605) 773-3378
F: (605) 773-3115
E: rich.sattgast
    @state.sd.us

TENNESSEE
Mr. John Gabriel
Director of Unclaimed Property
State Treasury
Andrew Jackson Building, 9th
Floor
502 Deaderick Street
Nashville, TN 37243
P: (615) 253-5354
F: (615) 734-6458
E: john.gabriel@tn.gov

Hon. David H. Lillard Jr.
State Treasurer
Department of Treasury
State Capitol, First Floor
600 Charlotte Avenue
Nashville, TN 37243
P: (615) 741-2956
F: (615) 253-1591
E: david.lillard@tn.gov

TEXAS
Hon. Glenn Hegar (R)
Comptroller of Public Accounts
Office of the Comptroller of
Public Accounts
LBJ State Office Building, 1st
Floor
111 East 17th Street
Austin, TX 78774
P: (512) 463-4444
F: (512) 463-4902
E: glenn.hegar
    @cpa.state.tx.us

UTAH
Hon. Richard K. Ellis (R)
State Treasurer
State Treasurer's Office
350 North State Street, Suite
180
P.O. Box 142315
Salt Lake City, UT 84114
P: (801) 538-1042
F: (801) 538-1465
E: sto@utah.gov

Mr. Dennis Johnston
Administrator
Division of Unclaimed Property
P.O. Box 140530
Salt Lake City, UT 84114
P: (801) 715-3321
F: (801) 715-3309
E: dljohnston@utah.gov

VERMONT
Mr. Albert LaPerle
Director of Unclaimed Property
State Treasury
109 State Street, 4th Floor
Montpelier, VT 05609
P: (802) 828-1452
F: (802) 828-2772
E: al.laperle@state.vt.us

Hon. Elizabeth Pearce
State Treasurer
Office of the State Treasurer
109 State Street
Montpelier, VT 05609
P: (802) 828-3322
F: (802) 828-2772
E: Beth.Pearce@state.vt.us

VIRGINIA
Ms. Vicki D. Bridgeman
Director of Unclaimed Property
State Treasury
P.O. Box 2478
Richmond, VA 23218
P: (804) 225-3156
F: (804) 786-4653
E: vicki.bridgeman
    @trs.virginia.gov

Hon. Manju Ganeriwala
State Treasurer
Department of the Treasury
P.O. Box 1879
Richmond, VA 23219
P: (804) 225-3131
F: (804) 786-0833
E: Manju.Ganeriwala
    @trs.virginia.gov

WASHINGTON
Ms. Celeste Monahan
Program Manager
Department of Revenue
P.O. Box 47454
Olympia, WA 98504
P: (360) 534-1301
F: (360) 664-8438
E: celestem@dor.wa.gov

Ms. Carol Nelson
Director
Department of Revenue
P.O. Box 47450
Olympia, WA 98504
P: (360) 534-1619

WEST VIRGINIA
Ms. Carolyn Atkinson
Deputy Treasurer of Unclaimed
Property
State Treasury
One Player's Club Drive
Charleston, WV 25311
P: (304) 341-0703
F: (304) 558-5063
E: carolyn.atkinson
    @wvsto.com

Hon. John D. Perdue (D)
State Treasurer
State Treasurer's Office
State Capitol Complex
Building 1, Room E-145
Charleston, WV 25305
P: (304) 558-5000
F: (304) 558-4097

WISCONSIN
Hon. Matt Adamczyk (R)
State Treasurer
Office of the State Treasurer
P.O. Box 2114
Madison, WI 53701
P: (608) 266-3714
F: (608) 266-2647
E: Matt.Adamczyk
    @wisconsin.gov

Ms. Mary Celentani
Administrator
Unclaimed Property Division
State Treasury
P.O. Box 2114
Madison, WI 53701
P: (608) 267-2208
F: (608) 261-6799
E: mary.celentani
    @wisconsin.gov

WYOMING
Hon. Mark Gordon
State Treasurer
Office of the State Treasurer
200 West 24th Street
Cheyenne, WY 82002
P: (307) 777-7408
F: (307) 777-5411
E: treasurer@wyo.gov

Ms. Nancy Russell
Director
Unclaimed Property Division
State Treasury
2515 Warren Avenue, Suite 502
Cheyenne, WY 82002
P: (307) 777-5590
F: (307) 777-5430
E: Nancy.Russell@wyo.gov

Veterans Affairs

Provides services and information to the state's veterans, their dependents and survivors.

ALABAMA
Mr. W. Clyde Marsh
Director
Department of Veterans Affairs
P.O. Box 1509
Montgomery, AL 36102
P: (334) 242-5077
F: (334) 242-5102
E: clyde.marsh
    @va.alabama.gov

ALASKA
Mr. Verdie Bowen
Administrator
Office of Veterans Affairs
4600 DeBarr Road, Suite 180
Ft. Richardson, AK 99508
P: (907) 334-0874
F: (907) 334-0869
E: verdie.bowen@alaska.gov

ARIZONA
Ms. Wanda Wright
Director
Department of Veterans'
Services
3839 North Third Street
Phoenix, AZ 85012
P: (602) 255-3373
F: (602) 255-1038
E: wwright@azdvs.gov

CALIFORNIA
Ms. Debbie Endsley
Acting Secretary
Department of Veterans Affairs
1227 O Street
Sacramento, CA 95814
P: (916) 653-2192
E: debbie.endsley
    @calvet.ca.gov

COLORADO
Mr. Ruben Mestas
Director
Division of Veteran Affairs
1355 South Colorado Boulevard
Suite 113
Denver, CO 80222
P: (303) 284-6077
E: reuben.mestas
    @dmva.state.co.us

CONNECTICUT
Lt. Col. Sean Connolly
Commissioner
Department of Veterans Affairs
287 West Street
Rocky Hill, CT 06067
P: (860) 721-5891
F: (860) 721-5919
E: Sean.Connolly@ct.gov

DELAWARE
Mr. Lawrence Kirby
Executive Director
Commission of Veterans Affairs
802 Silver Lake Boulevard
Dover, DE 19904
P: (302) 739-2792
F: (302) 739-2794
E: Lawrence.Kirby
    @state.de.us

DISTRICT OF COLUMBIA
Mr. Matthew J. Cary
Director
Office of Veterans Affairs
441 4th Street, Northwest
Suite 570 South
Washington, DC 20001
P: (202) 724-5454
F: (202) 724-7117
E: matt.cary@dc.gov

FLORIDA
Mr. Mike Prendergast
Executive Director
Department of Veterans Affairs
4040 Esplanade Way #180
Tallahassee, FL 32399
P: (850) 487-1533
F: (850) 488-4001
E: ExDir@fdva.state.fl.us

GEORGIA
Mr. Mike Roby
Interim Commissioner
Department of Veterans Service
205 Butler Street, Suite E-970
Atlanta, GA 30334
P: (404) 656-2300
F: (404) 657-9738
E: mroby@vs.state.ga.us

HAWAII
Mr. Ron Han
Director
Office of Veterans Services
459 Patterson Road
E-Wing, Room 1-A103
Honolulu, HI 96819
P: (808) 433-0420
F: (808) 433-0385
E: ovs@ovs.hawaii.gov

IDAHO
Mr. David Brasuell
Administrator
Division of Veterans Affairs
320 Collins Road
Boise, ID 83702
P: (208) 334-3513
F: (208) 334-2627
E: david.brasuell
    @veterans.idaho.gov

ILLINOIS
Ms. Erica Jeffries
Director
Department of Veterans Affairs
P.O. Box 19432
Springfield, IL 62794
P: (217) 785-4114
F: (217) 524-0344
E: erica.jeffries
    @illinois.gov

INDIANA
Sgt. James M. Brown
Director
Department of Veterans Affairs
302 West Washington Street,
Room E-120
Indianapolis, IN 46204
P: (317) 232-3910
F: (317) 232-7721
E: jbrown@dva.in.gov

IOWA
Colonel Robert King
Executive Director
Department of Veterans Affairs
Camp Dodge, Building 3663
7105 Northwest 70th Avenue
Johnston, IA 50131
P: (515) 727-3444
F: (515) 727-3713
E: Robert.King@iowa.gov

KANSAS
Mr. Gregg Burden
Executive Director
Commission on Veterans'
Affairs
700 Southwest Jackson Street
Jayhawk Towers, Suite 701
Topeka, KS 66603
P: (785) 296-3976
F: (785) 296-1462
E: gburden@kvva.org

KENTUCKY
Ms. Heather French Henry
Commissioner
Department of Veterans Affairs
1111 Louisville Road (NGAKY
Building)
Frankfort, KY 40601
P: (502) 564-9203
F: (502) 564-9240

LOUISIANA
Mr. David LaCerte
Secretary
Department of Veterans Affairs
P.O. Box 94095
Baton Rouge, LA 70804
P: (225) 922-0500
F: (225) 922-0511
E: david.lacerte@la.gov

MAINE
Ms. Adria O. Horn
Director
Bureau of Veterans Services
State House Station #117
Augusta, ME 04333
P: (207) 626-4464
F: (207) 626-4471
E: mainebvs@maine.gov

MARYLAND
Mr. George W. Owings III
Secretary
Department of Veterans Affairs
The Jeffrey Building, Fourth
Floor
16 Francis Street
Annapolis, MD 21401
P: (410) 260-3838
F: (410) 216-7928
E: secretary.mdva
    @maryland.gov

MASSACHUSETTS
Mr. Francisco Urena
Secretary
Department of Veterans Services
600 Washington Street, Room
1100
Boston, MA 02111
P: (617) 210-5951
F: (617) 210-5755
E: MDVS@vet.state.ma.us

MICHIGAN
Maj. Gen. Gregory J.
    Vadnais
Adjutant General
Department of Military &
Veterans Affairs
3411 North Martin Luther King
Boulevard
Lansing, MI 48906
P: (517) 481-8083
F: (517) 481-8125
E: gregory.vadnais
    @us.army.mil

Veterans Affairs

MINNESOTA
Maj. Gen. Larry W. Shellito
Commissioner
Department of Veterans Affairs
Veterans Services Building, 2nd
Floor
20 West 12th Street, Room 206
St. Paul, MN 55155
P: (651) 757-1555
F: (651) 296-3954
E: larry.shellito
@state.mn.us

MISSISSIPPI
Mr. Randy Reeves
Executive Director
Veterans Affairs Board
P.O. Box 5947
Pearl, MS 39288
P: (601) 576-4850
F: (601) 576-4868
E: rreeves@vab.ms.gov

MISSOURI
Mr. Larry D. Kay
Executive Director
Veterans Commission
P.O. Drawer 147
Jefferson City, MO 65102
P: (573) 522-1402
F: (573) 751-6836
E: larry.kay@mvc.dps.mo.gov

MONTANA
Mr. Joseph S. Foster
Administrator
Veterans Affairs Division
P.O. Box 5715
Helena, MT 59604
P: (406) 324-3740
F: (406) 324-3745
E: jofoster@mt.gov

NEBRASKA
Mr. John Hilgert
Director
Department of Veterans Affairs
P.O. Box 95083
Lincoln, NE 68509
P: (402) 471-2458
F: (402) 471-2491
E: john.hilgert
@nebraska.gov

NEVADA
Colonel Kat Miller
Executive Director
Department of Veterans Services
5460 Reno Corporate Drive,
Suite 131
Reno, NV 89511
P: (775) 688-1653
F: (775) 688-1656
E: millerk@veterans.nv.gov

NEW HAMPSHIRE
Ms. Mary E. Morin
Director
Office of Veterans Affairs
275 Chestnut Street, #517
Manchester, NH 03101
P: (603) 624-9230
F: (603) 624-9236
E: mary.morin@vba.va.gov

NEW JERSEY
Mr. Raymond Zawacki
Deputy Commissioner for
Veterans Affairs
Department of Military &
Veterans Affairs
Eggerts Crossing Road
P.O. Box 340
Trenton, NJ 08625
P: (609) 530-7045
F: (609) 530-7075
E: raymond.zawacki
@njdmava.state.nj.us

NEW MEXICO
Mr. Jack Fox
Secretary
Department of Veterans Services
407 Galisteo Street, Room 142
Santa Fe, NM 87504
P: (866) 433-8387

NEW YORK
Mr. Eric Hesse
Director
Division of Veterans Affairs
Corning Tower, Suite 2836
5 Empire State Plaza
Albany, NY 12223
P: (518) 474-6114
F: (518) 474-6924

NORTH CAROLINA
Mr. Ilario Pantano
Director
Division of Veterans Affairs
1315 Mail Service Center
325 North Salisbury Street
Raleigh, NC 27699
P: (919) 807-4250
F: (919) 807-4260
E: ilario.pantano
@doa.nc.gov

NORTH DAKOTA
Mr. Lonnie Wangen
Commissioner
Department of Veterans Affairs
P.O. Box 9003
Fargo, ND 58106
P: (701) 239-7165
F: (701) 239-7166
E: lwangen@nd.gov

OHIO
Mr. Timothy C. Gorrell
Director
Department of Veterans Services
77 South High Street, 17th Floor
Columbus, OH 43215
P: (614) 728-0221
F: (614) 728-9498
E: timothy.gorrell
@dvs.ohio.gov

OKLAHOMA
Maj. Gen. Myles L. Deering
Director
Department of Veterans Affairs
P.O. Box 53067
Oklahoma City, OK 73152
P: (405) 521-3684
F: (405) 521-6533
E: mdeering
@odva.state.ok.us

OREGON
Mr. Cameron Smith
Director
Department of Veterans Affairs
700 Summer Street, Northeast
Salem, OR 97310
P: (503) 373-2388
F: (503) 373-2362
E: smithc@odva.state.or.us

PENNSYLVANIA
Brigadier General Jerry G.
Beck Jr.
Deputy Adjutant General
Department of Military &
Veterans Affairs
Fort Indiantown Gap
Building S-O-47
Annville, PA 17003
P: (717) 861-8902
F: (717) 861-8589

RHODE ISLAND
Ms. Kim Ripoli
Associate Director
Division of Veterans Affairs
480 Metacom Avenue
Bristol, RI 02809
P: (401) 254-8350
F: (401) 254-2320
E: kripoli@dhs.ri.gov

SOUTH CAROLINA
Mr. Howard Metcalf
Director
Division of Veterans Affairs
1205 Pendleton Street, Suite 463
Columbia, SC 29201
P: (803) 734-0200
F: (803) 734-0197
E: hmetcalf@oepp.sc.gov

SOUTH DAKOTA
Maj. Gen. Timothy A. Reisch
Adjutant General
Department of the Military
2823 West Main Street, Building
420
Rapid City, SD 57702
P: (605) 737-6702
F: (605) 737-6677
E: tim.reisch@us.army.mil

Mr. Larry Zimmerman
Director
Department of Veterans Affairs
500 East Capitol Avenue
Pierre, SD 57501
P: (605) 773-3269
F: (605) 773-5380
E: larry.zimmerman
@state.sd.us

TENNESSEE
Ms. Many-Bears Grinder
Commissioner
Department of Veterans Affairs
215 Rosa L. Parks Avenue
Nashville, TN 37243
P: (615) 741-2931
F: (615) 741-4785

TEXAS
Mr. Thomas Palladino
Executive Director
Veterans Commission
P.O. Box 12277
Austin, TX 78711
P: (512) 463-5538
F: (512) 475-2395
E: executiveoffice
@tvc.texas.gov

UTAH
Mr. Gary R. Harter
Director
Department of Veterans Affairs
550 Foothill Boulevard, Room
202
Salt Lake City, UT 84108
P: (801) 326-2372
F: (801) 326-2369
E: gharter@utah.gov

VERMONT
Mr. Robert Burke
Veterans Services Director
Office of Veterans Affairs
118 State Street, Drawer 20
Montpelier, VT 05620
P: (802) 828-3379
F: (802) 828-5932
E: robert.burke@state.vt.us

VIRGINIA
Mr. John Newby
Commissioner
Department of Veterans Services
900 East Main Street
1st Floor, West Wing
Richmond, VA 23219
P: (804) 786-0286
F: (804) 786-0302
E: john.newby
 @dvs.virginia.gov

WASHINGTON
Ms. Lourdes Alvarado-Ramos
Director
Department of Veterans Affairs
1011 Plum Stret, Building 5
P.O. Box 41150
Olympia, WA 98504
P: (360) 725-2151
F: (360) 586-4393

WEST VIRGINIA
Mr. Rick Thompson
Secretary
Department of Veterans
Assistance
1514-B Kanawha Boulevard,
East
Charleston, WV 25311
P: (304) 558-3661
F: (304) 558-3662

WISCONSIN
Mr. John A. Scocos
Secretary
Department of Veterans Affairs
30 West Mifflin Street
P.O. Box 7843
Madison, WI 53707
P: (608) 266-1315
F: (608) 264-7616

WYOMING
Mr. Larry Barttlebort
Executive Director
Veterans Commission
5500 Bishop Boulevard
Cheyenne, WY 82009
P: (307) 772-5145
F: (307) 772-5202
E: lbartt@state.wy.us

Vital Statistics

Maintains a statewide file of birth, death, marriage and divorce records, and issues certified copies of those records.

ALABAMA
Ms. Catherine Donald
Director
Center for Health Statistics
Department of Public Health
Vital Records, P.O. Box 5625
Montgomery, AL 36103
P: (334) 206-5418
F: (334) 206-2659

ALASKA
Mr. Phillip Mitchell
Section Chief
Bureau of Vital Statistics
Department of Health & Social Services
P.O. Box 110675
Juneau, AK 99801
P: (907) 465-3391
F: (907) 465-3618
E: phillip.mitchell
    @alaska.gov

ARIZONA
Dr. Cara M. Christ
Director
Department of Health Services
150 North 18th Avenue
Phoenix, AZ 85007
P: (602) 542-1025
F: (602) 542-1062

ARKANSAS
Ms. Melinda Allen
Branch Chief
Division of Vital Records
4815 West Markham Street, Slot 44
Little Rock, AR 72205
P: (501) 661-2336
F: (501) 661-2717
E: Melinda.Allen
    @Arkansas.gov

CALIFORNIA
Ms. Veronica Wogec
Chief
Vital Records Issuance & Preservation Branch
1501 Capitol Avenue, MS 5000
P.O. Box 997410
Sacramento, CA 95899
P: (916) 552-8129

COLORADO
Mr. Bob O'Doherty
Director & Chief Information Officer
Health Statistics
Public Health & Environment
4300 Cherry Creek South, CHEIS-HS-A1
Denver, CO 80246
P: (303) 692-2160
F: (303) 691-7821
E: cdphe.healthstatistics
    @state.co.us

CONNECTICUT
Ms. Jane Purtill
State Registrar of Vital Records
Vital Records Office
Department of Public Health
410 Capitol Avenue, MS#11VRS
Hartford, CT 06134
P: (860) 509-7895
F: (860) 509-7964
E: jane.purtill@ct.gov

DELAWARE
Ms. Judy Chaconas
Director
Bureau of Health Planning & Resources Management
Jesse Cooper Building
417 Federal Street
Dover, DE 19901
P: (302) 744-4555
F: (302) 739-3313

DISTRICT OF COLUMBIA
Mr. David A. Berns
Director
Department of Human Services
64 New York Avenue, Northeast
6th Floor
Washington, DC 20002
P: (202) 671-4200
F: (202) 671-4326
E: dhs@dc.gov

FLORIDA
Mr. Ken T. Jones
Deputy State Registrar
Bureau of Vital Statistics
P.O. Box 210
Jacksonville, FL 32231
P: (904) 359-6900
F: (904) 359-6931
E: VitalStats@FLHealth.gov

GEORGIA
Dr. Brenda C. Fitzgerald
Commissioner
Department of Public Health
Two Peachtree Street, Northwest
15th Floor
Atlanta, GA 30303
P: (404) 657-2700

HAWAII
Dr. Alvin T. Onaka
Chief & State Registrar
Office of Health Status Monitoring
Department of Health
P.O. Box 3378
Honolulu, HI 96801
P: (808) 586-4600
F: (808) 586-4606

IDAHO
Ms. Jane S. Smith
State Registrar
Bureau of Vital Records & Health Statistics
450 West State Street
1st Floor, Pete T. Cenarrusa Building
Boise, ID 83720
P: (208) 334-5976
F: (208) 332-7260
E: smithj2@dhw.idaho.gov

ILLINOIS
Dr. Nirav D. Shah
Acting Director of Public Health
Department of Public Health
535 West Jefferson Street, 5th Floor
Springfield, IL 62761
P: (217) 782-4977
F: (217) 782-3987

INDIANA
Mr. Brian Carnes
Director
Vital Records Division
Department of Health
2 North Meridian Street, Room 2NLL077
Indianapolis, IN 46204
P: (317) 233-7523
F: (317) 233-5956
E: bcarnes@isdh.IN.gov

IOWA
Ms. Jill France
Bureau Chief
Bureau of Health Statistics
Lucas State Office Building
321 East 12th Street
Des Moines, IA 50319
P: (515) 281-6762
E: jill.france
    @idph.iowa.gov

KANSAS
Dr. Elizabeth W. Saadi
State Registrar
Office of Vital Statistics
Curtis State Office Building
1000 Southwest Jackson
Topeka, KS 66612
P: (785) 296-1400
F: (785) 296-8075
E: Vital.Records@kdheks.gov

KENTUCKY
Dr. Stephanie
    Mayfield Gibson
Commissioner
Department for Public Health
275 East Main Street
Frankfort, KY 40621

LOUISIANA
Ms. Devin D. George
Director
State Registrar & Vital Records
Department of Health & Hospitals
P.O. Box 629
Baton Rouge, LA 70821
P: (504) 593-5100
F: (504) 568-8716
E: devin.george@la.gov

MAINE
Ms. Roberta L. Fogg
Deputy State Registrar
Office of Data, Research & Vital Statistics
11 State House Station
220 Capitol Street
Augusta, ME 04333
P: (207) 287-3181
F: (207) 287-5470
E: roberta.l.fogg@maine.gov

MARYLAND
Dr. Isabelle L. Horon
Director
Vital Statistics Administration
Department of Health & Mental Hygiene
4201 Patterson Avenue
Baltimore, MD 21215
P: (410) 764-3513
F: (410) 358-4750
E: horoni@dhmh.state.md.us

MASSACHUSETTS
Dr. Monica Bharel
Commissioner
Department of Public Health
250 Washington Street
Boston, MA 02108
P: (617) 624-6000

MICHIGAN
Mr. Glenn Copeland
State Registrar & Division Director
Division for Vital Records & Health Statistics
Capitol View Building
201 Townsend Street
Lansing, MI 48913
P: (517) 335-8677
F: (517) 335-8711
E: CopelandG@michigan.gov

MINNESOTA
Dr. Edward Ehlinger
Commissioner of Health
Department of Health
625 North Robert Street
Box 64975
St. Paul, MN 55164
P: (651) 201-5810
F: (651) 201-4986
E: Ed.Ehlinger@state.mn.us

MISSISSIPPI
Ms. Judy Moulder
State Registrar
Public Health Statistics
571 Stadium Drive
P.O. Box 1700
Jackson, MS 39215
P: (601) 576-7960
F: (601) 576-7505
E: jmoulder
  @msdh.state.ms.us

MISSOURI
Ms. Michelle Zeilman
Chief
Bureau of Vital Records
Department of Health & Senior
Services
P.O. Box 570
Jefferson City, MO 65102
P: (573) 751-6387
F: (573) 526-3846
E: VitalRecordsInfo
  @health.mo.gov

MONTANA
Mr. Dean Vig
Supervisor
Office of Vital Records
111 North Sanders, Room 6
P.O. BOX 4210
Helena, MT 59604
P: (406) 444-5249
F: (406) 444-1803

NEVADA
Mr. Chad Westom
Bureau Chief
Bureau of Health Statistics,
Planning, Epidemiology &
Response
Department of Health & Human
Services
4150 Technology Way, Suite 200
Carson City, NV 89706
P: (775) 684-4155
F: (775) 684-4156

NEW HAMPSHIRE
Mr. Steven M. Wurtz
State Registrar
Division of Vital Records
Department of State
71 South Fruit Street
Concord, NH 03301
P: (603) 271-4650
F: (603) 271-3447
E: swurtz@sos.state.nh.us

NEW JERSEY
Ms. Mary E. O'Dowd
Commissioner
Department of Health & Senior
Services
P.O. Box 360
Trenton, NJ 08625
P: (609) 292-7837
F: (609) 292-0053

NEW YORK
Mr. Peter Carucci
Director
Vital Records
800 North Pearl Street
Albany, NY 12204
P: (518) 474-5245

NORTH CAROLINA
Ms. Catherine Ryan
Director & State Registrar
Department of Health & Human
Services
Vital Records Division
1903 Mail Service Center
Raleigh, NC 27699
P: (919) 733-3000
F: (919) 733-1511
E: catherine.c.ryan
  @dhhs.nc.gov

NORTH DAKOTA
Mr. Darin J. Meschke
State Registrar, Director
Division of Vital Records
600 East Boulevard Avenue
Department 301
Bismarck, ND 58505
P: (701) 328-2360
F: (701) 328-1850
E: dmeschke@nd.gov

**NORTHERN MARIANA
ISLANDS**
Mr. John G. Moore
Commonwealth Recorder
Vital Records Section
P.O. Box 500307
Saipan, MP 96950
P: (670) 236-9830
F: (670) 236-9831

OHIO
Dr. Robert J. Campbell
Deputy Director
Center for Public Health
Statistics & Informatics
Department of Health
246 North High Street
Columbus, OH 43215
P: (614) 995-5591
F: (614) 728-4638
E: datacenter@odh.ohio.gov

OKLAHOMA
Ms. Kelly Baker
Director
Center for Health Statistics
State Department of Health
1000 Northeast 10th Street
Oklahoma City, OK 73117
P: (405) 271-6225
F: (405) 270-9061
E: kellyb@health.ok.gov

OREGON
Ms. Jennifer A. Woodward
Section Manager/State Registrar
Center for Health Statistics
State Health Authority
800 Northeast Oregon Street,
Suite 205
Portland, OR 97232
P: (971) 673-1190
F: (971) 673-1203
E: jennifer.a.woodward
  @state.or.us

PENNSYLVANIA
Ms. Linda Caniglia
Director
Division of Vital Records
P.O. Box 1528
New Castle, PA 16103
P: (724) 656-3100
F: (724) 656-3079

PUERTO RICO
Mr. Nicolas
  Fernandez-Cornier
Executive Director
Demographic Registry
P.O. Box 11854
San Juan, PR 00910
P: (787) 281-8867
F: (787) 751-5003

RHODE ISLAND
Ms. Colleen Fontana
Chief, State Registrar
Office of Vital Records
Department of Health
3 Capitol Hill, Room 101
Providence, RI 02908
P: (401) 222-2811
F: (401) 222-6548
E: colleen.fontana
  @health.ri.gov

SOUTH CAROLINA
Ms. Shae Sutton
Director
Public Health Statistics &
Information Services
Dept. of Health &
Environmental Control
2600 Bull Street
Columbia, SC 29201
P: (803) 898-4144

SOUTH DAKOTA
Mr. Anthony Nelson
State Registrar
Vital Records
Department of Health
207 East Missouri Avenue, Suite
1A
Pierre, SD 57501
P: (605) 773-4961
F: (605) 773-2680
E: vitalrecords@state.sd.us

TENNESSEE
Ms. Catherine Haralson
State Registrar & Director
Vital Records
1st Floor, Central Services
Building
421 5th Avenue, North
Nashville, TN 37243
P: (615) 741-1763

TEXAS
Nagla Elerian
Director
Center for Health Statistics
Department of State Health
Services
1100 West 49th Street
Austin, TX 78756
P: (512) 776-7261
F: (512) 776-7332
E: chs-info
  @dshs.state.tx.us

Vital Statistics

Ms. Geraldine Harris
Vital Statistics
Department of State Health
Services
P.O.Box 149347
Austin, TX 78714
P: (888) 963-7111
F: (512) 458-7711
E: registrar
     @dshs.state.tx.us

U.S. VIRGIN ISLANDS
Darice Plaskett
Commissioner
Department of Health
Charles Harwood Complex
3500 Richmond
St. Croix, VI 00820

UTAH
Ms. Janice Houston
Director
Office of Vital Records &
Statistics
288 North 1460 West
P.O. Box 141010
Salt Lake City, UT 84114
P: (801) 538-6262
F: (801) 538-7012
E: jlhouston@utah.gov

VERMONT
Dr. William K. Apao
Director
Division of Health Surveillance
Department of Health
108 Cherry Street
Burlington, VT 05402
P: (802) 863-7300
F: (802) 865-7754

VIRGINIA
Dr. Marissa J. Levine
Commissioner of Health
Department of Health
109 Governor Street
P.O. Box 2448
Richmond, VA 23218
P: (804) 864-7026
F: (804) 864-7022
E: Marissa.Levine
     @vdh.virginia.gov

WASHINGTON
Ms. Jennifer Tebaldi
Assistant Secretary
Disease Control & Health
Statistics Division
P.O. Box 47811
Olympia, WA 98504
P: (360) 236-4202
F: (360) 236-4245
E: jennifer.tebaldi
     @doh.wa.gov

WEST VIRGINIA
Mr. Gary L. Thompson
State Registrar & Assistant
Director
Health Statistics Center
350 Capitol Street, Room 165
Charleston, WV 25301
P: (304) 558-2931
F: (304) 558-1051
E: Gary.L.Thompson@wv.gov

WYOMING
Mr. Jim McBride
Manager
Vital Statistics Services
Department of Health
2300 Capitol Avenue
Cheyenne, WY 82002
P: (307) 777-7591
F: (307) 777-2483

Vocational Rehabilitation

Assists and encourages disabled persons to find suitable employment through training programs.

ALABAMA
Dr. Cary F. Boswell
Commissioner
Department of Rehabilitation Services
602 South Lawrence Street
P.O. Box 4280
Montgomery, AL 36103
P: (334) 293-7200
F: (334) 293-7383

ALASKA
Mr. Mark Dale
Director
State Rehabilitation Services
Juneau Central Office
801 West 10th Street, Suite A
Juneau, AK 99801
P: (907) 465-6926

AMERICAN SAMOA
Mr. Pete Galea'i
Director
Vocational Rehabilitation
American Samoa Government
ASG Mail 3492
Pago Pago, AS 96799
P: (684) 699-1371
F: (864) 633-2393

ARIZONA
Ms. Letitia M. Labrecque
Administrator
State Rehabilitation Services
1789 West Jefferson, 2nd Floor
Northwest
P.O. Box 6123
Phoenix, AZ 85005
P: (602) 542-6295

ARKANSAS
Mr. Alan McClain
Commissioner
State Rehabilitation Services
525 West Capitol Avenue
Little Rock, AR 72201
P: (501) 296-1616

Ms. Katy Morris
Director
Division of Services for the Blind
700 Main Street, Slot S101
Little Rock, AR 72201
P: (501) 682-0360
F: (501) 682-0366
E: katy.morris@arkansas.gov

CALIFORNIA
Mr. Joe Xavier
Director
Department of Rehabilitation
721 Capitol Mall
Sacramento, CA 95814
P: (916) 558-5800

COLORADO
Ms. Joelle Brouner
Director
Division of Vocational Rehabilitation
Administration Office
1575 Sherman Street, 4th Floor
Denver, CO 80203
P: (303) 866-4886

CONNECTICUT
Ms. Amy Porter
Director
State Rehabilitation Services
Department of Social Services
25 Sigourney Street, 11th Floor
Hartford, CT 06106
P: (860) 424-4864
F: (860) 424-4850

Mr. Brian S. Sigman
Director of Education and Rehabilitation
Bureau of Rehabilitative Services
184 Windsor Avenue
Windsor, CT 06095
P: (860) 602-4008
F: (860) 602-4030
E: brian.sigman@ct.gov

DELAWARE
Ms. Andrea Guest
Director
Division of Vocational Rehabilitation
Department of Labor
4425 North Market Street, P.O. Box 9969
Wilmington, DE 19809
P: (302) 761-8275
F: (302) 761-6611

Mr. Daniel Madrid
Director
Division for the Visually Impaired
Health & Social Services, Biggs Building
1901 North DuPont Highway
New Castle, DE 19720
P: (302) 255-9800

DISTRICT OF COLUMBIA
Mr. Andrew Reese
Deputy Director
Department on Disability Services
1125 15th Street, Northwest, 9th Floor
Washington, DC 20005
P: (202) 442-8663

FLORIDA
Mr. Robert Doyle
Director, Division of Blind Services
Department of Education
325 West Gaines Street
Turlington Building, Room 1114
Tallahassee, FL 32399
P: (850) 245-0331

Ms. Aleisa McKinlay
Director
Division of Vocational Rehabilitation
Department of Education
4070 Esplanade Way, 2nd Floor
Tallahassee, FL 32399
P: (850) 245-3311
F: (850) 245-3316

GEORGIA
Mr. Greg Schmieg
Deputy Commissioner
Vocational Rehabilitation Agency
2 Peachtree Street, 6th Floor
Atlanta, GA 30303
P: (404) 232-7800

GUAM
Ms. Rita Sotomayor
Director, Division of Vocational Rehabilitation
Department of Integrated Services for Individuals with Disabilities
Suite 602 DNA Building
238 AFC Flores Street
Hagatna, GU 96910
P: (671) 475-5735

HAWAII
Mr. Albert Perez
Administrator
State Rehabilitation Services
1901 Bachelot Street
Honolulu, HI 96817
P: (808) 586-9741

IDAHO
Ms. Jane Donnellan
Administrator
Division of Vocational Rehabilitation
650 West State Street, Room 150
P.O. Box 83720-0096
Boise, ID 83720
P: (208) 287-6477

Ms. Angela Jones
Administrator
Commission for the Blind & Visually Impaired
341 West Washington Street
P.O. Box 83720
Boise, ID 82720
P: (208) 334-3220
F: (208) 334-2963

ILLINOIS
Ms. Kristine Smith
Director
Division of Rehabilitation Services
100 South Grand Avenue
P.O. Box 19429
Springfield, IL 62704
P: (217) 557-0401

INDIANA
Ms. Kylee Hope
Director, Division of Disability & Rehabilitative Services
Bureau of Rehabilitation Services
402 West Washington Street
IGCS/W453/MS 20
Indianapolis, IN 46204
P: (800) 545-7763

IOWA
Mr. David Mitchell
Administrator
Vocational Rehabilitation Services
Department of Education
510 East 12th Street
Des Moines, IA 50319
P: (515) 281-6731
F: (515) 281-4703
E: david.mitchell@iowa.gov

Mr. Richard Sorey
Director
Department for the Blind
524 Fourth Street
Des Moines, IA 50309
P: (515) 281-1293
F: (515) 281-1263
E: Richard.Sorey @blind.state.ia.us

Vocational Rehabilitation

KANSAS
Mr. Michael Donnelly
Director
State Rehabilitation Services
915 Southwest Harrison, 9th
Floor North
Docking State Office Building
Topeka, KS 66612
P: (785) 368-8204
F: (785) 368-7467

KENTUCKY
Ms. Allison Flanagan
Executive Director
Office for the Blind
275 East Main Street, Mail Stop
2 E-J
Frankfort, KY 40621
P: (502) 782-3416

Mr. Buddy Hoskinson
Executive Director
Office of Vocational
Rehabilitation
Education Cabinet
275 East Main Street, Mail Drop
2-EK
Frankfort, KY 40621
P: (502) 564-4440 Ext. 23437
F: (502) 564-6745
E: buddy.hoskinson@ky.gov

LOUISIANA
Mr. Mark Martin
Director
Rehabilitation Services
P.O. Box 91297
Baton Rouge, LA 70821
P: (225) 219-2231
F: (225) 219-2942

MAINE
Ms. Elizabeth Hopkins
Director
Division of Vocational
Rehabilitation
150 State House Station
Augusta, ME 04333
P: (207) 623-6745
F: (207) 287-5292

Mr. John McMahon
Director
Division for the Blind &
Visually Impaired
150 State House Station
Augusta, ME 04333
P: (207) 623-7956
F: (207) 287-5292

MARYLAND
Ms. Suzanne Page
Assistant State Superintendent
Division of Rehabilitation
Services
Department of Education
2301 Argonne Drive
Baltimore, MD 21218
P: (410) 554-9385
F: (410) 554-9384

MASSACHUSETTS
Ms. Adelaide Nicky Osborn
State Rehabilitation
Commission
27 Wormwood Street
Boston, MA 02210
P: (617) 204-3600
F: (617) 727-1354

Mr. Paul Saner
Commissioner
Commission for the Blind
48 Boylston Street
Boston, MA 02210
P: (617) 626-7503

MICHIGAN
Ms. Suzanne Howell
Director
Rehabilitation Services
201 North Washington Square
P.O. Box 30010
Lansing, MI 48909
P: (517) 373-7457

Mr. Edward Rodgers
Director
Commission for the Blind
201 North Washington Square
P.O. Box 30652
Lansing, MI 48909
P: (517) 373-2062

MINNESOTA
Ms. Carol Pankow
Director
State Services for the Blind
2200 University Avenue West,
Suite 240
St. Paul, MN 55114
P: (651) 539-2272

Ms. Kimberley T. Peck
Director, Rehabilitation Services
Branch
Department of Employment &
Economic Development
First National Bank Building
332 Minnesota Street, Suite
#E200
St. Paul, MN 55101
P: (651) 259-7345
F: (651) 297-5159

MISSISSIPPI
Mr. H. S. Butch McMillan
Executive Director
Department of Rehabilitation
Services
1281 Highway 51 (Madison,
MN 39110)
P.O. Box 1698
Jackson, MS 39215
P: (601) 853-5203
F: (601) 853-5205

MISSOURI
Mr. Kevin Faust
Deputy Director
Rehabilitation Services for the
Blind
615 Howerton Court
P.O. Box 2320
Jefferson City, MO 65102
P: (573) 751-4249
F: (573) 751-4984

Dr. C. Jeanne Loyd
Assistant Commissioner
Vocational Rehabilitation
3024 Dupont Circle
Jefferson City, MO 65109
P: (573) 751-3901
F: (573) 751-1441
E: info@vr.dese.mo.gov

MONTANA
Mr. Jim Marks
Administrator, Vocational
Rehabilitation
Disability Transitions Programs
111 North Last Chance Gulch,
Suite 4C
P.O. Box 4210
Helena, MT 59604
P: (406) 444-2591
F: (406) 444-3632

NEBRASKA
Mr. Mark Schultz
Assistant Commissioner &
Director, Vocational
Rehabilitation
Department of Education
6th Floor, 301 Centennial Mall
South
P.O. Box 94987
Lincoln, NE 68509
P: (402) 471-3649
F: (402) 471-0788

Ms. Pearl VanZandt
Executive Director
Commission for the Blind &
Visually Impaired
4600 Valley Road, Suite 100
Lincoln, NE 68510
P: (402) 471-2891
F: (402) 471-3009

NEVADA
Ms. Shelley Hendren
Administrator, Rehabilitation
Division
Department of Employment,
Training & Rehabilitation
3016 West Charleston Boulevard
Suite 215
Las Vegas, NV 89102
P: (702) 486-0372

NEW HAMPSHIRE
Ms. Lisa K. Hatz
Interim Director
State Rehabilitation Services
21 South Fruit Street, Suite 20
Concord, NH 03301
P: (603) 271-7080
F: (603) 271-7095
E: lhatz@ed.state.nh.us

NEW JERSEY
Mr. Daniel Frye
Executive Director
Commission for the Blind &
Visually Impaired
153 Halsey Street
P.O. Box 47017
Newark, NJ 07101
P: (973) 648-2324

Ms. Alice Hunnicut
Director
Division of Vocational
Rehabilitation Services
135 East State Street
P.O. Box 398
Trenton, NJ 08625
P: (609) 292-7318
F: (609) 292-4033

NEW MEXICO
Mr. Paul Aguilar
Director
Division of Vocational
Rehabilitation
Department of Education
435 St. Michael's Drive,
Building D
Santa Fe, NM 87505
P: (505) 954-8511
F: (505) 954-8562

Mr. Greg Trapp
Executive Director
Commission for the Blind
2200 Yale Boulevard, Southeast
Albuquerque, NM 87106
P: (505) 827-4479
F: (505) 827-4475

NEW YORK
Ms. Debora Brown-Johnson
Assistant Commissioner
Vocational & Educational
Services for People with
Disabilities
State Education Department
One Commerce Plaza, Room
1606
Albany, NY 12234
P: (518) 474-2714

Mr. Brian Daniels
Director
Commission for the Blind &
Visually Impaired
40 North Pearl Street
Albany, NY 12243
P: (518) 474-6812
F: (518) 486-5819

NORTH CAROLINA
Ms. Elizabeth Bishop
Director
Division of Vocational
Rehabilitation Services
Department of Health & Human
Services
2801 Mail Service Center
Raleigh, NC 27699
P: (919) 855-3500

Mr. Donald Edward Weaver
Director
Division of Services for the
Blind
309 Ashe Avenue, Fisher
Building
2601 Mail Service Center
Raleigh, NC 27699
P: (919) 733-9822 Ext. 212
F: (919) 733-9769

NORTH DAKOTA
Mr. Russell Cusack
Director
Division of Vocational
Rehabilitation
Prairie Hills Plaza
1237 West Divide Avenue, Suite
#1B
Bismarck, ND 58501
P: (701) 328-8926
F: (701) 328-8969

**NORTHERN MARIANA
ISLANDS**
Ms. Arlene Kay Yamagata
Director
Office of Vocational
Rehabilitation
Navy Hill Building, N-2
P.O. Box 501521
Saipan, MP 96950
P: (670) 322-6448

OHIO
Mr. Kevin Miller
Executive Director
Rehabilitation Services
Commission
400 East Campus View
Boulevard
Columbus, OH 43235
P: (614) 438-1210
F: (614) 985-7906

OKLAHOMA
Mr. Joe Cordova
Director
Department of Rehabilitation
Services
3535 Northwest 58th Street,
Suite 500
Oklahoma City, OK 73112
P: (405) 951-3400

OREGON
Ms. Dacia Johnson
Administrator
State Commission for the Blind
535 Southeast 12th Avenue
Portland, OR 97214
P: (971) 673-1588

Ms. Trina Lee
Administrator
Office of Vocational
Rehabilitation Services
Department of Human Services
500 Summer Street, Northeast,
E-87
Salem, OR 97301
P: (503) 945-5949

PENNSYLVANIA
Mr. David DeNotaris
Deputy Secretary
Office of Vocational
Rehabilitation
Department of Labor & Industry
1521 North 6th Street
Harrisburg, PA 17102
P: (717) 787-7312

PUERTO RICO
Mr. Ivan Clemente
Adminstrator
Vocational Rehabilitation
Administration
P.O. Box 191118
San Juan, PR 00919
P: (787) 727-0445

RHODE ISLAND
Mr. Ronald Racine
Administrator
Office of Rehabilitation
Services
Department of Human Services
40 Fountain Street
Providence, RI 02903
P: (401) 462-7888

SOUTH CAROLINA
Ms. Barbara G. Hollis
Commissioner
Vocational Rehabilitation
Department
1410 Boston Avenue
P.O. Box 15
West Columbia, SC 29170
P: (803) 896-6504
F: (803) 896-6529

Mr. James Kirby
Commissioner
Commission for the Blind
1430 Confederate Avenue
P.O. Box 2467
Columbia, SC 29202
P: (803) 898-8700
F: (803) 898-8852

SOUTH DAKOTA
Ms. Gaye Mattke
Director
Services for the Blind
East Highway 34
C/o 500 East Capitol
Pierre, SD 57501
P: (605) 773-5114
F: (605) 773-5483

Mr. Eric Weiss
Director
Division of Rehabilitation
Services
3800 East Highway 34
C/o 500 East Capitol
Pierre, SD 57501
P: (605) 773-3195
F: (605) 773-5483

TENNESSEE
Ms. Yovancha Lewis-Brown
Assistant Commissioner
Rehabilitation Services
10th Floor, Citizens Plaza
Building
400 Deaderick Street
Nashville, TN 37243
P: (615) 313-5004

TEXAS
Mr. Scott Bowman
Assistant Commissioner
DARS - Division for Blind
Services
4800 North Lamar Boulevard,
Suite 310
Austin, TX 78756
P: (512) 377-0602
F: (512) 377-0551

Mr. Cheryl Fuller
Assistant Commissioner
Division of Rehabilitation
Services
DARS
4900 North Lamar Boulevard,
Suite 5667
Austin, TX 78751
P: (800) 628-5115

U.S. VIRGIN ISLANDS
Mr. Felicia Blyden
Director, Division of Disabilities
& Rehabilitation Services
Department of Human Services
Knud Hansen Complex,
Building A
1303 Hospital Ground
St. Thomas, VI 00802
P: (340) 774-0930 Ext. 4289

UTAH
Mr. Aaron Thompson
Executive Director
State Office of Rehabilitation
250 East 500, South
P.O. Box 144200
Salt Lake City, UT 84114
P: (801) 538-7547

VERMONT
Ms. Diane P. Dalmasse
Director
Vocational Rehabilitation
Division
Department of Aging
103 South Main Street
Waterbury, VT 05676
P: (802) 241-2186
F: (802) 241-3359
E: Diane.Dalmasse
   @ahs.state.vt.us

Mr. Fred Jones
Director
Divsion of Services for the
Blind & Visually Impaired
Department of Aging
103 South Main Street
Waterbury, VT 05671
P: (802) 871-3068
F: (802) 241-2210
E: Fred.Jones
   @ahs.state.vt.us

Vocational Rehabilitation

VIRGINIA
Mr. Ray Hopkins
Commissioner
Department for the Blind &
Vision Impaired
397 Azalea Avenue
Richmond, VA 23227
P: (804) 371-3145
F: (804) 371-3157

Mr. James Rothrock
Commissioner
Department of Rehabilitative
Services
8004 Franklin Farms Drive
Henrico, VA 23229
P: (804) 662-7010
F: (804) 662-7644

WASHINGTON
Mr. Andres Aguirre
Interim Director
Division of Vocational
Rehabilitation
P.O. Box 45340
Olympia, WA 98504
P: (360) 725-3610
F: (360) 438-8011

Ms. Lou Oma Durand
Director
Department of Services for the
Blind
P.O. Box 40933
Olympia, WA 98504
P: (360) 725-3835
F: (360) 407-0679
E: loudurand@dsb.wa.gov

WEST VIRGINIA
Ms. Donna Ashworth
Acting Director
Division of Rehabilitation
Services
State Capitol
P.O. Box 50890
Charleston, WV 25305
P: (304) 356-2058
F: (304) 766-4905

WISCONSIN
Mr. Michael Greco
Acting Administrator, Division
of Vocational Rehabilitation
Department of Workforce
Development
201 East Washington Avenue,
Room A100
P.O. Box 7852
Madison, WI 53707
P: (608) 261-4576
F: (608) 260-2450

WYOMING
Mr. Jim McIntosh
Administrator
Division of Vocational
Rehabilitation
Department of Employment
1100 Herschler Building
Cheyenne, WY 82002
P: (307) 777-7389
F: (307) 777-5939

Waste Management

Develops and maintains a comprehensive waste management program in the state.

ALABAMA
Ms. Debi Thomas
Executive Assistant
Environmental Management
Commission
1400 Coliseum Boulevard
P.O. Box 301463
Montgomery, AL 36130
P: (334) 271-7706
F: (334) 279-3052

ARIZONA
Ms. Laura L. Malone
Waste Programs Division
Director
Department of Environmental
Quality
1110 West Washington Street
Phoenix, AZ 85007
P: (602) 771-4567
F: (602) 771-2302
E: malone.laura@azdeq.gov

CALIFORNIA
Ms. Caroll Mortensen
Director
Department of Resources,
Recycling & Recovery
1001 I Street
P.O. Box 4025
Sacramento, CA 95812
P: (916) 322-4025
F: (916) 319-7227
E: Caroll.Mortensen
    @calrecycle.ca.gov

COLORADO
Mr. Gary Baughman
Director
Hazardous Materials & Waste
Management Division
Public Health & Environment
4300 Cherry Creek Drive, South
Denver, CO 80246
P: (303) 692-3338
F: (303) 759-5355
E: gary.baughman
    @state.co.us

CONNECTICUT
Mr. Robert Isner
Director
Waste Engineering &
Enforcement Division
Energy & Environmental
Protection
79 Elm Street
Hartford, CT 06106
P: (860) 424-3264
F: (860) 424-4059
E: robert.isner@ct.gov

DELAWARE
Ms. Nancy C. Marker
Administrator
Solid & Hazardous Waste
Management Section
89 Kings Highway
Dover, DE 19901
P: (302) 739-9403
F: (302) 739-5060
E: nancy.marker@state.de.us

DISTRICT OF COLUMBIA
Mr. William O. Howland Jr.
Director
Department of Public Works
2000 14th Street, Northwest
Washington, DC 20009
P: (202) 673-6833
F: (202) 671-0642
E: dpw@dc.gov

FLORIDA
Mr. Jorge Caspary
Director
Division of Waste Management
Department of Environmental
Protection
2600 Blair Stone Road
Tallahassee, FL 32399
P: (850) 245-8693
E: jorge.caspary
    @dep.state.fl.us

GEORGIA
Mr. Jeff Cown
Branch Chief
Land Protection Branch
4244 International Parkway,
Suite 104
Atlanta, GA 30354
P: (404) 362-2692
F: (404) 362-2693

HAWAII
Mr. Steven Y.K. Chang
Branch Chief
Solid & Hazardous Waste
Branch
Department of Health
919 Ala Moana Boulevard, #212
Honolulu, HI 96814
P: (808) 586-4226
F: (808) 586-7509
E: schang
    @eha.health.state.hi.us

IDAHO
Mr. Orville Green
Administrator
Waste Management &
Remediation Division
DEQ State Office
1410 North Hilton
Boise, ID 83706
P: (208) 373-0148
F: (208) 373-0154
E: orville.green
    @deq.idaho.gov

ILLINOIS
Ms. Lisa Bonnett
Director
Environmental Protection
Agency
1021 North Grand Avenue, East
Springfield, IL 62706
P: (217) 782-9540
F: (217) 782-9039

INDIANA
Mr. Bruce Palin
Assistant Commissioner, Office
of Land Quality
Department of Environmental
Management
100 North Senate Avenue
Room IGCN 1154
Indianapolis, IN 46204
P: (317) 233-6591
F: (317) 233-6647
E: bpalin@idem.in.gov

KANSAS
Mr. William L. Bider
Director
Bureau of Waste Management
1000 Southwest Jackson Street
Suite 320
Topeka, KS 66612
P: (785) 296-1600
F: (785) 296-8909
E: wbider@kdheks.gov

KENTUCKY
Mr. Anthony R. Hatton
Division Director
Division of Waste Management
Department for Environmental
Protection
200 Fair Oaks Lane, 2nd Floor
Frankfort, KY 40601
P: (502) 564-6716
F: (502) 564-4049
E: tony.hatton@ky.gov

LOUISIANA
Ms. Lourdes Iturralde
Administrator
Public Participation & Permits
Support Services
Department of Environmental
Quality
P.O. Box 4313
Baton Rouge, LA 70821
P: (225) 219-3180
F: (225) 219-3309

MARYLAND
Ms. Hilary Miller
Acting Director
Land Management
Administration
Department of the Environment
1800 Washington Boulevard
Baltimore, MD 21230
P: (410) 537-3304
F: (410) 537-3321
E: hilary.miller
    @maryland.gov

MASSACHUSETTS
Mr. Martin Suuberg
Commissioner
Department of Environmental
Protection
One Winter Street
Boston, MA 02108
P: (617) 292-5856
F: (617) 574-6880

MINNESOTA
Mr. John Linc Stine
Commissioner
Pollution Control Agency
520 Lafayette Road North, Sixth
Floor
St. Paul, MN 55155
P: (651) 757-2016
F: (651) 296-6334
E: john.stine@state.mn.us

Waste Management

MISSISSIPPI
Mr. Gary Rikard
Executive Director
Department of Environmental
Quality
515 East Amite Street
Jackson, MS 39201
P: (601) 961-5001
F: (601) 961-5093
E: gary_rikard
    @deq.state.ms.us

MISSOURI
Mr. Chris Nagel
Program Director
Solid Waste Management
Program
P.O. Box 176
Jefferson City, MO 65102
P: (573) 751-5401
F: (573) 526-3902
E: swmp@dnr.mo.gov

NEBRASKA
Mr. Jim Macy
Director
Department of Environmental
Quality
1200 N Street, Suite 400
Lincoln, NE 68508
P: (402) 471-3585
F: (402) 471-2909
E: Jim.Macy@nebraska.gov

NEVADA
Mr. Leo Drozdoff
Director
Department of Conservation &
Natural Resources
901 South Stewart Street, Suite
5001
Carson City, NV 89701
P: (775) 687-9301
F: (775) 687-5856
E: ldrozdoff@dcnr.nv.gov

Mr. Eric Noack
Bureau Chief
Bureau of Waste Management
Division of Environmental
Protection
901 South Stewart Street, Suite
4001
Carson City, NV 89701
P: (775) 687-9366
F: (775) 687-5856
E: enoack@ndep.nv.gov

NEW HAMPSHIRE
Mr. John Duclos
Bureau Administrator
Hazardous Waste Management
Bureau
29 Hazen Drive
P.O. Box 95
Concord, NH 03301
P: (603) 271-1998
F: (603) 271-0869
E: john.duclos@des.nh.gov

NEW JERSEY
Mr. John Giordano
Assistant Commissioner,
Compliance & Enforcement
Department of Environmental
Protection
P.O. Box 420
Trenton, NJ 08625
P: (609) 984-3285

NEW MEXICO
Mr. John E. Kielng
Chief
Hazardous Waste Bureau
2905 Rodeo Park Drive, East
Building 1
Santa Fe, NM 87505
P: (505) 476-6000
F: (505) 476-6030
E: john.kielng@state.nm.us

NEW YORK
Mr. Joe Martens
Commissioner
Department of Environmental
Conservation
625 Broadway, 14th Floor
Albany, NY 12233
P: (518) 402-8540
F: (518) 402-8541
E: joemartens
    @gw.dec.state.ny.us

NORTH CAROLINA
Mr. Dexter Matthews
Director
Department of Environment &
Natural Resources
Division of Waste Management
1646 Mail Service Center
Raleigh, NC 27699
P: (919) 707-8238
F: (919) 715-0708
E: dexter.matthews
    @ncdenr.gov

NORTH DAKOTA
Mr. Scott Radig
Director
Division of Waste Management
Department of Health
918 East Divide Avenue, 3rd
Floor
Bismark, ND 58501
P: (701) 328-5166
F: (701) 328-5200
E: sradig@nd.gov

**NORTHERN MARIANA
ISLANDS**
Mr. Martin C. Sablan
Secretary
Department of Public Works
Caller Box 10007, Capitol Hill
Saipan, MP 96950
P: (670) 235-5827
F: (670) 235-6346

OHIO
Ms. Pam Allen
Chief
Division of Materials & Waste
Management
50 West Town Street, Suite 700
P.O. Box 1049
Columbus, OH 43216
P: (614) 644-2980
F: (614) 728-5315
E: pam.allen
    @epa.state.oh.us

OKLAHOMA
Ms. Kelly Dixon
Division Director
Land Protection Division
Department of Environmental
Quality
P.O. Box 1677
Oklahoma City, OK 73101
P: (405) 702-5100
F: (405) 702-5101
E: kelly.dixon@deq.ok.gov

OREGON
Mr. Dick Pedersen
Director
Department of Environmental
Quality
811 Southwest 6th Avenue
Portland, OR 97204
P: (503) 229-5300
F: (503) 229-5850
E: pedersen.dick
    @deq.state.or.us

PENNSYLVANIA
Mr. Kenneth R. Reisinger
Bureau Director
Bureau of Waste Management
Department of Environmental
Protection
P.O. Box 69170
Harrisburg, PA 17106
P: (717) 783-2388
F: (717) 787-1904
E: ra-epwaste@pa.gov

PUERTO RICO
Mr. Augustine F. Carbo Lugo
Director
Solid Waste Management
Authority
P.O. Box 40285
San Juan, PR 00918
P: (787) 765-7575
F: (787) 753-2220

Mr. Jose Maeso Gonzalez
Executive Director
Energy Affairs Administration
P.O. Box 41314
San Juan, PR 00940
P: (787) 999-2200 Ext. 2888
F: (787) 999-2246
E: jose.maeso@aae.pr.gov

RHODE ISLAND
Ms. Janet Coit
Director
Department of Environmental
Management
235 Promenade Street, 4th Floor
Providence, RI 02908
P: (401) 222-2771
F: (401) 222-6802
E: janet.coit@dem.ri.gov

SOUTH CAROLINA
Ms. Daphne G. Neel
Bureau Chief
Bureau of Land & Waste
Management
Dept. of Health &
Environmental Control
2600 Bull Street
Columbia, SC 29201
P: (803) 896-4007
F: (803) 896-4001
E: neeldg@dhec.sc.gov

SOUTH DAKOTA
Ms. Vonni Kallemeyn
Environmental Scientist
Manager
Department of Environment &
Natural Resources
Waste Management Program
523 East Capitol Avenue
Pierre, SD 57501
P: (605) 773-3153
F: (605) 773-6035
E: denrinternet@state.sd.us

TENNESSEE
Mr. Patrick J. Flood
Director
Division of Solid & Hazardous
Waste Management
William R. Snodgrass Tennessee
Tower
312 Rosa L Parks Ave, 14th
Floor
Nashville, TN 37243
P: (615) 532-0780
F: (615) 532-0886

TEXAS
Mr. Earl Lott
Director
Waste Permits Division
12100 Park 35 Circle
P.O. Box 13087
Austin, TX 78711
P: (512) 239-2047
F: (512) 239-0659

U.S. VIRGIN ISLANDS
Mr. Darryl A. Smalls
Commissioner
Department of Public Works
6002 Estate Anna's Hope
Christiansted, VI 00820
P: (340) 776-4844
F: (340) 773-1290

UTAH
Mr. Scott Anderson
Director
Division of Solid & Hazardous
Waste
195 North 1950 West, 2nd Floor
P.O. Box 144880
Salt Lake City, UT 84114
P: (801) 536-0203
F: (801) 536-0222
E: standerson@utah.gov

VERMONT
Mr. Chuck Schwer
Director
Waste Management &
Prevention Division
1 National Life Drive - Davis 1
Montpelier, VT 05620
P: (802) 760-8041
F: (802) 828-1011
E: chuck.schwer@state.vt.us

VIRGINIA
Mr. David K. Paylor
Director
Department of Environmental
Quality
629 East Main Street
Richmond, VA 23219
P: (804) 698-4390
F: (804) 698-4019
E: david.paylor
   @deq.virginia.gov

WASHINGTON
Ms. Maia Bellon
Director
Department of Ecology
300 Desmond Drive, Southeast
Lacey, WA 98503
P: (360) 407-7001
F: (360) 407-6989
E: maib461@ecy.wa.gov

WEST VIRGINIA
Mr. Scott G. Mandirola
Division Director
Division of Water & Waste
Management
601 57th Street, Southeast
Charleston, WV 25304
P: (304) 926-0499
F: (304) 926-0463
E: Scott.G.Mandirola@wv.gov

WISCONSIN
Mr. Bart Sponseller
Deputy Division Administrator
Division of Air, Waste &
Remediation & Redevelopment
P.O. Box 7921
Madison, WI 53707
F: (608) 267-2768
E: Bart.Sponseller
   @wisconsin.gov

WYOMING
Mr. Luke Esch
Administrator
Solid & Hazardous Waste
Division
Department of Environmental
Quality
122 West 25th Street, Herschler
Building
Cheyenne, WY 82002
P: (307) 777-7192
F: (307) 777-5973
E: luke.esch1@wyo.gov

Water Resources

Responsible for water conservation, development, use and planning in the state.

ALABAMA
Mr. Brian Atkins
Division Chief
Office of Water Resources
401 Adams Avenue
P.O. Box 5690
Montgomery, AL 36103
P: (334) 242-5499
F: (334) 242-5099
E: James.Atkins
    @adeca.alabama.gov

ALASKA
Mr. David W. Schade
Chief of the Water Resources
Section
Division of Mining, Land &
Water
Department of Natural
Resources
550 West 7th Avenue, Suite 1020
Anchorage, AK 99501
P: (907) 269-8645
F: (907) 269-8947
E: david.w.schade
    @alaska.gov

AMERICAN SAMOA
Ms. Andra Samoa
Chief Executive Officer
American Samoa Power
Authority
American Samoa Government
Pago Pago, AS 96799
P: (684) 699-5282

ARIZONA
Mr. Thomas Buschatzke
Director
Department of Water Resources
3550 North Central Avenue
Phoenix, AZ 85007
P: (602) 771-8426
F: (602) 771-8681

ARKANSAS
Mr. J. Randy Young
Executive Director
Natural Resources Commission
101 East Capitol Avenue, Suite
350
Little Rock, AR 72201
P: (501) 682-3961
F: (501) 682-3991
E: randy.young@arkansas.gov

CALIFORNIA
Mr. Mark W. Cowin
Director
Department of Water Resources
1416 Ninth Street
P.O. Box 942836
Sacramento, CA 94236
P: (916) 653-5791
F: (916) 653-4684
E: mcowin@water.ca.gov

COLORADO
Mr. Dick Wolfe
State Engineer
Division of Water Resources
Department of Natural
Resources
1313 Sherman Street, Suite 821
Denver, CO 80203
P: (303) 866-3581
F: (303) 866-3589
E: dick.wolfe@state.co.us

CONNECTICUT
Ms. Cheryl Chase
Director
Inland Water Resources
Division
Energy & Environmental
Protection
79 Elm Street
Hartford, CT 06106
P: (860) 424-3706
F: (860) 424-4075
E: cheryl.chase@ct.gov

DELAWARE
Ms. Kathleen M. Stiller
Director
Division of Water
89 Kings Highway
Dover, DE 19901
P: (302) 739-9950
F: (302) 739-7864

DISTRICT OF COLUMBIA
Mr. George S. Hawkins
General Manager
Water & Sewer Authority
5000 Overlook Avenue,
Southwest
P.O. Box 97200
Washington, DC 20090
P: (202) 787-2000
F: (202) 787-2333
E: info@dcwater.com

FLORIDA
Mr. Mark Thomasson
Director
Water Resource Management
Department of Environmental
Protection
2600 Blair Stone Road, M.S.
3500
Tallahassee, FL 32399
P: (850) 245-8336
F: (850) 245-8356
E: mark.thomasson
    @dep.state.fl.us

GEORGIA
Mr. James A. Capp
Branch Chief
Watershed Protection Branch
2 Martin Luther King Jr. Drive,
SW
Suite 1152, East Tower, Floyd
Building
Atlanta, GA 30334
P: (404) 463-4911
F: (404) 651-8455

GUAM
Mr. Martin L. Roush
General Manager
Waterworks Authority
P.O. Box 3010
Hagatna, GU 96910
P: (671) 647-2603
F: (671) 646-2335
E: roushm
    @guamwaterworks.net

HAWAII
Mr. W. Roy Hardy
Acting Deputy Director
Commission on Water Resource
Management
Department of Land & Natural
Resources
1151 Punchbowl Street, Room
227
Honolulu, HI 96813
P: (808) 587-0214
F: (808) 587-0219
E: dlnr.cwrm@hawaii.gov

IDAHO
Mr. Gary Spackman
Director
Department of Water Resources
322 East Front Street
P.O. Box 83720
Boise, ID 83720
P: (208) 287-4800
F: (208) 287-6700
E: gary.spackman
    @idwr.idaho.gov

ILLINOIS
Mr. Dan Injerd
Director
Office of Water Resources
1 Natural Resources Way, 2nd
Floor
Springfield, IL 62702
P: (217) 785-3334

INDIANA
Mr. Mike Neyer
Director
Division of Water
Department of Natural
Resources
402 West Washington Street,
Room W264
Indianapolis, IN 46204
P: (317) 232-4160
F: (317) 233-4579
E: mneyer@dnr.in.gov

IOWA
Mr. Bill Ehm
Administrator of Environmental
Services Division
Department of Natural
Resources
4th Floor, Wallace Building
502 East 9th Street
Des Moines, IA 50319
P: (515) 281-5817
F: (515) 281-8895
E: william.ehm@dnr.iowa.gov

KANSAS
Mr. David W. Barfield
Chief Engineer
Division of Water Resources
109 Southwest 9th Street, 2nd
Floor
Topeka, KS 66612
P: (785) 296-3717
F: (785) 296-1176
E: David.Barfield
    @kda.ks.gov

Mr. Tracy D. Streeter
Director
Kansas Water Office
901 South Kansas Avenue
Topeka, KS 66612
P: (785) 296-3185
F: (785) 296-0878
E: tracy.streeter
    @kwo.ks.gov

KENTUCKY
Ms. Sandy Gruzesky
Director
Division of Water
Department for Environmental
Protection
200 Fair Oaks Lane, Fourth
Floor
Frankfort, KY 40601
P: (502) 564-3410
F: (502) 564-0111
E: water@ky.gov

LOUISIANA
Mr. Jim H. Welsh
Commissioner of Conservation
Office of Conservation
Department of Natural
Resources
P.O. Box 94275
Baton Rouge, LA 70804
P: (225) 342-5540
F: (225) 342-3705
E: Jim.Welsh@la.gov

MAINE
Ms. Patricia Aho
Commissioner
Department of Environmental
Protection
17 State House Station
Augusta, ME 04333
P: (207) 287-2812
F: (207) 287-2814
E: patricia.aho@maine.gov

MARYLAND
Dr. David Goshorn
Assistant Secretary for Aquatic
Resources
Department of Natural
Resources
Tawes State Office Building, C4
580 Taylor Avenue
Annapolis, MD 21401
P: (410) 260-8110
F: (410) 260-8111
E: dgoshorn@dnr.state.md.us

MASSACHUSETTS
Mr. Matthew A. Beaton
Secretary of Energy and
Environmental Affairs
Executive Office of Energy &
Environmental Affairs
100 Cambridge Street, Suite 900
Boston, MA 02114
P: (614) 626-1000
F: (614) 626-1181

MICHIGAN
Mr. William Creal
Chief
Water Resources Division
3rd Floor, South Tower
525 West Allegan Street, P.O.
Box 30458
Lansing, MI 48909
P: (517) 284-5470
F: (517) 241-9003
E: CREALW@michigan.gov

MINNESOTA
Mr. John Linc Stine
Commissioner
Pollution Control Agency
520 Lafayette Road North, Sixth
Floor
St. Paul, MN 55155
P: (651) 757-2016
F: (651) 296-6334
E: john.stine@state.mn.us

MISSISSIPPI
Mr. Kay Whittington
Director
Office of Land & Water
Resources
700 North State Street
P.O. Box 2309
Jackson, MS 39225
P: (601) 961-5729
F: (601) 961-5228

MISSOURI
Ms. Andrea Collier
Director
Water Resources Center
P.O. Box 176
Jefferson City, MO 65102
P: (573) 751-1134
F: (573) 751-7627
E: andrea.collier
@dnr.mo.gov

MONTANA
Mr. John Tubbs
Director
Department of Natural
Resources & Conservation
1625 Eleventh Avenue
P.O. Box 201601
Helena, MT 59620
P: (406) 444-2074
F: (406) 444-2684

NEBRASKA
Mr. Jim Schneider
Director
Department of Natural
Resources
301 Centennial Mall South
Lincoln, NE 68509
P: (402) 471-2366
F: (402) 471-2900
E: jim.schneider
@nebraska.gov

NEVADA
Mr. Jason King
State Engineer/Administrator
Department of Conservation &
Natural Resources
Division of Water Resources
901 South Stewart Street, Suite
2002
Carson City, NV 89701
P: (775) 684-2800
F: (775) 684-2811
E: jking@water.nv.gov

NEW HAMPSHIRE
Mr. Eugene Forbes
Director
Water Division
Department of Environmental
Services
P.O. Box 95
Concord, NH 03302
P: (603) 271-3308
F: (603) 271-2867
E: eugene.forbes@des.nh.gov

NEW JERSEY
Mr. Fred Sickels
Acting Director
Division of Water Supply &
Geoscience
Department of Environmental
Protection
P.O. Box 402
Trenton, NJ 08625
P: (609) 292-7219
F: (609) 292-1654

NEW MEXICO
Mr. Tom Blaine
State Engineer/Secretary,
Interstate Stream Commission
Office of the State
Engineer/Interstate Stream
Commission
130 South Capitol Street, Pino
Building
P.O. Box 25102
Santa Fe, NM 87504
P: (505) 827-6091
F: (505) 827-3806

NEW YORK
Mr. Mark Klotz
Director
Division of Water
625 Broadway
Albany, NY 12233
P: (518) 402-8233
F: (518) 402-9029
E: dowinfo
@gw.dec.state.ny.us

NORTH CAROLINA
Mr. Tom Reeder
Director
Department of Environment &
Natural Resources
Division of Water Resources
1611 Mail Service Center
Raleigh, NC 27699
P: (919) 707-9027
F: (919) 733-3558
E: tom.reeder@ncdenr.gov

NORTH DAKOTA
Mr. Todd Sando
State Engineer
Water Commission
900 East Boulevard Avenue
Department 770
Bismarck, ND 58505
P: (701) 328-2750
F: (701) 328-3696
E: tsando@nd.gov

NORTHERN MARIANA ISLANDS
Mr. Jesus B. Castro
Division Manager
Water Division
P.O. Box 501220
Saipan, MP 96950
P: (670) 235-7025
F: (670) 235-7053

OHIO
Mr. Steven J. Grossman
Executive Director
Water Development Authority
480 South High Street
Columbus, OH 43215
P: (614) 466-5822
F: (614) 644-9964

OKLAHOMA
Mr. J.D. Strong
Executive Director
Water Resources Board
3800 North Classen Boulevard
Oklahoma City, OK 73118
P: (405) 530-8800
F: (405) 530-8900

Water Resources

OREGON
Mr. Tom Byler
Director
Water Resources Department
725 Summer Street, Northeast,
Suite A
Salem, OR 97301
P: (503) 986-0876
F: (503) 986-0903
E: thomas.m.byler
   @wrd.state.or.us

PENNSYLVANIA
Ms. Cindy Adams Dunn
Secretary
Department of Conservation &
Natural Resources
209 Finance Building
Harrisburg, PA 17120
P: (717) 787-5440
F: (717) 787-4523

PUERTO RICO
Ms. Carmen Guerrero Perez
Secretary
Department of Natural &
Environmental Resources
P.O. Box 366147
San Juan, PR 00936
P: (787) 999-2200
F: (787) 999-2303

RHODE ISLAND
Ms. Alicia M. Good
Assistant Director
Department of Environmental
Management
Office of Water Resources
235 Promenade Street
Providence, RI 02908
P: (401) 222-3961
F: (401) 222-3564
E: alicia.good@dem.ri.gov

SOUTH CAROLINA
Mr. Joe Gellici
Section Chief
Hydrology Section
Department of Natural
Resources
1000 Assembly Street
Columbia, SC 29201
P: (803) 734-6428
F: (803) 734-9200
E: gellicij@dnr.sc.gov

SOUTH DAKOTA
Mr. James Feeney
Division Director
Division of Financial &
Technical Assistance
Environment & Natural
Resources
523 East Capitol Avenue
Pierre, SD 57501
P: (605) 773-4254
F: (605) 773-6035

TENNESSEE
Mr. John McClurkan
Administrator
Water Resources Program
Department of Agriculture
440 Hogan Road
Nashville, TN 37220
P: (615) 837-5305
E: john.mcclurkan@tn.gov

TEXAS
Mr. Jeff Walker
Deputy Executive Administrator
Water Supply & Infrastructure
Water Development Board
1700 North Congress, P.O. Box
13231
Austin, TX 78711
P: (512) 463-7779
F: (512) 475-2053

U.S. VIRGIN ISLANDS
Mr. David Simon
Director
Division of Environmental
Protection
Cyril E. King Airport
Terminal Building, 2nd Floor
St. Thomas, VI 00802
P: (340) 774-3320
E: david.simon@dpnr.gov.vi

UTAH
Mr. Eric Millis
Director
Division of Water Resources
Department of Natural
Resources
P.O. Box 146201
Salt Lake City, UT 84116
P: (801) 538-7230
F: (801) 538-7229
E: ericmillis@utah.gov

VERMONT
Mr. Peter LaFlamme
Director
Watershed Management
Division
1 National Life Drive, Main 2
Montpelier, VT 05620
P: (802) 828-1535
F: (802) 828-1544
E: pete.laflamme
   @state.vt.us

VIRGINIA
Mr. David K. Paylor
Director
Department of Environmental
Quality
629 East Main Street
Richmond, VA 23219
P: (804) 698-4390
F: (804) 698-4019
E: david.paylor
   @deq.virginia.gov

WASHINGTON
Mr. Tom Loranger
Program Manager
Water Resources Programs
P.O. Box 47600
Olympia, WA 98504
P: (360) 407-6672
F: (360) 407-6989
E: tom.loranger@ecy.wa.gov

WEST VIRGINIA
Mr. Scott G. Mandirola
Division Director
Division of Water & Waste
Management
601 57th Street, Southeast
Charleston, WV 25304
P: (304) 926-0499
F: (304) 926-0463
E: Scott.G.Mandirola@wv.gov

WISCONSIN
Mr. Russell Rasmussen
Division Administrator
Division of Water
101 South Webster Street
P.O. Box 7921
Madison, WI 53707
P: (608) 264-6278
F: (608) 267-2800
E: Russell.Rasmussen@wi.gov

WYOMING
Mr. Kevin Frederick
Administrator
Water Quality Division
Water & Waste Advisory Board
122 West 25th Street, Herschler
Building
Cheyenne, WY 82002
P: (307) 777-5985
F: (307) 777-5973
E: Kevin.Frederick@wyo.gov

Welfare

Administers the delivery of financial and medical benefits to low-income families and individuals.

ALABAMA
Ms. Nancy T. Buckner
Commissioner
Department of Human Resources
Gordon Persons Building, Suite 2104
50 North Ripley Street
Montgomery, AL 36130
P: (334) 242-1310
F: (334) 353-1115
E: Nancy.Buckner
@dhr.alabama.gov

ALASKA
Mr. Sean O'Brien
Director
Division of Public Assistance
P.O. Box 110640
Juneau, AK 99801
P: (907) 465-2680
F: (907) 465-5154
E: sean.obrien@alaska.gov

AMERICAN SAMOA
Dr. Taeaoafua Meki Solomona
Director
Department of Human & Social Services
P.O. Box 997534
Pago Pago, AS 96799
P: (684) 633-1664
F: (684) 633-7449
E: mtsolomona@dhss.as

ARIZONA
Ms. Leona M. Hodges
Director
Division of Benefits & Medical Eligibility
Department of Economic Security
1717 West Jefferson Street
Phoenix, AZ 85007
P: (602) 542-3596

ARKANSAS
Ms. Delia Anderson
Director
Division of County Operations
P.O. Box 1437, Slot S301
Little Rock, AR 72203
P: (501) 682-8375
F: (501) 682-8367
E: delia.anderson
@arkansas.gov

CALIFORNIA
Mr. Will Lightbourne
Director
Department of Social Services
744 P Street
Sacramento, CA 95814
P: (916) 657-2598
F: (916) 651-6569

COLORADO
Mr. Reginald L. Bicha
Executive Director
Department of Human Services
1575 Sherman Street
Denver, CO 80203
P: (303) 866-3475
F: (303) 866-2606
E: reggie.bicha@state.co.us

CONNECTICUT
Mr. Roderick L. Bremby
Commissioner
Department of Social Services
55 Farmington Avenue
Hartford, CT 06105
P: (860) 424-5024
E: commis.dss@ct.gov

DELAWARE
Ms. Rita M. Landgraf
Secretary
Department of Health & Social Services
Main Building
1901 North DuPont Highway
New Castle, DE 19720
P: (302) 255-9040
F: (302) 255-4429

DISTRICT OF COLUMBIA
Mr. David A. Berns
Director
Department of Human Services
64 New York Avenue, Northeast
6th Floor
Washington, DC 20002
P: (202) 671-4200
F: (202) 671-4326
E: dhs@dc.gov

FLORIDA
Mr. Mike Carroll
Secretary
Department of Children & Families
1317 Winewood Boulevard
Building 1, Room 202
Tallahassee, FL 32399
P: (850) 487-1111
F: (850) 922-2993
E: mike_carroll
@dcf.state.fl.us

GEORGIA
Ms. Sharon Hill
Division Director
Division of Family & Children Services
Two Peachtree Street, Northwest
Suite 18-486
Atlanta, GA 30303
P: (404) 657-3433
F: (404) 657-5105

HAWAII
Dr. Rachael Wong
Director
Department of Human Services
1390 Miller Street, Room 209
P.O. Box 339
Honolulu, HI 96809
P: (808) 586-4997
F: (808) 586-4890
E: dhs@dhs.hawaii.gov

IDAHO
Mr. Russell Barron
Administrator
Division of Welfare
2nd Floor, Pete T. Cenarrusa Building
450 West State Street
Boise, ID 83720
P: (208) 334-5696
F: (208) 334-5571
E: barronr@dhw.idaho.gov

ILLINOIS
Ms. Julie Hamos
Director
Department of Healthcare & Family Services
201 South Grand Avenue East, 3rd Floor
Springfield, IL 62763
P: (217) 782-7755

INDIANA
Mr. Joe Moser
Director of Medicaid
Office of Medicaid Policy & Planning
Family & Social Services Administration
402 West Washington Street
Indianapolis, IN 46204
P: (317) 234-8725
E: Joe.Moser@fssa.IN.gov

IOWA
Ms. Ann Wiebers
Administrator
Division of Financial, Health & Work Supports
Hoover State Office Building
1305 East Walnut Street
Des Moines, IA 50319
P: (515) 281-6080
F: (515) 281-7791
E: awieber@dhs.state.ia.us

KANSAS
Ms. Sandra Kimmons
Director
Economic & Employment Services
915 Southwest Harrison Street
Topeka, KS 66612
P: (785) 296-6750
F: (785) 296-6960

KENTUCKY
Ms. Teresa James
Commissioner
Department for Community Based Services
275 East Main Street
Mail Stop 3W-A
Frankfort, KY 40621
P: (502) 564-3703
F: (502) 564-6907

MAINE
Ms. Stefanie Nadeau
Director
Office of MaineCare Services
Department of Health & Human Services
221 State Street
Augusta, ME 04333
P: (207) 287-2674
F: (207) 287-2675
E: Stefanie.Nadeau
@maine.gov

MARYLAND
Mr. Sam Malhotra
Secretary
Department of Human Resources
311 West Saratoga Street
Baltimore, MD 21201
P: (410) 767-7109
F: (410) 333-0099
E: sam.malhotra
@maryland.gov

MASSACHUSETTS
Mr. Jeff McCue
Commissioner
Department of Transitional Assistance
600 Washington Street
Boston, MA 02111
P: (617) 348-8400
F: (617) 348-8575

MICHIGAN
Ms. Maura D. Corrigan
Director
Department of Human Services
235 South Grand Avenue
P.O. Box 30037
Lansing, MI 48909
P: (313) 456-4887
F: (517) 335-6101
E: dhsweb@michigan.gov

Welfare

MISSISSIPPI
Ms. Cathy Sykes
Director
Division of Economic
Assistance
P.O. Box 352
Jackson, MS 39205
P: (601) 359-4093

MISSOURI
Ms. Janel Luck
Director
Family Support Division
Department of Social Services
P.O. Box 2320
Jefferson City, MO 65102
P: (573) 751-3221
F: (573) 751-3091

NEW HAMPSHIRE
Mr. Nicholas A. Toumpas
Commissioner
Department of Health & Human
Services
129 Pleasant Street
Concord, NH 03301
P: (603) 271-9200
F: (603) 271-4912
E: ntoumpas
   @dhhs.state.nh.us

NEW JERSEY
Ms. Jeanette Page-Hawkins
Director
Division of Family
Development
P.O. Box 716
Trenton, NJ 08625
P: (609) 588-2400
F: (609) 584-4404

NEW MEXICO
Ms. Marilyn Martinez
Director
Income Support Division
Human Services Department
2009 South Pacheco Street
Santa Fe, NM 87505
P: (505) 827-7250
F: (505) 827-7203

NEW YORK
Ms. Kristin M. Proud
Commissioner
Office of Temporary &
Disability Assistance
40 North Pearl Street
Albany, NY 12243
P: (518) 473-1090

NORTH CAROLINA
Mr. Wayne E. Black
Director
Division of Social Services
McBryde Building, 820 South
Boylan Ave.
2401 Mail Service Center
Raleigh, NC 27699
P: (919) 527-6335
F: (919) 334-1018
E: wayne.black@dhhs.nc.gov

NORTH DAKOTA
Ms. Maggie D. Anderson
Executive Director
Department of Human Services
State Capitol, Judicial Wing
600 East Boulevard Avenue,
Dept. 325
Bismarck, ND 58505
P: (701) 328-2538
F: (701) 328-1545
E: manderson@nd.gov

Ms. Carol K. Olson
Executive Director
Department of Human Services
State Capitol, Judicial Wing
600 East Boulevard Avenue,
Dept. 325
Bismarck, ND 58505
P: (701) 328-2538
F: (701) 328-1545
E: colson@nd.gov

**NORTHERN MARIANA
ISLANDS**
Ms. Eleanor S. Dela Cruz
Administrator
Nutrition Assistance Program
Caller Box 10007, Capital Hill
Saipan, MP 96950
P: (670) 235-9889
F: (670) 235-9250

OHIO
Ms. Cynthia J. Dungey
Director
Department of Job & Family
Services
30 East Broad Street, 32nd Floor
Columbus, OH 43215
P: (614) 466-9195
F: (614) 466-2815

OKLAHOMA
Mr. Jim Struby
Director
Adult & Family Services
Department of Human Services
P.O. Box 25352
Oklahoma City, OK 73125
P: (405) 521-3076
F: (405) 521-4158
E: fssinquiries@okdhs.org

OREGON
Ms. Erinn L. Kelley-Siel
Director
Department of Human Services
500 Summer Street, Northeast,
E-15
Salem, OR 97301
P: (503) 945-7001
F: (503) 378-2897
E: erinn.kelley-siel
   @state.or.us

PENNSYLVANIA
Mr. Theodore Dallas
Secretary
Department of Human
Resources
P.O. Box 2675
Harrisburg, PA 17105
P: (717) 787-2600

PUERTO RICO
Ms. Idalia Columbus Rondon
Secretary
Department of the Family
P.O. Box 11398
Hato Rey, PR 00917
P: (787) 294-4900
F: (787) 294-0732

RHODE ISLAND
Ms. Melba Depena Affigne
Director
Department of Human Services
600 New London Avenue
Cranston, RI
F: (401) 462-3677
E: Director@dhs.ri.gov

SOUTH DAKOTA
Ms. Lynne A. Valenti
Cabinet Secretary
Department of Social Services
700 Governors Drive
Pierre, SD 57501
P: (605) 773-3165
F: (605) 773-4855
E: DSSInfo@state.sd.us

TENNESSEE
Dr. Raquel Hatter
Commissioner
Department of Human Services
400 Deaderick Street, 15th Floor
Nashville, TN 37243
P: (615) 313-4700
F: (615) 741-4165
E: raquel.hatter@tn.gov

TEXAS
Dr. Kyle L. Janek
Executive Commissioner
Health & Human Services
Commission
4900 North Lamar Boulevard
P.O. Box 13247
Austin, TX 78711
P: (512) 424-6502
F: (512) 491-1967

Mr. Jon Weizenbaum
Commissioner
Department of Aging &
Disability Services
701 West 51st Street
P.O. Box 149030
Austin, TX 78714
P: (512) 438-3030
F: (512) 438-3011

U.S. VIRGIN ISLANDS
Mrs. Ermine Boschulte
Administrator
Division of Financial Programs
4401 Sion Farm , Christiansted
St. Thomas, VI 00802
P: (340) 774-2399
F: (340) 774-3466

UTAH
Mr. John Pierpont
Executive Director
Department of Workforce
Services
P.O. Box 45249
Salt Lake City, UT 84145
P: (801) 526-9210
F: (801) 526-9211
E: jpierpo@utah.gov

VERMONT
Mr. Ken Schatz
Commissioner
Department for Children &
Families
103 South Main Street
2nd Floor, 5 North
Waterbury, VT 05671
P: (802) 871-3385
E: ken.schatz@state.vt.us

VIRGINIA
Ms. Margaret Schultze
Commissioner
Department of Social Services
801 East Main Street
Richmond, VA 23219
P: (804) 726-7000
E: margaret.schultze
   @dss.virginia.gov

WASHINGTON
Mr. Kevin W. Quigley
Secretary
Department of Social & Health
Services
P.O. Box 45130
Olympia, WA 98504
P: (360) 902-7800

WEST VIRGINIA
Ms. Karen L. Bowling
Cabinet Secretary
Department of Health & Human
Resources
One Davis Square, Suite 100
East
Charleston, WV 25301
P: (304) 558-0684
F: (304) 558-1130
E: DHHRSecretary@wv.gov

WYOMING
Dr. Steve Corsi
Director
Department of Family Services
Hathaway Building, 3rd Floor
2300 Capitol Avenue
Cheyenne, WY 82002
P: (307) 777-7561
F: (307) 777-7747
E: steve.corsi@wyo.gov

Workers Compensation

Administers laws providing insurance and compensation for workers for job-related illnesses, injury or death.

ALABAMA
Mr. Scottie Spates
Director
Workers' Compensation
Division
649 Monroe Street
Montgomery, AL 36131
P: (334) 242-2868
F: (334) 353-8262
E: WC@labor.alabama.gov

ALASKA
Mr. Alan Ezzell
Acting Director
Division of Workers'
Compensation
P.O. Box 115512
Juneau, AK 99811
P: (907) 465-2790
F: (907) 465-2797
E: alan.ezzell@alaska.gov

AMERICAN SAMOA
Mr. Le'i S. Thompson
Director
Department of Human
Resources
Executive Office Building
AP Lutali, 2nd Floor
Pago Pago, AS 96799
P: (684) 644-4485
F: (684) 633-1139
E: sonnythompson
  @samoatelco.com

ARIZONA
Ms. Laura L. McGrory
Director
Industrial Commission
800 West Washington Street
Phoenix, AZ 85007
P: (602) 542-4411
F: (602) 542-7889
E: lmcgrory@ica.state.az.us

ARKANSAS
Ms. Barbara Womack Webb
Chief Executive Officer
Workers' Compensation
Commission
P.O. Box 950
Little Rock, AR 72203
P: (501) 682-3930
F: (501) 682-2786

CALIFORNIA
Ms. Destie Overpeck
Administrative Director
Division of Workers'
Compensation
1515 Clay Street, 17th Floor
P.O. Box 420603
Oakland, CA 94612
P: (510) 286-7100
E: doverpeck@dir.ca.gov

COLORADO
Mr. Paul Tauriello
Director
Division of Workers
Compensation
633 17th Street, Suite 400
Denver, CO 80202
P: (303) 318-8700
F: (303) 318-8710
E: workers.comp@state.co.us

CONNECTICUT
Mr. John A. Mastropietro
Chair
Workers' Compensation
Commission
Capitol Place
21 Oak Street
Hartford, CT 06106
P: (860) 493-1500
F: (860) 247-1361
E: wcc.chairmansoffice
  @po.state.ct.us

DELAWARE
Mr. John F. Kirk III
Administrator
Office of Workers'
Compensation
4425 North Market Street, 3rd
Floor
Wilmington, DE 19802
P: (302) 761-8200
F: (302) 761-6601
E: jkirk@state.de.us

DISTRICT OF COLUMBIA
Mr. F. Thomas Luparello
Acting Director
Department of Employment
Services
4058 Minnesota Avenue,
Northeast
Washington, DC 20019
P: (202) 724-7000
F: (202) 673-6993
E: does@dc.gov

FLORIDA
Mr. Tanner Holloman
Director
Division of Workers'
Compensation
200 East Gaines Street
Tallahassee, FL 32399
P: (850) 413-1600
E: Tanner.Holloman
  @myfloridacfo.com

GEORGIA
Delece A. Brooks
Executive Director/Chief
Operating Officer
State Board of Workers'
Compensation
270 Peachtree Street, Northwest
Atlanta, GA 30303
P: (404) 656-2048

GUAM
Mr. Manuel Q. Cruz
Director
Department of Labor
Government of Guam
P.O. Box 9970
Tamuning, GU 96931
P: (671) 647-6510
F: (671) 674-6517

HAWAII
Mr. Walter Kawamura
Administrator
Disability Compensation
Division
830 Punchbowl Street, Room
209
P.O. Box 3769
Honolulu, HI 96812
P: (808) 586-9151
F: (808) 586-9219
E: dlir.workcomp@hawaii.gov

IDAHO
Mr. Thomas Baskin
Chair
Industrial Commission
P.O. Box 83720
Boise, ID 83720
P: (208) 334-6000
F: (208) 334-2321
E: tom.baskin@iic.idaho.gov

ILLINOIS
Ms. Carolyn Parks
Executive Director
Workers' Compensation
Commission
100 West Randolph Street,
#8-200
Chicago, IL 60601
P: (312) 814-7268

INDIANA
Ms. Linda Hamilton
Chair
Worker's Compensation Board
402 West Washington Street,
Room W-196
Indianapolis, IN 46204
P: (317) 232-3809
F: (317) 233-5493
E: lhamilton@wcb.in.gov

IOWA
Mr. Christopher J. Godfrey
Commissioner
Division of Workers'
Compensation
Workforce Development
Organization
1000 East Grand Avenue
Des Moines, IA 50319
P: (515) 281-3504
F: (515) 281-6501
E: Christopher.Godfrey
  @iwd.iowa.gov

KANSAS
Mr. Larry Karns
Director
Division of Workers
Compensation
401 Southwest Topeka
Boulevard, Suite 2
Topeka, KS 66603
P: (785) 296-4000
F: (785) 296-0839
E: wc@dol.ks.gov

KENTUCKY
Mr. Dwight T. Lovan
Commissioner
Department of Workers' Claims
657 Chamberlin Avenue
Frankfort, KY 40601
P: (502) 782-4439
F: (502) 564-5934

LOUISIANA
Mr. Patrick Robinson
Interim Director
Office of Workers'
Compensation Administration
Workforce Commission
P.O. Box 94040
Baton Rouge, LA 70804
P: (225) 342-7555
F: (225) 342-5665
E: owca@lwc.la.gov

MAINE
Mr. Paul H. Sighinolfi
Executive Director/Chair
Workers' Compensation Board
27 State House Station
Augusta, ME 04333
P: (207) 287-7086
F: (207) 287-7198
E: phil.sighinolfi
   @maine.gov

MARYLAND
Ms. Mary K. Ahearn
Chief Executive Officer
Workers' Compensation
Commission
10 East Baltimore Street, 7th
Floor
Baltimore, MD 21202
P: (410) 864-5308
F: (410) 333-8122
E: Mahearn@Wcc.state.md.us

MASSACHUSETTS
Ms. Linda Edmonds
Director
Department of Industrial
Accidents
1 Congress Street, Suite 100
Boston, MA 02114
P: (617) 727-4900
F: (617) 727-7470

MICHIGAN
Mr. Jack A. Nolish
Deputy Director
Workers' Compensation Agency
7150 Harris Drive, First Floor
7150 Harris Drive, P.O. Box
30016
Lansing, MI 48909
P: (517) 322-1106
F: (517) 322-6012
E: nolishj@michigan.gov

MINNESOTA
Mr. Ken Peterson
Commissioner
Department of Labor & Industry
443 Lafayette Road North
St. Paul, MN 55155
P: (651) 284-5010
F: (651) 284-5720
E: ken.peterson@state.mn.us

MISSISSIPPI
Mr. Liles Williams
Chair
Workers' Compensation
Commission
1428 Lakeland Drive
P.O. Box 5300
Jackson, MS 39296
P: (601) 987-4200

MISSOURI
Mr. John J. Hickey
Director
Division of Workers'
Compensation
Labor and Industrial Relations
P.O. Box 58
Jefferson City, MO 65102
P: (573) 751-4231
F: (573) 751-2012
E: workerscomp@labor.mo.gov

MONTANA
Mr. Peter Van Nice
Bureau Chief
Workers' Compensation
Regulations Bureau
P.O. Box 8011
Helena, MT 59604
P: (406) 444-0566
F: (406) 444-7710

NEBRASKA
Mr. Glenn W. Morton
Administrator
Workers' Compensation Court
P.O. Box 98908
Lincoln, NE 68509
P: (402) 471-3602
F: (402) 471-2700
E: Glenn.Morton
   @nebraska.gov

NEVADA
Mr. Donald L. Soderberg
Director
Division of Industrial Relations
500 East Third Street
Carson City, NV 89713
P: (775) 684-3849
F: (775) 684-3850
E: dsoderberg
   @business.nv.gov

NEW HAMPSHIRE
Ms. Kathryn J. Barger
Deputy Commissioner
Department of Labor
95 Pleasant Street
Concord, NH 03301
P: (603) 271-3176
F: (603) 271-6194
E: kbarger
   @labor.state.nh.us

NEW JERSEY
Mr. Peter J. Calderone
Director/Chief Judge
Division of Workers'
Compensation
P.O. Box 381
Trenton, NJ 08625
P: (609) 292-2515
F: (609) 984-3924
E: dwc@dol.state.nj.us

NEW MEXICO
Mr. Darin A. Childers
Director
Workers' Compensation
Administration
2410 Centre Avenue, Southeast
P.O. Box 27198
Albuquerque, NM 87125
P: (505) 841-6000
F: (505) 841-6009

NEW YORK
Mr. Robert E. Beloten
Chair
Workers' Compensation Board
20 Park Street
Albany, NY 12207
P: (518) 462-8880
F: (518) 473-1415

NORTH DAKOTA
Mr. Bryan Klipfel
Director
Workforce Safety & Insurance
1600 East Century Avenue,
Suite 1
P.O. Box 5585
Bismarck, ND 58506
P: (701) 328-3762
F: (701) 328-3820
E: bklipfel@nd.gov

**NORTHERN MARIANA
ISLANDS**
Mr. Frank Cabrera
Workers' Compensation
Commission
P.O. Box 501247
Capitol Hill
Saipan, MP 96950
P: (670) 664-8024
E: cabreraF
   @NMIretirement.com

OHIO
Mr. Steve Buehrer
Administrator/CEO
Bureau of Workers'
Compensation
30 West Spring Street
Columbus, OH 43215
P: (614) 466-5223
F: (877) 520-6446

OKLAHOMA
Hon. Michael J. Harkey
Vice Presiding Judge
Workers' Compensation Court
1915 North Stiles Avenue
Oklahoma City, OK 73105
P: (405) 522-8600

OREGON
Mr. John L. Shilts
Division Administrator
Workers' Compensation
Division
P.O. Box 14480
350 Winter Street, Northeast
Salem, OR 97309
P: (503) 947-7810
F: (503) 947-7581
E: john.l.shilts
   @state.or.us

PENNSYLVANIA
Ms. Elizabeth A. Crum
Deputy Secretary for
Compensation & Insurance
Bureau of Workers'
Compensation
1171 South Cameron Street,
Room 324
Harrisburg, PA 17104
P: (717) 783-5421
E: ecrum@state.pa.us

RHODE ISLAND
Mr. Matthew P. Carey III
Assistant Director
Workers Compensation
Department of Labor & Training
Center General Complex, 1511
Pontiac Ave
Cranston, RI 02920
P: (401) 462-8100
F: (401) 462-8105
E: mcarey@dlt.ri.gov

SOUTH CAROLINA
Mr. Gary M. Cannon
Executive Director
Workers' Compensation
Commission
1333 Main Street, Suite 500
P.O. Box 1715
Columbia, SC 29202
P: (803) 737-5700
F: (803) 737-5768
E: gcannon@wcc.sc.gov

SOUTH DAKOTA
Mr. James E. Marsh
Director
Division of Workers
Compensation
Department of Labor &
Regulation
700 Governors Drive
Pierre, SD 57501
P: (605) 773-3101
F: (605) 773-6184
E: james.marsh@state.sd.us

Workers Compensation

TENNESSEE
Ms. Abbie Hudgens
Administrator
Workers' Compensation
Division
Labor & Workforce
Development
220 French Landing Drive
Nashville, TN 37243
P: (615) 741-2395
F: (615) 532-1468
E: wc.info@tn.gov

TEXAS
Mr. Ryan Brannan
Commissioner
Division of Workers'
Compensation
Department of Insurance
7551 Metro Center Drive, Suite
100
Austin, TX 78744
P: (512) 804-4400

UTAH
Mr. Ron Dressler
Director
Industrial Accidents Division
160 East 300 South, 3rd Floor
P.O. Box 146610
Salt Lake City, UT 84114
P: (801) 530-6841
F: (801) 530-6804
E: rdressler@utah.gov

VERMONT
Mr. J. Stephen Monahan
Director
Workers' Compensation &
Safety Division
5 Green Mountain Drive
P.O. Box 488
Montpelier, VT 05601
P: (802) 828-2138
F: (802) 828-4022
E: stephen.monahan
   @state.vt.us

VIRGINIA
Ms. Vivian R. Guidt
Interim Executive Director
Workers' Compensation
Commission
1000 DMV Drive
Richmond, VA 23220
P: (804) 205-3603
E: vivan.guidt
   @workcomp.virginia.gov

WASHINGTON
Mr. Frank E. Fennerty Jr.
Labor Member
Board of Industrial Insurance
Appeals
2430 Chandler Court, Southwest
P.O. Box 42401
Olympia, WA 98504
P: (360) 753-6823
F: (360) 586-5611
E: fennerty@biia.wa.gov

WEST VIRGINIA
Mr. Michael D. Riley
Commissioner
Offices of the Insurance
Commissioner
1124 Smith Street, Room 403
P.O. Box 50540
Charleston, WV 25305
P: (304) 558-3354
F: (304) 558-0412
E: michael.riley
   @wvinsurance.gov

WISCONSIN
Mr. John Metcalf
Division Administrator
Workers Compensation Division
201 East Washington Avenue
P.O. Box 7901
Madison, WI 53707
P: (608) 266-1340
F: (608) 267-0394
E: John.Metcalf
   @dwd.wisconsin.gov

WYOMING
Mr. Steven R. Czoschke
Interim Executive Secretary
Workers' Compensation Medical
Commission
P.O. Box 20247
Cheyenne, WY 82003
P: (307) 777-5422
F: (307) 777-5201

Workforce Development

Administers job training and services for the unemployed, underemployed and economically disadvantaged in the state.

ALABAMA
Mr. Fitzgerald Washington
Commissioner
Department of Labor
649 Monroe Street
Montgomery, AL 36131
P: (334) 242-8990

ALASKA
Ms. Heidi Drygas
Commissioner
Department of Labor &
Workforce Development
P.O. Box 111149
Juneau, AK 99811
P: (907) 465-2700
F: (907) 465-2784
E: heidi.drygas@alaska.gov

AMERICAN SAMOA
Mr. Le'i S. Thompson
Director
Department of Human
Resources
Executive Office Building
AP Lutali, 2nd Floor
Pago Pago, AS 96799
P: (684) 644-4485
F: (684) 633-1139
E: sonnythompson
    @samoatelco.com

ARIZONA
Mr. James Apperson
Assistant Director
Division of Employment &
Rehabilitation Services
Department of Economic
Security
1717 West Jefferson Street
Phoenix, AZ 85007
P: (602) 542-4910
E: japperson@azdes.gov

ARKANSAS
Mr. Daryl Bassett
Director
Department of Workforce
Services
#2 Capitol Mall
Little Rock, AR 72201
P: (501) 682-2121
F: (501) 682-8845
E: daryl.bassett
    @arkansas.gov

CALIFORNIA
Mr. Patrick W. Henning
Director
Employment Development
Department
P.O. Box 826880, MIC 83
Sacramento, CA 94280
P: (916) 654-8210
F: (916) 654-9069
E: patrick.henning
    @edd.ca.gov

COLORADO
Ms. Ellen Golombek
Executive Director
Department of Labor &
Employment
633 17th Street, Suite 201
Denver, CO 80202
P: (303) 318-8020
F: (303) 318-8047
E: Ellen.Golombek
    @state.co.us

Ms. Stephanie Steffens
Director
Workforce Development
Council
Department of Labor &
Employment
633 17th Street, Suite 1200
Denver, CO 80202
P: (303) 318-8038
F: (303) 318-8049
E: stephanie.steffens
    @state.co.us

CONNECTICUT
Ms. Sharon Palmer
Commissioner
Department of Labor
200 Folly Brook Boulevard
Westerfield, CT 06109
P: (860) 263-6505
F: (850) 263-6529
E: sharon.palmer@ct.gov

DELAWARE
Mr. John McMahon
Secretary of Labor
Department of Labor
4425 North Market Street
Wilmington, DE 19802
P: (302) 761-8000
F: (302) 761-6621
E: john.mcmahon@state.de.us

Ms. Lori Reeder
Director
Department of Labor
Division of Employment &
Training
4425 North Market Street
Wilmington, DE 19802
P: (302) 761-8085
E: lori.reeder@state.de.us

DISTRICT OF COLUMBIA
Ms. Deborah A. Carroll
Director
Department of Employment
Services
4058 Minnesota Avenue,
Northeast
Washington, DC 20019
P: (202) 724-7000
F: (202) 673-6993
E: does@dc.gov

FLORIDA
Mr. Jesse Panuccio
Director
Department of Economic
Opportunity
107 East Madison Street
Caldwell Building
Tallahassee, FL 32399
P: (850) 245-7105

GEORGIA
Hon. Mark Butler (R)
Commissioner
Department of Labor
148 International Boulevard
Northeast
Atlanta, GA 30303
P: (404) 232-7300
F: (404) 656-2683
E: commissioner@gdol.ga.gov

HAWAII
Ms. Linda Chu Takayama
Director
Department of Labor &
Industrial Relations
830 Punchbowl Street
Honolulu, HI 96813
P: (808) 586-8844
F: (808) 586-9099
E: dlir.director@hawaii.gov

IDAHO
Mr. Kenneth D. Edmunds
Director
Department of Labor
317 West Main Street
Boise, ID 83735
P: (208) 334-6110
F: (208) 334-6430
E: kenneth.edmunds
    @labor.idaho.gov

ILLINOIS
Mr. Julio Rodriguez
Deputy Director
Department of Commerce &
Economic Opportunity
Office of Employment &
Training
100 West Randolph Street, Suite
3-400
Chicago, IL 60601
P: (312) 814-6028

INDIANA
Mr. Steve Braun
Commissioner
Department of Workforce
Development
Government Center South
10 North Senate Avenue
Indianapolis, IN 46204
P: (317) 232-7676
E: SBraun@dwd.IN.gov

IOWA
Ms. Beth Townsend
Agency Director
Workforce Development
1000 East Grand Avenue
Des Moines, IA 50319
P: (515) 281-5364
E: beth.townsend
    @iwd.iowa.gov

KANSAS
Mr. Pat George
Secretary
Department of Commerce
1000 Southwest Jackson Street,
Suite 100
Topeka, KS 66612
P: (785) 296-2741
F: (785) 296-5055
E: pgeorge
    @kansascommerce.com

Ms. Lana Gordon
Secretary of Labor
Department of Labor
401 Southwest Topeka
Boulevard
Topeka, KS 66603
P: (785) 296-5058
F: (785) 368-5289
E: lana.gordon@dol.ks.gov

Workforce Development

KENTUCKY
Ms. Lori Collins
Division Director
Division of Workforce &
Employment Services
Office of Employment &
Training
275 East Main Street
Frankfort, KY 40621
P: (502) 564-7456
F: (502) 564-7459
E: Lori.Collins@ky.gov

LOUISIANA
Mr. Curt Eysink
Executive Director
Workforce Commission
1001 North 23rd Street
P.O. Box 94094
Baton Rouge, LA 70804
P: (225) 342-3111
F: (225) 342-3778
E: owd@lwc.la.gov

Mr. Bryan Moore
Director
Office of Workforce
Development
1001 North 23rd Street
P.O. Box 94094
Baton Rouge, LA 70804
P: (225) 342-3111
F: (225) 342-7960
E: bmoore@lwc.la.gov

MAINE
Ms. Jeanne Paquette
Commissioner
Department of Labor
54 State House Station
Augusta, ME 04333
P: (207) 623-7900
F: (207) 623-7934
E: jeanne.paquette
    @maine.gov

MARYLAND
Ms. Julie E. Squire
Assistant Secretary
Division of Workforce
Development & Adult Learning
Labor, Licensing and Regulation
1100 North Eutaw Street, Room
108
Baltimore, MD 21201
P: (410) 767-3011
E: julie.squire
    @maryland.gov

MASSACHUSETTS
Mr. Ronald L. Walker II
Secretary
Executive Office of Labor &
Workforce Development
One Ashburton Place, Suite
2112
Boston, MA 02108
P: (617) 626-7122
F: (617) 727-1090

MICHIGAN
Ms. Christine Quinn
Director
Workforce Development
Agency
201 North Washington Square
Lansing, MI 48913
P: (517) 335-5858
F: (517) 241-8217
E: QuinnC@michigan.gov

MINNESOTA
Mr. Thomas Norman
Director, Workforce
Development
Department of Employment &
Economic Development
1st National Bank Building
332 Minnesota Street, Suite
E200
St. Paul, MN 55101
P: (651) 894-3553

MISSISSIPPI
Mr. Mark Henry
Executive Director
Department of Employment
Security
1235 Echelon Parkway
P.O. Box 1699
Jackson, MS 39215
P: (601) 321-6000
F: (601) 321-6104
E: mhenry@mdes.ms.gov

MISSOURI
Mr. Mike Downing
Director
Department of Economic
Development
301 West High Street
P.O. Box 1157
Jefferson City, MO 65102
P: (573) 751-4962
F: (573) 526-7700
E: ecodev@ded.mo.gov

Mr. Ryan McKenna
Director
Department of Labor &
Industrial Relations
421 East Dunklin Street
P.O. Box 504
Jefferson City, MO 65102
P: (573) 751-4091
F: (573) 751-4135
E: ryan.mckenna
    @labor.mo.gov

MONTANA
Ms. Pam Bucy
Commissioner
Department of Labor & Industry
P.O. Box 1728
Helena, MT 59624
P: (406) 444-2840
F: (406) 444-1419
E: pbucy@mt.gov

Mr. Mike Cooney
Administrator
Workforce Services Division
Department of Labor & Industry
P.O. Box 1728
Helena, MT 59624
P: (406) 444-4100
F: (406) 444-3037

NEBRASKA
Ms. Brenda Hicks-Sorensen
Director
Department of Economic
Development
550 South 16th Street
Lincoln, NE 68508
P: (402) 471-3125
E: brenda.hicks-sorensen
    @nebraska.gov

NEVADA
Mr. Donald L. Soderberg
Director
Department of Employment,
Training & Rehabilitation
500 East Third Street
Carson City, NV 89713
P: (775) 684-3849
F: (775) 684-3850
E: dsoderberg
    @business.nv.gov

NEW JERSEY
Mr. Harold Wirths
Commissioner
Department of Labor &
Workforce Development
P.O. Box 110
Trenton, NJ 08625
P: (609) 292-2323
F: (609) 633-9271
E: hal.wirths
    @dol.state.nj.us

NEW MEXICO
Ms. Celina Bussey
Secretary
Department of Workforce
Solutions
401 Broadway, Northeast
P.O. Box 1928
Albuquerque, NM 87103
P: (505) 841-8405
F: (505) 841-8491
E: celina.bussey
    @state.nm.us

NEW YORK
Mr. Mario J. Musolino
Acting Commissioner
Department of Labor
W. Averell Harriman State
Office Campus
Building 12
Albany, NY 12240
P: (518) 457-9000
F: (518) 485-6297
E: mario.musolino
    @labor.state.ny.us

NORTH CAROLINA
Mr. Roger Shackleford
Assistant Secretary for
Workforce Solutions
Division of Workforce Solutions
313 Chapanoke Road, Suite 120
4316 Mail Service Center
Raleigh, NC 27699
P: (919) 814-0315
F: (919) 662-4770
E: roger.shackleford
    @nccommerce.com

NORTH DAKOTA
Ms. Beth Zander
Director
Workforce Development
Division
1600 East Century Avenue
P.O. Box 2057
Bismarck, ND 58502
P: (701) 328-5345
F: (701) 328-5320
E: bezander@nd.gov

OHIO
Ms. Cynthia J. Dungey
Director
Department of Job & Family
Services
30 East Broad Street, 32nd Floor
Columbus, OH 43215
P: (614) 466-9195
F: (614) 466-2815

Mr. Bruce Madson
Assistant Director, Employment
Services
Department of Job & Family
Services
30 East Broad Street, 32nd Floor
Columbus, OH 43215
P: (614) 466-9195
F: (614) 466-2815

Mr. John B. Weber
Deputy Director
Office of Workforce
Development
Department of Job & Family
Services
4020 East 5th Avenue
Columbus, OH 43219
P: (614) 752-3091
F: (614) 995-1298
E: john.weber@jfs.ohio.gov

OKLAHOMA
Mr. Richard McPherson
Executive Director
Employment Security
Commission
2401 North Lincoln Boulevard
P.O. Box 52003
Oklahoma City, OK 73152
P: (405) 557-7201

OREGON
Mr. Jim Middleton
Executive Director
Department of Community
Colleges & Workforce
Development
255 Capitol Street, Northeast
Third Floor
Salem, OR 97310
P: (503) 559-4340
F: (503) 378-3365
E: jim.middleton
   @state.or.us

PENNSYLVANIA
Ms. Kathy M. Manderino
Secretary
Department of Labor & Industry
651 Boas Street, Room 1700
Harrisburg, PA 17121
P: (717) 787-5279
F: (717) 787-8826

PUERTO RICO
Mr. Vance Thomas
Secretary
Department of Labor & Human
Resources
P.O. Box 195540
Hato Rey, PR 00918
P: (787) 754-2119
F: (787) 753-9550

RHODE ISLAND
Mr. Scott Jensen
Director
Department of Labor & Training
Center General Complex
1511 Pontiac Avenue
Cranston, RI 02920
P: (401) 462-8000
F: (401) 462-8872
E: director-dlt@dlt.ri.gov

SOUTH CAROLINA
Ms. Cheryl M. Stanton
Executive Director
Department of Employment &
Workforce
1550 Gadsden Street
P.O. Box 995
Columbia, SC 29202
P: (803) 737-2617
E: cstanton@dew.sc.gov

SOUTH DAKOTA
Ms. Marcia Hultman
Secretary
Department of Labor &
Regulation
700 Governors Drive
Pierre, SD 57501
P: (605) 773-3101
F: (605) 773-6184
E: marcia.hultman
   @state.sd.us

TENNESSEE
Mr. Burns Phillips
Commissioner
Department of Labor &
Workforce Development
220 French Landing Drive
Nashville, TN 37243
P: (615) 741-6642
F: (615) 741-5078
E: burns.phillips@tn.gov

Mr. Sterling Van Der Spuy
Administrator
Workforce Services Division
Labor & Workforce
Development
220 French Landing Drive
Nashville, TN 37243
P: (615) 741-1031
F: (615) 741-5078

TEXAS
Reagan Miller
Director
Workforce Development
Division
Workforce Commission
101 East 15th Street
Austin, TX 78701
P: (512) 936-3563
E: reagan.miller
   @twc.state.tx.us

Mr. Larry E. Temple
Executive Director
Workforce Commission
101 East 15th Street
Austin, TX 78778
P: (512) 463-0735
F: (512) 475-2321
E: larry.temple
   @twc.state.tx.us

UTAH
Mr. John Pierpont
Executive Director
Department of Workforce
Services
P.O. Box 45249
Salt Lake City, UT 84145
P: (801) 526-9210
F: (801) 526-9211
E: jpierpo@utah.gov

VERMONT
Ms. Annie Noonan
Commissioner
Department of Labor
5 Green Mountain Drive
P.O. Box 488
Montpelier, VT 05601
P: (802) 828-4301
F: (802) 828-4022
E: annie.noonan@state.vt.us

VIRGINIA
Ms. Ellen Marie Hess
Commissioner
Employment Commission
703 East Main Street
Richmond, VA 23219
E: ellen.hess
   @vec.virginia.gov

WASHINGTON
Ms. Eleni Papadakis
Executive Director
Workforce Training &
Education Coordinating Board
128 10th Avenue, Southwest
P.O. Box 43105
Olympia, WA 98504
P: (360) 709-4600
F: (360) 586-5862
E: eleni.papadakis
   @wtb.wa.gov

WEST VIRGINIA
Mr. Russell Fry
Acting Executive Director
Workforce West Virginia
112 California Avenue
Charleston, WV 25305
P: (304) 558-7024
F: (304) 558-1343
E: Russell.L.Fry@wv.gov

WISCONSIN
Mr. Reggie Newson
Secretary
Department of Workforce
Development
201 East Washington Avenue
GEF-1, Room A400, P.O. Box
7946
Madison, WI 53707
P: (608) 266-3131
F: (608) 266-1784
E: reggie.newson
   @dwd.wisconsin.gov

WYOMING
Ms. Joan K. Evans
Director
Department of Workforce
Services
122 West 25th Street
Herschler Building, 2nd Floor
East
Cheyenne, WY 82002
P: (307) 777-8728
F: (307) 777-5857
E: joan.evans@wyo.gov

Notes

Notes

Notes

Notes

Notes

Notes

Notes

Notes

Notes

Notes

Notes

Notes

Notes